The Greek Alphabet

Alpha	A	α	Iota	I	ι	Rho	P	ρ
Beta	B	β	Kappa	K	κ	Sigma	Σ	σ
Gamma	Γ	γ	Lambda	Λ	λ	Tau	T	τ
Delta	Δ	δ	Mu	M	μ	Upsilon	Υ	υ
Epsilon	E	ϵ	Nu	N	ν	Phi	Φ	ϕ
Zeta	Z	ζ	Xi	Ξ	ξ	Chi	X	χ
Eta	H	η	Omicron	O	o	Psi	Ψ	ψ
Theta	Θ	θ	Pi	Π	π	Omega	Ω	ω

Abbreviations for Units

A	ampere		ℓ	liter
Å	angstrom (10^{-10} m)		m	meter
atm	atmosphere		MeV	megaelectron volts
C	coulomb		mi	mile
°C	degree Celsius		min	minute
cal	calorie		mm	millimeter
cm	centimeter		msec	millisecond
eV	electron volt		N	newton
°F	degree Fahrenheit		nm	nanometer (10^{-9} m)
fm	femtometer, fermi (10^{-15} m)		pt	pint
ft	foot		qt	quart
G	gauss		rev	revolution
gm	gram		sec	second
H	henry		T	tesla
h	hour		u	unified mass unit
Hz	hertz		V	volt
in	inch		W	watt
J	joule		y	year
K	kelvin		yd	yard
kg	kilogram		μm	micrometer (10^{-6} m)
km	kilometer		μsec	microsecond
keV	kiloelectron volts		μC	microcoulomb
lb	pound		Ω	ohm

William J. Simms
MacGregor House   F-324

William J. Simms
MacGregor House   F-324

PHYSICS

VOLUME 1 # Physics

Paul A. Tipler

Oakland University
Rochester, Michigan

WORTH PUBLISHERS, INC.

Physics, Volume 1

Paul A. Tipler

Copyright © 1976 by Worth Publishers, Inc.

Printed in the United States of America

Library of Congress Catalog Card No. 78-55578

ISBN: 0-87901-094-X

First Printing, May 1978

Designed by Malcolm Grear Designers

Composition by Progressive Typographers, Inc.

Illustrated by Felix Cooper

Picture research by Susan Haggerty

Worth Publishers, Inc.

444 Park Avenue South

New York, NY 10016

For Libor Velinsky

Preface

This is a textbook for the standard two-semester or three-semester elementary physics course for engineering and science majors. It is assumed that the students have taken, or are concurrently taking, calculus. The usual topics in classical physics are presented: Mechanics (Chapters 1–16), Thermodynamics (Chapters 17–19), Waves (Chapters 20–27), and Electromagnetism (Chapters 29–41). In addition, special relativity is discussed in Chapter 28 and quantization in Chapter 42.

Although I have deviated only slightly from the traditional order of topics, I have tried to emphasize the unity of physics and the economy of physical theory by relating many phenomena through a common theoretical description. Many topics are introduced as examples illustrating more general physical principles. For example, there is no separate chapter on fluid mechanics. Instead, Archimedes' principle is discussed as an example of the application of Newton's laws in Chapter 5, and Bernoulli's equation is derived as an application of the work-energy theorem in Chapter 9. Similarly, the relationship between gas pressure and molecular kinetic energy is obtained in Chapter 11 as an application of the impulse-momentum equation. This immediate application of general principles to the description of interesting phenomena makes the theory less abstract for the beginning student.

The teaching of elementary physics is complicated by the wide range of student backgrounds and abilities in a typical class. Some have had good physics courses and a calculus course in high school; others have had no high school physics and are just beginning to struggle with their first calculus course. I have tried to write this book so that the least prepared students will be able to read it, enjoy it, and gain confidence because they can work most of the exercises. At the same time, optional sections and some difficult problems are included to challenge the better-prepared students. Because of these varied mathematical backgrounds, I have included a review of trigonometry in the first chapter and discussed differentiation and integration while introducing the kinematic concepts of velocity and acceleration in Chapter 2.

Although there is beauty and elegance in the mathematical derivation of specific results from a general theory, most students learn more easily when new concepts are introduced in an intuitive, nonmathe-matical way, proceeding from a specific example to the more general relation. I have followed this approach in many cases, supplying the general or formal derivation in an optional paragraph at the end of the section or chapter. Whenever possible, concepts are introduced in one dimension and later generalized to three dimensions.

Derivations are given without calculus whenever possible, with calculus-based derivations included for comparison. Simple differen-tiation and integration are illustrated in worked examples and in problems throughout the book. Material that is more difficult mathe-matically, or that can be omitted with no loss in continuity, is labeled "optional" and is set in the right column of the page, bounded on either side by colored rules. Many derivations are relegated to this optional column.

Frequently, to show the interrelatedness of phenomena, a concept is mentioned briefly even though it will be treated in detail later. For example, Newton's law of gravitation and Coulomb's law are intro-duced as examples of basic forces (Chapter 6) and later treated in detail (in Chapters 16 and 29). Similarly, gravitational potential energy is mentioned in terms of recovery of work (at the end of Chapter 7), then discussed more fully when the idea of conservative forces is introduced.

Material dealing with applications and techniques is often placed in "how-to-do-it" sections and chapters. This allows the use of many examples, graded in difficulty, without disturbing the continuity of the discussion of the concepts. For example, Newton's laws are discussed in Chapter 4, while their application to problems is shown by ex-amples in Chapter 5. The electric field and its properties are discussed in Chapter 29, while calculation of the electric field for various charge distributions is illustrated in Chapter 30.

A minor deviation from the traditional order of topics is the brief discussion of the four basic interactions presented early in classical mechanics (Chapter 6) along with a discussion of molecular forces and such empirical contact forces as support forces, friction, and the forces exerted by strings and springs. The mention of gravitational forces and electrostatic forces here allows for more varied examples of potential-energy functions in Chapter 8 than just those associated with constant forces or spring forces. It also permits discussions of such interesting phenomena as escape velocity, binding energy, and molecular dis-sociation as examples of the use of energy conservation in Chapter 9.

A more significant change from the traditional order is the unified treatment of waves. Reflection, refraction, interference, diffraction, dis-persion, etc., are discussed as general wave phenomena with applica-tions to waves on strings, sound, and light. This integration of various wave phenomena illustrates the wide applicability of physical theory while making it easier for students to understand the important prop-erties of sound and light. In particular, the general discussion of dif-fraction and the validity of the ray approximation in Chapter 25 lays the foundation for the understanding of the wave-particle duality of nature (Chapter 42), and for the student's future study of quantum theory. I have placed this material before electricity and magnetism for two reasons: 1. the study of simple harmonic motion is then relatively fresh in the students' minds, and 2. most students find the material on waves, with its many possibilities for classroom demonstrations, easier and more intuitive than the more abstract ideas in electricity and magnetism. Instructors who prefer to present electricity and magnetism first can easily do so by skipping to Chapter 29 after completing Chapter 19 and later returning to Chapter 20.

Within each chapter are questions placed at the ends of various sections. Some are routine and can easily be answered from the material in the preceding section. Others are open-ended and can serve as a basis for classroom discussion. At the end of each chapter is a review section. This section generally consists of a checklist of words and phrases which students are asked to "define, explain, or otherwise identify" and a set of true-false questions. The page number where the definition of the term is given appears after each item in the checklist, and answers to all the true-false questions are given in the back of the book. Following the review section, there is an extensive set of exercises (usually about 30) organized by the sections within the chapter. These exercises are not difficult, and each involves material in that section of the chapter only. The exercises are followed by a set of problems, which tend to be somewhat more difficult than the exercises, involve more mathematics, or require the student to use material from more than one section and perhaps supply reasonable data from his or her experience. Answers (and sometimes hints) to all the odd-numbered exercises and problems are given at the back of the book. I suggest the assignment of many more exercises than problems. It is my experience that self-confidence is an important factor in learning and can be easily destroyed by too many challenging problems. The exercises are designed to build the student's self-confidence.

Fifteen essays have been written especially for this book. Three are biographical (on Isaac Newton, Albert Einstein, and Benjamin Franklin), many are on applications (e.g., xerography, transistors, and radar astronomy), and others are on topics of current interest (e.g., thermal pollution, black holes, and energy resources). These brief essays are for the enjoyment and enlightenment of students and instructors. There are no exercises or problems connected with the essays.

Although the international system of units (SI) is used predominately, the British engineering system is introduced and used often in the mechanics chapters, and commonly used units such as the calorie, eV, atmosphere, etc., are also used where convenient.

For the sake of completeness and flexibility, the book contains more material than can be covered in two semesters. There should be enough for a three-semester course or, perhaps with some supplement in modern physics, a four-semester course. To use this book in a two-semester course such as I teach, some sections and chapters in addition to those labeled "optional" must be omitted or at least skimmed over. One method for broadening a course (while sacrificing some of the depth) is to assign a chapter or section to be read, without assigning the associated exercises or problems. I would recommend this to those who are tempted to omit Chapter 15, because the important ideas of resonance should be at least presented to students as early as possible. The inclusion or omission of certain topics naturally depends on the judgment of the instructor and the particular needs of the students. For a two-semester course, I would suggest, in addition to the optional sections, the omission of some of the following: Sections 5-4 (Motion with a Retarding Force Proportional to the Speed), 9-3 (Bernoulli's Equation), 10-6 (Using Integration to Find the Center of Mass), 11-7 (Elastic Collisions in Three Dimensions), 11-9 (Reaction Threshold), 11-10 (Coefficient of Restitution), 12-6 (Static Equilibrium of a Rigid Body), 13-6 (Motion of a Gyroscope), 14-8 (Combinations of Two Simple Harmonic Motions), 21-7 (Energy and Intensity of Harmonic Sound Waves), 23-3 (Harmonic Analysis and Synthesis), 23-4 (Wave Packets), 23-5 (Dispersion), 25-8 (Bragg Scattering), 26-8 (Diffraction Gratings), 29-8 (Electric Dipole in Electric Fields), 34-6 (Conservation of Charge and Approach to Electrostatic Equilibrium), 37-3 (Special Relativity and the Magnetic Field), and Chapters 28 (Special Relativity), 40 (Alternating-Current Circuits), 41 (Maxwell's Equations and Electromagnetic Waves), and 42 (Quantization).

Acknowledgments

Many people have contributed to this book. I would like to thank all those who have reviewed the various drafts and preliminary edition and have offered many helpful suggestions. In particular, James Gerhart was a constant source of information, inspiration, and encouragement through all the early drafts and preliminary edition. His generous hospitality during my pleasant and productive summer at the University of Washington and his help with writing problems, drawing figures, and criticizing the manuscript was largely responsible for getting the project off the ground. John McKinley's line-by-line review of the entire final manuscript, his checking of the final figures, and his overall help with all phases of the final production, including the reading of the galleys, was invaluable. Jerry Griggs suggested many of the interesting exercises and problems, and worked all the odd-numbered exercises and problems to check the answer section. Stanley Williams reviewed all the exercises and problems, supervised the working of them, and suggested exercises and problems for the latter chapters. Others who reviewed various parts of the manuscript include Reuben E. Alley, Jr., U.S. Naval Academy; Wallace Arthur, Fairleigh Dickinson University; Leo L. Baggerly, California State College, Bakersfield; Bill Beam, Rose-Hulman Institute of Technology; James R. Benbrook, University of Houston; Robert A. Boyer, Muhlenberg College; Morton K. Brussel, University of Illinois; Charles Buchanan, UCLA; Robert Folk, Lehigh University; Kenneth N. Geller, Drexel University; Sigmund P. Harris, Los Angeles Pierce College; Alvin M. Hudson, Occidental College; Granvil C. Kyker, Rose-Hulman Institute of Technology; David A. Nordling, U.S. Naval Academy; Jack Prince, Bronx Community College; Edward A. Saunders, U.S. Military Academy; D. J. Schlueter, Purdue University; Charles S. Shapiro, California State University, San Francisco; Stanley J. Shepherd, Pennsylvania State University; Dan Sober, UCLA; Martin Tiersten, CUNY; Miro M. Todorovich, Bronx Community College; and Al Verone, Oakland Community College.

I would like to thank the students at Oakland University and at Rose-Hulman Institute of Technology, who used the preliminary edition and various early drafts and who offered the kind of criticism only students can give. The preliminary edition was skillfully typed by La Verna Cole and the entire final manuscript, as well as several early drafts, by Sue Nast. I am grateful to my wife Sue for her continuing support and for her expert work on the index. Finally, I received much help and encouragement from Worth Publishers.

PAUL A. TIPLER

Supplements

Instructor's Manual   This comprehensive manual provides many aids and suggestions for teaching the course, including classroom demonstrations, additional applications and topics, suggestions for outside reading, and a guide to films that can be rented or purchased, keyed to the chapters in the text.

Student Study Guide   Available for student purchase, this includes the following for each chapter in the text:

A chapter summary including the fundamental equations.

A list of key items for review and self-testing.

True-false questions.

Essay questions to allow students to apply what they have learned.

Worked-out examples to supplement those in the text. Guidance in solving given problems is provided in three steps so students can take just as much help as they need.

Answers (and explanations) to all true-false and essay questions.

Contents in Brief

Contents in Brief

VOLUME 2

Contents

xvi   Contents

PHYSICS

CHAPTER 1   Introduction

Man has always been curious about the world around him. Since the beginnings of his recorded thought he has sought ways to impose order on the bewildering diversity of observed events. This search for order takes a variety of forms. One is religion, another is art, a third is science. The word science has its origins in a Latin verb meaning "to know," but science has come to mean not merely knowledge but knowledge specifically of the natural world and, most importantly, a body of knowledge organized in a specific and rational way.

Although the roots of science are as deep as those of religion or of art, its traditions are much more modern. Only in the last few centuries have there been methods for studying nature systematically. They include techniques of observation, rules for reasoning and prediction, the idea of planned experimentation, and ways for communicating experimental and theoretical results — all loosely referred to as the *scientific method*. An essential part of the advance of our understanding of nature is the open communication of experimental results, theoretical calculations, speculations, and summaries of knowledge. A textbook is one of these forms. An elementary textbook such as this has two purposes: It is designed, first, to introduce the newcomer in the field of science to material which is already widely known in the scientific and technical community and which will form the basis of his or her more advanced studies of this knowledge. It may also serve to acquaint a student not majoring in science with information and with a way of thinking that is having a cumulative effect upon our way of life.

This book concentrates on the subjects of *classical physics*, a term that usually refers to mechanics, light, heat, sound, electricity, and magnetism, subjects well understood in the late nineteenth century before the advent of relativity and quantum theory, which were developed in the early years of the twentieth century. The application of special relativity, and particularly quantum theory, to the description of such microscopic systems as atoms, molecules, and nuclei and to a detailed understanding of solids, liquids, and gases is often referred to as *modern physics*. Although modern physics has made many important contributions to technology, the great bulk of technical knowledge and skill is still based squarely on classical physics. While concentrating on classical physics, we shall often discuss modifications based on quantum theory and special relativity, and compare the predictions of the classical and modern theories with each other and with the results of experiments.

Except for the interior of the atom and for motion at speeds near the speed of light, classical physics correctly and precisely describes the behavior of the physical world. It is through applications of classical physics that we have been able to exploit natural resources successfully, and it is largely through applications of classical physics that we will find the technical means necessary to preserve our environment for successful and controlled future use. Moreover, modern physics builds on the concepts of classical physics and cannot be understood without them. Consider, for a moment, the modern descriptions of the atom. In the first successful theory of the atom, the Bohr theory of 1913, the atom was pictured as a miniature solar system with the electrons revolving around the nucleus in circular or elliptical orbits. The attraction of the electron to the nucleus was described by the classical theory of electricity. The fact that the orbits had to be circular or elliptical followed directly from Newton's laws of mechanics. In the Bohr theory, the classical principles of *conservation of mechanical energy* and of *angular momentum* were fundamental assumptions. In the modern quantum-mechanical theory of the atom, the electron is represented by a *wave packet*. The energy of the atom is *quantized* by postulating that the *electron wave function* obeys a *standing-wave condition*. As with the Bohr theory, *energy conservation* determines the possible *energies of radiation* when the atom changes *energy states*. When the atom is in a *magnetic field,* the *radiation spectrum* of the atom is slightly different. This difference is related to the frequency with which the *magnetic moment* precesses about the *magnetic field* due to the *torque* exerted by the *field* on the atom. This *precession* is similar to that of a spinning top or gyroscope.

Many of the terms and concepts mentioned in the above paragraph are probably unfamiliar to you now. Don't let this bother you. All of these concepts—angular momentum, energy, potential energy, torque, precession, wave packet, wave function, standing-wave condition, conservation of energy, magnetic field—are concepts of classical physics which we discuss in this book. With a thorough understanding of these concepts and familiarity with the role they play in classical physics, you will be well equipped to study the modern theory of the atom or any other topic in modern physics.

1-1   Mechanical Models

Classical mechanics, fascinating in its own right, is a particularly good subject to start with. Since so much of our everyday experience is directly applicable, classical mechanics is less abstract than subjects like electric and magnetic fields. Many abstract concepts in physics, e.g., potential energy, are easiest to learn in the framework of classical mechanics. But classical mechanics is important for other reasons. Many of the modern microscopic theories of matter are stated in terms

Marshall Lockman/Black Star

Mechanical model of a DNA molecule.

Eighteenth-century mechanical model of the solar system. (*Courtesy of Harvard University.*)

of mechanical models, like the Bohr model of the atom, already mentioned. We say, for example, that the magnetic moment of the electron precesses like the precession of a spinning top. In a useful mechanical model of solid matter, atoms are pictured as being connected to each other by springs, and the vibrations of the atoms are coupled to each other like those of coupled mechanical oscillators. The classical mechanical theory of oscillation is therefore central to the modern theory of solids.

There is great economy in the methods of physics. Consider the motion of a mass on a spring, which we shall look at in detail when we study simple harmonic motion. Later we shall consider different types of oscillation and resonance. What you learn from these studies is directly applicable to many other phenomena; e.g., the behavior of electric circuits with capacitance, inductance, and resistance is described by exactly the same kind of mathematical equations as a mass oscillating on a spring. The exchange between the electric energy in the capacitor and magnetic energy in the inductor and the dissipation of energy in the resistor are analogous to the exchange between potential and kinetic energy of a mass on a spring and the dissipation of energy by friction. This same study is applicable to wave motion, whether it is the simple harmonic motion of a string segment for standing waves on a string, the oscillations of air particles during the passage of sound waves through air, or the oscillations of the electric and magnetic field vectors in a light wave. In modern theory a thorough knowledge of the classical oscillator is necessary in many quantum-mechanical problems.

1-2   Mathematics and Physics

The laws of physics are generalizations from observations and experimental results. For example, Newton's law of universal gravitation was based on a variety of observations: the paths of planets in their motion about the sun, the acceleration of objects near the earth, the acceleration of the moon in its orbit, the daily and seasonal variation in the tides, etc. Physical laws are usually expressed as mathematical equations.[1] The law of gravitation states that any two objects attract each other with a force which is proportional to the mass of each object and inversely proportional to the square of the distance between them. It is written $F = Gm_1m_2/r^2$. The equation can then be used to make predictions about other phenomena and to test the range of validity of the law. For example, together Newton's law of gravitation and Newton's laws of motion can be used to predict the orbits of planets, comets, and satellites. Understanding such predictions requires knowledge of elementary calculus and the ability to manipulate and solve simple differential equations, for the laws of motion are expressed as second-order differential equations. The mathematical equations governing wave motion are partial differential equations. Thus to understand physics on any level beyond a qualitative description, a considerable amount of mathematics is needed. It is usually easiest to learn the physics and the necessary mathematics at about the same time since the immediate application of mathematics to a physical situation helps you understand both the physics and the mathematics. In this book it is assumed that you have taken or are now taking a course in calculus. Much of the calculus needed to understand physics is presented in outline form. Since calculus is a new and unfamiliar tool for most students beginning physics, it is used here as simply as possible. As this book is about physics and not mathematics, mathematical details and rigor are not stressed. In the more difficult mathematical problems, plausibility arguments are often substituted for rigorous derivations in order to appeal to your intuition.

1-3   How to Learn Physics

A textbook is only one tool for learning physics. A good teacher, lecture demonstrations, films, and experimental work in the laboratory are indispensible. Outside reading is highly recommended. While you concentrate on obtaining a rigorous understanding of classical physics in your introductory course, you should be broadening your familiarity with contemporary physics by reading widely in the many excellent popular and semipopular accounts of modern science, e.g., those in *Scientific American*.

At the end of each chapter are a review, exercises, and problems. The importance of solving problems to learn physics cannot be overemphasized. Only in working problems can you find out whether you have really grasped the text material. Many details can be brought out in problems that cannot be treated in any other way. You should do as many problems as possible, whether assigned or not. One way to gain practice and experience in problem solving is to use the examples in the text as problems. Read the statement or question in the example and then attempt to answer the question or work through the example without looking at the text. When you finish or if you get stuck, look at the worked example. This approach will demonstrate how well you understand the material and what mistakes you may be making.

[1] Some laws are expressed as mathematical inequalities; e.g., the second law of thermodynamics can be stated: the entropy change of the universe in any period of time is always greater than or equal to zero.

(Don't be discouraged if you are often stuck. Although many examples are rather direct applications of material discussed in the text, some introduce a new method of solution or approach. A few examples cover famous results and are really an extension of the text. In these cases, you cannot expect to work through the examples on your first try without difficulty.)

Scattered throughout the text are questions. Some are very easy and are answered in the previous discussion. If you have understood the discussion, you should be able to answer them with little trouble. Other questions are meant to extend or apply the discussion in the text. Some have no simple answers but are food for thought. Whether or not you are taking a simultaneous laboratory course, you should be alert to simple experiments or observations relating the concepts in the book to your experience in the real world. The questions should stimulate your ability to relate your study to everyday experience.

It is possible to state the laws of physics in concise statements and equations and use them to deduce the behavior of many systems under various conditions. Although there is a certain aesthetic appeal in this deductive approach, it is not an easy way to learn physics or to develop an understanding of the workings of nature. What we now know of nature results from the efforts of many different people and many years of experimentation, theoretical proposals, and debate. Sometimes discussing the history of an idea helps us learn the presently accepted view. Considering rather special cases can be a helpful preliminary to the general discussion of a physical law. For example, some familiarity with many new concepts can be obtained by treating one-dimensional problems. The extension to three dimensions is then much easier than starting with the general three-dimensional problem would be. We shall consider one-dimensional motion first to introduce some of the concepts of velocity and acceleration before generalizing to two- and three-dimensional motion. Similarly, the ideas of work, potential energy, conservative forces, and many of the properties of waves are first introduced in one dimension before the general three-dimensional situation is treated.

1-4   Units

The laws of physics express relationships between physical quantities such as length, time, force, energy, and temperature. Measuring such a quantity involves comparison with some unit value of the quantity. The most elementary measurement is probably that of distance. In order to measure the distance between two points we need a standard unit, e.g., a meter stick or a ruler. The statement that a certain distance is 25 meters means that it is 25 times the length of the unit meter; i.e., a standard meter stick fits into that distance 25 times. It is important to include the unit meters along with the number 25 in expressing a distance because there are other units of distance in common use. To say that a distance is 25 is meaningless.

The units of all physical quantities can be expressed in terms of a small number of fundamental units. For example, a unit of speed, e.g., meters per second or miles per hour, is expressed in terms of a unit of length and a unit of time. Similarly, any unit of energy can be expressed in terms of the units of length, time, and mass. In fact, all quantities occurring in the study of mechanics can be expressed in

Standard meter bar, kept at the National Bureau of Standards, Washington, D.C., the United States national standard from 1893 to 1960. The bar, made of a platinum-iridium alloy, is an exact duplicate of the international prototype meter housed at Sèvres, France. (*Courtesy of the National Bureau of Standards.*)

Figure 1-1
The standard of length, the meter, was chosen so that the distance from the equator to the North Pole along the meridian through Paris would be 10^7 m. The circumference of the earth is therefore 4×10^7 m, and the radius is $(2 \times 10^7)/\pi$ m $= 6.37 \times 10^6$ m.

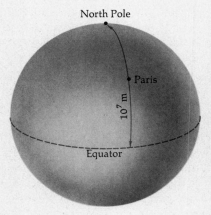

terms of these three fundamental units. The choice of standard units for these fundamental quantities determines a system of units for all mechanical quantities. In the system used universally in the scientific community, which we shall use most often, the standard length is the meter, the standard time is the second, and the standard mass is the kilogram. This system of units is called the mks system (after the meter, kilogram, and second). The standard of length, the meter (abbreviated m), was originally indicated by two scratches on a platinum-iridium alloy bar kept at the International Bureau of Weights and Measures in Sèvres, France. This length was chosen so that the distance between the equator and the North Pole along the meridian through Paris would be 10 million meters (Figure 1-1). (After construction of the standard meter bar, it was found that this distance differs by a few hundredths of a percent from 10^7 m.) The standard meter was used to construct secondary standards, which are used to calibrate measuring rods throughout the world. The standard meter is now defined in terms of the wavelength of a particular spectral line of an isotope of krypton. It is 1,650,763.73 wavelengths of this light. This change made comparison of lengths throughout the world easier and more accurate.

The unit of time, the second (sec), was originally defined in terms of the rotation of the earth to be $\frac{1}{60}(\frac{1}{60})(\frac{1}{24})$ of the mean solar day. The second is now defined in terms of a characteristic frequency associated with the cesium atom.

The unit of mass, the kilogram (kg), equal to 1000 grams (gm), is defined to be the mass of a particular standard body, also kept at Sèvres. We shall discuss the concept of mass in detail in Chapter 4.

The units of other quantities in mechanics, such as speed and momentum, are derived from the three fundamental units of length, time, and mass. The choice of these three as the fundamental quantities is somewhat arbitrary. For example, we could replace the choice of a standard length with a standard speed, e.g., the speed of light in vacuum, and give this unit a name. The unit of length would then be derived from the product of this speed unit and the unit of time.

In studying thermodynamics and electricity, we shall need two more fundamental physical units, the unit of temperature, the kelvin (formerly the degree kelvin), and the unit of current, the ampere. These five fundamental units, the meter (m), the second (sec), the kilogram (kg), the kelvin (K), and the ampere (A), constitute the international system of units (SI).[1] The unit of every physical quantity can be expressed in terms of these fundamental SI units. Some important combinations are given special names. For example, the SI unit of force, $kg\text{-}m/sec^2$, is called a newton (N). Similarly, the SI unit of power, $kg\text{-}m^2/sec^3 = N\text{-}m/sec$, is called a watt (W). Prefixes for common multiples and submultiples of SI units are listed in Table 1-1. These multiples are all powers of 10. Such a system is called a *decimal system;* the decimal system based on the meter is called the *metric system.* The prefixes can be applied to any SI unit; for example, 10^{-2} meter is 1 centimeter (cm); 10^{-3} watt is 1 milliwatt (mW).

In another system of units used in the United States, the *British engineering system,* the unit of force, the pound, is chosen to be a fundamental unit instead of mass. (We shall discuss the relation between force and mass in detail in Chapter 4.) The unit of force is defined in terms of the gravitational attraction of the earth at a particular place for a standard body. The other fundamental units in this system are the foot and the second. The second is defined as in the international system. The foot is defined as exactly one-third of a yard, which is now legally defined in terms of the meter

$$1 \text{ yd} = 0.9144 \text{ m}$$

$$1 \text{ ft} = \tfrac{1}{3} \text{ yd} = 0.3048 \text{ m}$$

making the inch exactly 2.54 cm. This system is not a decimal system. It is less convenient than the SI or other decimal systems because common multiples of the unit are not powers of 10. For example, 1 ft $= \tfrac{1}{3}$ yd, and 1 in $= \tfrac{1}{12}$ ft. We shall see in Chapter 4 that mass is a better choice of a fundamental unit than force because mass can be defined without reference to the gravitational attraction of the earth. Relations between the British engineering system and SI units are given in Appendix C.

Questions

1. What are the advantages and disadvantages of using the length of a person's arm for a standard of length?

2. A certain clock is consistently 10 percent fast when compared with the standard cesium clock. A second clock varies in a random way by 1 percent. Which clock would make a more useful secondary standard for a laboratory? Why?

1-5 Conversion of Units

We have said that the magnitude of a physical quantity must include both a number and a unit. When such quantities are added, sub-

Table 1-1
Prefixes for powers of 10

Multiple	Prefix	Abbreviation
10^{12}	tera	T
10^9	giga	G
10^6	mega	M
10^3	kilo	k
10^{-1}	deci	d
10^{-2}	centi	c
10^{-3}	milli	m
10^{-6}	micro	μ
10^{-9}	nano	n
10^{-12}	pico	p
10^{-15}	femto	f
10^{-18}	atto	a

Definition of yard and foot

Roman-Greek tablet showing the length of the standard foot about A.D. 300–500. (*Courtesy of the Science Museum, London.*)

---

[1] SI stands for *Système International.* The sixth SI unit, the candela, a unit of luminous intensity, we have no occasion to use in this book.

tracted, multiplied, or divided in an algebraic equation, the unit can be treated like any other algebraic quantity. For example, suppose you wish to find the distance traveled in 3 hours (h) by a car moving at a constant rate of 60 miles/hour (mi/h). The distance x is just the speed v times the time t:

$$x = vt = 60 \, \frac{\text{mi}}{\cancel{\text{h}}} \times 3 \, \cancel{\text{h}} = 180 \text{ mi}$$

We cancel the unit of time, the hour, just as we would any algebraic quantity to obtain the distance in the proper unit of length, the mile. This method makes it easy to convert from one unit of distance to another. Suppose we want to convert our answer of 180 mi into feet. We use the fact that

$$5280 \text{ ft} = 1 \text{ mi}$$

If we divide each side of this equation by 1 mi, we obtain

$$\frac{5280 \text{ ft}}{1 \text{ mi}} = 1$$

We can now change 180 mi to feet by multiplying by the factor 5280 ft/mi:

$$180 \text{ mi} = 180 \text{ mi} \times \frac{5280 \text{ ft}}{1 \text{ mi}} = 9.50 \times 10^5 \text{ ft}$$

We have rounded the result to three significant figures, consistent with the fact that the distance 180 mi is given to only three significant figures. The factor 5280 ft/mi is called a *conversion factor*. It has the value 1 and is used to convert a quantity expressed in one unit of measure into the equivalent in another unit of measure. By writing out the units explicitly, we need not think about whether we multiply by 5280 or divide by 5280 to change miles to feet or feet to miles because the units tell us if we have chosen the correct or incorrect factor.

Example 1-1 What is the equivalent of 60 mi/h in feet per second?

We use the above conversion factor plus the facts that 60 sec = 1 min and 60 min = 1 h. Then

$$60 \, \frac{\cancel{\text{mi}}}{\cancel{\text{h}}} \times \frac{5280 \text{ ft}}{1 \, \cancel{\text{mi}}} \times \frac{1 \, \cancel{\text{h}}}{60 \, \cancel{\text{min}}} \times \frac{1 \, \cancel{\text{min}}}{60 \text{ sec}} = 88 \, \frac{\text{ft}}{\text{sec}}$$

The quantity 60 mi/h is multiplied by a set of conversion factors each having the value 1, so that the value of the speed is not changed.

1-6   Dimensions of Physical Quantities

The area of a plane figure is found by multiplying one length by another. For example, the area of a rectangle of sides 2 and 3 in is $A = (2 \text{ in})(3 \text{ in}) = 6 \text{ in}^2$. The units of this area are square inches. Because area is the product of two lengths, it is said to have the *dimensions* of length times length, or length squared, often written L^2. The idea of dimensions is easily extended to other nongeometric quantities. For example, speed is said to have the dimensions of length divided by time, or L/T. The dimensions of any quantity in mechanics are written in terms of the fundamental quantities length, time, and mass. Adding two physical quantities makes sense only if the quantities have the same dimensions. For example, we cannot add an area to a speed to obtain a meaningful sum. If we have an equation like

$$A = B + C$$

the quantities A, B, and C must all have the same dimensions. Addition of B and C requires that these quantities be in the same units. For example, if B is an area of 500 in^2 and C is 4 ft^2, we must either convert B into square feet or C into square inches to find the sum of the two areas.

We can often find mistakes in a calculation by checking the dimensions or units of the quantities in the calculation. Suppose, for example, we are using a formula for distance x given by

$$x = x_0 + vt + \tfrac{1}{2}at$$

where t is the time, x_0 is the initial distance at time $t = 0$, v is the speed, and a is the acceleration, which (as we shall see in the next chapter) has dimensions of L/T^2 and SI units of meters per second per second (m/sec^2). We can see immediately that this formula cannot be correct: since x has dimensions of length, each term on the right side of the equation must have dimensions of length. Both x_0 and vt have dimensions of length, but the dimensions of $\tfrac{1}{2}at$ are $(L/T^2)T = L/T$. Since the last term does not have the correct dimensions, an error has been made somewhere in obtaining the formula. Dimensional consistency is a necessary condition for an equation to be correct. It is, of course, not sufficient. An equation can have the correct dimensions in each term without describing any physical situation.

Our knowledge of the dimensions of quantities often enables us to recall a formula or sometimes even guess at it. Suppose we remember that there is a simple formula relating the velocity of a wave v (dimensions L/T), the wavelength λ[1] (dimensions L), and frequency f (dimensions T^{-1}). There is only one dimensionally consistent equation expressing one of these quantities as the product of the other two; it is

$$v = f\lambda$$

This equation happens to be correct. If we were to write down $f = v\lambda$, we could see immediately by checking the dimensions that it is incorrect.

Questions

3. The speed v of an object dropped from rest depends on the time t and on the acceleration of gravity g, which is a constant and has dimensions LT^{-2}. From dimensional considerations only, guess at a possible relation between v, g, and t.

4. The distance d an object falls when dropped from rest also depends on the time t and the acceleration of gravity g. Guess at a relation among d, g, and t.

---

[1] λ is the Greek letter lambda. A list of the Greek alphabet will be found inside the front cover.

1-7   Review of Trigonometry

Since the elements of trigonometry are used in analyzing almost all physical problems, you must be able to use trigonometry easily, quickly, and correctly. With practice, the physical scientist or engineer can handle simple trigonometry almost as easily as algebra or arithmetic. This section gives the main results of trigonometry used in physics. You should read it through to be sure you are familiar with these results. If you encounter unfamiliar material, study it carefully. This section may also be a useful reference as you read further or work on problems.

The angle made by two intersecting straight lines is defined as follows. The two lines are connected with the arc of a circle whose center is at the intersection of the lines (see Figure 1-2). The angle made by the two lines is defined to be the ratio of the arc length and the radius. This ratio is the same no matter where the arc is drawn. If r is the radius of the arc and s the distance along it, i.e., the arc length, the angle θ is given by

Figure 1-2
The angle θ is defined to be the ratio s/r, where s is the arc length intercepted on a circle of radius r. The angle so defined is measured in radians.

$$\theta = \frac{s}{r}$$

1-1   *Definition of angle*

The angle expressed this way is measured in *radians* (rad). Since the angle is the ratio of two lengths, it is dimensionless. The radian is therefore a dimensionless unit. In dimensional analysis it can be ignored. A more familiar unit of angular measurement is the degree, defined as the angle for which the arc length s is $\frac{1}{360}$ times the circumference of the circle. Since the circumference of a circle has an arc length of $2\pi r$, the angle subtended by a full circle in radians is $2\pi r/r = 2\pi$. The degree and radian are related by

$$360° = 2\pi \text{ rad}$$

or

$$1 \text{ rad} = \frac{360°}{2\pi} = 57.3°$$

1-2

Figure 1-3 shows a right triangle formed by drawing the line BC perpendicular to AC. The lengths of the sides are labeled a, b, and c. The trigonometric functions $\sin \theta$, $\cos \theta$, and $\tan \theta$ are defined for an acute angle θ by

Figure 1-3
Right triangle used to define the trigonometric functions $\sin \theta$, $\cos \theta$, and $\tan \theta$.

$$\sin \theta = \frac{a}{c} = \frac{\text{opposite side}}{\text{hypotenuse}}$$

$$\cos \theta = \frac{b}{c} = \frac{\text{adjacent side}}{\text{hypotenuse}}$$

1-3   *Definition of trigonometric functions*

$$\tan \theta = \frac{a}{b} = \frac{\sin \theta}{\cos \theta} = \frac{\text{opposite side}}{\text{adjacent side}}$$

Three other trigonometric functions are defined by the inverse of these functions:

$$\sec \theta = \frac{c}{b} = (\cos \theta)^{-1} \qquad \csc \theta = \frac{c}{a} = (\sin \theta)^{-1}$$

$$\cot \theta = \frac{b}{a} = (\tan \theta)^{-1} = \frac{\cos \theta}{\sin \theta}$$

which are not often used in physics. The pythagorean theorem gives some useful identities:

$$a^2 + b^2 = c^2$$

1-4

If we divide each term in this equation by c^2, we obtain

$$\frac{a^2}{c^2} + \frac{b^2}{c^2} = 1 \qquad\qquad 1\text{-}5$$

or from the definitions of sin θ and cos θ,

$$\sin^2 \theta + \cos^2 \theta = 1 \qquad\qquad 1\text{-}6$$

Similarly we can divide each term in Equation 1-4 by a^2 or b^2 and obtain

$$1 + \cot^2 \theta = \csc^2 \theta \qquad\qquad 1\text{-}7$$

and

$$1 + \tan^2 \theta = \sec^2 \theta \qquad\qquad 1\text{-}8$$

Example 1-2 Use the isosceles right triangle shown in Figure 1-4 to find the sine, cosine, and tangent of 45°.

It is clear from the figure that the two acute angles of this triangle are equal. Since the sum of the three angles in a triangle must equal 180° and the right angle is 90°, each acute angle must be 45°. If we multiply each side of any triangle by a common factor, we obtain a similar triangle with the same angles as before. Since the trigonometric functions involve only ratios of two sides of a right triangle, we can choose any convenient length for one side. Let the equal sides of this triangle have the length 1 unit. The length of the hypotenuse is then found from the pythagorean theorem (Equation 1-4):

$$c = \sqrt{a^2 + b^2} = \sqrt{1^2 + 1^2} = \sqrt{2} \text{ units}$$

The trigonometric functions for the angle 45° are then given by Equation 1-3:

$$\sin 45° = \frac{1}{\sqrt{2}} = 0.707$$

$$\cos 45° = \frac{1}{\sqrt{2}} = 0.707$$

$$\tan 45° = \frac{1}{1} = 1.00$$

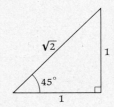

Figure 1-4
Isoceles right triangle for Example 1-2. This triangle is also called a 45-45-90 triangle.

Example 1-3 The sine of 30° is exactly $\frac{1}{2}$. Find the ratios of the sides of a 30-60 right triangle.

This common triangle is shown in Figure 1-5. We choose the length 1 unit for the side opposite the 30° angle. The hypotenuse is then obtained from the fact that sin 30° = 0.5:

$$c = \frac{a}{\sin 30°} = \frac{1}{0.5} = 2 \text{ units}$$

The length of the side opposite the 60° angle is then found from the pythagorean theorem:

$$b = \sqrt{c^2 - a^2} = \sqrt{2^2 - 1} = \sqrt{3}$$

From these results we can obtain the other trigonometric functions for the angles 30 and 60°:

$$\cos 30° = \frac{b}{c} = \frac{\sqrt{3}}{2} = 0.866$$

$$\tan 30° = \frac{a}{b} = \frac{1}{\sqrt{3}} = 0.577$$

$$\sin 60° = \frac{b}{c} = \cos 30° = \frac{\sqrt{3}}{2} = 0.866$$

Figure 1-5
A 30-60-90 triangle for Example 1-3.

$$\cos 60° = \frac{a}{c} = \sin 30° = \tfrac{1}{2} = 0.500$$

$$\tan 60° = \frac{b}{a} = \frac{\sqrt{3}}{1} = 1.732$$

Figure 1-6
For small angles, $\theta = s/c$, $\sin \theta = a/c$, and $\tan \theta = a/b$ are approximately equal.

The calculation of the trigonometric functions for another common right triangle, the 3-4-5 right triangle, is left as an exercise.

For small angles, the length a is nearly equal to the arc length s, as can be seen from Figure 1-6. Also, the lengths c and b are nearly equal. The angle $\theta = s/c$ is therefore nearly equal to $\sin \theta = a/c$:

$$\sin \theta \approx \theta \qquad \text{small } \theta \qquad\qquad\qquad 1\text{-}9$$

Small-angle approximations

Similarly, $\tan \theta = a/b$ is nearly equal to both θ and $\sin \theta$ for small θ:

$$\tan \theta \approx \sin \theta \approx \theta \qquad \text{small } \theta \qquad\qquad 1\text{-}10$$

Since $\cos \theta = b/c$ and these lengths are nearly equal for small θ, we have

$$\cos \theta \approx 1 \qquad \text{small } \theta \qquad\qquad\qquad 1\text{-}11$$

Equations 1-9 and 1-10 hold only if θ is measured in radians.

Example 1-4 By how much do $\sin \theta$, $\tan \theta$, and θ differ when $\theta = 15°$? This angle in radians is

$$\theta = 15° \frac{2\pi \text{ rad}}{360°} = 0.262 \text{ rad}$$

From a table of trigonometric functions,

$$\sin 15° = 0.259 \qquad \tan 15° = 0.268$$

Thus $\sin \theta$ and θ (in radians) differ by 0.003, or about 1 percent, and $\tan \theta$ and θ differ by 0.006, or about 2 percent. For smaller angles the approximation $\theta \approx \sin \theta \approx \tan \theta$ is even more accurate.

This example shows that if accuracy of a few percent is needed, these approximations can be used only for angles of about 15° or smaller. Figure 1-7 graphs θ, $\sin \theta$, and $\tan \theta$ versus θ for small θ.

Figure 1-7
Plots of $\sin \theta$, $\tan \theta$, and θ for small angles.

Other trigonometric identities which we shall use occasionally follow directly from the definitions given:

$$\sin(\theta_1 + \theta_2) = \sin\theta_1 \cos\theta_2 + \cos\theta_1 \sin\theta_2$$

$$\cos(\theta_1 + \theta_2) = \cos\theta_1 \cos\theta_2 - \sin\theta_1 \sin\theta_2$$

$$\sin\theta_1 + \sin\theta_2 = 2\sin\tfrac{1}{2}(\theta_1 + \theta_2)\cos\tfrac{1}{2}(\theta_1 - \theta_2)$$

$$\cos\theta_1 + \cos\theta_2 = 2\cos\tfrac{1}{2}(\theta_1 + \theta_2)\cos\tfrac{1}{2}(\theta_1 - \theta_2)$$

1-12

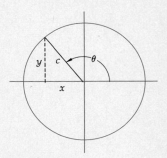

Figure 1-8
Diagram defining trigonometric functions for an obtuse angle.

Figure 1-8 shows an obtuse angle with vertex at the origin and one side along the x axis. The trigonometric functions are defined for a general angle by

$$\sin\theta = \frac{y}{c} \qquad \cos\theta = \frac{x}{c} \qquad \tan\theta = \frac{y}{x}$$

1-13

Figure 1-9 plots these functions versus θ. Some useful relations which can be obtained from these figures are

$$\sin(\pi - \theta) = \sin\theta \qquad \cos(\pi - \theta) = -\cos\theta$$

$$\sin(\tfrac{1}{2}\pi - \theta) = \cos\theta \qquad \cos(\tfrac{1}{2}\pi - \theta) = \sin\theta$$

1-14

All trigonometric functions have a period of 2π. That is, when an angle changes by 2π or 360°, the original value of the function is obtained again. Thus $\sin(\theta + 2\pi) = \sin\theta$, etc.

(a)

Figure 1-9
The trigonometric functions $\sin\theta$, $\cos\theta$, and $\tan\theta$ versus θ.

(b)

(c)

1-8 The Binomial Expansion

The binomial theorem is very useful for making approximations. One form of this theorem is

$$(1 + x)^n = 1 + nx + \frac{n(n-1)}{2} x^2 + \frac{n(n-1)(n-2)}{(3)(2)} x^3$$

$$+ \frac{n(n-1)(n-2)(n-3)}{(4)(3)(2)} x^4 + \cdots \qquad \text{1-15}$$

If n is a positive integer, there are just $n + 1$ terms in this series. If n is a real number other than a positive integer, there are an infinite number of terms. The series converges (is valid) for any value of n if x^2 is less than 1. It also converges for $x^2 = 1$ if n is positive. The series is particularly useful if $|x|$ is much less than 1. Then each term in Equation 1-15 is much smaller than the previous term and we can drop all but the first two or three terms in the equation. If $|x|$ is much less than 1, we have

---

$$(1 + x)^n \approx 1 + nx \qquad |x| << 1 \qquad \text{1-16}$$

Binomial approximation

Example 1-5 Use Equation 1-16 to find an approximate value for the square root of 101.

First state the problem to give an expression of the form $(1 + x)^n$ with x much less than 1:

$$(101)^{1/2} = (100 + 1)^{1/2} = (100)^{1/2}(1 + 0.01)^{1/2} = 10(1 + 0.01)^{1/2}$$

Now we can use Equation 1-16 with $n = \frac{1}{2}$ and $x = 0.01$:

$$(1 + 0.01)^{1/2} \approx 1 + \tfrac{1}{2}(0.01) = 1.005$$

$$(101)^{1/2} = 10(1 + 0.01)^{1/2} \approx 10(1.005) = 10.05$$

We can get an idea of the accuracy of this approximation by looking at the first term in Equation 1-15 that is neglected. This term is

$$\frac{n(n-1)}{2} x^2$$

Since x in this case is 1 percent of 1, the quantity x^2 is 0.01 percent of 1. By dropping this term, we are making an error of the order of

$$\frac{n(n-1)}{2} x^2 = \tfrac{1}{8}(0.01)^2 \approx 0.001\%$$

We thus expect our answer to be correct to within about 0.001 percent. The actual value of $(101)^{1/2}$ is 10.049876. The difference between this value and our approximation is 0.000124, which is about 0.001 percent of 10.05.

Example 1-6 Using $\sin \theta \approx \theta$ and $\cos \theta = (1 - \sin^2 \theta)^{1/2}$, find an approximation for $\cos \theta$ for small θ.

We have

$$\cos \theta = (1 - \sin^2 \theta)^{1/2} \approx (1 - \theta^2)^{1/2} \approx 1 + \tfrac{1}{2}(-\theta^2) = 1 - \tfrac{1}{2}\theta^2$$

This approximation is often useful as a correction to the more drastic approximation $\cos \theta \approx 1$ given by Equation 1-11.

Review

A. Define, explain, or otherwise identify the following (the numbers give the page on which the term is discussed or defined):

Units, 5   Fundamental units, 5

B. True or false. State whether each statement is true or false and explain your reasoning. If you can, give an example supporting a true statement and a counterexample contradicting a false statement.

1. Two quantities which are to be added must have the same dimensions.

2. Two quantities which are to be multiplied must have the same dimensions.

3. All conversion factors have the value 1.

4. If the angle θ is very small, sin θ and tan θ are approximately equal.

5. If the angle θ is very small, cos θ and θ are approximately equal.

Exercises

Section 1-4, Units; Section 1-5, Conversion of Units; and Section 1-6, Dimensions of Physical Quantities

1. In the following equations, the distance x is in meters and the time t is in seconds. What are the SI units of the constants C_1, C_2, and C_3?

(a) $x = C_1 + C_2 t + C_3 t^2$

(b) $x = C_1 \cos C_2 t$

(c) $x = C_1 \sin C_2 t$

Hint: The arguments of trigonometric functions and exponentials must be dimensionless.

2. What are the dimensions of the constants in Exercise 1?

3. An equation relating the speed v to the distance x is

$$v^2 = C_1 x$$

(a) What are the dimensions of the constant C_1? (b) If the speed is in meters per second and the distance in meters, what are the SI units of C_1?

4. If x is in feet and t in seconds in the equations in Exercise 1, what are the units of the constants in that exercise in the British engineering system?

5. The speed of a particle as a function of time is given by $v = C_1 \cos C_2 t$. Find the dimensions and the SI units of the constants C_1 and C_2.

6. From the original definition of the meter in terms of the distance from the equator to the North Pole, find in meters (a) the circumference and (b) the radius of the earth.

7. Find the circumference and radius of the earth in miles by converting your answers in Exercise 6 from meters to miles.

8. Find the conversion factor to convert miles per hour to kilometers per hour.

9. (a) Find the number of seconds in a year. (b) If one could count \$1 per second, how many years would it take to count 1 billion dollars (1 billion $= 10^9$)? (c) If one could count one molecule per second, how many years would it take to count the molecules in a mole? (The number of molecules in a mole is Avogadro's number, $N_A = 6 \times 10^{23}$.)

10. The SI unit of force, the kilogram-meter per second per second (kg-m/sec²), is called the newton (N). Find the dimensions and the SI units of the constant G in Newton's law of gravitation $F = Gm_1 m_2/r^2$.

11. Sometimes a conversion factor can be derived from the knowledge of a constant in two different systems. (a) The speed of light in vacuum is 186,000 mi/sec $= 3 \times 10^8$ m/sec. Use this fact to find the number of kilometers in a mile. (b) The weight of 1 ft^3 of water is 62.4 lb. Use this and the fact that 1 cm^3 of water has a mass of 1 gm to find the weight in pounds of a 1-kg mass.

Section 1-7, Review of Trigonometry

12. Find the measure of a right angle in radians directly from the definition $\theta = s/r$.

13. Find: (a) $\sin \frac{1}{2}\pi$; (b) $\cos \frac{1}{2}\pi$; (c) $\tan \pi$; (d) $\tan (\pi/4)$; (e) $\sin (\pi/4)$; (f) $\cos (3\pi/4)$.

14. Convert from radians to degrees: (a) $\pi/4$; (b) $3\pi/2$; (c) $\pi/2$; (d) $\pi/6$; (e) $5\pi/6$.

15. Convert from degrees to radians: (a) 60°; (b) 90°; (c) 30°; (d) 45°; (e) 180°; (f) 37°; (g) 720°.

16. Find conversion factors for revolutions per minute to radians per second and degrees per second.

17. A record rotates at a rate of 33.3 revolutions per minute (rev/min). Find the angle in radians and in degrees through which the record rotates in 1 sec.

18. The diameter of a record is 12 in, and the record rotates at 33.3 rev/min. (a) What is the distance traveled by a point on the rim (measured along the circular arc) during 1 rev? (b) At what rate in inches per second does this point travel?

19. A right triangle has sides 3, 4, and 5 m. If θ_1 is the smaller acute angle and θ_2 the larger acute angle of the triangle, find the sine, cosine, and tangent of each of these angles. Find the measures of these angles in degrees using Appendix F.

20. A right triangle has sides $a = 2$ in, $b = 8$ in, and $c = ?$ (a) Find the length of the hypotenuse c. (b) Find the sine, cosine, and tangent of the angles of the triangle. (c) From Appendix F find the angles.

21. Use the small-angle approximations to find approximate values for (a) $\sin 8°$ and (b) $\tan 5°$. Hint: First convert these angles to radian measure.

22. The angle subtended by the moon's diameter at a point on the earth is about 0.524°. Use this and the fact that the moon is about 2.36×10^5 mi away to find the diameter of the moon.

Section 1-8, The Binomial Expansion

23. Write out the complete binomial expansion (Equation 1-15) for $(1 + x)^3$ and check by finding $(1 + x)^3$ directly by multiplication.

24. The quantity $1/(1 + x)^2$ can be written as an infinite power series $1/(1 + x)^2 = 1 + a_1 x + a_2 x^2 + a_3 x^3 + \cdots + \cdots + a_n x^n + \cdots$, where a_n are constants. Find these constants using the binomial equation 1-15.

25. Use the approximation $(1 + x)^n \approx 1 + nx$, $|x| << 1$, to find approximate values for: (a) $\sqrt{99}$; (b) $1/1.01$; (c) $124^{1/3}$.

26. Use the approximation $(1 + x)^n \approx 1 + nx$ to find approximate values for: (a) 9.8^2; (b) 0.999^5; (c) 1.002^{-2}.

Problems

1. The accompanying table gives experimental results for a measurement of the period of motion T of an object of mass m suspended on a spring versus the mass of the object.

Mass m, kg	0.10	0.20	0.40	0.50	0.75	1.00	1.50
Period T, sec	0.56	0.83	1.05	1.28	1.55	1.75	2.22

These data are consistent with a simple equation expressing T as a function of m of the form $T = Cm^n$, where C and n are constants (n is not necessarily an integer). (a) Find n and C. (There are several ways to do this. One is to guess the value of n and check by plotting T versus m^n on ordinary graph paper. If your guess is right, the plot will be a straight line. Another is to plot T versus m on log log paper. The slope of the straight line on this paper is n.) (b) Which data points deviate the most from a straight-line plot of T versus m^n?

2. The table below gives the period T and orbit radius r for the motions of four satellites orbiting a dense, heavy asteroid.

Period T, y	0.44	1.61	3.88	7.89
Radius r, 10^5 km	0.88	2.08	3.74	6.00

(a) These data can be fitted by the formula $T = Cr^n$. Find C and n. (b) A fifth satellite is discovered to have a period of 6.20 y. Find the radius for the orbit of this satellite, which fits the same formula.

3. The period T of a simple pendulum depends on the length L of the pendulum and the acceleration of gravity g (dimensions L/T^2). (a) Find a simple combination of L and g which has the dimensions of time. (b) Check the dependence of the period T on the length L by measuring the period (time for a complete to-and-fro swing) of a pendulum for two different values of L. (c) The correct formula relating T to L and g involves a constant which is a multiple of π and cannot be obtained by the dimensional analysis of part (a). It can be found by experiment as in part (b) if g is known. Using the value $g = 9.8$ m/sec^2 and your experimental results from part (b), find the formula relating T to L and g.

4. A projectile fired at an angle of 45° travels a total distance R, called the range, which depends only on the initial speed v and the acceleration of gravity g (dimensions L/T^2). Using dimensional analysis, find how R depends on the speed and on g.

5. A ball thrown horizontally from a height H with speed v travels a total horizontal distance R. (a) Do you expect R to increase or decrease with increasing H? With increasing v? (b) From dimensional analysis, find a possible dependence of R on H, v, and g.

6. Show that $\sin 2\theta = 2 \sin \theta \cos \theta$. Hint: Use Equation 1-12.

7. From Equation 1-12, and the identity $\tan \theta = (\sin \theta)/(\cos \theta)$, find an expression for $\tan (\theta_1 + \theta_2)$ in terms of $\tan \theta_1$ and $\tan \theta_2$.

8. A man begins at an intersection of a north-south road with an east-west road and walks 10 mi in the direction north of east along a line which makes an angle of 30° with the easterly direction. (a) How far is he from the north-south road? From the east-west road? (b) He now walks along a line perpendicular to his original direction until he reaches the north-south road. How far must he walk?

9. For each case in Exercise 25, compute the next term $\frac{1}{2}n(n-1)x^2$ in the binomial expansion used and express this term as a percentage of your answer found in that exercise. (b) Find the difference between your approximate answer for each case in that exercise and the exact calculation (from tables or from any exact method of calculation) and express this difference as a percentage of the exact answer.

10. Repeat Problem 9 using the data of Exercise 26.

CHAPTER 2   Motion in One Dimension

To simplify our discussion of motion, we start with objects whose position can be described by locating one point. Such an object is called a *particle*. One tends to think of a particle as a very small object, e.g., a piece of shot, but actually no size limit is implied by the word particle. If we are not interested in the extension of an object or in its rotational motion, any object can be considered as a particle. For example, it is sometimes convenient to consider the earth as a particle moving around the sun in a nearly circular path. In this case we are interested only in the motion of the center of the earth and are ignoring the size of the earth and its rotation. In some astronomical problems, the solar system or even a whole galaxy is treated as a particle.

When we are interested in the internal motion or internal structure of an object, it can no longer be treated as a particle. However, our study of particle motion is useful even in these cases because any complex object can be treated as a system of particles. Even so small a thing as an atomic nucleus, with a diameter of only about 10^{-15} m (1 fm), turns out to be a rather complicated system of particles when its structure is examined in detail. In the first nine chapters of this book we shall concentrate on the motion of a single particle (or, at times, two particles) while we develop the important concepts and methods of classical mechanics. In Chapter 10 we extend our discussion to systems of particles.

To describe the motion of a particle, we need the concepts of *displacement*, *velocity*, and *acceleration*. In the general motion of a particle in three dimensions, these quantities are vectors, which have direction as well as magnitude. We study vectors and the general motion of a particle in Chapter 3; in this chapter, we confine our discussion to motion along a straight line, i.e., motion in one dimension. For such restricted motion, there are only two possible directions. They are distinguished by designating one positive and the other negative. A simple example of one-dimensional motion is a car moving along a flat, straight, narrow road. We can choose any convenient point on the

Size and structure are unimportant for particles

The simplest motion is one-dimensional

car for the location of this "particle." Since we are interested for the moment only in one-dimensional motion, we can neglect the width of the road and consider it a line.

Questions

1. Give several examples of the motion of large objects where treating the object as a particle is an adequate approximation. Give other examples where it is not.

2. In many respects the motion of a body along any curved line is similar to straight-line motion. Can you suggest reasons why these two cases require separate treatment?

2-1 Displacement and Average Velocity

Let us set up a coordinate system by choosing some reference point on a line for the origin O. To every other point on the line we assign a number x which indicates how far the point is from the origin. The value of x depends on the unit chosen as the measure of distance. The sign of x depends on its position relative to the origin O; if it is to the right, it is positive; to the left, negative.

Suppose that our particle is at position x_1 at some time t_1 and at point x_2 at time t_2. We determine its position at several other times along the way. Figure 2-1 shows a graph of the function $x(t)$. The measured points have been connected with a smooth curve. How accurately this curve represents the motion of the particle depends upon the number of points used and on the complexity of the motion. The change in the position of the particle, $x_2 - x_1$, is called the *displacement* of the particle. It is customary to use the Greek letter Δ (capital delta) to indicate the change in a quantity. Thus the change in x is written Δx. The notation Δx (read "delta x") stands for a single quantity, the change in x (it is not a product of Δ and x any more than cos x is a product of cos and x):

$$\Delta x = x_2 - x_1 \qquad \text{2-1}$$

Displacement defined

Figure 2-1
Plot of x versus t for a particle moving in one dimension. Measured points are connected with a smooth curve.

$$\frac{\Delta x}{\Delta t} = \text{slope} = v_{av}$$

Figure 2-2
A plot of x versus t for a particle moving in one dimension, as in Figure 2-1. Here, a straight line is drawn from position P_1 to position P_2. The average velocity for the time interval $t_2 - t_1$ is defined to be the slope of this line $v_{av} = \Delta x / \Delta t$. The average velocity depends on the time interval, as indicated by the fact that the line from P_1 to P_2' has a greater slope than that from P_1 to P_2.

The average velocity of the particle is defined to be the ratio of the displacement Δx and the time interval $\Delta t = t_2 - t_1$:

$$v_{av} = \frac{\Delta x}{\Delta t} = \frac{x_2 - x_1}{t_2 - t_1} \qquad \text{2-2}$$

Average velocity defined

Note that the displacement and the average velocity may be either positive or negative, depending on whether x_2 is greater or less than x_1 (assuming positive Δt). A positive value indicates motion to the right; a negative value indicates motion to the left.

In Figure 2-2 a straight line has been drawn from point (x_1, t_1) to point (x_2, t_2). This line is the hypotenuse of a triangle with sides Δt and Δx. The ratio $\Delta x / \Delta t$ is called the *slope* of this straight line. In geometric terms, it is a measure of the steepness of the straight line in the graph. For a given interval Δt, the steeper the line, the greater the value of $\Delta x / \Delta t$. Since the slope of this line is just the average velocity for the time interval Δt, we have a geometric interpretation of average velocity. It is the slope of the straight line connecting the points (x_1, t_1) and (x_2, t_2). In general, the average velocity depends on the time interval chosen. For example, in Figure 2-2, if we chose a smaller time interval by choosing a time t_2' closer to t_1, the average velocity would be greater, as indicated by the greater steepness of the line connecting points P_1 and P_2'.

Slope: a measure of steepness

Example 2-1 If $x_1 = 18$ m at $t_1 = 2$ sec and $x_2 = 3$ m at $t_2 = 7$ sec, find the displacement and the average velocity for this time interval.

By the definition, the displacement is

$$\Delta x = x_2 - x_1 = 3 \text{ m} - 18 \text{ m} = -15 \text{ m}$$

and the average velocity is

$$v_{av} = \frac{\Delta x}{\Delta t} = \frac{x_2 - x_1}{t_2 - t_1} = \frac{3 \text{ m} - 18 \text{ m}}{7 \text{ sec} - 2 \text{ sec}} = \frac{-15 \text{ m}}{5 \text{ sec}} = -3 \text{ m/sec}$$

The displacement and average velocity are negative, indicating that the particle moved to the left, toward decreasing values of x.

Note that the unit meters per second is included as part of the answer for the average velocity found in Example 2-1. Since there are many other possible choices for units of length and time (feet, inches, miles, light-years, etc., for length and hours, days, years, etc., for time) it is essential to include the unit with a numerical answer. The statement "the average velocity of a particle is −3" is meaningless.

Example 2-2 How far does a car go in 5 min if its average velocity is 60 mi/h?

In this example we are interested in the displacement during a time interval of 5 min. From Equation 2-2 the displacement Δx is given by

$$\Delta x = v_{av}\, \Delta t$$

Thus

$$\Delta x = 60 \text{ mi/h} \times 5 \text{ min} = 300\, \frac{\text{mi-}\cancel{\text{min}}}{\cancel{\text{h}}}\, \frac{1\, \cancel{\text{h}}}{60\, \cancel{\text{min}}} = 5 \text{ mi}$$

We use the conversion factor 1 h = 60 min to change the unit of displacement from mi-min/h to miles.

Questions

3. What sense, if any, does the following statement make? "The average velocity of the car at 9 A.M. was 60 mi/h."

4. Is it possible that the average velocity for some interval may be zero although the average velocity for a shorter interval included in the first interval is not zero? Explain.

2-2 Instantaneous Velocity

At first glance, it might seem impossible to define the velocity of a particle at a single instant, i.e., at a specific time. At a time t_1, the particle is at a single point x_1. If it is at a single point, how can it be moving? On the other hand, if it is not moving, shouldn't it stay at the same point? This is an age-old paradox, which can be resolved when we realize that to observe motion and thus define it, we must look at the position of the object at more than one time. It is then possible to define the velocity at an instant by a limiting process.

Figure 2-3 is the same x-versus-t curve as Figure 2-2, showing a sequence of time intervals indicated, $\Delta t_1, \Delta t_2, \Delta t_3 \ldots$, each smaller

Velocity at a point

Figure 2-3
Plot of $x(t)$ from Figures 2-1 and 2-2. As the time interval beginning at t_1 is decreased, the average velocity for that interval approaches the slope of the line tangent to the curve at time t_1. The instantaneous velocity at time t_1 is defined to be the slope of the line tangent to the curve at t_1.

A. J. Wyatt

Ken Regan/Camera 5

Motion depicted by an artist in Duchamp's "Nude Descending a Staircase." (*Marcel Duchamp, No. 2, 1912, Louise and Walter Arensberg Collection, Philadelphia Museum of Art.*) What features in the photograph of a runner imply motion? Can we tell with certainty from a single high-speed photograph that the athlete is moving?

than the previous one. For each time interval Δt, the average velocity is the slope of the dashed line appropriate for that interval. This figure shows that as the time interval becomes smaller, the dashed lines get steeper but never incline more than the line tangent to the curve at point t_1. We define the slope of this tangent line to be the *instantaneous velocity* at the time t_1. The instantaneous velocity is the limit of the ratio $\Delta x / \Delta t$ as Δt approaches zero:

$$v(t) = \lim_{\Delta t \to 0} \frac{\Delta x}{\Delta t} = \text{slope of line tangent to } x(t) \text{ curve} \qquad 2\text{-}3$$

Instantaneous velocity defined

This limit is called the *derivative of x with respect to t* at the point t_1. In the usual calculus notation[1] the derivative is written dx/dt:

$$v(t) = \lim_{\Delta t \to 0} \frac{\Delta x}{\Delta t} = \frac{dx}{dt} \qquad 2\text{-}4$$

Derivative defined

It is important to realize that the displacement Δx depends on the time interval Δt. As Δt approaches zero, Δx does also (as can be seen from Figure 2-3) and the ratio $\Delta x / \Delta t$ approaches the slope of the line tangent to the curve. In computing this limit, we do not set Δt equal to zero since then Δx would be zero also and the ratio $\Delta x / \Delta t$ would not be defined.

This concept of the limit of a function can be understood only with careful study. We omit further discussion here, assuming that it is covered in your calculus course.

---

[1] Strictly speaking, the notation dx/dt stands for the single quantity, the derivative of x with respect to t, which is the slope of the line tangent to the $x(t)$ curve. Later, we shall define the quantities dx and dt (called *differentials*) so that their ratio is in fact this slope. If Δx and Δt are chosen small enough, the ratio $\Delta x / \Delta t$ is *nearly* equal to the slope of the tangent line. Therefore it is convenient, though not mathematically rigorous, to think of dt as a very small change in t, and dx as the corresponding very small change in x.

Figure 2-4
Plot of x versus t for Example 2-3. The instantaneous velocity at time $t = 2$ sec can be found by measuring the slope of the line tangent to the curve at that time.

Example 2-3 The position of a particle is given by the function shown in Figure 2-4. Find the instantaneous velocity at the time $t = 2$ sec. When is the velocity greatest? When is it zero? Is it ever negative?

In the figure we have sketched the line tangent to the curve at time $t = 2$ sec. The slope of this line is measured from the figure to be $(3 \text{ m})/(2 \text{ sec}) = 1.5$ m/sec. Thus $v = 1.5$ m/sec at time $t = 2$ sec. According to the figure, the slope is greatest at about $t = 4$ sec. The velocity is zero at times $t = 0$ and $t = 6$ sec, as indicated by the fact that the tangent lines at these times are horizontal with zero slope. After $t = 6$ sec, the curve has a negative slope, indicating that the velocity is negative. (The slope of the line tangent to a curve is often referred to merely as the *slope of the curve*.)

Example 2-4 A particle is at point $x = 5$ ft at time $t = 0$ and moves with a constant velocity of 10 ft/sec. Sketch its position x as a function of time.

A constant velocity means that the slope of the x-versus-t curve is constant. The curve which has a constant slope is a straight line. The general expression for a straight-line curve is

$$x = mt + b$$

where m is the slope and b is the value of x at $t = 0$, called the *intercept*. Thus $m = 10$ ft/sec, $b = 5$ ft, and the equation for the curve is

$$x = 5 \text{ ft} + (10 \text{ ft/sec})t$$

This curve is sketched in Figure 2-5. In general, if a particle is at posi-

Figure 2-5
Plot of the position function $x = 5$ ft $+ (10$ ft/sec$)t$ from Example 2-4.

Figure 2-6
Plot of the function $x(t) = 16t^2$. Tangent lines are drawn at times t_1, t_2, and t_3. The slope of these tangent lines increases steadily from t_1 to t_2 to t_3, indicating that the instantaneous velocity increases steadily with time.

tion x_0 at time $t = 0$ and has a constant velocity v, its position is given by

$$x = x_0 + vt$$

Example 2-5 The position of a stone dropped from rest from a cliff is given by $x = 16t^2$, where x is in feet measured downward from the original position at $t = 0$ and t is in seconds. Find the velocity at any time. (We omit explicit indication of the units to simplify the notation.)

This function is shown in Figure 2-6, where tangent lines are drawn for three different times, t_1, t_2, and t_3. The slopes of these lines differ. As time passes, the slope of the curve increases, indicating that the instantaneous velocity is increasing with time. We can compute the velocity at some time t_1 by computing the derivative dx/dt directly from the definition in Equation 2-3. At time t_1 the position is

$$x_1 = 16t_1{}^2$$

At a later time $t_2 = t_1 + \Delta t$ the position is x_2, given by

$$\begin{aligned}
x_2 &= 16t_2{}^2 = 16(t_1 + \Delta t)^2 \\
&= 16\,[t_1{}^2 + 2t_1\,\Delta t + (\Delta t)^2] \\
&= 16t_1{}^2 + 32t_1\,\Delta t + 16(\Delta t)^2
\end{aligned}$$

The displacement for this time interval is thus

$$\Delta x = x_2 - x_1 = 32t_1\,\Delta t + 16(\Delta t)^2$$

The average velocity for this time interval is

$$v_{av} = \frac{\Delta x}{\Delta t} = 32\,t_1 + 16\Delta t$$

As we consider shorter and shorter time intervals, Δt approaches zero and the second term $16\Delta t$ approaches zero, though the first is unaltered. The instantaneous velocity at time t_1 is thus

$$v = \lim_{\Delta t \to 0} \frac{\Delta x}{\Delta t} = 32 t_1$$

This function, the instantaneous velocity, is proportional to the time. For any general time t, the instantaneous velocity is $v(t) = 32t$.

It is instructive to examine the limiting process numerically by computing the average velocity for smaller and smaller time intervals. Table 2-1 gives the average velocity for Example 2-5 computed for $t_1 = 2$ sec and various time intervals Δt, each smaller than the previous one. The table shows that for very small time intervals, the average velocity is very nearly equal to the instantaneous velocity 64 ft/sec. The difference between $\Delta x/\Delta t$ and $\lim_{\Delta t \to 0} (\Delta x/\Delta t)$ can be made arbitrarily small by choosing Δt sufficiently small.

It is important to distinguish carefully between average and instantaneous velocity. By custom, however, the word velocity alone is assumed to mean instantaneous velocity. The magnitude of the instantaneous velocity is called the *speed*.

Speed defined

Questions

5. If the instantaneous velocity does not change from instant to instant, will the average velocities for different intervals differ?

6. If $v_{av} = 0$ for some time interval Δt, must the instantaneous velocity v be zero at some time in the interval? Support your answer by a sketch of a possible x-versus-t curve which has $\Delta x = 0$ for some interval Δt.

2-3 Acceleration

When the instantaneous velocity of a particle is changing with time, as in Example 2-5, the particle is said to be *accelerating*. The average acceleration for a particular time interval $\Delta t = t_2 - t_1$ is defined as the ratio $\Delta v/\Delta t$, where $\Delta v = v_2 - v_1$ is the change in instantaneous velocity for that time interval:

$$a_{av} = \frac{\Delta v}{\Delta t} \qquad 2\text{-}5$$

Average acceleration defined

The dimensions of acceleration are length divided by time². Convenient units are meters per second per second (m/sec²) or feet per second per second (ft/sec²). For automobile accelerations miles per hour per second (mi/h-sec) is often used. *Instantaneous acceleration* is the limit of this ratio as Δt approaches zero. If we plot the velocity versus time, the instantaneous acceleration is defined to be the slope of the tangent line to this curve:

$$a = \lim_{\Delta t \to 0} \frac{\Delta v}{\Delta t} = \text{slope of } v\text{-versus-}t \text{ curve} \qquad 2\text{-}6$$

Instantaneous acceleration defined

The acceleration is thus the derivative of the velocity with respect to time. The calculus notation for this derivative is dv/dt. Since the velocity is also the derivative of the position x with respect to t, the acceleration is the *second* derivative of x with respect to t. The common nota-

Table 2-1
Displacement and average velocity for various time intervals Δt beginning at $t = 2$ sec for the function $x = 16t^2$

Δt, sec	Δx, ft	$\Delta x/\Delta t$, ft/sec
1.00	80	80
0.50	36	72
0.20	13.44	67.2
0.10	6.56	65.6
0.05	3.24	64.8
0.01	0.6416	64.16
0.005	0.3204	64.08
0.001	0.064016	64.016
0.0001	0.00640016	64.0016

tion for the second derivative of x with respect to t is d^2x/dt^2. We can see the origin of this notation by writing the acceleration as dv/dt and replacing v with dx/dt:

$$a = \frac{dv}{dt} = \frac{d(dx/dt)}{dt} = \frac{d^2x}{dt^2} \qquad\qquad 2\text{-}7$$

Notation for second derivative

If the velocity is constant, as in Example 2-4, the acceleration is zero since $\Delta v = 0$ for all time intervals. In this case the slope of the x-versus-t curve does not change. In Example 2-5 we found that for the position function $x = (16 \text{ ft/sec}^2)t^2$ the velocity increases linearly with time according to $v = (32 \text{ ft/sec}^2)t$. In this case the acceleration is constant and equal to 32 ft/sec², the constant slope of the v-versus-t curve. We can get at least a qualitative idea of the acceleration from the x-versus-t curve. From Figure 2-6 we can see that the velocity is increasing with time, as indicated by the increasing steepness of the tangent lines; i.e., this curve shows that the acceleration is positive.

Example 2-6 From the x-versus-t curve in Figure 2-7, discuss qualitatively the velocity and acceleration at the point $t = 5$ sec.

At $t = 5$ sec the tangent line to the curve is horizontal with zero slope. Thus the instantaneous velocity at this point is zero. However, the fact that the velocity is zero does *not* imply that the acceleration must be zero also. The acceleration is the rate of change of the instantaneous velocity. To find the acceleration at some time we must know how the velocity is changing at that time. For this example, to find the acceleration at $t = 5$ sec we must know the velocity at other times in the neighborhood of $t = 5$ sec. From the figure we see that the slope of the curve is positive just before $t = 5$ sec and negative just after. Thus the velocity changes from a positive value, to zero, to a negative value, and acceleration at this time is negative. In Figure 2-8 we have sketched the velocity-versus-t curve corresponding to the position function given in Figure 2-7. Note that at $t = 5$ sec, the velocity is zero; nevertheless the slope of the v-versus-t curve is not zero but negative.

Figure 2-7
x-versus-t curve for Example 2-6. The slope of the tangent line at $t = 5$ sec is zero, indicating that the instantaneous velocity is zero at this time. Just before $t = 5$ sec, the slope is positive; just after $t = 5$ sec, the slope is negative. Since the slope is decreasing at $t = 5$ sec, the acceleration at this time is negative.

Figure 2-8
Velocity-versus-time curve corresponding to the position curve in Figure 2-7. At $t = 5$ sec, the velocity is zero and decreasing.

Example 2-7 The position of a particle is given by $x = Ct^3$, where C is a constant with the dimensions of m/sec^3. Find the velocity and acceleration as functions of time.

The graph of x versus t (not shown) resembles the graph in Example 2-5 except that the increase of x with time is faster. The slope of the curve increases with time, indicating an increasing velocity. As in that example, we can compute the velocity by computing the derivative dx/dt directly from its definition (Equation 2-3). At some time t_1 the position is $x_1 = Ct_1^3$. At a later time $t_2 = t_1 + \Delta t$ the position is

$$x_2 = Ct_2^3 = C(t_1 + \Delta t)^3 = Ct_1^3 + 3Ct_1^2\,\Delta t + 3Ct(\Delta t)^2 + C(\Delta t)^3$$

The displacement is thus

$$\Delta x = x_2 - x_1 = 3Ct_1^2\,\Delta t + 3Ct_1(\Delta t)^2 + C(\Delta t)^3$$

The average velocity for this time interval is

$$v_{av} = \frac{\Delta x}{\Delta t} = 3Ct_1^2 + 3Ct\,\Delta t + C(\Delta t)^2$$

As $\Delta t \to 0$, the two right-hand terms also approach zero and the term $3Ct_1^2$ remains unchanged. The instantaneous velocity at time t is thus

$$v = 3Ct^2$$

(Having computed the velocity at time t_1, we can drop the subscript 1 on the time and write the velocity for a general time t.) We find the acceleration by repeating the process and thus finding the derivative of v with respect to t, which is the second derivative of x with respect to t. We omit some of the algebra in this derivation because it is similar to that shown above and in Example 2-5. The change in velocity for the time interval from t to $t + \Delta t$ is

$$\Delta v = 3C(t + \Delta t)^2 - 3Ct^2 = 6Ct\,\Delta t + 3C(\Delta t)^2$$

We divide this expression by Δt to obtain the average acceleration for this interval:

$$a_{av} = \frac{\Delta v}{\Delta t} = 6Ct + 3C\,\Delta t$$

The instantaneous acceleration is thus

$$a = \lim_{\Delta t \to 0} \frac{\Delta v}{\Delta t} = 6Ct$$

In this example the acceleration is not constant but increases with time.

In the examples so far we have computed derivatives directly from the definition by taking the appropriate limit explicitly. It is useful to examine various properties of the derivative and to develop rules permitting us to calculate the derivatives of many functions quickly without applying the definition each time. Table E-1 in Appendix E contains a list of such rules, followed by a brief discussion of their origin. We use these rules without comment and leave their detailed study to your calculus course.

Rule 7 in Table E-1 is used so often we repeat it here. If x is a simple power function of t, such as

$$x = Ct^n$$

where C and n are any constants, the derivative of x with respect to t is given by

$$\frac{dx}{dt} = Cnt^{n-1}$$

We have already seen applications of this rule for $n = 1, 2,$ and 3 in the examples; e.g., for the position function of Example 2-7, $x = Ct^3$, we found $v = dx/dt = 3Ct^2$ and $a = dv/dt = 6Ct$.

Questions

7. Give an example of a motion for which the velocity is negative but the acceleration is positive; e.g., sketch a graph of v versus t.

8. Give an example of a motion for which both the acceleration and velocity are negative.

9. Is it possible for a body to have zero velocity and nonzero acceleration?

2-4   Finding $x(t)$ from $v(t)$: The Initial-Value Problem

We have learned how to obtain the velocity and acceleration functions from a given position function by differentiation. The inverse problem is to find the position function x given the velocity v or the acceleration a. To solve this problem of finding a function which has a given derivative we make use of our knowledge of the derivatives of various types of functions, e.g., those listed in Appendix Table E-1. Consider, for example, constant velocity $v = v_0$. We have already found the position function x corresponding to this given velocity in Example 2-4. We make use of our knowledge that the curve x versus t which has a constant slope is a straight line. Thus x must vary linearly with t. One such function is

Finding the position from the velocity

$$x = v_0 t$$

However, this is not a general solution to the problem.

We can add any constant to the right-hand side of this equation without changing the derivative since the derivative of a constant is zero. Calling this constant x_0, we have for the general position function of a particle with constant velocity v_0

$$x = x_0 + v_0 t$$

The constant x_0 is the position at time $t = 0$, as can be seen by substituting $t = 0$ into this equation.

Let us consider a slightly more difficult example, a particle whose velocity is proportional to time:

$$v = a_0 t$$

The proportionality constant a_0 is just the acceleration, as can be seen by computing $dv/dt = a_0$. We now ask: What function $x(t)$ has the derivative $a_0 t$? We note from rule 7 in Table E-1 that the derivative of t^n is nt^{n-1}. Our position function must therefore be proportional to t^2, and we can verify that the correct function is $\frac{1}{2}a_0 t^2$. Again, we can add any constant to this function without changing its derivative. The general position function having the derivative $a_0 t$ is

$$x = x_0 + \tfrac{1}{2}a_0 t^2$$

where the additive constant x_0 is the value of x when $t = 0$. If the value of x is given for any particular time, we can determine the value of x_0.

Finding the function from its given derivative is called *antidifferentiation*. The function determined is the *antiderivative* (often called the indefinite integral) of the function. It always contains an additive constant which is related to the choice of origin. If the derivative of a function is given everywhere and the value of the function is known at one point, the function is uniquely determined because the actual value of the additive constant can be determined from the given information.

Antiderivatives

Let us now consider an example in which the acceleration is given.

Example 2-8 The acceleration of a particle is constant, $a(t) = a_0$. Find the position function $x(t)$.

We must first find the velocity $v(t)$ and use it to find $x(t)$. We thus go through the process of antidifferentiation twice. Each antiderivative contains an additive constant. Consequently there will be two constants in the function $x(t)$ which are as yet unspecified. These constants are usually determined from the velocity at some given time and from the position at some given (and perhaps different) time. We are given $dv/dt = a_0$. We did this type of problem earlier in the example at the beginning of this section. The general function which has a constant derivative is $v(t) = a_0 t + v_0$. Here the additive constant v_0 is the value of $v(t)$ at $t = 0$. We now need to find the function $x(t)$ which has the derivative $dx/dt = a_0 t + v_0$. On the basis of rule 2 in Appendix Table E-1 (the derivative of a sum of terms is the sum of the derivatives of the terms), we can treat each term separately. The function $\tfrac{1}{2}a_0 t^2$ has the derivative $a_0 t$, and the function $v_0 t$ has the derivative v_0. The additive constant in the antiderivatives can be combined into one constant. Calling this constant x_0, we have for the complete solution

$$x(t) = x_0 + v_0 t + \tfrac{1}{2}a_0 t^2$$

In Example 2-8 we saw that when $x(t)$ is found from the acceleration $a(t)$, two constants appear. We were able to relate these constants to the initial position x_0 and the initial velocity v_0. The problem "given $a(t)$, find $x(t)$" is called the *initial-value problem*. The solution depends on the form of the function $a(t)$, on the value of v at some particular time, and on the value of x at some particular time; these are often taken as initial values, i.e., values at time $t = 0$. The problem is particularly important in physics because the acceleration of a particle is determined by the forces acting on it. Thus if we know the forces acting on a particle and its position and velocity at some particular time, we can find its position uniquely at all other times.

Finding position from acceleration

2-5   The Antiderivative and Integration

The problem of finding the antiderivative is related to the problem of *integration*, or finding the area under a curve. This fundamental

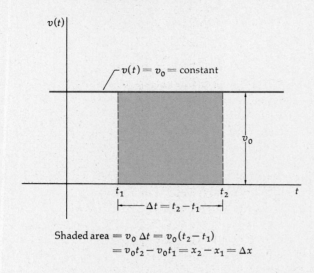

$v(t)$

$v(t) = v_0 = $ constant

v_0

t_1 t_2 t

$\longmapsto \Delta t = t_2 - t_1 \longmapsto$

Shaded area $= v_0 \, \Delta t = v_0(t_2 - t_1)$
$= v_0 t_2 - v_0 t_1 = x_2 - x_1 = \Delta x$

Figure 2-9
The displacement for the interval Δt equals the area under the velocity-versus-time curve for that interval. For $v(t) = v_0 = $ constant, the displacement equals the area of the rectangle shown.

problem in calculus will be discussed only briefly.

Consider the case of constant velocity v_0. The displacement during some time interval Δt is just the velocity times the time interval:

$$\Delta x = v_0 \, \Delta t$$

This is the area under the v-versus-t curve, as can be seen in Figure 2-9. The geometric interpretation of displacement as the area under the v-versus-t curve is quite general. Figure 2-10 is the v-versus-t curve when the velocity is proportional to time $v = a_0 t$. In the previous section, we found the position function to be $x = x_0 + \frac{1}{2}a_0 t^2$. The displacement during the time interval $t = 0$ to $t = t_1$ is

$$\Delta x = x_1 - x_0 = \tfrac{1}{2}a_0 t_1{}^2$$

As can be seen from the figure, again this equals the area under the curve for this time interval.

Figure 2-11 shows a general v-versus-t curve. If we know the algebraic function $v(t)$ for this curve, we can always compute the antiderivative and determine the position function $x(t)$ except for the initial value x_0, which must be found from additional information, e.g., the value of x at some specified time. We then can find the displacement during any interval $\Delta t = t_2 - t_1$ by subtracting $x(t_1)$ from $x(t_2)$ (this gives us Δx even if x_0 is not known since it subtracts out).

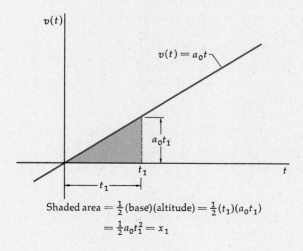

$v(t)$

$v(t) = a_0 t$

$a_0 t_1$

t_1 t

$\longmapsto t_1 \longmapsto$

Shaded area $= \frac{1}{2}$ (base)(altitude) $= \frac{1}{2}(t_1)(a_0 t_1)$
$= \tfrac{1}{2}a_0 t_1^2 = x_1$

Figure 2-10
For $v(t) = a_0 t$, the displacement during the interval from $t = 0$ to $t = t_1$ equals the triangular area indicated. Since the base of the triangle is t_1 and the height is $a_0 t_1$, the area is $\frac{1}{2}(a_0 t_1)(t_1) = \frac{1}{2}a_0 t_1{}^2$.

Figure 2-11
Plot of general $v(t)$ versus t. The displacement for the interval Δt_i is approximately $v(t_i)\,\Delta t_i$, indicated by the shaded rectangular area. The total displacement from t_1 to t_2 is the area under the curve for this interval, which can be approximated by summing the areas of the rectangles.

However, even if we do not know the algebraic function for $v(t)$, we can obtain the displacement Δx for some time interval $t_2 - t_1$ directly from the curve $v(t)$ versus t by finding the area under the curve for this time interval.

In Figure 2-11 the interval $t_2 - t_1$ is divided into a number of small intervals Δt_i. At time t_i, which is any time in the interval Δt_i, the instantaneous velocity is

$$v(t_i) = \lim_{\Delta t_i \to 0} \frac{\Delta x_i}{\Delta t_i}$$

If Δt_i is very small, the instantaneous velocity is approximately the average velocity:

$$v(t_i) \approx \frac{\Delta x_i}{\Delta t_i}$$

The displacement during the small interval Δt_i is thus

$$\Delta x_i \approx v(t_i)\,\Delta t_i$$

The approximation improves if we make Δt_i smaller. From the figure we see that Δx_i is the area of the rectangle indicated. This area is approximately the area under the curve for small Δt_i. The total displacement from t_1 to t_2 is then the sum of all the Δx_i:

$$\Delta x = \sum_{t_1}^{t_2} \Delta x_i \approx \sum_{t_1}^{t_2} v(t_i)\,\Delta t_i$$

where the sum is taken from the first rectangle at t_1 to the last one at t_2. The number of terms in the sum depends on the number of subintervals chosen. As we take smaller and smaller intervals Δt_i, the number of terms increases and the sum becomes a better approximation of the area under the curve and displacement Δx. Thus

$$\Delta x = x(t_2) - x(t_1) = \lim_{\Delta t \to 0} \sum_{t_1}^{t_2} v(t_i)\,\Delta t_i$$

$$= \text{area under } v(t)\text{-versus-}t \text{ curve from } t_1 \text{ to } t_2 \qquad \text{2-8}$$

Equation 2-8 is actually the definition of the area under a curve. The area under a curve can be measured in various ways. One is to plot the curve on graph paper containing many small squares of known area, count the squares, and estimate the fractional squares cut by the curve. Another is to cut the paper out along the curve, weigh it, and compare the weight with that of a standard rectangle of known area.

The definite integral is the area under a curve

The limit of the sum in Equation 2-8 is called a *definite integral,* usually written

$$\lim_{\Delta t_i \to 0} \sum_{t_1}^{t_2} v(t_i)\,\Delta t_i = \int_{t_1}^{t_2} v(t)\,dt = x(t_2) - x(t_1) \qquad 2\text{-}9$$

(The integral sign $\int$ is an elongated S, denoting a sum.) Equation 2-9 is also useful in finding the area under a curve for which the algebraic function is given. Since this area is just $x(t_2) - x(t_1)$, where $x(t)$ is the antiderivative, we need only compute the antiderivative at t_1 and t_2 and subtract. The antiderivative is also called the indefinite integral and written without limits on the integral sign:

$$x(t) = \int v(t)\,dt$$

Example 2-9 Find the area under the curve $v = Ct^2$ from $t = 0$ to $t = 4$, where $C = 1$ m/sec³.

Using rule 7, the antiderivative, or indefinite integral, of Ct^2 is $Ct^3/3$ plus any constant. (This can be checked, of course, by differentiating $Ct^3/3$.) Then

$$x(4) - x(0) = \int_0^4 Ct^2\,dt = \frac{4^3 C}{3} - \frac{0^3 C}{3} = \frac{64}{3}\,C = 21\frac{1}{3}\,C$$

You should check this by plotting the curve $v = Ct^2$ versus t and measuring the area by counting the squares.

The average velocity has a simple geometric interpretation in terms of area under a curve. Consider the v-versus-t curve in Figure 2-12. The displacement during the time interval $\Delta t = t_2 - t_1$ is indicated by the shaded area. By definition of the average velocity for this interval (Equation 2-2), the displacement is also the product of v_{av} and Δt:

$$\Delta x = v_{av}\,\Delta t$$

The average velocity is indicated in Figure 2-12 by the horizontal line, drawn so that the area under it from t_1 to t_2 equals the area under the actual v-versus-t curve:

$$v_{av}\,\Delta t = \Delta x = \int_{t_1}^{t_2} v\,dt \qquad 2\text{-}10$$

Figure 2-12
Geometric interpretation of average velocity. By definition, $v_{av} = \Delta x/\Delta t$. Thus the rectangular area $v_{av}(t_2 - t_1)$ must equal the displacement in the time interval $t_2 - t_1$. It follows that the rectangular area $v_{av}(t_2 - t_1)$ and the shaded area under the curve must be equal.

2-6   Motion with Constant Acceleration

In Example 2-8 we found the expressions for $v(t)$ and $x(t)$ for motion with constant acceleration. This type of motion is common in nature. Near the surface of the earth, all objects fall vertically with the constant acceleration of gravity $g = 32$ ft/sec^2 = 9.8 m/sec^2 if air resistance can be neglected and if there are no forces on the objects other than the pull of gravity. The examples in this section will increase your familiarity with the concepts of velocity and acceleration.

Free fall has constant acceleration

The equations found in Example 2-8 for constant acceleration a_0 are

$$v(t) = v_0 + a_0 t \qquad\qquad\qquad\qquad\qquad\qquad 2\text{-}11$$

Equations for constant acceleration

$$x(t) = x_0 + v_0 t + \tfrac{1}{2} a_0 t^2 \qquad\qquad\qquad\qquad 2\text{-}12$$

A third equation which is sometimes useful can be obtained by eliminating the variable t between these two equations. Using $t = (v - v_0)/a_0$ from Equation 2-11 in Equation 2-12, we have

$$x = x_0 + v_0 \frac{v - v_0}{a_0} + \tfrac{1}{2} a_0 \left(\frac{v - v_0}{a_0} \right)^2$$

This can be simplified and rearranged to yield

$$v^2 = v_0{}^2 + 2a_0 (x - x_0) \qquad\qquad\qquad\qquad 2\text{-}13$$

Constant acceleration with time eliminated

In Figure 2-13 the velocity is plotted versus time. The average velocity for some time interval $\Delta t = t_2 - t_1$ is indicated in the figure. The average velocity is just the arithmetic mean of the value v_1 at the beginning of the time interval and v_2 at the end of the interval:

$$v_{\text{av}} = \tfrac{1}{2}(v_1 + v_2) \qquad \text{for constant acceleration only}$$

This simple result for average velocity holds only when the instantaneous velocity varies linearly with time, i.e., when the acceleration is constant. When the acceleration is not constant, v_{av} is not generally the arithmetic mean of v_1 and v_2, as can be seen from Figure 2-12.

Since Equation 2-13 was obtained from Equations 2-11 and 2-12, these three equations are not independent. Only two of them (sometimes only one) are needed to solve any problem in which the acceleration is constant. Which equation is chosen depends on the problem.

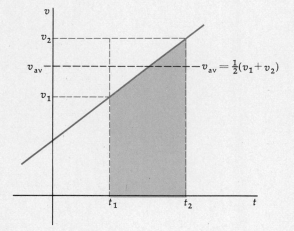

Figure 2-13
For constant acceleration, the average velocity for some time interval is just the mean of the initial and final velocities for that interval.

Example 2-10 A ball is dropped from rest from the top of a 100-ft building and has a constant acceleration downward of 32 ft/sec². (*a*) How fast is it moving just before it hits the ground? (*b*) How long does it take to reach the ground?

Let us choose our coordinate system with the origin at the top of the building with the positive *x* axis *down*. Then $x_0 = 0$, $v_0 = 0$, and $a_0 = +32$ ft/sec². Equations 2-11 to 2-13 for this problem become

(1) $v(t) = (32 \text{ ft/sec}^2)t$

(2) $x(t) = (16 \text{ ft/sec}^2)t^2$

(3) $v^2 = (64 \text{ ft/sec}^2)x$

(*a*) One way to find the speed at the bottom is to find the time it takes to fall from Equation (2) and then find $v(t)$ for this time from Equation (1). This amounts to doing part (*b*) first. If we are interested only in the final velocity, we can use Equation (3), which relates v to x without involving the time. For $x = 100$ ft, we have

$$v^2 = (64 \text{ ft/sec}^2)(100 \text{ ft}) = 6400 \text{ ft}^2/\text{sec}^2$$
$$v = 80 \text{ ft/sec}$$

Note how the units are treated as algebraic quantities in this calculation.

(*b*) Having found the velocity v at the bottom, we can find the time from Equation (1):

$$80 \text{ ft/sec} = (32 \text{ ft/sec}^2)t$$

$$t = \frac{80 \text{ ft/sec}}{32 \text{ ft/sec}^2} = 2.5 \text{ sec}$$

We could also find the time from $\Delta t = \Delta x / v_{\text{av}}$. Since the initial velocity is zero and the final velocity is 80 ft/sec, $v_{\text{av}} = \frac{1}{2}(0 + 80 \text{ ft/sec}) = 40$ ft/sec. Then $\Delta t = (100 \text{ ft})/(40 \text{ ft/sec}) = 2.5$ sec. If we had not found v in part (*a*), we could find the time from Equation (2), which relates distance to time, $100 \text{ ft} = (16 \text{ ft/sec}^2)t^2$:

$$t^2 = \frac{100 \text{ ft}}{16 \text{ ft/sec}^2} = (\tfrac{10}{4})^2 \text{ sec}^2 \quad \text{or} \quad t = \tfrac{10}{4} \text{ sec} = 2.5 \text{ sec}$$

Figure 2-14 shows a plot of $x(t)$ versus t for this problem. The slope of

Fundamental Photographs

Multiflash photograph of a golf ball falling with constant acceleration. The position of the ball is recorded at 1/25-sec intervals using a strobe light which flickers 25 times per second. The increase in spacing between successive positions indicates that the speed is increasing.

Figure 2-14
Plot of $x(t) = (16 \text{ ft/sec}^2)t^2$ for Example 2-10. The slope is zero at $t = 0$ and increases with t, indicating that the velocity is initially zero and increases with t.

Figure 2-15
Plot of $v(t) = (32 \text{ ft/sec}^2)t$ for
Example 2-10. Note that $v(t)$
versus t is a straight line, indicating that the acceleration
in this example is a constant.

this curve is zero at the origin (indicating that the initial velocity is
zero), and the slope increases with increasing t. Figure 2-15 is a plot of
$v(t)$ versus t. This curve has a constant slope equal to 32 ft/sec².

Example 2-11 A ball thrown vertically upward with an initial velocity of 96 ft/sec has a constant acceleration downward of 32 ft/sec². (*a*)
How high will the ball go? (*b*) How long is the ball in the air? (*c*) At
what times is the ball 80 ft above the ground?

Let us choose our coordinate system with origin at the initial position of the ball and with x positive *upward*. Then $x_0 = 0$, $v_0 = 96$ ft/sec,
and $a_0 = -32$ ft/sec². For these conditions the constant-acceleration
equations 2-11 to 2-13 become

(1) $v = 96 - 32t$

(2) $x = 96t - 16t^2$

(3) $v^2 = 96^2 - 64x$

In this example, we omit the units in the equations except when giving
the results. In the above equations it is to be understood that x is in feet,
t in seconds, and v in feet per second. Figure 2-16 shows a sketch of
x versus t [Equation (2)]. We see that x increases to a maximum value
and then decreases to zero and that the time to reach maximum equals
the time to fall back to $x = 0$. The slope of this curve is 96 ft/sec at $t = 0$

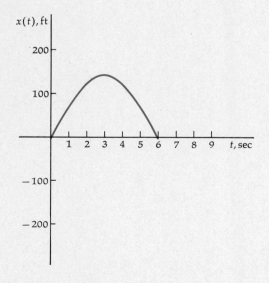

Figure 2-16
Plot of $x = 96t - 16t^2$ for Example 2-12. The slope is positive at $t = 0$, decreases to 0 at
$t = 3$ sec, and continues to decrease with increasing t. The
acceleration has the constant
negative value of -32 ft/sec².

(the original velocity) and decreases to zero at the highest point. After that the slope *continues to decrease*, becoming more and more negative. The symmetry of the figure means that just before the ball hits the ground, the velocity must be −96 ft/sec. Figure 2-17 shows a plot of $v(t)$ versus t from Equation (1). As observed from the slope of the $x(t)$ curve, the velocity begins at 96 ft/sec and always decreases, with a constant negative slope which is the constant acceleration −32 ft/sec. Note that when $v = 0$, the acceleration is *not zero* (despite the common misconception). When $v = 0$, the velocity is decreasing at the same rate as at any other time.

(*a*) Since $v = 0$ when the ball reaches the maximum height, the easiest way to find the maximum height is to set $v = 0$ in Equation (3) and find x:

$$0 = 96^2 - 64x$$

$$x = \frac{96^2}{64} = 144 \text{ ft}$$

(*b*) We can find the total time in the air by finding the times for which $x = 0$ from Equation (2):

$$0 = 96t - 16t^2 = 16t(6 - t)$$

Hence, $t = 0$ and $t = 6$ sec are the two times for which $x = 0$. The first is the time when the ball leaves the ground. The second is the time when it returns to the ground. Another way would be to recognize the symmetry from the figure, find the time to reach the highest point, and multiply by 2. Since $v = 0$ at the highest point, we set $v = 0$ in Equation (1) and obtain $96 - 32t = 0$, or $t = 3$ sec. The total time to reach the ground again is thus 2×3 sec $= 6$ sec.

(*c*) We can see from the sketch of $x(t)$ versus t that there will be two times when $x = 80$ ft. We can find them from Equation (2):

$$80 = 96t - 16t^2 \qquad t^2 - 6t + 5 = 0$$

$$(t - 1)(t - 5) = 0 \qquad \text{or} \qquad t = 1 \text{ sec and } t = 5 \text{ sec}$$

At $t = 1$ sec, the ball passes the height 80 ft on its way up. At $t = 5$ sec, the ball passes the same point on the way down.

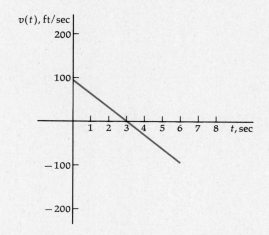

Figure 2-17
Plot of $v(t) = 96 - 32t$ for Example 2-11. The slope is the constant acceleration of −32 ft/sec².

Questions

10. Two boys standing on a bridge throw rocks straight down into the water below. They throw two rocks at the same time, but one hits the water before the other. How can this be if the rocks have the same acceleration g?

11. A ball is thrown straight up. What is its velocity at the top of its flight? What is its acceleration at that point?

Optional

2-7   The Differential

An important quantity related to the derivative and useful in making approximations is the differential. Consider the position function we have studied several times,

$$x = 16t^2$$

The distance traveled between times t_1 and $t_2 = t_1 + \Delta t$ is

$$\Delta x = x(t_1 + \Delta t) - x(t_1) = 16(t_1 + \Delta t)^2 - 16t_1^2$$
$$= 32t_1 \, \Delta t + 16(\Delta t)^2 \qquad\qquad 2\text{-}14$$

The first term in the equation is Δt times the derivative of x with respect to t. This quantity is called the *differential of* x, written dx,

Definition of differential

$$dx = \left(\lim_{\Delta t \to 0} \frac{\Delta x}{\Delta t} \right) \Delta t \qquad\qquad 2\text{-}15$$

Equation 2-14 is then

$$\Delta x = dx + 16(\Delta t)^2$$

If the time interval Δt is very small, the second term in this equation is small compared with the first term because $(\Delta t)^2$ will be small compared to Δt. Thus, to a good approximation,

$$\Delta x \approx dx$$

This approximation is useful because it is often easier to calculate dx than Δx when Δx is wanted.

Figure 2-18 illustrates the difference between the actual change Δx in x, and its approximation, the differential dx. This approximation is essentially that of replacing the curve $x(t)$ by the straight line tangent

Figure 2-18
Comparison of the differential approximation dx with the actual change Δx for the interval t_1 to t_2. The differential dx is the change in x which would result if the slope of $x(t)$ versus t did not change in the interval t_1 to t_2. The approximation is good if the time interval is small.

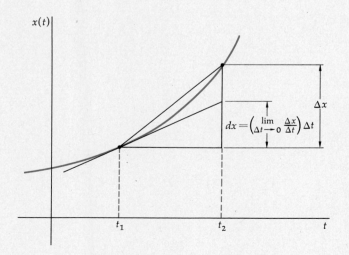

to the curve at t_1. The validity of the approximation obviously depends on how small Δt is and on how much the curve $x(t)$ deviates from a straight line in the range t_1 to $t_1 + \Delta t$. For the curve $x(t) = Ct$, the differential $dx = C\,\Delta t$ equals Δx for all Δt.

It is customary to write dt for the change Δt in the independent variable t. Then the differential dx is just the derivative of x with respect to t times dt. This is the origin of the traditional notation for the derivative we have been using

$$\frac{dx}{dt} = \lim_{\Delta t \to 0} \frac{\Delta x}{\Delta t}$$

We may regard dx/dt as the single quantity, the derivative of x with respect to t, as we have been doing up to now, or we may regard it as the ratio of the differentials dx and dt.

Example 2-12 For a falling body whose position is given by $x = (16 \text{ ft/sec}^2)t^2$, find the distance fallen during the 0.5-sec time interval between $t_1 = 10$ sec and $t_2 = 10.5$ sec.

The derivative of this function is just the velocity:

$$v = \frac{dx}{dt} = (32 \text{ ft/sec}^2)t$$

and the differential dx is

$$dx = (32 \text{ ft/sec}^2)t\, dt$$

Substituting $t = 10$ sec and $dt = 0.5$ sec gives

$$dx = (32 \text{ ft/sec}^2)(10 \text{ sec})(0.5 \text{ sec}) = 160 \text{ ft}$$

This is the distance the particle would fall during 0.5 sec if its velocity were equal to 320 ft/sec, the value of the instantaneous velocity at $t = 10$ sec. Thus the differential approximation here neglects the fact that the velocity increases slightly during the 0.5-sec interval from $t = 10$ sec to $t = 10.5$ sec. Since the velocity at $t = 10.5$ is $32 \times 10.5 = 336$ ft/sec, the average velocity during this interval is 328 ft/sec. The actual distance the body falls during this interval is 164 ft. This result is greater by 4 ft than that found using the differential approximation, an error of about $2\frac{1}{2}$ percent.

Review

A. Define, explain, or otherwise identify:

Particle, 18

Displacement, 19

Average velocity, 20

Instantaneous velocity, 21

Derivative, 22

Slope, 23

Speed, 25

Average acceleration, 25

Instantaneous acceleration, 25

Initial-value problem, 29

Antiderivative, 29

Definite integral, 32

Indefinite integral, 32

Differential, 37

B. True or false: If the statement is true, explain; if it is false, give a counterexample, i.e., a known example which contradicts the statement.

1. The equation $x = x_0 + v_0 t + \frac{1}{2}a_0 t^2$ holds for all motion in one dimension.

2. If the acceleration is zero, the particle cannot be moving.

3. The displacement equals the area under the velocity-versus-time curve.

4. The average velocity always equals the mean value of the initial and final velocities.

Exercises

Unless instructed otherwise, use the approximate value $g = 32$ ft/sec² $= 9.8$ m/sec² for the acceleration of gravity in Exercises and Problems.

Section 2-1, Displacement and Average Velocity

1. A particle is at $x = +5$ m at $t = 0$, $x = -7$ m at $t = 6$ sec, and $x = +2$ m at $t = 10$ sec. Find the average velocity of the particle during the intervals (*a*) $t = 0$ to $t = 6$ sec; (*b*) $t = 6$ sec to $t = 10$ sec; (*c*) $t = 0$ to $t = 10$ sec.

2. A driver begins a 300-mi trip at noon. (*a*) He drives nonstop and arrives at his destination at 5:30 P.M. Calculate his average velocity for the trip. (*b*) He drives for 3 h, rests for $\frac{1}{2}$h, and continues driving, arriving at 5:30 P.M. Calculate his average velocity. (*c*) After resting 2 h, he drives back home, taking 6 h for the return trip. What is his average velocity for the total round trip? (*d*) What is his displacement?

3. A car travels in a straight line with average velocity of 60 mi/h for 2.5 h and then with average velocity of 30 mi/h for 1.5 h. (*a*) What is the total displacement for the 4-h trip? (*b*) What is the average velocity for the total trip?

4. Figure 2-19 shows the position of a particle versus time. Find the average velocity for the time intervals *a, b, c,* and *d* indicated.

Figure 2-19
x versus *t* for Exercise 4.

Section 2-2, Instantaneous Velocity

5. For each of the four graphs of x versus t in Figure 2-20, indicate whether the velocity at time t_2 is greater than, less than, or equal to the velocity at time t_1. Compare also the speeds at these times.

(*a*)

(*b*)

Figure 2-20
x-versus-*t* curves for Exercise 5. (Continued on next page)

(c)   (d)

Figure 2-20
(Continued)

6. In the graph of x versus t in Figure 2-21, (a) find the average velocity between the times $t = 0$ and $t = 2$ sec. (b) Find the instantaneous velocity at $t = 2$ sec by measuring the slope of the tangent line indicated.

Figure 2-21
x versus t for Exercise 6 with tangent line drawn at $t = 2$ sec.

7. For the graph of x versus t in Figure 2-22 find the average velocity for the time intervals $\Delta t = t_2 - 0.75$ sec when t_2 is 1.75, 1.5, 1.25, and 1.0 sec. What is the instantaneous velocity at $t = 0.75$ sec?

Figure 2-22
x-versus-t curve for Exercise 7.

8. For the graph of x versus t shown in Figure 2-23, (a) find the average velocity for the interval $t = 1$ sec to $t = 5$ sec. (b) Find the instantaneous velocity at $t = 4$ sec. (c) At what time is the velocity of the particle zero?

9. The position of a particle depends on the time according to $x = (1 \text{ m/sec}^2)t^2 - (5 \text{ m/sec})t + 1$ m. (a) Find the displacement and average velocity for the interval $t = 3$ sec to $t = 4$ sec. (b) Find a general formula for the displacement for the time interval from t to $t + \Delta t$. (c) Find the instantaneous velocity for any time t.

10. The height of a certain projectile is related to time by $y = -5(t - 5)^2 + 125$, where y is in meters and t in seconds. (a) Sketch y versus t for $t = 0$ to $t = 10$ sec. (b) Find the average velocity for each of the 1-sec time intervals between

Figure 2-23
x-versus-t curve for Exercise 8 with tangent line drawn at $t = 4$ sec.

integral time values from $t = 0$ to $t = 10$ sec. Sketch v_{av} versus t. (c) Find the instantaneous velocity as a function of time.

Section 2-3, Acceleration

11. A fast car can accelerate from 0 to 60 mi/h in 5 sec. What is the average acceleration during this interval? What is the ratio of this acceleration to the free-fall acceleration of gravity?

12. A car is traveling at 45 mi/h at time $t = 0$. It accelerates at a constant rate of 10 mi/h-sec. (a) How fast is the car going at $t = 1$ sec? At $t = 2$ sec? (b) What is its speed at a general time t?

13. At $t = 5$ sec an object is traveling at 5 m/sec. At $t = 8$ sec its velocity is -1 m/sec. Find the average acceleration for this interval.

14. A particle moves with velocity given by $v = 8t - 7$, where v is in meters per second and t in seconds. (a) Find the average acceleration for the 1-sec intervals beginning at $t = 3$ sec and $t = 4$ sec. (b) Sketch v versus t. What is the instantaneous acceleration at any time?

15. State whether the acceleration is positive, negative, or zero for each of the *position* functions $x(t)$ in Figure 2-24.

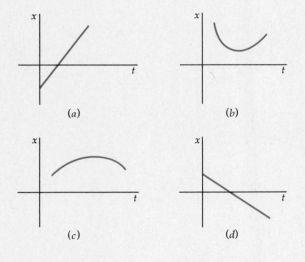

Figure 2-24
x-versus-t curves for Exercise 15.

16. The position of a particle versus time is given by

t, sec	0	1	2	3	4	5	6	7	8	9	10	11
x, m	0	5	15	45	65	70	60	-30	-50	-50	-55	-55

Plot x versus t and draw a smooth curve $x(t)$. Indicate the times or time intervals for which (a) the velocity is greatest; (b) the velocity is least; (c) the velocity is zero; (d) the velocity is constant; (e) the acceleration is positive; (f) the acceleration is negative.

17. The position of an object is related to time by $x = 4t^2 - 8t + 6$, where x is in feet and t in seconds. Find the instantaneous velocity and acceleration as functions of time.

18. A mass oscillating on a spring has a position function given by $x = A \sin \omega t$, where A and ω (the Greek letter omega) are constants. Find the instantaneous velocity and acceleration functions. (Rules 3 and 8 in Appendix Table E-1 may be helpful in finding the derivatives.) Show that the acceleration is proportional to the displacement x and that the velocity is greatest when the acceleration is zero.

19. The velocity of a particle under the influence of viscous forces (such as air resistance) is given by $v = Ae^{-bt}$, where A and b are constants. (a) What is the physical significance of the constant A? What are the dimensions of b? (b) Show that the acceleration is proportional to the velocity.

Section 2-4, Finding $x(t)$ from $v(t)$: The Initial-Value Problem

20. The velocity of a particle is given by $v = 6$ m/sec for all time t. Find the most general position function $x(t)$.

21. The velocity of a particle in meters per second is given by $v = 7t + 5$, where t is in seconds. Find the most general position function $x(t)$.

22. An object is dropped from rest at $t = 0$ from a height of 100 m. Its acceleration is $a = -9.8$ m/sec². (a) Find the velocity v at any time t. (b) Find the position x at any time t.

23. The velocity of an oscillating particle is given by $v = v_0 \cos \omega t$, where v_0 and ω are constants. Find the most general position function $x(t)$.

24. The acceleration of a certain rocket is given by $a = Ct$, where C is a constant. (a) Find the most general position function $x(t)$. (b) Find the position and velocity at $t = 5$ sec if $x = 0$ and $v = 0$ at $t = 0$ and $C = 3$ m/sec³.

25. A particle moves with a constant acceleration of 3 m/sec². At $t = 4$ sec it is at $x = 100$ m. At $t = 6$ sec it has a velocity $v = 15$ m/sec. Find its position at $t = 6$ sec.

Section 2-5, The Antiderivative and Integration

26. The velocity of a particle is given by $v = 6t + 3$, where t is in seconds and v in meters per second. (a) Sketch $v(t)$ versus t and find the area under the curve for the interval $t = 0$ to $t = 5$ sec. (b) Find the most general position function $x(t)$. Use this to calculate the displacement during the interval $t = 0$ to $t = 5$ sec.

27. The velocity of a particle in meters per second is given by $v = 7 - 4t$, where t is in seconds. (a) Sketch $v(t)$ versus t and find the area between the curve and the t axis from $t = 2$ sec to $t = 6$ sec. (b) Find the position function $x(t)$ by integration and use it to find the displacement during the interval $t = 2$ sec to $t = 6$ sec. (c) What is the average velocity for this interval?

28. Figure 2-25 shows the velocity of a particle versus time. (a) What is the magnitude in meters of the area of the rectangle indicated? (b) Find the displacement of the particle for the 1-sec intervals beginning at $t = 1$ sec and $t = 2$ sec. (c) What is the average velocity for the interval from $t = 1$ sec to $t = 3$ sec?

Figure 2-25
v-versus-t curve for Exercise 28.

29. Figure 2-26 shows the acceleration of a particle versus time. (*a*) What is the magnitude of the area of the rectangle indicated? (*b*) The particle starts from rest at $t = 0$. Find the velocity at the times $t = 1$, 2, and 3 sec by counting the squares under the curve. (*c*) Sketch the curve $v(t)$ versus t from your results of part (*b*) and estimate how far the particle traveled in the interval $t = 0$ to $t = 3$ sec.

Figure 2-26
a-versus-t curve for Exercise 29.

30. The equation of the curve shown in Figure 2-25 is $v = (0.5 \text{ m/sec})t^2$. Find the displacement of the particle for the interval $t = 1$ to $t = 3$ sec by integration and compare with your answer for Exercise 28. Is the average velocity equal to the mean of the initial and final velocities for this case?

Section 2-6, Motion with Constant Acceleration

31. A car accelerates from rest at a constant rate of 8 m/sec². (*a*) How fast is it going after 10 sec? (*b*) How far has it gone after 10 sec? (*c*) What is its average velocity for the interval $t = 0$ to $t = 10$ sec?

32. An object with initial velocity of 5 m/sec has a constant acceleration of 2 m/sec. When its speed is 15 m/sec, how far has it traveled?

33. An object with constant acceleration has velocity $v = 10$ m/sec when it is at $x = 6$ m and $v = 15$ m/sec when it is at $x = 10$ m. What is its acceleration?

34. An object has constant acceleration $a = 4$ m/sec². Its velocity is 1 m/sec at $t = 0$, at which time it is at $x = 7$ m. How fast is it moving when it is at $x = 8$ m? At what time is this?

35. How long does it take for a particle to travel 100 m if it begins from rest and accelerates at 10 m/sec²? What is the velocity when it has traveled 100 m? What is the average velocity for this time?

36. A ball is thrown upward with initial velocity of 80 ft/sec. Its acceleration is constant, equal to 32 ft/sec² downward. (*a*) How long is the ball in the air? (*b*) What is the greatest height reached by the ball? (*c*) When is the ball 96 ft above the ground?

37. A ball is dropped from a height of 3 ft and rebounds from the floor to a height of 2 ft. (*a*) What is the velocity of the ball just as it reaches the floor? (*b*) What is its velocity just as it leaves the floor? (*c*) If it is in contact with the floor for 0.02 sec, what are the magnitude and direction of its average acceleration during this interval?

38. The minimum distance for a controlled stop with no wheels locked for a certain car is 170 ft for level braking from 60 mi/h. Find the acceleration, assuming it to be constant, and express your answer as a fraction of the free-fall acceleration of gravity. How long does it take to stop?

Section 2-7, The Differential

39. The distance a body falls from rest in a time t is $x = (16 \text{ ft/sec}^2)t^2$. (*a*) Find the exact distance the body falls from time $t_1 = 20$ sec to time $t_2 = 20.3$ sec. (*b*) Find the velocity at time $t = 20$ sec and use the differential approximation to find the distance fallen during this interval.

40. The area of a circle of radius r is $A = \pi r^2$. Use the differential approximation to find the change in area ΔA for a small change in the radius Δr. Interpret the quantity dA geometrically.

41. Show that the fractional change in area of a circle is approximately related to the fractional change in radius by $\Delta A/A = 2\Delta r/r$. If the radius changes by 1 percent, what is the percentage change in the area?

42. The volume of a sphere of radius r is $V = (4\pi/3)r^3$. (*a*) Find the approximate small change in the volume dV for a small change in radius dr and interpret dV geometrically. (*b*) Show that the fractional changes are related by $dV/V = 3dr/r$. (*c*) The volume of a sphere is determined by measuring its radius. If a 2 percent error is made in this measurement, what is the resulting percentage error in the volume?

Problems

1. A car traveling at a constant speed of 20 m/sec passes an intersection at time $t = 0$, and 5 sec later a second car passes the same intersection traveling 30 m/sec in the same direction. (*a*) Sketch the position functions $x_1(t)$ and $x_2(t)$ for the two cars. (*b*) Find when the second car overtakes the first. (*c*) How far have the cars traveled when this happens?

2. Hare and Tortoise begin a 10-km race at time $t = 0$. Hare runs at 4 m/sec and quickly outdistances Tortoise, who runs at 1 m/sec (about 10 times faster than a tortoise can actually run but convenient for this problem). After running 5 min, Hare stops and falls asleep. His nap lasts 135 min. He awakes and again runs at 4 m/sec but loses the race. Plot an x-versus-t graph for each on the same axes. At what time does Tortoise pass Hare? How far behind is Hare when Tortoise crosses the finish line? How long can Hare nap and still win the race?

3. According to a mean-value theorem in calculus, in any time interval Δt there is at least one time t' at which the instantaneous velocity equals the average velocity for the whole interval. Sketch any continuous smooth curve x versus t and choose two times t_1 and t_2. Draw the line whose slope is the average velocity for the time interval $\Delta t = t_2 - t_1$ and find a time t' in your interval at which the tangent line to your curve has the same slope.

4. Figure 2-27 shows the position of a car plotted as a function of time. At which of the times t_0 to t_7 is (*a*) the velocity negative, (*b*) the velocity positive, (*c*) the velocity zero, (*d*) the acceleration negative, (*e*) the acceleration positive, (*f*) the acceleration zero?

Figure 2-27
Position of a car versus time
for Problem 4.

5. Sketch a single v-versus-t curve in which there are points or segments for which (a) the acceleration is zero and constant while the velocity is not zero; (b) the acceleration is zero but not constant; (c) the velocity and acceleration are both positive; (d) the velocity and acceleration are both negative; (e) the velocity is positive and the acceleration negative; (f) the velocity is negative and the acceleration positive; (g) the velocity is zero, but the acceleration is not.

6. For each of the graphs in Figure 2-28 indicate (a) at what times the acceleration of the object is positive, negative, and zero. (b) At what times is the acceleration constant? (c) At what times is the instantaneous velocity zero?

Figure 2-28
(a) v-versus-t curve and (b) x-versus-t curve for Problem 6.

7. A car is traveling 50 mi/h in a school zone. A police car starts from rest just as the speeder passes it and accelerates at a constant rate of 5 mi/h-sec. (a) Make a sketch of $x(t)$ for both cars. (b) When does the police car catch the speeding car? (c) How fast is the police car traveling when it finally catches the speeder?

8. The police car in Problem 7 chases a speeder traveling 80 mi/h. The maximum speed of the police car is 120 mi/h. The police car travels from rest with constant acceleration, 5 mi/h-sec, until its speed reaches 120 mi/h and then moves at constant speed. (a) When does it catch the speeder if it starts just as the speeder passes? (b) How far has each car traveled? (c) Sketch $x(t)$ for each car.

9. When the police car of Problem 8 traveling at 120 mi/h is 100 yd behind the speeder (traveling 80 mi/h), the speeder sees the car and slams on his brakes, locking the wheels. (a) Assuming that each car can brake at 20 ft/sec^2 and that the driver of the police car brakes as soon as he sees the brake lights of the

speeder, i.e., with no reaction time, show that the cars collide. (*b*) What is the speed of the police car relative to the speeder when they collide? At what time do they collide after the brakes are applied? (*c*) The time interval between the policeman's seeing the brake lights and putting on his own brakes is called his *reaction time T*. Estimate or measure your reaction time and discuss how it affects this problem.

10. When a car traveling at speed v_1 rounds a corner, the driver sees another car traveling at a slower speed v_2 a distance d ahead of him. (*a*) If the maximum acceleration his brakes can provide is a, show that the distance d must be greater than $(v_1 - v_2)^2/2a$ if a collision is to be avoided. (*b*) Evaluate this distance for $v_1 = 60$ mi/h, $v_2 = 30$ mi/h, and $a = 20$ ft/sec². (*c*) Estimate or measure your reaction time and calculate its effect on the distance found in part (*b*).

11. Figure 2-29 shows a plot of x versus t for a body moving along a straight line. Sketch rough graphs of v versus t and a versus t for this motion.

Figure 2-29
x-versus-t curve for Problem 11.

12. Figure 2-30 is a graph of v versus t for a particle moving along a straight line. The position of the particle at time $t = 0$ is $x_0 = 5$ m. (*a*) Find x for various times t by counting squares and sketch x versus t. (*b*) Sketch the acceleration a versus t.

Figure 2-30
v-versus-t curve for Problem 12.

13. A passenger is running at his maximum velocity of 10 ft/sec to catch a train. When he is a distance d from the nearest entry to the train, the train starts from rest with constant acceleration $a = 1.0$ ft/sec² away from the passenger. (*a*) If $d = 40$ ft and he keeps running, will he be able to jump onto the train? (*b*) Sketch the position function $x(t)$ for the train, choosing $x = 0$ at $t = 0$. On the same graph sketch $x(t)$ for the passenger for various values of initial separation distances d including $d = 40$ ft and the critical value d_c such that he just catches the train. (*c*) For the critical separation distance d_c, what is the speed of the train when the passenger catches it? What is its average speed for the time $t = 0$ until he catches it? What is the value of d_c?

14. A load of bricks is being lifted by a crane at the steady velocity of 16 ft/sec, but 20 ft above the ground one brick falls off. Describe the motion of the free brick by sketching $x(t)$. (*a*) What is the greatest height the brick reaches above the ground? (*b*) How long does it take to reach the ground? (*c*) What is its speed just before it hits the ground?

15. The position of a body oscillating on a spring is given by $x = A \sin \omega t$, where A and ω are constants and have the values $A = 5$ cm and

$\omega = 10°/\text{sec} = 0.175$ rad/sec. Sketch x versus t for times from $t = 0$ to $t = 36$ sec. (a) Measure the slope of your graph at $t = 0$ to find the velocity at this time. (b) Using sine tables, calculate the average velocity for a series of intervals beginning at $t = 0$ and ending at $t = 6, 3, 2, 1, 0, 0.5$, and 0.25 sec. (c) Compute dx/dt and find the velocity at time $t = 0$.

16. The kinetic energy of a particle is $E_k = \frac{1}{2}mv^2$, where m is the mass of the particle and v is its speed. Show that if the kinetic energy is plotted as a function of x the slope of this curve is proportional to the acceleration dv/dt. *Hint:* Use the chain rule

$$\frac{dv}{dt} = \frac{dv}{dx}\frac{dx}{dt}$$

17. Table 2-2 lists some world track records for short sprints. A simple model of sprinting assumes that a sprinter starts from rest, accelerates with constant acceleration a for a short time T, and then runs with constant speed $v_0 = aT$. According to this model, for times t greater than T, the distance x varies linearly with time. (a) Make a graph of distance x versus time t from the data in the table. (b) Set up an equation for x versus t according to the simple model described and show that for $t > T$, x can be written $x = v_0(t - \frac{1}{2}T)$. (c) Connect the points on your graph with a straight line and determine the slope and the intercept of the line with the time axis. From the fact that the slope is v_0 and the intercept is $\frac{1}{2}T$, compute the acceleration a. (d) The record for $x = 200$ m is 19.5 sec. Discuss the applicability of this simple model to races of 200 m or more.

Table 2-2

yd	m	t, sec
50		5.1
	50	5.5
60		5.9
	60	6.5
100		9.1
	100	9.9

18. The acceleration of a particle falling under the influence of gravity and a resistive force such as air resistance is given by

$$a = \frac{dv}{dt} = g - Bv$$

where g is the free-fall acceleration of gravity and B is a constant which depends on the mass and shape of the particle and on the medium. Suppose the particle begins with zero velocity at time $t = 0$. (a) Discuss qualitatively how the speed v varies with time from your knowledge of the rate of change dv/dt given by this equation. What is the value of the velocity when the acceleration is zero? This is called the *terminal velocity*. (b) Sketch the solution $v(t)$ versus t without solving the equation. This can be done as follows. At $t = 0$, v is zero and the slope is g. Sketch a straight-line segment, neglecting any change in slope for a short time interval. At the end of the interval the velocity is not zero, and so the slope is less than g. Sketch another straight-line segment with a smaller slope. Continue until the slope is zero and the velocity equals the terminal velocity.

19. (a) Show that the equation in Problem 18 can be written $df/f = -B\,dt$, where $f = g - Bv$. (b) Find the indefinite integral of each side of this equation and solve for v, using the fact that $\exp(\ln f) = f$. Find the constant of integration in terms of g and B from the initial condition $v = 0$ at $t = 0$. (c) Write your solution in the form $v = v_t(1 - e^{-t/T})$, where v_t is the terminal velocity and $T = 1/B$. (d) Plot the points for $t = 0, 1, 3, 6, 10$, and 20 sec for $B = 0.1$ sec^{-1}.

20. Show that if $y = Cx^n$, where c and n are any constants, the differential dy is related to dx by

$$\frac{dy}{y} = n\frac{dx}{x}$$

CHAPTER 3

Motion in Two and Three Dimensions

We now extend our description of the motion of a particle to the more general cases of motion in two and three dimensions. For this more general motion, displacement, velocity, and acceleration are vectors, which have direction in space as well as magnitude. In this chapter, we investigate the properties of vectors in general and of these three vectors in particular. We also discuss two important special cases of motion in a plane, projectile motion and circular motion.

When the motion of a particle is confined to a plane, its position can be described by two numbers. For example, we might choose the distance x from the y axis and the distance y from the x axis, where the x and y axes are perpendicular axes which intersect at origin O, as in Figure 3-1. Alternatively, we can specify the same position by giving the distance r from the origin, and the angle θ made by the x axis and the line from the origin to the point. There are of course other choices, but in each case two numbers are needed to specify the location of a point on a plane.

Position on a plane

If the particle is not confined to a plane but moves in three dimensions, three numbers are needed to specify its position. A convenient method is to use the three coordinates x, y, and z. An alternative is to use the spherical coordinates r, θ, and ϕ. The relations between spher-

Position in space

Figure 3-1
Coordinates of a point P in a plane. The rectangular coordinates (x,y) and polar coordinates (r,θ) are related by $x = r \cos \theta$, $y = r \sin \theta$, $r = \sqrt{x^2 + y^2}$, $\tan \theta = y/x$.

Figure 3-2
Coordinates of a point P in
three dimensions. The rectangular coordinates (x,y,z) and
spherical coordinates (r,θ,ϕ)
are related by
$x = r \sin \theta \cos \phi$
$y = r \sin \theta \sin \phi$
$z = r \cos \theta$
$r = \sqrt{x^2 + y^2 + z^2}$
$\tan \theta = \sqrt{x^2 + y^2}/z$
$\tan \phi = y/x$

ical and rectangular coordinates are shown in Figure 3-2. Spherical
coordinates are convenient when there is spherical symmetry. For example, if a particle moves on the surface of a sphere, these coordinates
are useful because r is constant and only θ and ϕ vary.

Most of the interesting features of motion in more than one dimension can be brought out in two-dimensional motion, which is easier to
illustrate on paper or a blackboard. Most of our examples are therefore
limited to two dimensions, with an indication of the extension to
three-dimensional motion.

3-1   The Displacement Vector

Consider a particle which moves from some point P_1 to another P_2. As
in one-dimensional motion, we call the change in position of a particle
its *displacement*. In two or three dimensions, we indicate the displacement by an arrow from the original position P_1 to the new position P_2,
as in Figure 3-3. We see that the displacement has direction as well as
magnitude. We should note also that the displacement as we have   *Displacement in space*
defined it does not depend on the path taken by the particle as it
moves from P_1 to P_2 but only on the end points P_1 and P_2. A second
displacement is indicated in Figure 3-3 by an arrow from point P_2 to
P_3. The arrow from the original point P_1 to P_3 indicates the *resultant*
displacement from the original position P_1 to the last position P_3; it is
called the sum of the two successive displacements. Quantities which
have magnitude and direction *and* which obey the addition law illus-

Figure 3-3
The addition of vectors. The
displacement **C** is equivalent
to the successive displace-
ments **A** and **B**; that is, **C** =
A + **B**.

trated by these displacements are called *vectors*. Many quantities in physics besides displacements are vectors, e.g., velocity, acceleration, force, momentum, and electric field. We denote vector quantities by boldface type, as in **A**, **B**, and **C** for the three displacements in Figure 3-3. (In handwriting, we indicate a vector by drawing an arrow over the symbol.) The addition law for vectors illustrated in this figure is simply

Notation for vectors

$$\mathbf{C} = \mathbf{A} + \mathbf{B} \qquad \text{3-1}$$

The *magnitude*, or length, of the vector **A** is written as $|\mathbf{A}|$ or A. The magnitude of a vector ordinarily has physical units, like speed or acceleration, discussed in Chapter 2. A displacement vector, for example, has a magnitude which can be expressed in feet or meters or any other measure of distance. Note that the sum of the magnitudes of **A** and **B** does not equal the magnitude of $\mathbf{C} = \mathbf{A} + \mathbf{B}$ unless **A** and **B** are in the same direction:

$$C \neq A + B \qquad \text{unless } \mathbf{A} \text{ and } \mathbf{B} \text{ are in the same direction}$$

Quantities which are completely specified by only a number (with units), e.g., distance, mass, or temperature, are called *scalars*.[1]

Questions

1. Can the displacement of a particle in any time interval have a magnitude which is less than the distance traveled by the particle along its path in that interval? Can its magnitude be more than the distance traveled? Explain.

2. Give an example in which the distance traveled is a significant amount yet the corresponding displacement is zero.

3. Is displacement always in the direction of motion?

4. If $A = 7$ m and $B = 3$ m, what are the greatest and least values possible for C if $\mathbf{C} = \mathbf{A} + \mathbf{B}$?

3-2   Components of a Vector

The projection of a vector on a line is called a *component* of the vector in the direction of that line. An important example of vector components is the projections of the vector on the axes of a rectangular coordinate system. These projections, called the *rectangular* components of the vector, are denoted by A_x, A_y, and A_z for the vector **A**. Figure 3-4 illustrates the rectangular components of the displacements **A**, **B**, and **C** of Figure 3-3. We denote the coordinates of P_1 by (x_1, y_1) and use similar designations for P_2 and P_3; then the components of these vectors are

Rectangular components

$$\begin{aligned} A_x &= x_2 - x_1 & A_y &= y_2 - y_1 \\ B_x &= x_3 - x_2 & B_y &= y_3 - y_2 \\ C_x &= x_3 - x_1 & C_y &= y_3 - y_1 \end{aligned} \qquad \text{3-2}$$

[1] Strictly speaking, only quantities which are independent of the choice of coordinate system are scalars. Thus distance, mass, and temperature are scalars, but, for example, the x coordinate of a point is not strictly a scalar because it depends on the coordinate system. This distinction will not be important for our work.

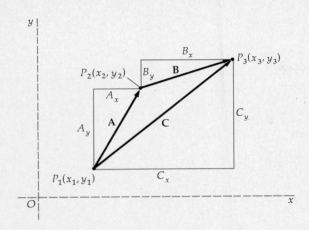

Figure 3-4
The x and y components of vectors $\mathbf{A}$, $\mathbf{B}$, and $\mathbf{C}$ from Figure 3-3. $A_x = x_2 - x_1$, $A_y = y_2 - y_1$, $B_x = x_3 - x_2$, $B_y = y_3 - y_2$, $C_x = x_3 - x_1 = A_x + B_x$, $C_y = y_3 - y_1 = A_y + B_y$.

Note that the *components* of a vector are not vectors. They are positive or negative numbers with units.[1] It should be clear from the figure that

$$\mathbf{C} = \mathbf{A} + \mathbf{B} \text{ implies both } C_x = A_x + B_x \text{ and } C_y = A_y + B_y \qquad 3\text{-}3$$

The magnitude of a vector can be written in terms of the rectangular components of the vector. As shown in Figure 3-4, the rectangular components A_x and A_y form the two legs of a right triangle whose hypotenuse is the magnitude A. Hence, from the theorem of Pythagoras,

$$A = \sqrt{A_x{}^2 + A_y{}^2} \qquad 3\text{-}4$$

We can also specify the direction in terms of the rectangular components. If θ is the angle between the vector and a line parallel to the x axis,

$$\tan \theta = \frac{A_y}{A_x} \qquad 3\text{-}5$$

Example 3-1 A man walks 4.00 mi northeast and then 3.00 mi southeast. If the origin of coordinates is taken at his starting point and the x axis points straight east, (*a*) what are the rectangular components of his two displacements? (*b*) What are the rectangular components of his overall displacement? (*c*) What are his final distance and direction from the starting point?

(*a*) The successive displacements are shown in Figure 3-5. Displace-

[1] The component of a vector is not strictly a scalar because it depends on the choice of coordinate system. (see previous footnote).

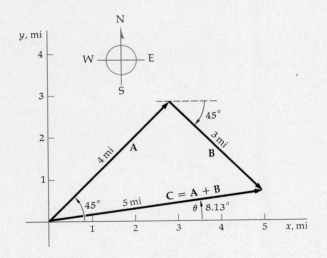

Figure 3-5
A plot of the displacements from Example 3-1. North is plotted in the $+y$ direction; east in the $+x$ direction.

ment **A** has magnitude 4.00 mi and is 45° north of east. Displacement **B** has magnitude 3.00 mi and is 45° south of east. The components of **A** are

$$A_x = A \cos 45° = (4.00 \text{ mi})(0.707) = 2.83 \text{ mi}$$

$$A_y = A \sin 45° = (4.00 \text{ mi})(0.707) = 2.83 \text{ mi}$$

The components of **B** are

$$B_x = B \cos 45° = (3.00 \text{ mi})(0.707) = 2.12 \text{ mi}$$

$$B_y = -B \sin 45° = -(3.00 \text{ mi})(0.707) = -2.12 \text{ mi}$$

The component B_y is negative, indicating that it is in the direction of decreasing, or negative, values of y rather than of increasing, or positive, values of y.

(b) The components of the resultant displacement **C** = **A** + **B** are calculated as follows:

$$C_x = A_x + B_x = 2.83 \text{ mi} + 2.12 \text{ mi} = 4.95 \text{ mi}$$

$$C_y = A_y + B_y = 2.83 \text{ mi} - 2.12 \text{ mi} = 0.71 \text{ mi}$$

(c) The man's final distance from his starting point is the magnitude of **C**:

$$C = \sqrt{C_x^2 + C_y^2} = \sqrt{4.95^2 + 0.71^2} = 5.0 \text{ mi}$$

The direction of the man's final position can be specified by giving the angle θ:

$$\tan \theta = \frac{C_y}{C_x} = \frac{0.71}{4.95} = 0.143$$

or

$$\theta = 8.13°$$

That is, the direction of the net displacement is 8.13° north of east.

We can write a vector conveniently in terms of its rectangular components by making use of *unit vectors*. A unit vector is a dimensionless vector which has the magnitude of 1 and points in any convenient direction. For example, let **i**, **j**, and **k** be unit vectors which point in the x, y, and z directions, respectively. A general vector **A** can then be written as the sum of three vectors each parallel to a coordinate:

$$\mathbf{A} = A_x\mathbf{i} + A_y\mathbf{j} + A_z\mathbf{k} \qquad\qquad 3\text{-}6 \qquad \textit{Unit vectors}$$

The vector $A_x\mathbf{i}$ is the product of the component A_x and the unit vector **i**. It is a vector parallel to the x axis with magnitude A_x. The vector sum indicated in Equation 3-6 is illustrated in Figure 3-6. The addition of

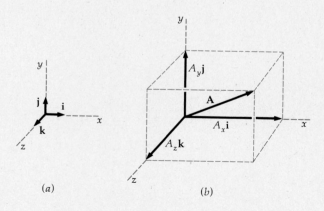

(a)   (b)

Figure 3-6
(a) The unit vectors **i**, **j**, and **k** in a rectangular coordinate system. (b) The vector **A** can be written in terms of the unit vectors **i**, **j**, **k**; that is, $\mathbf{A} = A_x\mathbf{i} + A_y\mathbf{j} + A_z\mathbf{k}$.

two vectors **A** and **B** can be written in terms of these unit vectors as

$$A + B = (A_x\mathbf{i} + A_y\mathbf{j} + A_z\mathbf{k}) + (B_x\mathbf{i} + B_y\mathbf{j} + B_z\mathbf{k})$$
$$= (A_x + B_x)\mathbf{i} + (A_y + B_y)\mathbf{j} + (A_z + B_z)\mathbf{k} \qquad 3\text{-}7$$

For example, the resultant displacement found in Example 3-1 is written

$$C = 4.95\mathbf{i} + 0.71\mathbf{j}$$

where **C** is in miles.

We shall frequently want to use components of vectors along lines other than the rectangular axes. For these cases, discussed later, we define other unit vectors pointing in directions convenient for the particular problem.

Questions

5. Can a component of a vector have a magnitude greater than the magnitude of the vector? Under what circumstances can a component of a vector have a magnitude equal to the magnitude of the vector?

6. Can a vector be equal to zero and still have one or more components not equal to zero?

7. Are the components of $C = A + B$ necessarily larger than the corresponding components of either **A** or **B**?

3-3   Properties of Vectors

This section summarizes some important properties of vectors.

Equality

Two vectors **A** and **B** are defined to be equal if they have the same magnitude *and* the same direction:

$$A = B \qquad \text{if } A = B \text{ } and \text{ their directions are the same} \qquad 3\text{-}8$$

Note that we do not require that the end points of the vectors be the same for them to be equal. All the vectors in Figure 3-7 are equal. Thus a vector is completely specified by its magnitude and direction. Since these properties can be written in terms of the rectangular components of the vector, we can also specify the vector completely by giving its

Figure 3-7
Vectors are equal if their magnitudes and directions are the same. The vectors in this figure are all equal.

rectangular components. Two vectors are equal if their corresponding rectangular components are equal:

$$\mathbf{A} = \mathbf{B} \qquad \text{if } A_x = B_x, A_y = B_y, \text{ and } A_z = B_z \qquad \text{3-9}$$

Vector Addition

The addition of two vectors **A** and **B** is defined geometrically as in Figure 3-8. Here, the tail of vector **B** is placed at the head of vector **A**. The sum $\mathbf{C} = \mathbf{A} + \mathbf{B}$ is the vector from the tail of **A** to the head of **B**, as shown.

An alternative construction for finding the sum of two vectors is to put the tails of the vectors together and construct a parallelogram, as in Figure 3-9. The resultant vector is along the diagonal of the parallelogram. The vector-addition law is sometimes referred to as the *parallelogram law of addition*. Figure 3-9 shows that this construction gives the same result as Figure 3-8, i.e., putting the tail of **B** at the head of **A** and drawing vector $\mathbf{C} = \mathbf{A} + \mathbf{B}$ from the tail of **A** to the head of **B**.

By geometric construction, we can see that the sum of the two vectors is independent of the order of the vectors. This is the *commutative law of addition*:

$$\mathbf{A} + \mathbf{B} = \mathbf{B} + \mathbf{A} \qquad \text{3-10}$$

The sum of three or more vectors is independent of the order in which they are added. This *associative law of addition*,

$$(\mathbf{A} + \mathbf{B}) + \mathbf{C} = \mathbf{A} + (\mathbf{B} + \mathbf{C}) \qquad \text{3-11}$$

is illustrated for three vectors in Figure 3-10.

Negative of a Vector

The vector $-\mathbf{A}$ is defined to be the vector which when added to **A** gives zero:

$$\mathbf{A} + -\mathbf{A} = 0$$

The vector $-\mathbf{A}$ has the same magnitude as **A** but points in the opposite direction (sometimes stated by saying that $-\mathbf{A}$ is antiparallel to **A**). The components of $-\mathbf{A}$ are each the negative of the components of **A**. That is, if **A** has components (A_x, A_y, A_z), then $-\mathbf{A}$ has components $(-A_x, -A_y, -A_z)$.

Subtraction of Vectors

The definition of the negative of a vector allows us to define vector subtraction in a simple way. **B** subtracted from **A** is defined to be $-\mathbf{B}$ added to **A**:

$$\mathbf{A} - \mathbf{B} = \mathbf{A} + (-\mathbf{B}) \qquad \text{3-12}$$

Vector subtraction is illustrated in Figure 3-11. It is often useful to think of $\mathbf{A} - \mathbf{B}$ as the vector which is added to vector **B** to obtain vector **A**. This idea is illustrated in Figure 3-11*b*, where the vectors **A** and **B** are drawn tail to tail. Then the vector $\mathbf{A} - \mathbf{B}$ is drawn from the tip of **B** to the tip of **A**.

Figure 3-8
Addition of two vectors. The vector $\mathbf{C} = \mathbf{A} + \mathbf{B}$ is drawn from the tail of **A** to the head of **B** when the tail of **B** is placed at the head of **A**.

Figure 3-9
Parallelogram method of addition of vectors. The vector $\mathbf{C} = \mathbf{A} + \mathbf{B}$ is along the diagonal of the parallelogram formed by **A** and **B**. The result is the same as that in Figure 3-8. It can be seen from this figure that $\mathbf{A} + \mathbf{B}$ is the same as $\mathbf{B} + \mathbf{A}$.

Figure 3-10
Vector addition is associative. $(\mathbf{A} + \mathbf{B}) + \mathbf{C} = \mathbf{A} + (\mathbf{B} + \mathbf{C})$.

Figure 3-11
Subtraction of vectors. (a) **C** =
A − **B** is found by adding −**B**
to **A**. (b) An alternative
method of finding **C** = **A** − **B**.
Here **C** is the vector which
when added to **B** gives the
vector **A**.

Multiplication of a Vector by a Scalar

If we multiply a vector **A** by a positive scalar c, we obtain the vector $c\mathbf{A}$, which has the same direction as **A** and magnitude cA.[1] We used this definition when we expressed a vector in terms of its rectangular components and the unit vectors **i**, **j**, and **k**. Note that this definition is consistent with the result that when we add two equal vectors **A** + **A**, we obtain a vector parallel to **A** with twice the magnitude, which is $2A$.

If c is a negative scalar, the vector $c\mathbf{A}$ has the magnitude $|c|A$ and is antiparallel to **A**.

Questions

8. Can two vectors of unequal magnitudes be added to give zero?

9. Are the magnitudes of **A** and −**A** equal, or do they have opposite signs? What about the components of **A** and −**A**?

10. Does the magnitude of a vector change if the units in which it is expressed change? Does the magnitude of $c\mathbf{A}$ have the same units as **A**?

11. If **A**, **B**, and **C** are three successive displacement vectors, the total displacement resulting from all three can be obtained by adding the three vectorially in any order; but is the path described by displacement **B** followed by **C** followed by **A** the same as the path corresponding to displacements **A**, **B**, and **C** taken in that order?

3-4   The Velocity Vector

We are now ready to extend our concepts of velocity and acceleration to the general motion of a particle. Consider a particle moving along a curve in two dimensions, as in Figure 3-12. At some time t_1 it is at

[1] This result holds whether c is a strict scalar or any numerical quantity.

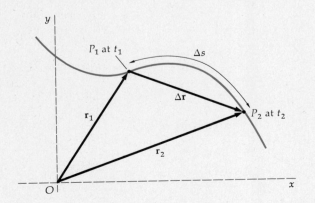

Figure 3-12
The position, or radius, vector **r** is the vector from the origin to the position of the particle. The displacement vector $\Delta\mathbf{r}$ for the time interval from t_1 to t_2 is then the difference in the position vectors $\Delta\mathbf{r} = \mathbf{r}_2 - \mathbf{r}_1$.

point P_1, and at a later time t_2 it is at point P_2. We can describe the position of the particle by a vector **r** from the origin to the position of the particle. This *position vector*, or *radius vector* as it is sometimes called, is special in that we specify in its definition the location of its tail. From the figure we see that the displacement vector is the difference of the two position vectors $\mathbf{r}_2 - \mathbf{r}_1$. By analogy with our one-dimensional notation, in which we wrote $\Delta \mathbf{r}$ for a displacement in two (or three) dimensions,

$$\Delta \mathbf{r} = \mathbf{r}_2 - \mathbf{r}_1 \qquad\qquad 3\text{-}13$$

Radius vector

Displacement vector

The new position vector $\mathbf{r}_2$ is thus the sum of the original position vector $\mathbf{r}_1$ and the displacement vector $\Delta \mathbf{r}$, as can be seen from the figure:

$$\mathbf{r}_2 = \mathbf{r}_1 + \Delta \mathbf{r}$$

We define the average velocity vector as the ratio of the displacement vector $\Delta \mathbf{r}$ and the time interval for this displacement $\Delta t = t_2 - t_1$:

$$\mathbf{v}_{\text{av}} = \frac{\Delta \mathbf{r}}{\Delta t} \qquad\qquad 3\text{-}14$$

Average-velocity vector

The average velocity is the product of a scalar $(1/\Delta t)$ and a vector $\Delta \mathbf{r}$ and is therefore a vector. We note from Figure 3-12 that the magnitude of the displacement vector is *not* equal to the distance of travel Δs as measured along the curve. It is, in fact, less than this distance (unless the particle travels in a straight line between points P_1 and P_2). However, if we consider smaller and smaller time intervals, as indicated in Figure 3-13, the magnitude of the displacement approaches the distance traveled by the particle along the curve, and the direction of $\Delta \mathbf{r}$ approaches the direction of the line tangent to the curve at point P_1. We define the instantaneous-velocity vector as the limit of the average velocity as the time interval Δt approaches zero:

$$\mathbf{v} = \lim_{\Delta t \to 0} \frac{\Delta \mathbf{r}}{\Delta t} = \frac{d\mathbf{r}}{dt} \qquad\qquad 3\text{-}15$$

Instantaneous-velocity vector

The instantaneous velocity is thus the derivative of the position vector with respect to time. The direction of the instantaneous velocity is along the line tangent to the curve traveled by the particle in space. The magnitude of the instantaneous velocity is called the *speed ds/dt*, where s is the distance measured along the curve. The position vector

Speed is the magnitude of the velocity vector

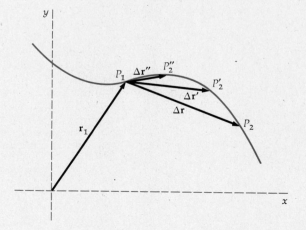

Figure 3-13
As smaller and smaller time intervals are considered, the magnitude of the displacement vector approaches the distance traveled along the curve and the direction of the displacement vector approaches the direction of the line tangent to the curve at point P_1.

Figure 3-14
A particle moving along a radial line has a position vector which does not change in direction but may change in magnitude.

Figure 3-15
A particle moving in a circle has a position vector which does not change in magnitude but does change in direction. The velocity vector is tangent to the circle and perpendicular to the radius vector.

r can change in magnitude, direction, or both. If the particle moves along a radial line through the origin, as in Figure 3-14, **r** changes in magnitude only and the velocity vector is parallel to **r**. Our discussion of one-dimensional motion in Chapter 2 applies for this special case.

Figure 3-15 shows a particle moving around the origin in a circle of radius r. In this case, the position vector has a constant magnitude but is changing in direction. The velocity vector for this motion is tangent to the circle and therefore perpendicular to the radius vector. In the general case illustrated in Figure 3-12 the radius vector is changing in both magnitude and direction.

Example 3-2 A sailboat with initial coordinates $(x_1,y_1) = (100$ ft, 200 ft) has the coordinates 1.00 min later $(x_2,y_2) = (120$ ft, 210 ft). What are the components, magnitude, and direction of its average velocity for this 1-min interval?

$$v_{x,\mathrm{av}} = \frac{x_2 - x_1}{\Delta t} = \frac{120 - 100 \text{ ft}}{1.00 \text{ min}} = 20.0 \text{ ft/min}$$

$$v_{y,\mathrm{av}} = \frac{y_2 - y_1}{\Delta t} = \frac{210 - 200 \text{ ft}}{1.00 \text{ min}} = 10.0 \text{ ft/min}$$

$$v_{\mathrm{av}} = \sqrt{(v_{x,\mathrm{av}})^2 + (v_{y,\mathrm{av}})^2}$$
$$= \sqrt{20.0^2 + 10.0^2} = \sqrt{500} = 22.4 \text{ ft/min}$$

$$\tan \theta = \frac{v_{y,\mathrm{av}}}{v_{x,\mathrm{av}}} = \frac{10 \text{ ft/min}}{20 \text{ ft/min}} = 0.500$$

or

$$\theta = 26.6°$$

Questions

12. For an arbitrary motion of a given particle does the direction of the velocity vector have any particular relationship to the direction of the position vector?

13. Give examples in which the directions of the velocity and position vectors are (*a*) opposite, (*b*) the same, (*c*) mutually perpendicular.

14. Can the velocity vector change direction without changing magnitude? If so, give an example.

3-5   The Acceleration Vector

The *average-acceleration vector* is defined as the ratio of the change in the instantaneous-velocity vector $\Delta \mathbf{v}$ and the time interval Δt:

$$\mathbf{a}_{av} = \frac{\Delta \mathbf{v}}{\Delta t} = \frac{\mathbf{v}_2 - \mathbf{v}_1}{\Delta t} \qquad \text{3-16}$$

Average-acceleration vector

The *instantaneous-acceleration vector* is defined as the derivative of the velocity vector with respect to time:

$$\mathbf{a} = \lim_{\Delta t \to 0} \frac{\Delta \mathbf{v}}{\Delta t} = \frac{d\mathbf{v}}{dt} \qquad \text{3-17}$$

Instantaneous-acceleration vector

It is particularly important to note that the velocity vector may be changing in magnitude, direction, or both. If the velocity vector is changing in any way, the particle is accelerating according to our definition. We are perhaps most familiar with acceleration in which the velocity vector changes in magnitude. In this case the speed changes (since the speed is just the magnitude of the velocity vector). However, a particle can be traveling with constant speed and still be accelerating if the direction of the velocity vector is changing. (A particularly important example of this is circular motion, discussed in Section 3-7.) This acceleration is just as real as when the speed is changing. We shall see in the next chapter that a force is necessary to produce an acceleration of a particle. The force required to produce a given acceleration (say 1 m/sec² downward) on a given particle is the same whether this acceleration is associated with a change in the magnitude of the velocity vector, a change in its direction, or a combination of both.

Changing direction involves acceleration

Questions

15. How is it possible for a particle moving at constant speed to be accelerating? Can a particle with constant velocity be accelerating at the same time?

16. Is it possible for a particle to round a curve without accelerating?

17. Show that the acceleration of a particle always points toward the concave side of its path.

18. Describe a circumstance in which a particle's velocity is horizontal and its acceleration is vertical.

3-6   Motion with Constant Acceleration: Projectile Motion

An important special case of motion in two or three dimensions occurs when the acceleration is constant in both magnitude and direction. An example of motion with constant acceleration is that of a projectile near the surface of the earth if air resistance can be neglected.

Let $\mathbf{a}_0$ be the instantaneous acceleration vector. Since $\mathbf{a}_0$ is constant, it is equal to the average acceleration for any time interval Δt. Equation 3-16 is then

$$\Delta \mathbf{v} = \mathbf{a}_0 \, \Delta t$$

If $\mathbf{v}_0$ is the velocity at time $t = 0$ and $\mathbf{v}$ is the instantaneous velocity at a general time t, we have

$$\mathbf{v} - \mathbf{v}_0 = \mathbf{a}_0 (t - 0)$$

or

$$\mathbf{v} = \mathbf{v}_0 + \mathbf{a}_0 t \qquad\qquad 3\text{-}18$$

The relation between the vectors $\mathbf{v}$, $\mathbf{v}_0$, and $\mathbf{a}_0$ is shown in Figure 3-16a.

The position vector $\mathbf{r}$ which has the derivative given by Equation 3-16 is

$$\mathbf{r} = \mathbf{r}_0 + \mathbf{v}_0 t + \tfrac{1}{2}\mathbf{a}_0 t^2 \qquad\qquad 3\text{-}19$$

where $\mathbf{r}_0$ is the position vector at $t = 0$. The validity of Equation 3-19 can be verified by computing the derivative $d\mathbf{r}/dt$ directly. Let $\mathbf{r}_1$ and $\mathbf{r}_2$ be the position vectors at times t and $t + \Delta t$, respectively. Then

$$\begin{aligned}
\mathbf{r}_2 &= \mathbf{r}_0 + \mathbf{v}_0(t + \Delta t) + \tfrac{1}{2}\mathbf{a}_0(t + \Delta t)^2 \\
&= \mathbf{r}_0 + \mathbf{v}_0 t + \mathbf{v}_0\,\Delta t + \tfrac{1}{2}\mathbf{a}_0 t^2 + \mathbf{a}_0 t\,\Delta t + \tfrac{1}{2}\mathbf{a}_0(\Delta t)^2 \\
&= \mathbf{r}_1 + \mathbf{v}_0\,\Delta t + \mathbf{a}_0 t\,\Delta t + \tfrac{1}{2}\mathbf{a}_0(\Delta t)^2
\end{aligned}$$

The average velocity for this time interval is

$$\begin{aligned}
\mathbf{v}_{\text{av}} &= \frac{\Delta \mathbf{r}}{\Delta t} = \frac{\mathbf{r}_2 - \mathbf{r}_1}{\Delta t} = \frac{\mathbf{v}_0\,\Delta t + \mathbf{a}_0 t\,\Delta t + \tfrac{1}{2}\mathbf{a}_0(\Delta t)^2}{\Delta t} \\
&= \mathbf{v}_0 + \mathbf{a}_0 t + \tfrac{1}{2}\mathbf{a}_0\,\Delta t
\end{aligned}$$

The limit of $\mathbf{v}_{\text{av}}$ as Δt approaches zero is the instantaneous velocity $\mathbf{v} = \mathbf{v}_0 + \mathbf{a}_0 t$.

Equations 3-18 and 3-19 are the three-dimensional generalizations of the one-dimensional constant-acceleration equations 2-11 and 2-12. Figure 3-16b shows the relation between the displacement vector $\mathbf{r} - \mathbf{r}_0$, the initial velocity $\mathbf{v}_0$, and the acceleration $\mathbf{a}_0$. The displacement at any time t is in the plane formed by $\mathbf{v}_0$ and $\mathbf{a}_0$. The motion is therefore two-dimensional.

Let us choose the z axis to be perpendicular to the plane of $\mathbf{v}_0$ and $\mathbf{a}_0$ and assume that the initial position of the particle is in the xy plane (Figure 3-17). The motion is then in the xy plane. The x and y components of Equations 3-18 and 3-19 are

$$v_x = v_{0x} + a_{0x} t \qquad\qquad 3\text{-}20$$

$$x = x_0 + v_{0x} t + \tfrac{1}{2}a_{0x} t^2$$

(a)

(b)

Figure 3-16
(a) The velocity vector $\mathbf{v}$ is the sum of the initial velocity $\mathbf{v}_0$ and the vector $\mathbf{a}_0 t$. (b) The displacement vector $\mathbf{r} - \mathbf{r}_0$ is the sum of $\mathbf{v}_0 t$ and $\tfrac{1}{2}\mathbf{a}_0 t^2$. The vector $\mathbf{v}_0 t$ would be the displacement if there were no acceleration, whereas the vector $\tfrac{1}{2}\mathbf{a}_0 t^2$ would be the displacement with constant acceleration if the initial velocity were zero. The displacement vector is in the plane of $\mathbf{v}_0$ and $\mathbf{a}_0$, indicating that motion with constant acceleration is confined to this plane.

Motion with constant acceleration is in a plane

(a)

(b)

and

$$v_y = v_{0y} + a_{0y}t$$

$$y = y_0 + v_{0y}t + \tfrac{1}{2}a_{0y}t^2$$

3-21

(If the particle is not assumed to be initially in the xy plane, the motion is parallel to the xy plane with the additional equations $v_z = 0$ and $z = z_0$.)

When the acceleration is constant, the motion takes place in a plane and the x and y motions can be described separately by equations identical to those for motion in one dimension with constant acceleration.

We can apply these results to the motion of a projectile, i.e., any body launched into the air and allowed to move freely. If air resistance is neglected, the acceleration of a projectile is the acceleration of gravity $\mathbf{g}$. (We shall neglect the effects of air resistance for simplicity although such effects are important in the motion of real projectiles.) If the motion is near the surface of the earth and we can neglect the curvature of the earth, the acceleration $\mathbf{g}$ is a constant vector directed downward with magnitude of about 32 ft/sec² $\approx$ 9.8 m/sec². We choose the xy plane to be the plane of motion with the y axis vertical and the x axis parallel to the surface of the earth. If the positive y direction is chosen to be up, the acceleration of the projectile is

$$\mathbf{a} = -g\mathbf{j}$$

Equations 3-20 and 3-21 apply with $a_{0x} = 0$ and $a_{0y} = -g$. We have then

$$v_x = v_{0x}$$

3-22

$$x = x_0 + v_{0x}t$$

3-23

and

$$v_y = v_{0y} - gt$$

3-24

$$y = y_0 + v_{0y}t - \tfrac{1}{2}gt^2$$

3-25

(These equations can be slightly simplified by choosing the origin at the point of projection so that $x_0 = y_0 = 0$.)

The x and y components of the initial velocity are related to the ini-

Figure 3-17
The rectangular components of (a) the velocity vector and (b) the position vector $\mathbf{r}$ assuming that the motion is in the xy plane.

Acceleration of gravity

Projectile motion

tial speed v_0 and the angle of projection θ_0 (the angle between the initial velocity and the horizontal), as shown in Figure 3-18:

$$v_{0x} = v_0 \cos \theta_0 \qquad v_{0y} = v_0 \sin \theta_0$$

Example 3-3 A ball is thrown into the air with initial velocity of 100 ft/sec at 53° to the horizontal. Find the total time the ball is in the air and the total horizontal distance traveled.

The rectangular components of the initial velocity vector are

$$v_{0x} = (100 \text{ ft/sec}) \cos 53° = 60 \text{ ft/sec}$$

$$v_{0y} = (100 \text{ ft/sec}) \sin 53° = 80 \text{ ft/sec}$$

Figure 3-19 shows the height y versus t for this case. This curve is of course the same as that in Example 2-11 except for different initial velocity. Since for each second the projectile moves 60 ft in the x direction, we can also interpret this sketch as that of y versus x if we change the scale of the horizontal axis from a time scale to a distance scale by multiplying the time values by 60 ft/sec. Thus the path of the ball $y(x)$ is a parabola.

The time for the ball to reach the top of its path can be calculated from Equation 3-24, just as for one dimension in Example 2-11. Here

$$v_y = 80 \text{ ft/sec} - (32 \text{ ft/sec}^2)t$$

$$v_y = 0 \qquad \text{at } t = \tfrac{80}{32} \text{ sec} = 2.5 \text{ sec}$$

The total time the ball is in the air is twice this time, or 5 sec. The total horizontal distance traveled, called the *range*, is $(60 \text{ ft/sec})(5 \text{ sec}) = 300$ ft.

We can apply these methods to find the range R for a general v_0 and θ_0. The time to reach the highest point is found by setting $v_y = 0$ in Equation 3-24:

$$t = \frac{v_{0y}}{g}$$

The range is then the horizontal distance traveled in twice this time:

$$R = v_{0x} \frac{2v_{0y}}{g} = \frac{2v_{0x}v_{0y}}{g} \qquad \qquad 3\text{-}26a$$

Figure 3-18
The components of the initial velocity of a projectile are $v_{0x} = v_0 \cos \theta_0$ and $v_{0y} = v_0 \sin \theta_0$, where θ_0 is the angle made by $\mathbf{v}_0$ and the horizontal x axis.

Fundamental Photographs

Multiflash photograph of a ball thrown into the air. The position of the ball is recorded at approximately 0.43-sec intervals.

Figure 3-19
Plot of $y(t)$ and $y(x)$ for Example 3-3. Here $y = 80t - 16t^2$, where y is in feet and t in seconds. The scale can be converted to a horizontal distance scale by multiplying each time by 60 ft/sec because x (in feet) is related to t (in seconds) by $x = 60t$.

Illuminated fountains, St. Louis, Missouri, showing parabolic paths of water.

Ralph Krubner/Black Star

In terms of the initial speed v_0 and angle θ_0, the range is

Range of a projectile

$$R = \frac{2(v_0 \cos \theta_0)(v_0 \sin \theta_0)}{g} = \frac{v_0^2}{g}(2 \sin \theta_0 \cos \theta_0)$$

$$= \frac{v_0^2}{g} \sin 2\theta_0 \qquad\qquad 3\text{-}26b$$

where we have used the trigonometric identity $2 \cos \theta_0 \sin \theta_0 = \sin 2\theta_0$.

Since the maximum value of $\sin 2\theta_0$ is 1 when $2\theta_0 = 90°$ or $\theta_0 = 45°$, the range is a maximum v_0^2/g when $\theta_0 = 45°$. (This calculation and the formulas used assume that there is no air resistance acting on the projectile. This often is a poor approximation, so that the correct launch angle θ_0 for maximum range is generally somewhat less than 45°.)

The general equation for the path $y(x)$ can be obtained from Equations 3-23 and 3-25 by eliminating the variable t between these equations. Choosing $x_0 = y_0 = 0$ and using $t = x/v_{0x}$ in Equation 3-25, we obtain

$$y = v_{0y}\frac{x}{v_{0x}} - \frac{1}{2}g\left(\frac{x}{v_{0x}}\right)^2$$

or

$$y = \frac{v_{0y}}{v_{0x}}x - \frac{1}{2}\frac{g}{v_{0x}^2}x^2 \qquad\qquad 3\text{-}27$$

Equation of projectile's path

This equation is of the same form as $y(t)$ in Equation 3-25. Figure 3-20 shows the path of a projectile with the velocity vector and its components indicated at several points.

If we view the motion of the projectile in a second coordinate system parallel to the first but moving with speed v_{0x} relative to it, the motion is in one dimension. Let us call the origin of our second coordinate system O′ and the axes x' and y'. If we let the two coordinate systems be coincident at $t = 0$, the coordinates are related by

$$y' = y \qquad x' = x - v_{0x}t \qquad\qquad 3\text{-}28$$

Figure 3-20
Path of a projectile with the velocity vector and its rectangular components indicated at several points. The total horizontal distance traveled is the range R.

The equations for the projectile in this coordinate system are found from Equations 3-23 and 3-25. Choosing x_0 and y_0 to be zero, we have

$$y' = v_{0y}t - \tfrac{1}{2}gt^2 \qquad\qquad 3\text{-}29$$

$$x' = 0 \qquad\qquad 3\text{-}30$$

In this coordinate system, the projectile moves in one dimension along the y' axis.

According to our analysis of projectile motion, an object dropped from a height h above the ground will hit the ground in the same time as one projected horizontally from the same height. In each case, the distance the object *falls* is given by $d = \tfrac{1}{2}gt^2$ (measuring d downward from the original height). This remarkable fact can easily be demonstrated.

It was first commented upon during the Renaissance. Galileo Galilei (1564–1642), the first to give the modern, quantitative description of projectile motion we have discussed, used this observation to illustrate the validity of treating the horizontal and vertical components of a projectile's motion as independent motions. Galileo wrote:[1]

> Let the ship be motionless and the fall of the stone from the mast take two pulse beats. Then cause the ship to move, and drop the same stone from the same place; from what has been said, it will take two

[1] Galileo Galilei, *Dialogue Concerning Two Chief World Systems—Ptolemaic and Copernican*, pp. 154–155, trans. Stillman Drake, University of California Press, Berkeley, 1953; reprinted by permission of The Regents of the University of California.

Path of cannonballs for various angles of projection, drawn by Diego Ufano in 1621. Which features of the motion are correct, and which are incorrect? (*Courtesy of the New York Public Library, Rare Book Division, Astor, Lenox, and Tilden Foundations.*)

pulse beats to arrive at the deck. In these two pulse beats, the ship will have gone, say, twenty yards so that the natural motion of the stone will have been a diagonal line much longer than the first straight and perpendicular one, which was merely the length of the mast; nevertheless, it will have traversed this distance in the same time. Now, assuming the ship to be speeded up still more, so that the stone in falling must follow a diagonal line very much longer still than the other, eventually the velocity of the ship may be increased by any amount while the falling rock will describe always longer and longer diagonals, and still pass over them in the same two pulse beats. Similarly, if a perfectly level cannon on a tower were fired parallel to the horizon, it would not matter whether a small charge or a great one was put in, so that the ball would fall a thousand yards away, four thousand, or six thousand, or ten thousand or more; all these shots would require equal times and each time would be equal to that which the ball would have taken in going from the mouth of the cannon to the ground if it were allowed to fall straight down without any other impulse.

Portrait of Galileo by Ottavio Leoni. (*Courtesy of Cabinet de Dessins, Musée du Louvre, Paris.*)

Example 3-4 A hunter with a blowgun wishes to shoot a monkey hanging from a branch. The hunter aims right at the monkey, not realizing that the dart will follow a parabolic path and thus fall below the monkey. The monkey, however, seeing the dart leave the gun, lets go of the branch and drops out of the tree, expecting to avoid the dart. Show that the monkey will be hit no matter what the initial velocity of the dart is so long as it is great enough to travel the horizontal distance to the tree before hitting the ground.

   This problem is often demonstrated using a target suspended by an electromagnet. When the dart leaves the gun, the circuit is broken and the target falls. Let the horizontal distance to the tree be x and the original height of the monkey be H, as shown in Figure 3-21. Then the dart will be projected at an angle given by $\tan \theta = H/x$. If there were no gravity, the dart would reach the height H in the time t taken for it to travel the horizontal distance x:

$$y = v_{0y}t = H \qquad \text{in time } t = \frac{x}{v_{0x}} \qquad \text{with no gravity}$$

However, because of the gravity, the dart has an acceleration vertically

$$y_2 = v_{0y}t - \tfrac{1}{2}gt^2$$
$$= H - \tfrac{1}{2}gt^2$$

Figure 3-21
The monkey and the dart from Example 3-4. The height of the dart is given by $y_2 = v_{0y}t - \frac{1}{2}gt^2$. The height of the monkey is given by $y = H - \frac{1}{2}gt^2$. But since $H = v_{0y}t$, the height of the dart and the monkey will coincide if the monkey is released the instant the dart is fired.

down. In time $t = x/v_{0x}$, the dart reaches a height given by

$$y = v_{0y}t - \tfrac{1}{2}gt^2 = H - \tfrac{1}{2}gt^2$$

This is lower than H by $\tfrac{1}{2}gt^2$, which is just the amount the monkey falls in this time. In the usual lecture demonstration, the initial velocity of the dart is varied so that for large v_0 the target is hit very near its original height and for small v_0 it is hit just before it reaches the floor.

Comparison of a ball dropped with one projected horizontally. The vertical position is independent of the horizontal motion. (*From* PSSC Physics, *3d ed., p. 248, D. C. Heath and Company, Lexington, Mass., 1971.*)

Questions

19. What is the acceleration of a projectile at the top of its flight?

20. Can the velocity of an object change direction while its acceleration is constant in both magnitude and direction? If so, cite an example.

21. A projectile is launched horizontally at the top of a cliff. Describe how the angle between its velocity and the acceleration varies as it falls.

3-7 Circular Motion with Constant Speed

A particle moving in a circular path illustrates many of the important features of velocity and acceleration vectors in two dimensions. In many natural phenomena the motion is circular or nearly circular, e.g., satellite motion or motion of the earth around the sun.

Consider first a particle moving in a circle of radius r with constant speed v. Though the magnitude of the velocity vector does not change, its direction does. Thus the particle is accelerating even though its speed is constant. Figure 3-22 shows the origin at the center of the circle, the position vectors $\mathbf{r}_1$ and $\mathbf{r}_2$ at t_1 and t_2, and the corresponding velocity vectors $\mathbf{v}_1$ and $\mathbf{v}_2$, which are tangent to the circle. The change in velocity in the time interval Δt is the difference of these two velocity vectors $\Delta \mathbf{v} = \mathbf{v}_2 - \mathbf{v}_1$, and the average acceleration is this change in velocity divided by Δt. We see from Figure 3-22 that for very small Δt, the velocity change (and therefore the average acceleration) is approxi-

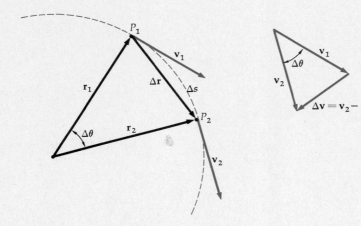

Figure 3-22
Calculation of the acceleration of a particle moving with constant speed in a circle of radius r. The position and velocity vectors are shown at times t_1 and t_2. Since $\mathbf{v}_1$ is perpendicular to $\mathbf{r}_1$ and $\mathbf{v}_2$ to $\mathbf{r}_2$, the angle between $\mathbf{v}_1$ and $\mathbf{v}_2$ is $\Delta\theta$, the same as between $\mathbf{r}_2$ and $\mathbf{r}_1$. For very short time intervals, the angle $\Delta\theta$ is very small and the change in velocity $\Delta\mathbf{v}$ is nearly perpendicular to $\mathbf{v}_1$ and points toward the center of the circle.

mately perpendicular to the velocity vectors in the direction pointing toward the center of the circle.

To calculate the magnitude of the acceleration, let Δs be the distance moved along the arc of the circle in Δt. The angular change measured in radians is

$$\Delta\theta = \frac{\Delta s}{r} \qquad 3\text{-}31$$

Thus

$$\Delta s = r\,\Delta\theta$$

The average speed equals the magnitude of the velocity since the speed is constant:

$$v = \frac{\Delta s}{\Delta t} = r\frac{\Delta\theta}{\Delta t}$$

From the similar triangles in Figure 3-22 we have

$$\frac{|\Delta\mathbf{v}|}{v} \approx \Delta\theta = \frac{\Delta s}{r} \qquad 3\text{-}32$$

or

$$|\Delta\mathbf{v}| \approx v\frac{\Delta s}{r} \qquad 3\text{-}33$$

The magnitude of the acceleration (assuming small Δt) is

$$a \approx \frac{|\Delta\mathbf{v}|}{\Delta t} \approx v\frac{\Delta s}{\Delta t}\frac{1}{r} = \frac{v^2}{r} \qquad 3\text{-}34$$

Acceleration for circular motion at constant speed

In the limit as Δt approaches zero, these approximate relations become exact. Thus the magnitude of the instantaneous acceleration is v^2/r, and the direction is radially in, toward the center.

As with projectile motion, the position, velocity, and acceleration vectors are not parallel. In projectile motion the acceleration vector points down, the velocity vector is tangent to the parabolic path, and the position vector points from the origin to the projectile. In circular motion, the velocity vector is tangent to the circle and perpendicular to the position vector, whereas the acceleration vector (for motion with constant speed) points toward the center of the circle, perpendicular to the velocity vector, and antiparallel to the position vector.

It is convenient to express the velocity and acceleration vectors in terms of radial and tangential components, i.e., components along lines which are parallel or perpendicular to the radius vector. We then have for the velocity

$$v_r = 0 \qquad v_t = v \qquad 3\text{-}35$$

and for the acceleration

$$a_r = -\frac{v^2}{r} \qquad 3\text{-}36$$

$$a_t = 0$$

Acceleration that points in toward the center of the circle is called *centripetal acceleration*. The minus sign in the expression for a_r indicates that this acceleration is toward the center and antiparallel to the radius vector.

Centripetal acceleration

Example 3-5 A satellite moves at constant speed in a circular orbit about the center of the earth and near the surface of the earth. Its acceleration has the magnitude 32.2 ft/sec². What is the speed, and how long does it take for one complete revolution?

This acceleration is the same as for any body falling freely near the surface of the earth. We take the radius of the earth, about 3960 mi, to be approximately the radius of the orbit. (For actual satellites put into orbit a few hundred miles above the earth's surface, the orbit radius is of course somewhat larger. The acceleration is slightly less than 32.2 ft/sec², due to the decrease in the gravitational attraction of the earth with distance from the center of the earth.) The speed of the satellite can be found from Equation 3-34:

$$v^2 = rg = (3960 \text{ mi})(32.2 \text{ ft/sec}^2)(5280 \text{ ft/mi})$$
$$= 6.73 \times 10^8 \text{ ft}^2/\text{sec}^2$$
$$v = 2.59 \times 10^4 \text{ ft/sec}$$

We can change this to miles per hour using the conversion factor 60 mi/h = 88 ft/sec:

$$v = 2.59 \times 10^4 \text{ ft/sec} \; \frac{60 \text{ mi/h}}{88 \text{ ft/sec}} = 1.77 \times 10^4 \text{ mi/h}$$

The time for a satellite of this speed to make one complete revolution is called the *period T*. Since it goes a distance of $2\pi r$ in this time T at speed v, the period is

$$T = \frac{2\pi r}{v} = \frac{2\pi (3960 \text{ mi})}{1.77 \times 10^4 \text{ mi/h}}$$
$$= 1.41 \text{ h} = 84.3 \text{ min}$$

People often wonder why a satellite does not fall toward the earth. The answer is that it does. However, because of its tangential velocity, it continually misses the earth. Consider Figure 3-23. If there were no force exerted on the satellite by the earth, the satellite would travel along a straight line as indicated. (This follows from Newton's laws as discussed in Chapter 4.) In a short time t it would move from point P_1 to point P_2. However, because it is accelerating toward the earth, it is actually at point P_2' after this time. If we take the time t small enough, points P_2 and P_2' are approximately on a radius, as shown in the figure. The distance fallen in this time is h, which is much smaller than the

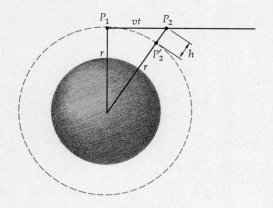

Figure 3-23
Satellite moving with speed v in a circular orbit of radius r about the earth. If the satellite did not accelerate toward the earth, it would move in a straight line from point P_1 to P_2 in time t. Because of its acceleration, it falls a distance h in this time. For small t, $h = \frac{1}{2}(v^2/r)t^2 = \frac{1}{2}at^2$.

orbit radius r for small t. We can calculate h from the right triangle of sides vt, r, and $r + h$. We have

$$(r + h)^2 = (vt)^2 + r^2$$

$$r^2 + 2hr + h^2 = v^2t^2 + r^2$$

If we cancel the r^2 terms and neglect h^2 compared with $2rh$, we obtain

$$2rh \approx v^2t^2$$

$$h = \frac{1}{2} \frac{v^2}{r} t^2$$

The distance the satellite falls in time t is thus $\frac{1}{2}at^2$, where the acceleration a is v^2/r. (The formula $\frac{1}{2}at^2$ applies to this case only if the time t is very small.)

Figure 3-24 is a drawing from Newton's *Principia* illustrating the connection between projectile motion and satellite motion. Newton's description reads:[1]

> That by means of centripetal forces the planets may be retained in certain . . . orbits, we may easily understand, if we consider the motions of projectiles; for a stone that is projected is by the pressure of its own weight forced out of the rectilinear path, which by the initial projection alone it should have pursued, and made to describe a curved line in the air; and through that crooked way is at last brought down to the ground; and the greater the velocity is with which it is projected, the farther it goes before it falls to the earth. We may therefore suppose the velocity to be so increased, that it would describe an arc of 1, 2, 5, 10, 100, 1000 miles before it arrived at the earth, till at last, exceeding the limits of the earth, it should pass into space without touching it.

Figure 3-24
Drawing from Newton's *System of the World*, published in 1728, illustrating the connection between projectile motion and satellite motion. (*Courtesy of the Niels Bohr Library, American Institute of Physics.*)

3-8   Circular Motion with Varying Speed

Let us assume that the speed of the particle discussed in Section 3-7 is increasing as the particle moves around the circle instead of remaining constant. Then the velocity vector $\mathbf{v}_2$ will be greater than $\mathbf{v}_1$ in magnitude and different in direction, as shown in Fig. 3-25. The change in velocity is $\Delta\mathbf{v} = \mathbf{v}_2 - \mathbf{v}_1$. The change can be considered to consist of two parts:

$$\Delta\mathbf{v} = \Delta\mathbf{v}_r + \Delta\mathbf{v}_t$$

The first term, $\Delta\mathbf{v}_r$, is the change that would occur if the speed were constant. We computed this term in Section 3-7. For small Δt, this change in the velocity vector is approximately radial. The second term, $\Delta\mathbf{v}_t$, is due to the increase in magnitude of the velocity vector. For small time intervals Δt this term is approximately tangential to the circle.

The average acceleration is

$$\mathbf{a}_{av} = \frac{\Delta\mathbf{v}_r}{\Delta t} + \frac{\Delta\mathbf{v}_t}{\Delta t} \qquad\qquad 3\text{-}37$$

[1] *Philosophiae Naturalis Principia Mathematica*, 1686, trans. Andrew Motte, 1729, University of California Press, Berkeley, 1960; reprinted by permission of The Regents of the University of California.

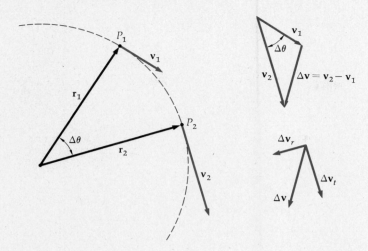

Figure 3-25
Calculation of the acceleration of a particle moving in a circle with variable speed. Here the velocity change $\Delta \mathbf{v}$ is due partly to the change in direction of motion and partly to the change in speed. For very small time intervals, $\Delta \theta$ is very small, and the change in $\mathbf{v}$ due to changing direction is approximately radial toward the center of the circle, while the change in $\mathbf{v}$ due to changing speed is approximately tangential to the motion. The instantaneous acceleration has an inward radial component of magnitude v^2/r and a tangential component of magnitude dv/dt.

In the limit as Δt approaches zero, the first term in Equation 3-24 has the magnitude v^2/r and points toward the center of the circle, as shown above. The second term has the magnitude dv/dt and is tangential to the circle and parallel to the velocity vector. Thus, in general, for circular motion of a particle with varying speed, the acceleration has both a radial and a tangential component:

$$a_r = -\frac{v^2}{r} \qquad a_t = \frac{dv}{dt} \qquad\qquad 3\text{-}38$$

Radial and tangential components of acceleration

This result, that *the radial component of the acceleration is associated with the change in direction of the velocity vector while the tangential component of acceleration is associated with the change in magnitude of the velocity,* is a general one not limited to circular motion. Consider a particle moving along any arbitrary curve in space. A small segment of the curve can be considered as the arc of a circle, as shown in Figure 3-26. The acceleration has a component dv/dt parallel to the velocity vector and a component v^2/r perpendicular to the velocity.

Figure 3-26
Particle moving along an arbitrary curve in space. A small segment of any curve in space can be considered to be the arc of a circle of radius r. The instantaneous-acceleration vector has a component a_t of magnitude dv/dt tangent to the curve and a component a_r of magnitude v^2/r toward the center of curvature of the arc.

3-9 Radial and Tangential Unit Vectors

We have seen that for circular motion it is convenient to use radial and tangential components of the velocity and acceleration vectors. We can write these vectors in terms of these components using radial and tangential unit vectors (Figure 3-27). In this figure, the angle θ and the distance s are measured from the x axis. The distance s is related to the polar coordinates r and θ by

$$\theta = \frac{s}{r} \qquad s = r\theta \qquad\qquad \text{3-39}$$

Since r is constant, the speed of the particle is

$$v = \frac{ds}{dt} = r\frac{d\theta}{dt} \qquad\qquad \text{3-40}$$

We define $\hat{\mathbf{r}}$ to be a unit vector parallel to the position vector $\mathbf{r}$ and $\hat{\boldsymbol{\theta}}$ to be a unit vector perpendicular to $\mathbf{r}$, tangent to the circle in the direction of increasing θ and s.

The position, velocity, and acceleration vectors for a particle moving in a circle of radius r are

$$\mathbf{r} = r\hat{\mathbf{r}} \qquad\qquad \text{3-41}$$

$$\mathbf{v} = v\hat{\boldsymbol{\theta}} = \frac{ds}{dt}\,\hat{\boldsymbol{\theta}} = \frac{r\,d\theta}{dt}\,\hat{\boldsymbol{\theta}} \qquad\qquad \text{3-42}$$

$$\mathbf{a} = -\frac{v^2}{r}\,\hat{\mathbf{r}} + \frac{dv}{dt}\,\hat{\boldsymbol{\theta}} = -\frac{(ds/dt)^2}{r}\,\hat{\mathbf{r}} + \frac{d^2s}{dt^2}\,\hat{\boldsymbol{\theta}} \qquad\qquad \text{3-43}$$

We can relate the unit vectors $\hat{\mathbf{r}}$ and $\hat{\boldsymbol{\theta}}$ to the rectangular unit vectors $\mathbf{i}$ and $\mathbf{j}$. From Figure 3-28 we have

$$\mathbf{r} = r\cos\theta\,\mathbf{i} + r\sin\theta\,\mathbf{j} \qquad\qquad \text{3-44}$$

Therefore

$$\hat{\mathbf{r}} = \frac{\mathbf{r}}{r} = \cos\theta\,\mathbf{i} + \sin\theta\,\mathbf{j} \qquad\qquad \text{3-45}$$

Similarly from Figure 3-28 we see that $\hat{\boldsymbol{\theta}}$ has rectangular components $\hat{\boldsymbol{\theta}}_x = -\sin\theta$ and $\hat{\boldsymbol{\theta}}_y = \cos\theta$; thus

$$\hat{\boldsymbol{\theta}} = -\sin\theta\,\mathbf{i} + \cos\theta\,\mathbf{j} \qquad\qquad \text{3-46}$$

The unit vectors $\hat{\mathbf{r}}$ and $\hat{\boldsymbol{\theta}}$ differ from $\mathbf{i}$ and $\mathbf{j}$ in that their direction depends on r and θ, that is, on the location of the particle. Thus the unit vectors $\hat{\mathbf{r}}$ and $\hat{\boldsymbol{\theta}}$ change with time as the particle moves in a circle, while the unit vectors $\mathbf{i}$ and $\mathbf{j}$ are true constant vectors.

Figure 3-27
Definition of the unit vectors $\hat{\mathbf{r}}$ and $\hat{\boldsymbol{\theta}}$.

Unit vectors $\hat{\mathbf{r}}$ and $\hat{\boldsymbol{\theta}}$

Figure 3-28
The unit vectors $\hat{\mathbf{r}}$ and $\hat{\boldsymbol{\theta}}$ are related to $\mathbf{i}$ and $\mathbf{j}$ by $\hat{\mathbf{r}} = \cos\theta\,\mathbf{i} + \sin\theta\,\mathbf{j}$ and $\hat{\boldsymbol{\theta}} = -\sin\theta\,\mathbf{i} + \cos\theta\,\mathbf{j}$.

2. If a body has no acceleration, can you conclude that no forces act on it?

3. If only a single force acts on a body, must it be accelerated? Can it ever have zero velocity?

4. Is there a net force acting (*a*) when a body moves at constant speed along a circle, (*b*) when a body that is moving in a straight line slows down, (*c*) when a body moves at constant speed in a straight line?

5. Is it possible for an object to round any curve without a force being impressed upon it?

6. When a body rounds a curve, can the net force on it be toward the convex side of the curve?

7. If a single known force acts on a body, can you tell *in which direction* the body will *move* from this information alone?

8. If several forces of different magnitudes and directions are applied to a body initially at rest, how can you predict the direction in which it will move?

9. A string is just barely capable of supporting a 10-lb weight suspended at rest from it. What happens if the weight is set swinging? Explain.

10. The maximum tension a rope can withstand without breaking is 90 lb. Could the rope be used to lower a 100-lb weight? How? Is it possible that the rope might break in raising an 80-lb weight? Under what conditions?

4-2   Mass

So far we have discussed how to compare forces quantitatively by comparing the accelerations they produce in some particular single object. We now investigate the effect of a given force on different objects. Let us use one of our calibrated springs to produce a given force on a different body. We note that the acceleration produced for a given spring extension is not the same, in general, as it was for our first body. If our second body is "more massive" (according to our everyday use of this term), the acceleration produced by a force of 1 unit is observed to be less than 1 m/sec^2. If it is less massive, the acceleration produced is greater. For example, if we connect two identical bodies, the acceleration produced by a given force is exactly half that produced by the same force acting on just one of the bodies. This suggests that we quantify the concept of mass by considering the acceleration a given force will produce in different bodies.

Specifically, we define the ratio of the mass of one body to that of another body to be the *inverse* ratio of the accelerations produced in those two bodies by the *same force*. If a given force produces an acceleration a_1 when it acts on body 1 and an acceleration a_2 on body 2, the ratio of the masses of the two bodies is defined to be

$$\frac{m_2}{m_1} = \frac{a_1}{a_2}$$

4-5   *Definition of mass*

We find the ratio of the masses of any two bodies by applying the same force to each and comparing their accelerations. Having defined the ratio of masses for any two bodies, we can set up a mass scale by choosing one particular body to be a standard body and arbitrarily calling its mass 1 unit. The SI unit of mass is the *kilogram*. The international standard body is a cylinder of platinum carefully kept at the International Bureau of Weights and Measures at Sèvres, France. Its mass is defined to be one kilogram. (This was originally intended to be equal to the mass of 1000 cm³ of water, but the relationship proved inexact by a very small amount.) Theoretically, the mass of any other body can be compared to the standard mass, as described above, and assigned an appropriate number. For example, if a certain force produces an acceleration of $a_1 = 1$ m/sec² on the standard body and the same force produces an acceleration $a_2 = 2$ m/sec² on a second body, the mass of the second body is $m_2 = (a_1/a_2)m_1 = 0.5$ kg.

The standard kilogram, kept at the International Bureau of Weights and Measures, Sèvres, France. (*Courtesy of the Science Museum, London.*)

The ratio of accelerations a_2/a_1 produced by the same force on two bodies is independent of the magnitude and direction of the force. It is also independent of the kind of force used, i.e., whether the force is due to springs, the pull of gravity, electric or magnetic attraction or repulsion, etc. We note also that if mass m_2 is found to be twice the standard mass by direct comparison and mass m_3 is found to be 4 times the standard mass, m_3 is found to be twice m_2 when compared with it directly. Thus mass is an *intrinsic* property of the body which does *not* depend on the surroundings of the body, any external agent, or on the type of force used to measure it. It is a scalar quantity which obeys the ordinary rules of arithmetic and algebra.

Mass is an intrinsic property

The concept of mass, as we have defined it, is associated with the size of the acceleration produced by a given force. The larger the mass the smaller the acceleration produced by a given force. Thus mass is a quantitative measure of the property of *inertia*, or resistance to acceleration, which all objects have.

Mass is a quantitative measure of inertia

Questions

11. Can you judge the mass of an object by its size? If A is twice as big as B, does that mean that $m_A = 2m_B$?

12. Could a body have a different mass for electric forces than for gravitational forces?

13. Can the mass of a body be negative?

14. How do we know that we can add masses as scalars? That is, if one body has a mass of 2 kg and another of 3 kg, how do we know that the two bodies taken together have a mass of 5 kg?

15. Mass is sometimes said to be the measure of the quantity of matter in a body. How does this unscientific definition compare with the definition discussed above?

4-3   Newton's Second Law

The definitions we have given for force and mass are summarized in Newton's second law, which states that the net, or resultant, force $\Sigma \mathbf{F}$ acting on a body is proportional to its mass and its acceleration. In symbols

$$\Sigma \mathbf{F} = Km\mathbf{a}$$

where K represents a constant we are still free to determine. (The actual operational definitions we have used are not convenient for practical work. Their value is in clarifying our quantitative concepts, not in their direct application. More practical definitions, however, can be shown to be equivalent to ours though they are much more difficult to phrase.) It is convenient to define the unit of force so that the constant of proportionality is unity. Then a force of 1 unit acting on a mass of 1 kg produces an acceleration of 1 m/sec², or 1 unit of force = 1 kg-m/sec². This combination of units, 1 kg-m/sec², is called a newton (N):

$$1 \text{ N} = 1 \text{ kg-m/sec}^2 \qquad 4\text{-}6$$

Definition of the newton

The unit of force is so defined that Newton's second law holds in the form

$$\Sigma \mathbf{F} = m\mathbf{a} \qquad 4\text{-}7$$

Newton's second law

Our definitions of force and mass agree with our intuitive notions of the meaning of these words. These definitions are useful because they allow us to describe a wide variety of physical phenomena using just a few relatively simple force laws. For example, with the addition of Newton's law of gravitational attraction between two bodies we can calculate and explain such phenomena as the motion of the moon, the orbits of all the planets around the sun, the orbits of artificial satellites, the variation in the acceleration of gravity g with latitude due to the rotation of the earth, the variations in the acceleration of gravity due to the presence of mineral deposits, the paths of ballistic missiles, and many other motions.

Note that Newton's statement of the second law does not refer to mass and acceleration but to the change in "motion." What Newton called motion is now called *momentum*. The momentum of a particle is a dynamic quantity defined as the product of the mass and the velocity of a particle. Writing $\mathbf{a} = d\mathbf{v}/dt$ for the acceleration and assuming the mass of the particle to be constant, we have

$$\Sigma \mathbf{F} = m\,\frac{d\mathbf{v}}{dt} = \frac{d(m\mathbf{v})}{dt}$$

or

$$\Sigma \mathbf{F} = \frac{d\mathbf{p}}{dt} \qquad 4\text{-}8$$

where

$$\mathbf{p} = m\mathbf{v} \qquad 4\text{-}9$$

Momentum defined

is the momentum of the particle. Momentum is a vector parallel to the velocity vector. A body of mass 0.5 kg moving at 2000 m/sec has the same momentum as a body of mass 4 kg moving in the same direction at 250 m/sec. A force of 1 N will change the momentum of any body by 1 kg-m/sec in 1 sec.

In classical mechanics the mass of a particle is always constant, and Equations 4-7 and 4-8 are equivalent. However, when a particle moves with a speed near the speed of light (about 3×10^8 m/sec), the ratio of the force to the acceleration depends on the speed. As we shall see in Chapter 28, for high-speed particles, classical mechanics must be modified according to Einstein's theory of special relativity. In this theory, Equation 4-8 holds if the expression for momentum is taken to be

$$\mathbf{p} = \frac{m\mathbf{v}}{\sqrt{1 - v^2/c^2}} \qquad \text{4-10}$$

where c is the speed of light in vacuum. When the speed of the particle is much less than that of light, the quantity $\sqrt{1 - v^2/c^2}$ is very nearly equal to 1 and the relativistic and classical expressions for momentum (Equations 4-9 and 4-10) are approximately equal.

4-4 Weight

The force most common in our everyday experience is the force of attraction of the earth for various bodies. This force is called the *weight* of the body. We can find the weight of a 1-kg mass by measuring its acceleration when the mass is falling freely so that the only force on it is its weight. The resulting acceleration is about 9.81 m/sec² downward. The weight w of a 1-kg mass thus has the magnitude

$$w = ma = 1 \text{ kg} \times 9.81 \text{ m/sec}^2 = 9.81 \text{ N}$$

The free-fall acceleration of any body (about 9.81 m/sec² at sea level) is independent of the mass of the body as long as air resistance can be neglected. Since the acceleration is the ratio of the resultant force (the weight in this case) and the mass, the fact that it is independent of the mass implies that the weight of a body is proportional to its mass,

$$\mathbf{w} = m\mathbf{g} \qquad \text{4-11}$$

Weight is the gravitational force on a body

where $\mathbf{g}$ is the free-fall acceleration of gravity. Careful measurements of the free-fall acceleration of a body at various places show that this acceleration is not the same everywhere. Thus weight, unlike mass, is not an intrinsic property of the body. The force of attraction of the earth for a body varies with location. In particular, for points above the surface of the earth, this force varies inversely with the square of the distance of the body from the center of the earth. Thus a body weighs less at very high altitude than it does at sea level. The weight of a body also varies slightly with latitude because the earth is not exactly spherical but is flattened at the poles.[1]

Near the surface of the moon, the gravitational attraction of the moon is much stronger than that of the earth. The force exerted on the body by the moon is usually called the weight of the body when it is near the moon. Note again that the mass of a body is the same whether it is on the earth, on the moon, or somewhere in space. Mass is a property of the body itself, whereas weight depends on the nature and distance of other objects which exert gravitational forces on the body.

Since at any particular location the weight of a body is proportional to its mass, we can conveniently compare the mass of one body with that of another by comparing their weights as long as we determine the weights at the same place.

[1] If the free-fall acceleration of a body is measured relative to a point on the surface of the earth, there is a variation with latitude because the reference point has an acceleration due to the rotation of the earth. This variation, discussed in Section 4-7, is not a variation in $\mathbf{g}$, which we define as the gravitational force on the body divided by its mass.

NASA

Edward H. White II in a space walk during the third orbit of the Gemini-Titan 4 flight. He experiences weightlessness whether he is inside or outside the space capsule because the only force acting on him is gravity. He is in free fall accelerating toward the earth with the acceleration of gravity.

Our sensation of our own weight usually comes from other forces which balance it. For example, sitting on a chair, we feel the force exerted by the chair which balances our weight. When we stand on a spring scale, our feet feel the force exerted on us by the scale. The scale is calibrated to read the force it must exert (by compression of its springs) to balance our weight. The force which balances our weight is called our *apparent weight*. It is the apparent weight that is given by a spring scale. If there is no force to balance your weight, as in free fall, your apparent weight is zero. This condition, called *weightlessness*, is experienced by astronauts in orbiting satellites. Consider a satellite in a circular orbit near the surface of the earth with a centripetal acceleration v^2/r, where r is the orbit radius and v is the speed. The only force acting on the satellite is its weight. Thus it is in free fall with the acceleration of gravity. The astronaut is also in free fall. The only force on him is his weight, which produces the acceleration $g = v^2/r$. Since there is no force balancing the force of gravity, the astronaut's apparent weight is zero.

Apparent weight defined

Questions

16. From our definitions of mass and weight, would it be conceivable to use the same units for both?

17. Suppose an object were sent far out in space away from galaxies, stars, or other bodies. How would its mass change? Its weight?

18. How would an astronaut in a condition of weightlessness be aware of his mass?

19. We commonly compare the masses of objects by comparing their weights. Would this be possible if g depended on the kind of material an object is made of?

20. Under what circumstances would your apparent weight be greater than your true weight?

4-5   Units of Force and Mass

The definition of the unit of mass, the kilogram, as the mass of a particular standard body completes our definition of the three fundamental units of mechanics in the mks system. In this system, the unit of force, the newton (that force which produces an acceleration of 1 m/sec² on a 1-kg mass) is a derived unit; i.e., it can be expressed in terms of the three fundamental units, as in Equation 4-6. As mentioned in Chapter 1, the mks system of mechanics units is a subset of the international system of units (SI), which also includes units of temperature, electric current, and luminous intensity. These units are used almost exclusively throughout the world except in the United States, where they will also eventually become standard. Although we generally use SI units in this book, we need to know about two other systems, the *cgs system*, a metric system based on the centimeter, gram, and second, which is closely related to the mks system and used by many scientists, and the British engineering system, based on the foot, the second, and a force unit (the pound), which is still used today in the United States.

The unit of time, the second, is common to all three systems of units. In the cgs system, the unit of length is the centimeter (cm), now defined to be one-hundredth the length of the meter:

$$1 \text{ cm} = 10^{-2} \text{ m} \qquad\qquad 4\text{-}12$$

The unit of mass, the gram (gm), is now defined to be exactly one-thousandth the mass of the standard kilogram:

$$1 \text{ gm} = 10^{-3} \text{ kg} \qquad\qquad 4\text{-}13$$

Definition of centimeter and gram

The gram was originally chosen to be the mass of one cubic centimeter of water at standard pressure and temperature. The unit of force in the cgs system, called the dyne, is the force which applied to a one-gram mass produces an acceleration of one centimeter per second per second:

$$1 \text{ dyne} = 1 \text{ gm-cm/sec}^2 \qquad\qquad 4\text{-}14$$

Because the units are so small, the cgs system is less convenient than the mks system for practical work. For example, the mass of a penny is about 3 gm. Since the free-fall acceleration of gravity is 981 cm/sec², the weight of a penny in the cgs system is about

$$w = mg = (3 \text{ gm})(981 \text{ cm/sec}^2) = 2.94 \times 10^3 \text{ dynes}$$

The dyne is a very small unit of force. The relation between the dyne and the newton is

$$1 \text{ dyne} = \frac{1 \text{ gm-cm}}{\text{sec}^2} \frac{1 \text{ kg}}{10^3 \text{ gm}} \frac{1 \text{ m}}{10^2 \text{ cm}} = 10^{-5} \text{ kg-m/sec}^2$$

or

$$1 \text{ dyne} = 10^{-5} \text{ N} \qquad\qquad 4\text{-}15$$

The British engineering system differs from both the mks and cgs systems in that a unit of force is chosen as a fundamental unit rather than a unit of mass. (Another difference is that it is not a decimal system.) The pound was originally defined as the weight of a particular standard body at point where the acceleration of gravity is exactly 9.80665 m/sec² = 32.1740 ft/sec². It is now defined in terms of the standard kilogram. One pound is defined to be the weight of a body of

Definition of pound

mass 0.45359237 kg at a point where the acceleration of gravity has the value given above. The relation between the standard pound and the newton is thus

$$1 \text{ pound} = (0.45359237 \text{ kg})(9.80665 \text{ m/sec}^2) = 4.448222 \text{ N}$$

or

$$1 \text{ lb} \approx 4.45 \text{ N} \hspace{4cm} 4\text{-}16$$

Since 1 kg weighs 9.81 N, its weight in pounds is

$$9.81 \text{ N} \times \frac{1 \text{ lb}}{4.45 \text{ N}} = 2.20 \text{ lb} \hspace{3cm} 4\text{-}17$$

Weight of 1 kg in pounds

The unit of mass in the British system is that mass which will be given an acceleration of one foot per second per second when a force of one pound is applied to it. This unit is called a *slug*. From its definition

Definition of slug

$$1 \text{ slug} = \frac{1 \text{ lb}}{1 \text{ ft/sec}^2} = 1 \text{ lb-sec}^2/\text{ft} \hspace{2.5cm} 4\text{-}18$$

The weight of a slug near sea level is about

$$w = mg = (1 \text{ lb-sec}^2/\text{ft})(32.2 \text{ ft/sec}^2) = 32.2 \text{ lb} \hspace{1cm} 4\text{-}19$$

In practice, the slug is seldom used. It is more convenient to work problems in this system by writing the mass as w/g, where w is the weight and g is the acceleration of gravity.

Example 4-3 The net force acting on a 10.0-lb body is 3.00 lb. What is its acceleration?

The acceleration is the force divided by the mass:

$$a = \frac{F}{m} = \frac{F}{w/g} = \frac{3.00 \text{ lb}}{(10.0 \text{ lb})/(32.2 \text{ ft/sec}^2)} = 9.66 \text{ ft/sec}^2$$

Although the weight of an object varies from place to place because of changes in the acceleration of gravity, this variation is too small to be noticed in most practical applications. Thus, in our everyday experience, the weight of a body appears to be as much a constant characteristic of the body as its mass.[1]

Questions

21. What is your weight in newtons?

22. What is your mass in kilograms? In slugs?

23. What would your weight be in pounds on the moon, where objects fall freely with acceleration of about $5\frac{1}{3}$ ft/sec²?

24. What is the weight at sea level of a 10-kg mass? Give your answer in newtons and in pounds. What would be the weight of this same mass on the moon, where the acceleration of gravity is about one-sixth what it is at sea level? What is the mass of this object on the moon?

---

[1] This fact has led to everyday use of two other units, which often is confusing. One is a unit of force, the kilogram force, which is the weight of a 1-kg mass. A kilogram force is equal to 9.81 N or 2.20 lb. A second practical unit is the pound mass, which is the mass of a body which weighs 1 lb. Since by definition, a pound force is the weight of 0.454 kg, a pound mass is equivalent to 0.454 kg. We shall not use these practical but confusing units.

4-6   Newton's Third Law and Conservation of Momentum

Newton's third law describes an important property of forces: they always occur in pairs. For each force exerted on some body A there must be some external agent, say another body B, exerting the force. The third law states that body A exerts an equal but opposite force on the agent B. For example, earth exerts a gravitational force on a projectile, causing it to accelerate toward the earth with acceleration $\mathbf{g} = \mathbf{F}/m = \mathbf{w}/m$, where $\mathbf{w}$ is the weight of the projectile and m its mass. According to the third law, the projectile in turn exerts a force on the earth equal in magnitude and opposite in direction. Thus the projectile exerts a force $\mathbf{w}'$ on the earth toward the projectile. The earth, in response to the force exerted by the projectile, must accelerate. Because of the great mass of the earth, this contribution to its total acceleration is negligible and unobserved.

In discussions of Newton's third law the words action and reaction are frequently used. If the force exerted on body A is called the *action* of B upon A, then the force body A exerts back on body B is called the *reaction* of A upon B. It does not matter which force in such a pair is called the action and which the reaction. The important point is that forces always occur in action-reaction pairs and that the reaction force is equal in magnitude and opposite in direction to the action force.

Action and reaction

Note that the action and reaction forces can never balance each other because they act on different objects. This is illustrated in Figure 4-6, which shows two action-reaction pairs of forces for a block resting on a table. The force acting downward on the block is the weight $\mathbf{w}$ due to the attraction of the earth. An equal and opposite force $\mathbf{w}'$ is exerted by the block *on the earth*. These are an action-reaction pair. If they were the only forces acting, the block would accelerate down because it would have only a single force acting on it. However, the table in contact with the block exerts a force $\mathbf{N}$ upward on it. This force balances the weight of the block. The block also exerts a force $\mathbf{N}'$ downward on the table. The forces $\mathbf{N}$ and $\mathbf{N}'$ are also an action-reaction pair.

Action-reaction forces can never balance

There is a simple but important consequence of the third law for two objects isolated from their surroundings so that the only forces on them are the ones they exert on each other. *The sum of the momenta of the two objects remains constant in time.* This can be seen from the form of Newton's second law in Equation 4-8. The rate of change of the momentum of each object equals the force acting on it. Each object has a single force acting on it, and the two forces are equal but opposite.

Figure 4-6
Action-reaction forces. The weight $\mathbf{w}$ is the force exerted on the block by the earth. The equal and opposite reaction force is $\mathbf{w}'$, exerted on the earth by the block. Similarly, the table exerts a force $\mathbf{N}$ on the block, and the block exerts an equal and opposite force $\mathbf{N}'$ on the table. Action-reaction forces are exerted on different objects.

Thus the change of momentum of one object equals the negative of the change of momentum of the other, and the sum of the changes is zero. Let $\mathbf{F}_1$ be the force on object 1 and $\mathbf{p}_1 = m_1\mathbf{v}_1$ be its momentum. Then Newton's second law for this object is

$$\mathbf{F}_1 = \frac{d\mathbf{p}_1}{dt}$$

Similarly, if $\mathbf{F}_2$ is the force acting on object 2 and $\mathbf{p}_2 = m_2\mathbf{v}_2$ is its momentum, we have

$$\mathbf{F}_2 = \frac{d\mathbf{p}_2}{dt}$$

But $\mathbf{F}_2 = -\mathbf{F}_1$, and so

$$\frac{d\mathbf{p}_2}{dt} = -\frac{d\mathbf{p}_1}{dt}$$

or

$$\frac{d\mathbf{p}_1}{dt} + \frac{d\mathbf{p}_2}{dt} = \frac{d}{dt}(\mathbf{p}_1 + \mathbf{p}_2) = 0$$

Thus the rate of change of the sum of the momenta $\mathbf{p}_1 + \mathbf{p}_2$ is zero. Then

$\mathbf{p}_1 + \mathbf{p}_2 = $ constant	4-20

Conservation of momentum

We can take Equation 4-20 as an equivalent statement of Newton's third law. In fact, Newton seems to have arrived at his statement of action-reaction by studying the momentum of two bodies before and after collisions. When two bodies collide, they exert very large forces on each other during the short time they are in contact. Even if there are other forces on the bodies, they are usually much smaller than these contact forces and can be neglected. From the careful measurements made by his predecessors Newton knew that no matter what kind of collision occurs, the sum of the momenta of the two colliding bodies is the same after the collision as before. Starting from Equation 4-20, which describes this result, he arrived at his statement that action equals reaction. We need only differentiate Equation 4-20 and substitute $\mathbf{F}_1$ for $d\mathbf{p}_1/dt$ and $\mathbf{F}_2$ for $d\mathbf{p}_2/dt$. This result is known as the *law of conservation of momentum*. We have shown that it applies to two bodies each of which experiences only a force exerted by the other. That is, the total momentum of the two bodies is constant (conserved) if they are isolated from influences from other sources. By a straight-forward generalization, the same law can be shown to apply to any isolated system of bodies, no matter how great their number.

The extrapolation of the action-reaction principle for forces exerted by bodies in contact to bodies far apart presents conceptual difficulties of which Newton was well aware. We have seen that the statement that action equals reaction is equivalent to the statement that the rate at which one body gains momentum equals the rate at which the second body loses momentum. This is easily imagined if the bodies are in contact, but if they are widely separated, it implies that momentum is instantaneously transmitted from one to the other across the intervening space. This concept, called *action at a distance*, is difficult to accept. For example, applied to the earth-sun system, it suggests that the momentum lost by one travels instantly across the 93 million miles between them to be taken up by the other (Figure 4-7). Newton justified his extension of the third law to action-at-a-distance forces

Action at a distance

$$\mathbf{F}_2 = -\mathbf{F}_1$$

$$\mathbf{F}_1$$

Figure 4-7
Action-reaction forces for
widely separated bodies.
Modern theory treats the
action-at-a-distance problem
by introducing the concept of
a field.

because the assumption enabled him to calculate the orbits of the planets correctly from the law of gravitation. He perceived action at a distance as a flaw in his theory but avoided giving any other hypothesis. In 1692 Newton made a famous comment[1] about the concept of action at a distance:

> It is inconceivable that inanimate, brute matter should, without the mediation of something else, which is not material, operate upon, and affect other matter without mutual contact, as it must be if gravitation, in the sense of Epicurus, be essential and inherent in it. And this is one reason why I desired you would not ascribe innate gravity to me. That gravity should be innate, inherent, and essential to matter, so that one body may act upon another at a distance through a vacuum, without the mediation of anything else, by and through which their action and force may be conveyed from one to another, is to me so great an absurdity that I believe no man who has in philosophical matters a competent faculty of thinking can ever fall into it.

Today, we treat the problem of action at a distance by introducing the concept of a field. For example, we consider the attraction of the earth by the sun in two steps. The sun creates a condition in space which we call the *gravitational field*. This field produces a force on the earth. The field is thus the intermediary agent. Similarly, the earth produces a gravitational field which exerts a force on the sun. If the earth suddenly moves to a new position, the field of the earth is changed. This change is not propagated through space instantly but with the velocity $c = 3 \times 10^8$ m/sec $= 1.86 \times 10^5$ mi/sec, which is also the velocity of light. If we can neglect the time it takes for propagation of the field, we can ignore this intermediary agent and treat the forces as if they were exerted by the sun and the earth directly on each other. For example, during the 8 min it takes for propagation of the gravitational field from the earth to the sun, the earth moves only a small fraction of its total orbit around the sun. (The angular displacement of the earth after 8 min is only 9.6×10^{-5} rad $= 5.5 \times 10^{-3}$ deg.)

The field concept

The third law is only an approximate law for two separated bodies. It holds if we can neglect the time of propagation of momentum between the interacting bodies. The law of conservation of momentum for *two bodies* is also only approximate: it takes time for the momentum to be transferred from one body to another. However, the

[1] Isaac Newton, Third Letter to Bentley (Feb. 25, 1692), R. and J. Dodsley, London, 1756.

conservation of momentum can be rephrased as an exact law by introducing the idea that the field itself can have momentum. Then during the time of transit, the momentum lost by the two bodies is carried by the field. It can be demonstrated in the analogous case of the electromagnetic force between two separated charges that the electromagnetic field can indeed transport momentum. It is more difficult to demonstrate this for the gravitational field.

Newton's extension of the action-reaction law to separated bodies generated the conceptual difficulties we have discussed, but the difficulties were indeed conceptual and not practical. The action-reaction law is generally an exceptionally good approximation and is very useful in practical problems.

Questions

25. When a ball is bounced from the ground, the earth exerts the force on the ball necessary to reverse its velocity. Is there a simultaneous force exerted on the earth? If so, why don't we perceive any acceleration of the earth?

26. When an object absorbs or reflects light, it experiences a very small but measurable force. Consider the following case. A supernova (stellar explosion) occurs in which the star becomes millions of times brighter than normal for a few weeks. Light from the star reaches the earth centuries after the explosion and causes the deflection of a delicately balanced mirror. Does the action-reaction law apply to the interaction of the star and the mirror?

27. In a tug of war the forces each team exerts on the other are equal in magnitude and opposite in direction. How can either team win?

4-7   Reference Frames

It might appear that the first law is merely a special case of the second when $\Sigma \mathbf{F} = 0$, since then $\mathbf{a} = 0$ and $\mathbf{v} = $ constant. However, we shall interpret the first law as a definition of an *inertial reference frame*. If the net force on a body is zero and it maintains a constant velocity relative to some reference frame, the reference frame is called an inertial frame. Before examining this concept of an inertial reference frame more fully, we must discuss what is meant by a reference frame.

To measure the velocity and acceleration of a particle, we need a coordinate system, as illustrated in Figure 4-8. Consider another coordinate system $x'y'z'$ *at rest* relative to xyz. For convenience, we have

Figure 4-8
Two coordinate systems at rest relative to each other. A particle with position (x,y,z) relative to O has position $x' = x - x_0$, $y' = y$, $z' = z$ relative to O'. The velocity $\mathbf{v}$ and acceleration $\mathbf{a}$ of the particle are the same in both systems. These coordinate systems are said to be in the same reference frame.

assumed the axes parallel and the origin O' to be on the x axis at a distance x_0 from O. A particle at x with velocity $\mathbf{v}$ and acceleration $\mathbf{a}$ relative to O will have the same velocity $\mathbf{v}' = \mathbf{v}$ and acceleration $\mathbf{a}' = \mathbf{a}$ relative to O', but its coordinate will be different, $x' = x - x_0$. *The set of coordinate systems at rest relative to a given system is called a reference frame.* Clearly, any one coordinate system in a reference frame is as good as any other for describing the motion of a particle, for $\mathbf{v}$ and $\mathbf{a}$ are the same in all such coordinate frames.

Reference frame defined

Now consider the case in which two coordinate systems are in motion relative to each other. Let axes x', y', z' move with *constant velocity* $\mathbf{v}_0$ relative to axes x, y, z. (For example, the axes x', y', z' might be fixed to a train moving at constant velocity relative to the track.) For convenience, let the origins coincide at $t = 0$, and take $\mathbf{v}_0$ along the x or x' axes, as in Figure 4-9. We now have two different reference frames, which we shall call S and S'. S' moves with velocity $v_x = v_0$ relative to S whereas S moves with velocity $v'_x = -v_0$ relative to S'. A particle at rest in one frame is not at rest in the other. The coordinates are still related by

$$x' = x - x_0 \qquad\qquad 4\text{-}21$$

but now x_0 is not a constant. It is given by $x_0 = v_0 t$; thus

$$x' = x - v_0 t \qquad\qquad 4\text{-}22$$

The velocities of the particle measured in the two reference frames are related by

$$v'_x = \frac{dx'}{dt} = \frac{d}{dt}(x - v_0 t) = \frac{dx}{dt} - v_0 = v_x - v_0 \qquad\qquad 4\text{-}23$$

Differentiating again, we find that the accelerations in the two frames are equal, since the relative velocity v_0 was assumed to be constant.

$$a'_x = \frac{dv'_x}{dt} = \frac{d}{dt}(v_x - v_0) = \frac{dv_x}{dt} = a_x \qquad\qquad 4\text{-}24$$

Suppose we have a body of mass m attached to a spring which is extended by an amount Δx and thus exerts a force F_x in reference frame S. The acceleration will be $a_x = F_x/m$ assuming that Newton's law holds in this frame.

In frame S', the position x' and velocity v'_x of the body are not the same, but the acceleration a'_x is the same as a_x. Furthermore, the extension of the spring is the same (see Exercise 34). Thus the force is the same, and if $\Sigma \mathbf{F} = m\mathbf{a}$ holds in S, it holds in S' also.

Figure 4-9
Two coordinate systems moving relative to each other are in different reference frames. The reference frame S' containing coordinate system $x'y'z'$ moves with velocity $\mathbf{v}_0$ relative to reference frame S containing coordinate system xyz. The position and velocity of a particle are different in the two reference frames, but the acceleration of a particle is the same if $\mathbf{v}_0$ is constant.

Figure 4-10
The two coordinate systems
of Figure 4-9 from the point
of view of reference frame S'.
In this frame, the coordinate
system $x'y'z'$ is at rest, and
the system xyz moves to the
left with speed v_0. Only the
relative speed v_0 between the
reference frames is of significance.

We could just as well have made the drawing from the point of
view of S' and had S moving with speed v_0 to the left (Figure 4-10). Is
there any way to determine which frame is really at rest and which
frame is moving? That is, is it possible to determine absolute velocity?
Since only acceleration and not velocity appears in Newton's laws,
there are no mechanics experiments available for distinguishing absolute motion. This *principle of relativity* was discussed in the fourteenth
century, but it became well known only with the work of Galileo early
in the seventeenth century. It is interesting to read Galileo's remarks
on the impossibility of observing absolute motion:[1]

Principle of relativity

Shut yourself up with some friend in the main cabin below decks on
some large ship, and have with you there some flies, butterflies, and
other small flying animals. Have a large bowl of water with some fish
in it; hang up a bottle that empties drop by drop into a wide vessel
beneath it. With the ship standing still, observe carefully how the
little animals fly with equal speed to all sides of the cabin. The fish
swim indifferently in all directions; the drops fall into the vessel
beneath; and, in throwing something to your friend, you need throw
it no more strongly in one direction than another, the distances being
equal; jumping with your feet together, you pass equal spaces in
every direction. When you have observed all these things carefully
(though there is no doubt that when the ship is standing still everything must happen in this way), have the ship proceed with any
speed you like, so long as the motion is uniform and not fluctuating
this way and that. You will discover not the least change in all the effects named, nor could you tell from any of them whether the ship
was moving or standing still. In jumping you will pass on the floor
the same spaces as before, nor will you make larger jumps toward the
stern than toward the prow even though the ship is moving quite
rapidly, despite the fact that during the time you are in the air the
floor under you will be going in a direction opposite to your jump. In
throwing something to your companion, you will need no more force
to get it to him whether he is in the direction of the bow or the stern,
with yourself situated opposite. The droplets will fall as before into
the vessel beneath without dropping toward the stern, although
while the droplets are in the air the ship runs many spans. The fish in
their water will swim toward the front of their bowl with no more effort than toward the back, and will go with equal ease toward bait
placed anywhere around the edges of the bowl. Finally the butterflies

[1] Galileo Galilei, *Dialogue Concerning Two Chief World Systems—Ptolemaic and Copernican,*
pp. 186–187, trans. Stillman Drake, University of California Press, Berkeley, 1953; reprinted by permission of The Regents of the University of California.

DPI

and flies will continue their flights indifferently toward every side, nor will it ever happen that they are concentrated toward the stern, as if tired out from keeping up with the course of the ship, from which they have been separated during long intervals by keeping themselves in the air. And if smoke is made by burning some incense, it will be seen going up in the form of a little cloud, remaining still and moving no more toward one side than the other.

In the late nineteenth century it was thought that a careful measurement of the velocity of light relative to the earth would reveal absolute motion of the earth through space. Such an observation would contradict the principle of relativity, which was not yet accepted as a fundamental law of nature. Careful experiments by Michelson and Morley, however, gave a null result for the absolute velocity of the earth: they could not detect motion of the earth by measuring the velocity of light. The principle of relativity was again enunciated as a universal law by Poincaré and Einstein: absolute uniform motion cannot be detected by any experiment. The consequences of this principle, along with the assumption, based on experiment, that the speed of light is the same for all observers independent of their motion relative to the light source, were investigated by Einstein in 1905. His revolutionary results are known as the *special theory of relativity*. We shall study Einstein's theory in detail in Chapter 28.

A reference frame in which Newton's laws hold is called an inertial reference frame. All reference frames moving with constant velocity relative to an inertial frame are also inertial reference frames. Consider now the case in which S is an inertial reference frame and S' is *accelerating* relative to S. S' might be, for example, a coordinate frame at rest in a railroad car which is accelerating with acceleration $\mathbf{a}_0$ relative to the tracks. We find that Newton's laws do not hold in the railroad car. For example, a body on a smooth table does not remain at rest or move with constant velocity relative to the car; instead it has an acceleration $-\mathbf{a}_0$. Figure 4-11 shows a body suspended by a cord from the ceiling of the car. There is an unbalanced force to the right, but there is no acceleration (relative to the car). Since Newton's laws do not hold in S', this is not an inertial reference frame.

Accelerated reference frames

It is important to note that in order to classify a reference frame as inertial or not, we need to know all the possible forces acting on a

Figure 4-11
Body suspended by a cord from the ceiling of an acceler-ated car. The horizontal com-ponent of the tension in the cord is unbalanced, causing the body to accelerate to the right relative to the inertial reference frame S attached to the tracks. Reference frame S' attached to the car is not an inertial reference frame be-cause Newton's laws do not hold in this frame. Although there is an unbalanced force to the right, the body remains at rest and does not accelerate in frame S'.

body. We can identify the possible forces by finding the agent, i.e., the other body, responsible for each force. If we suspect the existence of a force because of an observed acceleration of the body but cannot find any agent responsible for it, we must conclude that the observed accel-eration results because our reference frame is a noninertial frame.

Consider a body dropped in the accelerating railroad car. Its acceler-ation (relative to the car) is

$$a_y = -g \qquad a_x = -a_0$$

We describe the y component of acceleration as being due to the pull of gravity of the earth. Might not the x component be due to a similar cause, i.e., a large mass to the left of the car? To determine whether the car is in an inertial frame we must look outside for possible forces. Because there is no apparent agent (such as a large massive object to the left of the car) responsible for the observed acceleration to the left, we label the reference frame in the car as noninertial.

Two questions now arise. Can absolute acceleration be detected? Is there any natural inertial reference frame? Newton gave the following demonstration of the absoluteness of acceleration. Consider a pail of water suspended by a rope. The surface of the water is level. Now give the pail a twist. At first the pail rotates, but the water does not. Because of viscosity, the water begins to rotate, and the surface is no longer level but assumes a parabolic shape. Eventually the water and pail have the same angular velocity, and thus no relative velocity or acceleration. If the pail is now suddenly stopped, the water continues to rotate. The shape of the water surface does not depend on the rela-tive motion of the water and pail but only on the absolute rotation of the water, or the rotation relative to the "fixed stars." Suppose, how-ever, that we could rotate *all* the surroundings of the water including the fixed stars while leaving the water at "rest." What shape would the surface of the water take? If it remained flat, we would have to believe in absolute acceleration. If instead it assumed the parabolic shape as when it was rotating, we would conclude that only relative accelera-tion is observable.

We can state this question in terms of our accelerating box car. Sup-pose we leave the box car at rest and give all the stars in the universe an acceleration $-\mathbf{a}_0$ relative to the box car. Would a body dropped in the box car accelerate toward the earth, i.e., obey Newton's laws, or would it accelerate also to the left, as when we accelerated only the box car? These questions cannot be answered with certainty, for no such experiment or its equivalent has been performed. We may, with Newton, believe in absolute acceleration.

A reference frame attached to the surface of the earth is certainly useful in describing the motion of everyday objects, but it is not an inertial frame. Because of the earth's rotation, such a frame has an acceleration directed toward the axis of rotation. At the equator, this acceleration is

$$a = \frac{v^2}{R_E} = \frac{(2\pi R_E/T)^2}{R_E} = \frac{4\pi^2 R_E}{T^2}$$

$$\approx 3.4 \times 10^{-2} \text{ m/sec}^2 \qquad \qquad 4\text{-}25$$

using $T \approx 86{,}400$ sec for the period of rotation, 1 day (d), and $R_E = 6.4 \times 10^6$ m for the radius of the earth.[1] When this acceleration is very small compared to others, it can be neglected and the surface of the earth taken as approximately an inertial frame. Alternatively we can compensate for the earth's rotation by choosing a frame which rotates *relative to the earth* with a period of 1 d. Even this frame is accelerating, however, because of the revolution of the earth about the sun. Since $T = 1$ y $\approx 3.16 \times 10^7$ sec for the period and $r \approx 1.49 \times 10^{11}$ m for the radius of the orbit, this acceleration is

$$a_{\text{rev}} \approx 5.9 \times 10^{-3} \text{ m/sec}^2 \qquad \qquad 4\text{-}26$$

Suppose we choose a reference frame at rest relative to the sun and other fixed stars. To Newton, such a choice seemed a likely possibility for an inertial reference frame. Today we know more about the motion of the fixed stars. The acceleration of the sun corresponding to the rotation of the galaxy is about 10^{-10} m/sec^2, which is small enough to be neglected for most purposes. There is apparently no simple physical system such as the earth or the sun that is exactly at rest in an inertial reference frame. We can of course set up an inertial reference frame without dependence on this result. We need merely to take a first approximation, such as a rectangular coordinate system at rest relative to the sun, project masses along the axis, and measure any deviation from constant velocity. We can then correct for any observed acceleration by choosing a second coordinate system accelerating relative to the first. In practice, we need only find a frame in which $\Sigma \mathbf{F} = m\mathbf{a}$ holds within the accuracy of our measuring apparatus.

Questions

28. Suppose you are inside a closed railroad car (no sound or light from outsides reaches you). How can you decide whether the car is moving? How can you tell whether it is speeding up? Slowing down? Rounding a curve?

29. According to the principle of relativity you cannot detect your own constant velocity. Yet even a deaf and blind man riding at constant velocity along a freeway can tell that the car is not at rest. How?

30. Should it be possible to tell that the earth itself is moving by any experiment conducted in a closed room? Can you think of any possible experiments?

---

[1] The free-fall acceleration of a body *relative to the surface of the earth* is thus less than g by 3.4 cm/sec^2 at the equator.

Isaac Newton (1642–1727)

I. Bernard Cohen
Harvard University

When Isaac Newton was once asked how he had made his great discoveries, he replied, "By always thinking unto them." He is also reported to have said, "I keep the subject constantly before me and wait till the first dawnings open little by little into the full light." This ability to concentrate is a particular quality of Newton's genius, and it fits in well with his character and personality. For he was a solitary man, without close and intimate friends or confidants. He never married, and spent his early boyhood deprived of father (who died before young Isaac was born on Christmas day in 1642) and of mother (who remarried within 2 years and left Isaac to be reared by an aged grandmother).

A lonesome man, he developed "unusual powers of continuous concentrated introspection." In these words, his biographer Lord Keynes, the economist, epitomized Newton's "power of holding continuously in his mind a purely mental problem . . . for hours and days and weeks until it surrendered to him its secret." And then, in keeping with this character of inwardness, he was satisfied to keep his discoveries to himself, neither rushing into print, as his contemporary fellow scientists were wont to do, nor even communicating to his associates what he had accomplished. Accordingly, it has been said that every discovery of Newton's had two phases; Newton made the discovery, and then others had to find out that he had done so.

In 1684, Edmund Halley (the astronomer, after whom Halley's comet is named) went from London to Cambridge, where Newton was a professor, to ask him about a fundamental problem that had baffled the major scientists of the Royal Society (the world's oldest existing scientific organization), including Robert Hooke (of Hooke's law) and Christopher Wren (architect as well as scientist). What "curve would be described by the Planets," Halley asked Newton, "supposing the force of attraction towards the Sun to be reciprocal to the square of their distance from it?" Newton "replied immediately that it would be an Ellipsis," i.e., an ellipse. Halley, "struck with joy and amazement asked him how he knew it. Why, saith he, I have calculated it." In these final four words, Newton revealed that he had solved the major scientific problem of the century: to find the law of force that holds the solar system together, that causes the planets to move around the sun according to Kepler's laws, and that equally produces the same keplerian motion in satellites moving around planets.

Once Christiaan Huygens, in 1673, had published the law of "centrifugal force" (as he named it), one might easily compute that in uniform *circular motion* the central force is inversely proportional to the square of the distance from the center; and so, in fact, it was no great feat to *guess*, as Halley, Hooke, and Wren had done, that the same inverse-square law might apply to the *elliptical* orbits of planets and their satellites. However Newton had done far more. He had not only proved rigorously that an inverse-square force produces a keplerian elliptical orbit, he had also found the dynamical significance of Kepler's two other laws. He then went on to show that it is one and the same universal gravitational force that keeps the planets in their observed orbits around the sun and the satellites in their orbits around the planets, that (by the pull of the moon) produces tides in the oceans, and that causes bodies to fall to earth with the observed acceleration. And he computed the law of this force, directly proportional to the product of the masses of any gravitating bodies and inversely proportional to the distance between them. His actual reply to Halley ("I have calculated it") reveals the character of the man, since he had been satisfied merely to have made the calculations and had not rushed to make known the primary scientific discovery of the age: the law of universal gravitation.

The seeds of Newton's great achievements in science go back to a period of some 18 months after graduation from college (1665–1667), when fear of the plague had caused the university to be shut and Newton returned to the family farm in Woolsthorpe, Lincolnshire, where he had been born. Here he worked out his most fundamental contributions to mathematics, the methods of the differential and integral calculus (an innovation for which he must share the credit with the German philosopher and mathematician Leibniz, an independent codiscoverer). During this same time, he found the law of the inverse square and tested it by a rough calculation of the moon's motion. In this work he independently discovered the law of centrifugal force: that in uniform circular motion along a circle of radius r at speed v this force or acceleration must be proportional to v^2/r. He knew that for any system of bodies moving about a central body (such as the planets going around the sun or the set of moons around Jupiter) there holds a form of Kepler's third law: that in each such system r^3/T^2 is a constant k, where T is the period of revolution. Thus, considering the orbits to be circular (an approximation, but a rather good one at a first stage), the speed v is $2\pi r/T$, and so $v^2/r = 4\pi^2 r^2/T^2 r$. A clever man would see at once that multiplying by r/r gives

$$\frac{v^2}{r} = \frac{4\pi^2 r^3}{T^2 r^2} = \frac{4\pi^2}{r^2}\frac{r^3}{T^2} = \frac{4\pi^2 k}{r^2}$$

That is, v^2/r is equal to a constant multiplied by $1/r^2$; or the force is inversely proportional to the square of the distance. But is it? Newton's test was to note that the moon is about 60 times as far from the center of the earth as an apple. Accordingly, the "force" or acceleration of the moon, as it "falls" toward the earth and constantly "falls" away from straight-line inertial motion, should be just $1/60^2$, or 1/3600 of the acceleration of free fall of an apple. The calculations, Newton said, agreed "pretty nearly." In his own words, "I thereby compared the force requisite to keep the Moon in her orb with the force of gravity at the surface of the Earth, and found them answer pretty nearly."

Later, Newton had to show that this inverse-square law also holds in elliptical orbits, and he had to take account of the modification required of Kepler's laws in an earth-moon system, because he proved that each of these two bodies (and any other pair) will move about their common center of mass. And he had to use his mathematical prowess to prove the fundamental theorem, that a uniform sphere (or a sphere made up of concentric uniform shells) will attract gravitationally as if all its mass were concentrated at its geometric center. Eventually, Newton cast out the misleading concept of centrifugal force, and introduced a new kind of force which he named *centripetal*.

A third set of discoveries made by Newton during his period of retreat during the plague years was in the field of optics. Newton is celebrated not only for his work in pure mathematics and for having founded the science of celestial mechanics; he is also known as an experimental scientist, primarily for his discoveries relating to light and color and that class of effects known today as *interference phenomena*. He bought a triangular glass prism, he tells us,

Manuscript drawing in Newton's papers, showing the "crucial experiment." Sunlight enters a darkened room at the left-hand side from *S*, producing a spectrum on passing through the first prism *A*. A hole at *Y* in the board *DE* permits light of a single color to pass through the second prism *F*, with the result of a deviated beam of light, without any further alteration in color. (*Courtesy of Cambridge University Library.*)

to try "the celebrated phenomenon of colours." But where others had played around with the colored spectrum produced by such a prism, Newton proceeded to analyze the phenomena of dispersion and the composition of white light and was led to devise and construct a new form of telescope, which in the succeeding three centuries has been astronomy's most powerful tool.

Newton's experiments on color showed that "white" light, or sunlight, is composite, a mixture of light of all the different colors. He demonstrated that the prism produces a spectrum, or separates out the different colors, because each color has its own index of refraction or degree of being turned or deviated from the original path. The violet light he found to be deviated the most, the red light the least. In order to prove that this is so, he devised what he called a "crucial experiment." He allowed a narrow beam of sunlight to enter a darkened room through a small hole in a window shutter. This beam then passed through a prism and produced a spectrum. Using an opaque board with a small hole in it, Newton could separate out of this spectrum a beam of light of a single color—red, orange, green, blue—and allow this monochromatic light to pass through a second prism. If prisms produce a spectrum by "altering" the incident light in some way, this effect should be apparent in the way the second prism would alter or affect an incident beam of monochromatic light. When monochromatic light entered the second prism, it emerged with no change of color; the second prism had produced only a further deviation, or change of path by refraction.

These investigations not only led Newton to an understanding of why objects appear to have the colors they display, in terms of the colors of the light they absorb or transmit or reflect, but also showed him that telescopes with simple or single lenses have definite limitations. Since a biconvex lens can be thought of as a pair of prisms base to base (Figure 1), we can see at once that there will be a different focus for each color, or a poor image due to *chromatic aberration*. Newton accordingly proceeded to invent a wholly new kind of telescope, a reflector rather than a refractor, which by using the front surface of a concave mirror to form the image avoided chromatic aberration.

A most notable set of optical investigations centered on the effects produced by thin plates, or films, as in the familiar colored patterns seen on films of oil. Newton studied the alternating fringed rings of darkness and light that are produced by the thin layer of air between a flat glass surface and the convex side of a plano-convex lens of large focal length, a phenomenon known today as *Newton's rings.* His measurements were so precise that they were used a hundred years later by Thomas Young to compute the wavelength of light.

Figure 1
Two prisms, one on top of the other, act like a lens.

The alternating circles of brightness and darkness in monochromatic light, known as *Newton's rings.* (*From Newton's* Opticks, *1704.*)

Newton's explanation of the phenomenon of Newton's rings, produced by the thin "film" of air trapped between a plane glass surface *AB* and the convex side of the plano-convex lens *CED.* This diagram shows Newton's conception of the alternation of transmission and reflection of the light from the curved surface. (*From Newton's* Opticks, *1704.*)

This is a remarkable set of discoveries for any lifetime, and we can only contemplate in amazement how in so short a time a young man barely out of college should have made such fundamental contributions to pure mathematics, to theoretical celestial mechanics and dynamics, and to experimental physics. As Newton himself later said, "All this was in the two plague years of 1665 and 1666, for in those days I was in the prime of my age for invention, and minded mathematics and philosophy[1] more than at any time since."

The remainder of Newton's scientific life was devoted to elaboration of the fundamental discoveries we have described. He became Lucasian Professor of Mathematics at Cambridge, and in 1672 his paper on light and color, together with a description of the newly invented telescope, was read to the Royal Society. After some aspects of his work had been misunderstood and criticized, he decided that he would publish no more. His mathematical innovations were distributed only in manuscript until later in his life when some were printed. Then, in 1684, after Halley's visit—and with Halley's urging—he wrote up his discoveries in dynamics and celestial mechanics in the *Philosophiae Naturalis Principia Mathematica* (London, 1687), which may be translated as *The Mathematical Principles of Celestial Mechanics*. Here he not only set forth and applied the law of universal gravitation but produced the three famous laws of motion that bear his name and that were the "axioms" on which his system of dynamics was constructed. In this work, too, he set forth for the first time a clear concept of mass and momentum and set up a series of beautiful experiments to show that mass (as measured by inertia) is proportional to weight.

In the 1690s, Newton became bored or disenchanted with the cloistered life of a university professor and moved to London, where he became director of the Mint, a post he held until his death in 1727. He became president of the Royal Society and ruled British science with a firm control. During the London years, he brought out two revised editions of his *Principia* (1713, 1726), published his book of optics (1704 and later editions) and various tracts on mathematics. He died in 1727 and was buried with state honors in Westminster Abbey.

From early manhood, Newton devoted only a small fraction of his creative intellectual life to orthodox scientific pursuits: pure and applied mathematics, astronomy and celestial mechanics, dynamics, experimental physics, and optics. During all these years he was an ardent student of theology, reading and taking innumerable notes, and writing tracts and even whole books on religious subjects. Some of these dealt with fundamental questions of interpretation of theological doctrines, others with the meaning of the prophetic books of the Bible, and yet others with the problem of unraveling Church history. He also developed a whole new system of world chronology, in part based on astronomy, that proved to be of little value. And his chief subject of study was alchemy—reading extensively, copying out whole sections of books, making experiments, all to what end we do not know.

Through his readings of mystical philosophers, theologians, and speculative alchemists, Newton may have gained a vision of a unified system of knowledge that would embrace both physical and divine science, revealing both the laws of the created world and the plan of its Creator. Various hints of this aspect of Newton's thought appear in his writings, e.g., "And thus to discourse about God from phenomena does belong to experimental philosophy." It is this vision of a knowledge which he never attained that may have caused him to devalue his monumental scientific achievements. For shortly before his death he said, "I do not know what I may appear to the world; but to myself I seem to have been only like a boy, playing on the sea-shore, and diverting myself in now and then finding a smoother pebble or a prettier shell than ordinary, whilst the great ocean of truth lay all undiscovered before me."

---

[1] The word "philosophy" as used at that time meant "natural philosophy," or science.

Review

A. Define, explain, or otherwise identify:

Force, 81	Dyne, 90
Mass, 85	Newton, 90
Kilogram, 86	Pound, 90
Inertia, 86	Slug, 91
Momentum, 87	Inertial reference frame, 95
Weight, 88	Reference frame, 96
Apparent weight, 89	Principle of relativity, 97
Gram, 90	

B. True or false:

1. If there are no forces acting on a body, the body will not accelerate.

2. If a body is not accelerating, there must be no forces acting on it.

3. The motion of a body is always in the direction of the resultant force.

4. Action-reaction forces never act on the same body.

5. The mass of a body depends on its location.

6. The weight of a body depends on its location.

7. Action equals reaction only if the bodies are not accelerating.

8. Newton's laws hold only in inertial reference frames.

Exercises

Unless otherwise instructed, use the approximate value $g = 32$ ft/sec^2 = 9.8 m/sec^2 for the acceleration of gravity in Exercises and Problems.

Section 4-1, Force, and Section 4-2, Mass

1. An object experiences an acceleration of 4 m/sec^2 when a certain force $\mathbf{F}_0$ acts on it. (*a*) What is its acceleration when the force is doubled? (*b*) A second object experiences an acceleration of 8 m/sec^2 under the influence of the force $\mathbf{F}_0$. What is the ratio of the masses of the two objects? (*c*) If the two objects are tied together, what acceleration will the force $\mathbf{F}_0$ produce?

2. An electric field gives a charged object an acceleration of 6×10^6 m/sec^2. Another field gives the same object an acceleration of 9×10^6 m/sec^2. (*a*) If the force exerted by the first field is $\mathbf{F}_0$, what is the force exerted by the second field? What is the acceleration of the object (*b*) if the two fields act together on the same object in the same direction and (*c*) if the two fields act in opposite directions on the object?

3. Figure 4-12 shows the path taken by an automobile. It consists of straight lines and arcs of circles. The automobile starts from rest at point A and accelerates until it reaches point B. It then proceeds at constant speed until it reaches point E. From point E on it slows down, coming to rest at point F. What is the direction of the net force, if any, on the automobile at the midpoint of each section of the path?

Figure 4-12
Path taken by automobile in Exercise 3.

4. The graph in Figure 4-13 shows a plot of v_x versus t for an object of mass 10 kg moving along a straight line. Make a plot of the net force on the object as a function of time.

Figure 4-13
Graph of velocity v_x versus time t for Exercise 4.

5. Figure 4-14 shows the position versus time of a particle moving in one dimension. During what periods of time is there a net force acting on the particle? Give the direction ($+$ or $-$) of the net force for these times.

Figure 4-14
Graph of position x versus time t for Exercise 5.

6. In each part of Figure 4-15 illustrate the forces acting on the designated object: (a) a golf ball in midflight; (b) a box sliding down a rough-surfaced ramp at constant speed; (c) a test tube in a centrifuge on a table top, (d) a pendulum bob swinging in vacuum.

Figure 4-15
(a) Golf ball in flight; (b) box sliding down rough ramp; (c) test tube in centrifuge; and (d) pendulum in vacuum for Exercise 6.

(a)

(b)

(c)

Vacuum jar

m

(d)

Figure 4-16
Forces acting on object for Exercise 7.

7. A force $\mathbf{F}_0$ causes an acceleration of 5 m/sec^2 when acting on an object of mass m. Find the acceleration of the same mass when acted on by the forces shown in Figure 4-16a and b.

8. A certain force applied to mass m_1 gives it an acceleration of 20 ft/sec^2. The same force applied to m_2 gives it an acceleration of 30 ft/sec^2. If the two masses are tied together and the same force applied to the combination, find the acceleration.

9. A mass is pulled in a straight line along a level, frictionless surface with a constant force. The increase in its speed in a 10-sec interval is 5 mi/h. When a second constant force is applied in the same direction in addition to the first force, the speed increases by 15 mi/h in a 10-sec interval. How do the magnitudes of the two forces compare?

Section 4-3, Newton's Second Law

10. A 12-kg mass undergoes an acceleration of 4 m/sec^2. What is the magnitude of the resultant force acting on it?

11. A force of 15 N is applied to a mass m. The mass moves in a straight line with its speed increasing by 10 m/sec every 2 sec. Find the mass m.

12. A force of $\mathbf{F} = 6\mathbf{i} - 3\mathbf{j}$ N acts on a mass of 2 kg. Find the acceleration $\mathbf{a}$. What is the magnitude a?

13. A single force of 10 N acts on a mass m. The mass starts from rest and travels in a straight line a distance of 18 m in 6 sec. Find the mass.

14. A 10-kg block slides down a straight incline. When first observed, its speed is 3 m/sec. One second later its speed is 5 m/sec. After two seconds its speed is 7 m/sec. After three seconds it is 9 m/sec. What is the magnitude and direction of the resultant force on the block?

15. A 3-kg mass is acted on by a single force $\mathbf{F}_0$ perpendicular to the velocity of the mass. The mass travels in a circle of radius 2 m. It makes one complete revolution in each 3 sec. (a) What is the magnitude of the acceleration? (b) What is the magnitude of $\mathbf{F}_0$?

16. In order to drag a 100-kg log along the ground at constant velocity you have to pull on it with a force of 300 N (horizontally). (a) What is the resistive force exerted by the ground? (b) What force must you exert if you want to give the log an acceleration of 2 m/sec^2?

17. Show that a newton-second is a unit of momentum.

18. A 3-kg mass moves with speed 4 m/sec in the x direction. (a) What is its momentum? (b) If a 3-N force also in the x direction acts on the mass, what will its momentum be after 2 sec? (c) If this force acts in the negative x direction, what will the momentum of the mass be after 2 sec? After 5 sec? (Assume that it is moving at 4 m/sec initially in the positive x direction.)

19. For each case the momentum of a certain particle is given in kilogram-meters/second as a function of time in seconds; find the force $\mathbf{F}$ as a function of time: (a) $\mathbf{p} = (6t + 7)\mathbf{i}$, (b) $\mathbf{p} = 2t\mathbf{i} + 3t\mathbf{j}$, (c) $\mathbf{p} = 3t^2\mathbf{i} + 3t\mathbf{j}$, (d) $\mathbf{p} = 6e^{-3t}\mathbf{i}$.

Section 4-4, Weight, and Section 4-5, Units of Force and Mass

20. Find the weight of a 50-kg girl in newtons and pounds.

21. Find the mass of a 175-lb man (a) in slugs, (b) in kilograms, and (c) in grams.

22. A newspaper reports that 3 tons of marijuana was found in a ship docked at Los Angeles. What is its mass in kilograms?

23. Find the weight of a 50-gm mass in dynes and newtons.

24. An 140-lb girl weighs herself by standing on a scale in an elevator. What does the scale read when (a) the elevator is descending at a constant rate of 10 ft/sec; (b) the elevator is accelerating downward at 4 ft/sec²; (c) the elevator is ascending at 10 ft/sec but the speed is decreasing by 4 ft/sec in each second?

25. The acceleration of gravity can be written $a = gR_E^2/(R_E + h)^2$, where R_E is the radius of the earth, h is the height above the earth, and $g = 32$ ft/sec². (a) Find the weight of an 160-lb man at a height of 500 mi above the earth. (b) What is the mass of the man at this altitude? (Take the radius of the earth to be 4000 mi.)

Section 4-6, Newton's Third Law and Conservation of Momentum

26. A 2-kg mass hangs at rest from a string attached to the ceiling. (a) Draw a diagram showing the forces acting on the mass and indicate each reaction force. (b) Do the same for the forces acting on the string.

27. A hand pushes two masses on a smooth horizontal surface, as shown in Figure 4-17. One mass is 2 kg, and the other is 1 kg. The hand exerts a force of 5 N on the 2-kg mass. (a) What is the acceleration of the system? (b) What is the acceleration of the 1-kg mass? What force is exerted on it? What is the origin of this force? (c) Show all the forces acting on the 2-kg mass. What is the net force acting on this mass?

Figure 4-17
Exercise 27

28. A box slides down a rough inclined plane. Draw a diagram showing the forces acting on the box. For each force in your diagram, indicate the reaction force.

29. A 1-kg mass and a 2-kg mass are moving toward each other with equal speed. They collide head on and rebound, moving away from each other with unequal speed. Compare the change in (a) momentum and (b) velocity of the 1-kg mass with that of the 2-kg mass.

30. A 10-ton freight car rolls along a horizontal track at 5 ft/sec with negligible friction. It hits a second stationary car weighing 15 tons. They couple together and roll with speed v. (a) Find the initial momentum of the 10-ton car (1 ton = 2000 lb). (b) Find the speed v.

31. A 2000-lb car traveling north at 60 mi/h collides with a 5000-lb car traveling east at 40 mi/h. The cars stick together after the collision. Find the velocity (magnitude and direction) of the cars just after the collision.

Section 4-7, Reference Frames

32. Two coordinate frames S and S' are coincident at $t = 0$. The origin O' is moving in the x direction with speed 3 m/sec relative to O. A 2-kg mass is moving along the x axis with velocity v'_x relative to the origin O'. (a) What is the velocity relative to O? (b) A force of 5 N in the x direction acts on the mass. If it starts from rest in frame S' at $t = 0$, find its velocity v'_x at times $t = 1$ sec, $t = 2$ sec, and $t = 3$ sec. (c) Use your result from part (a) to find the velocity v_x in S at these times. (d) What is the acceleration of the mass in frame S'? In frame S?

33. Water in a river flows in the x direction at 4 m/sec. A boat crosses the river with speed 10 m/sec relative to the water. Set up a reference frame with its origin fixed relative to the water and another with its origin fixed relative to the shore. Write expressions for the velocity of the boat in each reference frame.

34. A spring parallel to the x axis has extension $\Delta x = x_2 - x_1$ measured in reference frame S. Show that the extension is the same when measured in frame S' if the coordinates x and x' are related by Equation 4-22.

Problems

1. The acceleration versus spring length observed when a 0.5-kg mass is pulled along a frictionless table by a single spring is

L, cm	4	5	6	7	8	9	10	11	12	13	14
a, m/sec²	0	2.0	3.8	5.6	7.4	9.2	11.2	12.8	14.01	14.6	14.6

(a) Make a plot of the force exerted by the spring versus length L. (b) If the spring is extended to 12.5 cm, what force does it exert? (c) By how much is the spring extended when the mass is at rest suspended from it near sea level, where $g = 9.8$ m/sec²?

2. Explain how you could measure the mass of an object if you were in a spaceship moving with constant velocity far from the earth or any other planet or large gravitational mass.

3. A 4000-lb car traveling at 60 mi/h can be brought to rest in 242 ft by a constant braking force. (a) How long does it take to stop? (b) What is the force necessary to stop the car in this distance? (c) If the same force were applied, how far would the car travel before stopping if it were initially traveling 30 mi/h? If it were traveling 80 mi/h?

4. A 2-ton load is being moved by a crane. (a) As the load is lifted off the ground, its upward acceleration is 4 ft/sec². What is the tension in the cable that supports it? (b) After a brief period of acceleration, the load is lifted at constant speed. What is the tension then? (c) When the load has nearly reached the desired height, it accelerates downward at 4 ft/sec². What is the tension in the cable?

5. A platform scale calibrated in newtons is placed on the bed of a truck driven at a constant speed of 14 m/sec. A box weighing 500 N is placed on the

scale. (*a*) When the truck passes over the crest of a hill with radius of curvature 100 m, what is the reading on the scale? (*b*) When the truck passes through the bottom of a dip with radius of curvature 80 m, what is the scale reading?

6. Two men pull with equal force on the ends of a rope. A weight *w* is suspended at the center of the rope, as shown in Figure 4-18. (*a*) For any given angle θ made by the rope with the horizontal, find the tension in the rope. (*b*) If the mass of each man is *m*, what force must be exerted by the ground on the man to keep him stationary? (*c*) Evaluate parts (*a*) and (*b*) for $\theta = 5°$, $w = 10$ lb, and $mg = 160$ lb. (*d*) Is it possible for the men to hold the weight suspended with the rope horizontal? Is it possible for them to pull in such a way that the rope is horizontal momentarily? How?

Figure 4-18
Two 160-lb men supporting a 10-lb weight on a rope (Problem 6).

7. A 100-kg mass is pulled along a frictionless surface by a force **F** so that its acceleration is 6 m/sec² (see Figure 4-19). A 20-kg mass slides along the top of the 100-kg mass and has an acceleration of 4 m/sec². (It thus slides back relative to the 100-kg mass.) (*a*) What is the frictional force exerted by the 100-kg mass on the 20-kg mass? (*b*) What is the net force on the 100-kg mass? What is the force **F**? (*c*) After the 20-kg mass falls off the 100-kg mass, what is the acceleration of the 100-kg mass?

Figure 4-19
Problem 7.

8. A 50-gm mass which slides freely on a horizontal frictionless surface is attached by a light string 5 cm long to a pivot fixed on the surface (Figure 4-20). The mass is circling the pivot at a constant speed of 10 cm/sec. (*a*) What is the acceleration of the mass? (*b*) What is the force exerted by the string? (*c*) If the speed is doubled, what force must be exerted by the string? (*d*) If the mass moves at 10 cm/sec but the length of the string is doubled, what is the force? (*e*) If the string is 5 cm but the mass makes twice the number of revolutions per minute as originally, what is the force?

Figure 4-20
Mass moving in horizontal circle for Problem 8.

9. The velocity of a particle is 1 percent that of the velocity of light. (*a*) What is the velocity in meters per second? In miles per hour? (*b*) Expand $(1 - v^2/c^2)^{-1/2}$ using the binomial theorem. What percentage error is made if the relativistic correction to the momentum of the particle is ignored?

10. A small rocket with a mass of 10 kg is initially moving horizontally near the earth's surface with a speed of 10 m/sec. (*a*) What is the initial momentum of the rocket? (*b*) The rocket engine produces a force of 300 N on the rocket at an angle of 30° above the horizontal. (The force is in the plane determined by **g** and the initial momentum.) What is the resultant force on the rocket (use $g = 10$ m/sec²)? (*c*) Find the speed and momentum of the rocket 10 sec after the engine is turned on (assume the mass of the rocket is constant).

11. (*a*) Show that a point on the surface of the earth at latitude θ has an acceleration relative to the center of the earth of magnitude $3.4 \cos \theta$ cm/sec². What is the direction of this acceleration? (*b*) Discuss the effect of this acceleration on the apparent weight of an object near the surface of the earth. (*c*) The free-fall acceleration of an object at sea level measured *relative to the earth's surface* has the value 978 cm/sec² at the equator and 981 cm/sec² at latitude $\theta = 45°$. What are the values of the acceleration of gravity g at these points?

12. A 100-kg mass is near the surface of the earth at the equator. It is at rest relative to the surface of the earth. What is its acceleration relative to the center of the earth when (*a*) it has zero acceleration relative to the surface of the earth and (*b*) it has acceleration 9.81 m/sec² downward relative to the surface of the earth? (*c*) What is its weight mg? (*d*) What is its apparent weight read on a scale on which it rests?

13. A simple accelerometer (a device for measuring acceleration) can be made by suspending a small mass from a string attached to a fixed point in the accelerating object, e.g., from the ceiling of a passenger car. When there is an acceleration, the mass will deflect and the string will make some angle with the vertical. (*a*) How is the direction in which the suspended mass deflects related to the direction of the acceleration? (*b*) Show that the acceleration a is related to the angle θ the string makes with the vertical by $a = g \tan \theta$. (*c*) Suppose the accelerometer is attached to the ceiling of an automobile which brakes to rest from 30 mi/h in a distance of 200 ft. What angle will the accelerator make? Will the mass swing forward or back?

14. An accelerometer of the type described in Problem 13 is suspended in a railroad car moving at a constant speed of 50 mi/h. The angle of the string with the vertical is 10°. The deflection is toward the right-hand side of the car when the observer faces the direction of motion. Which way is the car turning? What is the radius of the curve?

CHAPTER 5   Applications of Newton's Laws

Newton's laws are applied in two ways: (1) to determine the acceleration, velocity, and position of a particle as functions of time given all
the forces acting on the particle and (2) to determine the forces acting
on a particle given the acceleration, velocity, or position of the particle
as a function of time. If all the forces acting on a particle are known,
the acceleration is found from $\mathbf{a} = \Sigma \mathbf{F}/m$, and the velocity and position
of the particle can be found (if their initial values are known) by integration. On the other hand, if the position or velocity of a particle is
known as a function of time, the acceleration can be determined by
differentiation and the *resultant* force from $\Sigma \mathbf{F} = m\mathbf{a}$. In this chapter we
shall treat rather simple problems carefully in order to illustrate the
general methods of solution. Careful study of these simple examples
will make you aware of the content of newtonian mechanics and how
it is applied. Practical problems are generally more complex than these
examples, but the means of solving them are natural extensions of the
methods illustrated here.

We begin in Section 5-1 by looking at examples in which the forces
are constant and each object moves in a straight line. After illustrating
a general method of attack which is useful in the solution of a wide
variety of mechanics problems, we apply this method to problems involving circular motion in Section 5-2 and to Archimedes' principle in
Section 5-3. Finally, we examine the motion of a particle under the
influence of a velocity-dependent retarding force, the situation when a
particle moves through a fluid such as air or water.

5-1 Linear Motion with Constant Forces

Example 5-1 A block resting on a smooth horizontal table is pulled
horizontally by a light string. Find the acceleration of the block and
the force exerted by the table.

Figure 5-1
A block on a smooth surface with a horizontal force exerted upon it through a string. The first step in solving the problem is to isolate the system to be analyzed. In this case, the gray circle isolates the block from its surroundings.

To find the motion of the block, we need to find the resultant force acting on it. A first step in applying the newtonian laws is to choose the object whose acceleration is to be determined and upon which the forces to be considered act. Although this seems simple enough, many students' errors can be traced to failure to identify clearly what mass is being considered and what all the forces acting upon it are. In Figure 5-1 a circle is drawn around the block to help isolate it mentally from its surroundings. Forces acting on the block are due to agents external to the block. Our problem is to determine what those forces are. As a general rule, external forces may be exerted on a body at any point where the body touches something else. Such forces are called *contact forces*. For the block in this simple example, we would expect a contact force to be exerted on the block where it touches the surface supporting it. We also know that a force is exerted at the point where the string is attached to the block. We anticipate that forces will be exerted where the air touches the block. These are forces of air resistance, which for low speeds and heavy objects are usually negligible. We shall neglect them in this example.

Choose the object

Find what forces act on it

Contact forces

In addition to contact forces, there usually are *action-at-a-distance forces*, i.e., forces which act over a space between the mass whose motion is being analyzed and the body which exerts the force. The force of gravity, or weight, of the mass is the most familiar example. Electric and magnetic forces are also of this kind. To determine whether such forces act we must know whether there is any body nearby which can exert a significant gravitational force or whether there are electric charges nearby which can account for electric or magnetic forces.

Action-at-a-distance forces

Three significant external forces act on the block in this example. They are indicated in a *free-body diagram* in Figure 5-2:

Free-body diagram

w the weight, or force of gravity, pulling down on the block. This is an action-at-a-distance force.

N the contact force exerted by the table. In general, a surface like the table exerts a force which has both a tangential component, called the *force of friction*, and a perpendicular component, called the *normal* force

Friction
Normal force

Figure 5-2
A *free-body diagram* for the block of Figure 5-1. The three significant forces acting on the block are its weight **w**, the normal force exerted by the table **N**, and the force exerted by the tension in the string **T**.

(the word normal means perpendicular). The phrase "smooth table" means that the frictional force is negligible compared with other forces in the problem. Thus the force exerted by a smooth surface is perpendicular, or normal, to the surface.

T   the contact force exerted by the string, called the *tension* in the string.   *Tension*

A convenient coordinate system is also indicated in Figure 5-2. Note that **N** and **w** are drawn with equal magnitude. If this were not the case, there would be a net vertical force and either the block would crash through the table ($N < w$) or the block would accelerate up off the table ($N > w$). If the table is strong enough to hold the block and has no unusual properties that would make the block jump up, there will be no acceleration in the y direction; thus $\mathbf{N} + \mathbf{w} = 0$. Here we have used a known fact about the motion, namely $a_y = 0$, in combination with Newton's second law, $\Sigma F_y = ma_y = 0$, to infer something about the force exerted by the table. For the x component of $\Sigma \mathbf{F} = m\mathbf{a}$, we have, since **T** is the only horizontal force,

$$T = ma_x \qquad \text{or} \qquad a_x = \frac{T}{m} \qquad\qquad\qquad\qquad 5\text{-}1$$

Equation 5-1 thus gives a_x in terms of T and m assumed to be known. If T is *constant*, a_x is also constant and we can immediately write down the position x of the block by using the constant-acceleration equations from Chapter 2:

$$x(t) = x_0 + v_0 t + \frac{1}{2} \frac{T}{m} t^2 \qquad\qquad\qquad\qquad 5\text{-}2$$

where x_0 is the position at $t = 0$ and v_0 is the velocity at $t = 0$. The quantities x_0 and v_0 must be given in order to specify $x(t)$ completely, as discussed in Chapter 2.

Even in this simple example, both kinds of applications of Newton's laws were used: the horizontal acceleration, velocity, and position were found in terms of the given horizontal force **T**, and the vertical force exerted by the table **N** was found from the fact that the block remains on the table and thus $a_y = 0$. This second type of information, which limits the kind of motion possible for the block, is called a *constraint*.   *Constraints*

According to Newton's third law, forces always act in pairs. In Figure 5-2 we have only three forces. What are the action-reaction pairs in this example? Figure 5-3 shows three forces not shown in Figure 5-2, the gravitational force **w'** exerted *by the block on the earth*, the force **N'** exerted *by the block on the table*, and the force **T'** exerted *by the block on the string*. Note that none of these forces is exerted *on* the block. Therefore they have nothing to do with the motion of the block and must be omitted in the application of the second law to the motion of the block.

Example 5-1 illustrates a general method of attack for problems using Newton's laws. This method consists of the following steps.

1. Draw a neat diagram.   *General method of attack*

2. Isolate the body (particle) of interest and draw a free-body diagram

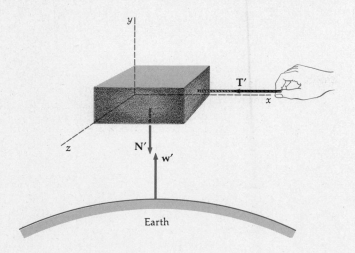

Figure 5-3
The reaction forces corresponding to the three forces shown in Figure 5-2. Note that these forces *do not* act on the block; **T'** acts on the man's hand, **N'** acts on the table, and **w'** acts on the earth.

indicating every external force acting on the body.[1] Do this for each body if there is more than one in the problem, drawing a separate diagram for each.

3. Choose a convenient coordinate system for each body and apply Newton's law $\Sigma\mathbf{F} = m\mathbf{a}$ in component form.

4. Solve the resulting equations for the unknowns using whatever additional information is available, e.g., constraints. The unknowns generally will include the components of both the acceleration and some of the forces.

5. Finally, inspect the results carefully, checking whether they correspond to reasonable expectations. Particularly valuable is to determine what your solution predicts when variables in the solution are assigned extreme values. In this way you can check your work for errors.

Example 5-2 Find the acceleration of a block of mass m which moves on a smooth, fixed surface inclined to the horizontal at an angle θ.

There are only two forces acting on the block, the weight **w** and the force **N** exerted by the incline (see Figure 5-4). We neglect air resistance, and we are instructed that there is no friction at the contact with

[1] We assume that all conceivable forces that act on a body can be conveniently separated into two classes: (1) a small number of dominant forces which can be enumerated and (2) an unspecified number of other forces, e.g., air resistance in Example 5-1, the gravitational attraction of the moon or other bodies, etc., which are too small to affect the motion of the body and can reasonably be neglected. Only forces in the first class are indicated in the free-body diagram.

Figure 5-4
Forces acting on mass m on a smooth incline. It is convenient to choose the x axis parallel to the incline.

the incline. Since the two forces are not in the same direction, they cannot add to zero and the block must therefore accelerate. As in Example 5-1, we have a constraint: the acceleration is along the incline. It is convenient for this problem to choose a coordinate frame with one axis parallel to the incline and the other perpendicular, as shown in Figure 5-4. Then the acceleration has only one component, a_x. For this choice, **N** is in the y direction, and the weight **w** has the components

$$w_x = w \sin \theta = mg \sin \theta$$

5-3

$$w_y = -w \cos \theta = -mg \cos \theta$$

where m is the mass and g is the acceleration of gravity (Figure 5-5). The resultant force in the y direction is $N - mg \cos \theta$. From Newton's second law and the fact that $a_y = 0$

$$\Sigma F_y = ma_y = N - mg \cos \theta = 0$$

and thus

$$N = mg \cos \theta$$

5-4

Similarly, for the x components

$$\Sigma F_x = ma_x = mg \sin \theta$$
$$a_x = g \sin \theta$$

5-5

The acceleration down the incline is constant and equal to $g \sin \theta$. It is useful to check our results at the extreme values of inclination, $\theta = 0$ and $\theta = 90°$. At $\theta = 0$, the surface is horizontal. The weight has only a y' component, which is balanced by the normal force $N =$

When friction is neglected, the body slides down the incline with acceleration $g \sin \theta$. (*Courtesy of the Museum of Modern Art/Film Archives, New York.*)

Figure 5-5
The weight of the block in Example 5-2 can be replaced by its components, $mg \cos \theta$ in the $-y$ direction and $mg \sin \theta$ in the $+x$ direction. Note that the normal force **N** exerted on the block by the incline has been omitted. Since there is no acceleration in the y direction, $\mathbf{N} = mg \cos \theta \; \mathbf{j}$.

$mg \cos 0° = mg$. The acceleration is of course zero; $a_x = g \sin 0° = 0$. At the opposite extreme, $\theta = 90°$, the incline is vertical. There the weight has only an x component along the incline, and the normal force is zero; $N = mg \cos 90° = 0$. The acceleration is $a_x = g \sin 90° = g$ since the block is in free fall.

Example 5-3 A 2-lb picture is supported by two wires of tension $\mathbf{T}_1$ and $\mathbf{T}_2$, as shown in Figure 5-6a. Find the tension in the wires.

This is a problem in static equilibrium. Since the picture does not accelerate, the net force acting on it must be zero. The three forces acting on the picture, its weight $m\mathbf{g}$, the tension $\mathbf{T}_1$, and the tension $\mathbf{T}_2$, must therefore sum to zero. Since the weight has only a vertical component mg downward, the horizontal components of the tensions $\mathbf{T}_1$ and $\mathbf{T}_2$ must be equal in magnitude and the vertical components of the tensions must balance the weight.

$$\Sigma F_x = T_1 \cos 30° - T_2 \cos 60° = 0$$

$$\Sigma F_y = T_1 \sin 30° + T_2 \sin 60° - mg = 0$$

Using $\cos 30° = \sqrt{3}/2 = \sin 60°$ and $\sin 30° = \frac{1}{2} = \cos 60°$ and solving for the tensions, we obtain

$$T_1 = \tfrac{1}{2}mg = 1 \text{ lb}$$

$$T_2 = \sqrt{3} \; T_1 = \frac{\sqrt{3}}{2} \, mg = 1.73 \text{ lb}$$

Example 5-4 Two blocks on a smooth table are connected by a light string (Figure 5-7), and one is drawn along by a second horizontal string. Find the acceleration of each block.

We assume that the given quantities in this problem are the masses m_1 and m_2 and the tension $\mathbf{T}_3$. We choose the x axis to be along the table, as in Figure 5-7.

Figure 5-6
(a) Picture supported by two wires in Example 5-3. (b) Choice of coordinate system and resolution of forces into x and y components. Since the picture is not accelerating,
$F_x = 0 = T_{1x} - T_{2x}$
$F_y = 0 = T_{2y} + T_{1y} - w$

(a)

(b)

Figure 5-7
The two connected blocks of Example 5-4. The gray circles remind us to isolate each block separately.

The free-body diagrams for these blocks are shown in Figure 5-8. There are three forces acting on m_1, its weight $\mathbf{w}_1 = m_1\mathbf{g}$, the normal force $\mathbf{N}_1$ exerted by the table, and the force $\mathbf{T}_1$ exerted by the connecting string. The x component of Newton's second law for this body is

$$T_1 = m_1 a_{x1} \tag{5-6}$$

The block of mass m_2 experiences four forces: its weight $\mathbf{w}_2 = m_2\mathbf{g}$, the normal supporting force $\mathbf{N}_2$ exerted by the table, the force $\mathbf{T}_2$ exerted by the connecting string, and the force $\mathbf{T}_3$ exerted by the second string. The x component of Newton's second law for this body is

$$T_3 - T_2 = m_2 a_{x2} \tag{5-7}$$

For each of the bodies we have neglected frictional forces and forces of air resistance. As in our earlier examples, we have the constraint imposed by the table that there is no vertical acceleration (the blocks neither leap up from the table nor sink into it). Thus the weight of each block is supported fully by the corresponding normal force of the table; $N_1 = w_1 = m_1 g$ and $N_2 = w_2 = m_2 g$. The connecting string provides an additional constraint. If the string does not break or become slack, the distance between the two blocks remains constant. Thus the accelerations a_{x1} and a_{x2} must be equal. If we write a for this common acceleration, Equations 5-6 and 5-7 become

$$T_1 = m_1 a \tag{5-8}$$

and

$$T_3 - T_2 = m_2 a \tag{5-9}$$

We still have three unknowns, a, T_1, and T_2, and only two equations. (We are considering T_3 to be given.) We can relate the force T_1 and T_2 by applying Newton's laws to the connecting string. The free-body diagram for the connecting string (Figure 5-9) neglects the weight of the string. The forces $\mathbf{T}_1'$ and $\mathbf{T}_2'$ are the contact forces exerted *on the string* by the blocks at either end. According to Newton's third law, $\mathbf{T}_1'$ is equal and opposite to $\mathbf{T}_1$, and $\mathbf{T}_2'$ is equal and opposite to $\mathbf{T}_2$. (If the weight of the string is not negligible, the string will sag and the tensions will have vertical components. The fact that there is little sag in the string in practice indicates that we can neglect its weight.) Newton's second law applied to the connecting string is

$$T_2' - T_1' = m_s a \tag{5-10a}$$

where m_s is the mass of the string and a is the acceleration, which is the same as that of the blocks. Since the magnitudes T_1' and T_1 are equal, as are T_2 and T_2', we can write

$$T_2 - T_1 = m_s a \tag{5-10b}$$

Equation 5-10b gives us a third relation between the three unknowns T_1, T_2, and a. In most cases, the mass of the string is very small and can be neglected. Then the tensions T_1 and T_2 are equal; i.e., the tension in the connecting string is the same throughout the string. We can then simplify our notation by dropping the subscripts 1 and 2 from the forces $\mathbf{T}_1$ and $\mathbf{T}_2$. Equations 5-8 and 5-9 become

$$T = m_1 a \tag{5-11}$$

$$T_3 - T = m_2 a \tag{5-12}$$

Figure 5-8
The free-body diagrams for the two blocks of Example 5-4. $\mathbf{T}_1$ and $\mathbf{T}_2$ are an action-reaction pair and therefore equal in magnitude.

Figure 5-9
Forces acting on the connecting string in Figure 5-7. According to Newton's second law, $T_2' - T_1' = m_s a$, where m_s is the mass of the string. If the string is very light, T_2' and T_1' are approximately equal in magnitude.

These two equations are easily solved for the two unknowns T and a. (For example, simply adding them eliminates T.) The results are

$$a = \frac{T_3}{m_1 + m_2} \qquad\qquad 5\text{-}13$$

and

$$T = \frac{m_1}{m_1 + m_2} T_3 \qquad\qquad 5\text{-}14$$

The acceleration is the same as if there were only one body of mass $m = m_1 + m_2$ because the acceleration of each mass is the same in magnitude and direction. That is, they could be considered to be rigidly connected or one combined mass (Figure 5-10).

The results obtained in Equations 5-13 and 5-14 can be checked as follows. One extreme case is $m_1 = 0$; that is, this block is absent. Then our result for a should be the same as in Example 5-1 when a single block was being pulled by a horizontal string. In fact, putting $m_1 = 0$ in Equation 5-13 gives $a = T_3/m_2$, the expected result. In this same extreme case we would expect the tension in the connecting string to be zero (since it has nothing to pull). Putting $m_1 = 0$ in Equation 5-14 gives $T = 0$, as expected. The reader should check for himself that Equations 5-13 and 5-14 give the expected results in other extreme cases, such as $m_2 = 0$, $m_1 = \infty$, and $m_2 = \infty$.

The analysis in Example 5-3 of the forces associated with the connecting string is complete and rigorously correct. It is a lengthy argument, however, for a very common situation. The result is just that *a light string connecting two points has a tension which has constant magnitude throughout and which acts in the direction of the string at any point.* This approximation is valid if the mass of the string is negligible, so that there is no need for a difference between the forces at the ends to account for the acceleration of the string. It also assumes, of course, that no forces are applied to the string at intermediate points. In the next example we shall show that this statement is also true when a string passes over a smooth peg. The general conditions for the validity of this approximation are that (1) the mass of the string is negligible and (2) there are no forces on the string between the two points with component tangential to the string.

You use this approximation without going through the elaborate analysis as long as you recognize that it is only an approximation valid under the above conditions. In some practical applications these conditions do not hold because the string is massive or there is a tangential frictional force. In these situations, a more complete analysis must be used.

Example 5-5 A block hangs by a string which passes over a smooth peg and is connected to another block on a smooth table. Find the acceleration of each block and the tension in the string.

Figure 5-10
The two connected blocks of Example 5-4 treated as a single body. The forces exerted by the connecting string (T_1 and T_2 in Figure 5-8) are now forces internal to the system and have no effect on the acceleration of the system.

(a)

(b)   (c)

Figure 5-11
(a) The two blocks of Example
5-5. The free-body diagrams
(b) for m_1 and (c) for m_2.

Figure 5-11 shows the important elements of this problem. For block 1 on the table, the vertical forces, **N** and $\mathbf{w}_1$, have equal magnitudes because of the constraint that the vertical acceleration is zero for m_1. Newton's second law applied to the horizontal components gives

$$T_1 = m_1 a_1 \qquad\qquad 5\text{-}15$$

where a_1 is the acceleration of m_1 along the horizontal surface. If we take the downward direction to be positive for the acceleration a_2 of block 2, the equation of motion for m_2 is

$$m_2 g - T_2 = m_2 a_2 \qquad\qquad 5\text{-}16$$

We can simplify these equations by noting that if the connecting string does not stretch, the accelerations a_1 and a_2 are both positive and equal in magnitude (but not in direction). Let us call this magnitude a. We shall now show that the tensions $\mathbf{T}_1$ and $\mathbf{T}_2$ are equal in magnitude.

Figure 5-12 shows a small segment of the string subtending an angle $\Delta\theta$ in contact with the peg. The tangent to the segment at the midpoint is shown as a dashed line. Since the peg is smooth (frictionless), the force it exerts on the segment is perpendicular to this tangent at the midpoint and bisects $\Delta\theta$. The other forces on the segment are the tensions $\mathbf{T}_A$ and $\mathbf{T}_B$ at the ends of the segment. If we assume the string to be massless, the three forces on the segment must add vectorially to zero. From the symmetry of the figure we see that this implies that the tensions $\mathbf{T}_A$ and $\mathbf{T}_B$ are equal in magnitude. We can extend this argument to other segments of the string. If there is no tangential force exerted on a string between two points and the mass of the string is negligible, the tension has the same magnitude at the two points.

Again we simplify our notation by dropping the subscripts and calling the magnitude of the tension T. Equations 5-15 and 5-16 then become

$$T = m_1 a \qquad\qquad 5\text{-}17$$

$$m_2 g - T = m_2 a \qquad\qquad 5\text{-}18$$

Figure 5-12
Forces on a small segment of string in contact with a smooth peg. The force **F** exerted by the peg is perpendicular to the peg at the midpoint and bisects the angle $\Delta\theta$ subtended by the segment. The forces $\mathbf{T}_A$ and $\mathbf{T}_B$ are due to the tension in the string. If the string is massless, these three forces must balance. Then the magnitudes T_A and T_B are equal.

Solution of these equations gives

$$a = \frac{m_2}{m_1 + m_2} g \qquad\qquad 5\text{-}19$$

$$T = \frac{m_1 m_2}{m_1 + m_2} g \qquad\qquad 5\text{-}20$$

Note that although the result for a appears to be the same as that for a mass $m = m_1 + m_2$ acted on by a force $m_2 g$, this is not the case because the magnitude of the acceleration of each mass is the same but the direction is not.

Example 5-6 Apparent Weight in an Accelerating Elevator A block rests on a scale in an elevator, as in Figure 5-13. What is the scale reading when the elevator is accelerating (*a*) up and (*b*) down?

(*a*) Since the block is at rest relative to the elevator, it is also accelerating up. The forces on the block are **N**, exerted by the scale platform on which it rests, and **w**, the force of gravity. If we call the upward acceleration **a**, Newton's second law gives

$$\mathbf{N} + \mathbf{w} = m\mathbf{a}$$

or, in terms of the upward components,

$$N - w = ma$$

$$N = w + ma = mg + ma \qquad\qquad 5\text{-}21$$

The force **N'** exerted by the block on the scale determines the reading on the scale, the apparent weight. Since **N'** and **N** are an action-reaction pair, they are equal in magnitude. Thus when the elevator accelerates up, the apparent weight of the block is greater than its true weight by the amount ma.

(*b*) Let us call the acceleration **a'**. Again Newton's second law gives

$$\mathbf{N} + \mathbf{w} = m\mathbf{a}'$$

but in this case the acceleration is downward. In terms of the magnitudes, we have

$$w - N = ma'$$

or

$$N = w - ma' = mg - ma' \qquad\qquad 5\text{-}22$$

Again, the scale reading, or apparent weight, equals N. In this case, the apparent weight is less than mg. If $a' = g$, as it would if the elevator were in free fall, the block would be apparently weightless. What if the acceleration of the elevator is greater than g? Assuming that the surface of the scale is not sticky, the scale cannot exert a force down on the block. (We assume that the scale is fastened to the floor of the elevator.) Since the downward force on the block cannot be greater than w, the scale will soon leave the block. The block will have the acceleration g, which is less than that of the elevator; so relative to the elevator, the block will accelerate up until it hits the ceiling. (As described in an inertial reference frame outside the elevator, the ceiling accelerates down faster than the block until it hits the block.) Then if the ceiling is strong enough, it can provide the force downward necessary to give the block the acceleration a'.

(*a*)

(*b*)

Figure 5-13
The block on a scale in an accelerating elevator for Example 5-6. The scale indicates the *apparent weight,* i.e., the upward force exerted on the block by the scale. The apparent weight is greater than mg when the acceleration is upward and is less than mg when the acceleration is downward.

Questions

1. A picture is supported by two wires as in Example 5-3. Do you expect the tension to be greater or less in the wire which is more nearly vertical?

2. A weight is hung on a wire which is originally horizontal. Can the wire remain horizontal? Explain.

3. Give an example in which the tension in a string does not have the same magnitude throughout.

4. If the two blocks in Example 5-4 were connected by a very light rod, would the analysis change?

5. What effect does the velocity of the elevator have on the apparent weight of the block in Example 5-6?

5-2   Circular Motion

If a particle moves with speed v in a circle of radius r, it has an acceleration of magnitude v^2/r toward the center of the circle. This centripetal acceleration is related to the change in the direction of the velocity of the particle, as discussed in Chapter 3. As with any acceleration, there must be a resultant force in the direction of the acceleration to produce it. If the speed of the particle is changing, there is also a component of the acceleration tangential to the circle of magnitude dv/dt. In this case, the resultant force has both radial and tangential components.

Example 5-7 A particle of mass m is suspended from a string of length L and travels at constant speed in a horizontal circle of radius r. The string makes an angle θ given by $\sin \theta = r/L$. Find the tension in the string and the speed of the particle.

This is known as a *conical pendulum* (Figure 5-14). The two forces acting on the particle are its weight $\mathbf{w} = m\mathbf{g}$, acting down, and the tension $\mathbf{T}$, which acts along the string. In this problem we know that the

This racetrack is banked so that the normal force exerted by the track on the car has a horizontal component toward the center of the circle to provide the centripetal force.

Ken Regan/Camera 5

acceleration is horizontal, toward the center of the circle, and of magnitude v^2/r. Thus the vertical component of the tension must balance the weight. The horizontal component of the tension is the resultant force. The vertical and horizontal components of $\Sigma\mathbf{F} = m\mathbf{a}$ therefore give

$$T\cos\theta - mg = 0 \qquad\qquad 5\text{-}23$$

$$T\sin\theta = ma = m\frac{v^2}{r} \qquad\qquad 5\text{-}24$$

The tension is found directly from Equation 5-23 since θ is given. We can find the speed v in terms of the known quantities r and θ by dividing one equation by the other to eliminate T:

$$\tan\theta = \frac{v^2}{rg} \qquad \text{or} \qquad v = \sqrt{rg\tan\theta}$$

Example 5-8 A ball on a string moves in a vertical circle with speed v_t at the top and speed v_b at the bottom. What is the tension in the string (*a*) at the top and (*b*) at the bottom of the circle?

(*a*) The forces on the ball at the top of the circle are shown in Figure 5-15*a*. At this point both the contact force **T** exerted by the string and the force of gravity $\mathbf{w} = m\mathbf{g}$ point down. The acceleration is also down (toward the center of the circle) with magnitude v_t^2/r. Newton's second law gives

$$T_t + mg = m\frac{v_t^2}{r}$$

or

$$T_t = m\frac{v_t^2}{r} - mg \qquad\qquad 5\text{-}25$$

(*b*) At the bottom of the circle, the tension points up and the force of gravity down. The acceleration is still toward the center of the circle (which at this point is up) with magnitude v_b^2/r. Newton's second law gives

$$T_b - mg = m\frac{v_b^2}{r}$$

or

$$T_b = m\frac{v_b^2}{r} + mg \qquad\qquad 5\text{-}26$$

Figure 5-14
(*a*) The conical pendulum of Example 5-7 and (*b*) its free-body diagram.

Figure 5-15
The forces on a ball moving in a vertical circle, as in Example 5-8. (The string is not shown.) (*a*) At the top of the circle, both the weight and the tension in the string (**w** and **T**) act downward and toward the center of the circle. (*b*) At the bottom of the circle, **w** and **T** act in opposite directions.

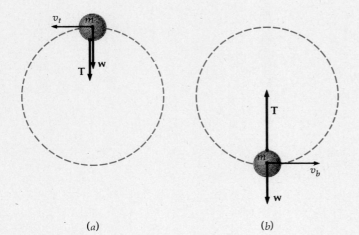

124   CHAPTER 5   Applications of Newton's Laws

At the bottom of the circle, the tension exceeds the weight mg by the amount mv_b^2/r. If the ball were simply suspended at rest from the string, the tension in the string would have to just equal the weight. But if the ball is moving, it has a net upward acceleration. Thus, according to the second law, there must be a net upward force acting on it. In other words, the upward tension must exceed the downward weight in magnitude.

At the top of the circle, the tension in the string must be positive (otherwise the string would fall slack). For this to be true, the first term in Equation 5-25 must be greater than the second. That is,

$$\frac{mv_t^2}{r} > mg \quad \text{or} \quad v_t > \sqrt{rg}$$

If the speed of the ball becomes less than this value at any point in its swing, the string will become slack and the ball will begin to move in a parabola, since it then will be in free fall.

Example 5-9 A block on a string moves in a vertical circle. What is the tension when the string makes an angle θ with the vertical, as shown in Figure 5-16, and the speed is v?

From the diagram (Figure 5-16) we see that the tension and weight are not collinear. It is convenient to use the radial and tangential directions for the application of $\Sigma \mathbf{F} = m\mathbf{a}$. The only force in the tangential

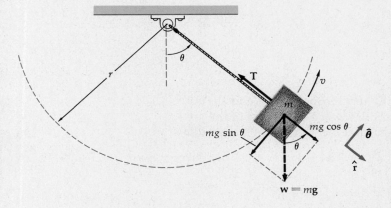

Figure 5-16
The forces on a block moving in a vertical circle (Example 5-9). The weight $\mathbf{w} = mg$ is resolved into radial and tangential components. The tangential component of the weight is the only tangential force acting, and so the block has a tangential acceleration related to a change in its speed. The net radial force in the inward direction, $T - mg \cos \theta$, provides the centripetal acceleration v^2/r.

direction is the component of the weight, of magnitude $mg \sin \theta$. If we choose the direction of increasing θ for the positive tangential direction, this component is negative. The tangential component of Newton's second law thus gives

$$-mg \sin \theta = ma_t \qquad \text{5-27}$$

or

$$a_t = -g \sin \theta \qquad \text{5-28}$$

The tangential acceleration varies with the angle θ. The rate of change of the speed is thus

$$\frac{dv}{dt} = a_t = -g \sin \theta$$

This rate of change of speed is the same as that for a mass sliding down a smooth incline tangent to the circle at this point. Taking the outward direction for the positive radial direction, we have for the radial components of $\Sigma \mathbf{F} = m\mathbf{a}$,

$$mg \cos \theta - T = ma_r = \frac{-mv^2}{r}$$

or

$$T = \frac{mv^2}{r} + mg \cos \theta \qquad 5\text{-}29$$

This result includes both results of Example 5-8. At the bottom of the circle, $\theta = 0$, $\cos \theta = 1$, and $T = mv_b^2/r + mg$. At the top of the circle, $\theta = 180°$, $\cos \theta = -1$, and $T = mv_t^2/r - mg$.

Questions

6. Explain why the following statement is incorrect: In the circular motion of a ball on a string, the ball is in equilibrium because the outward force of the ball due to its motion is balanced by the tension in the string.

7. Could we simplify Example 5-8 by assuming that the ball on the string moves in a vertical circle with constant speed? Explain.

8. How would Example 5-9 be changed if the ball were attached to a very light rod instead of a flexible string?

5-3 Buoyant Forces; Archimedes' Principle

If a heavy object submerged in water is "weighed" by suspending it from a scale (Figure 5-17a), the scale reads less than when the object is weighed in air. Evidently the water exerts an upward force partially supporting the weight of the object. This force is even more evident when we submerge a piece of cork: it accelerates up toward the surface, where it floats partially submerged. The submerged cork experiences an upward force from the water greater than its weight.

The force exerted by a fluid on a body submerged in it, called the *buoyant force*, depends on the density of the fluid and the volume of the body but not on the composition or shape of the body. It is equal in magnitude to the weight of the fluid displaced by the body. This result is known as *Archimedes' principle:*

A body wholly or partially submerged in a fluid is buoyed up by a force equal to the weight of the displaced fluid.

Archimedes' principle is a direct consequence of Newton's laws applied to a fluid. In deriving this result we shall first assume that the fluid is not accelerating relative to an inertial reference frame. We shall then investigate an accelerating fluid and show that the principle still holds if we interpret weight as meaning apparent weight. For example, if the fluid is in free fall, the apparent weight of the displaced fluid is zero and the buoyant force is zero.

Figure 5-17b shows the vertical forces acting on an object being weighed while submerged, i.e., the weight $\mathbf{w}$ down, which is the attraction of the earth; the force of the spring balance $\mathbf{F}_s$ acting up; a

Figure 5-17
(a) Weighing a mass m submerged in a fluid. (b) The corresponding free-body diagram. $F_2 > F_1$ because of the greater pressure on the bottom surface of the object. The difference $F_2 - F_1$ is the buoyant force on the object.

(a)

(b)

force $\mathbf{F}_1$ acting down because of the fluid pressing on the top surface of the object, and a force $\mathbf{F}_2$ acting up because of the fluid pressing on the bottom surface of the object. Since the spring balance reads a force less than the weight, the force $\mathbf{F}_2$ must be greater in magnitude than the force $\mathbf{F}_1$. The difference in magnitude of these two forces is the buoyant force $B = F_2 - F_1$. The buoyant force occurs because the pressure of the fluid at the bottom of the object is greater than that at the top.

Pressure is defined as follows. Consider a small surface of area A submersed in a fluid. Let F be the force normal to the surface exerted by the fluid on one side of the surface on the fluid on the other side. The pressure P is then

$$P = \frac{F}{A} \qquad\qquad 5\text{-}30$$

Pressure of a fluid

The pressure so defined is independent of the size of A (assuming A to be small) and is independent of the orientation of the surface.

The force exerted by a fluid on a small area element of a submerged object is perpendicular to the area element and has the magnitude of the pressure times the area of the element. The vector sum of these forces over the total area of the object is the resultant force exerted by the fluid on the object which is the buoyant force. It is independent of the composition of the object.

In Figure 5-18 we have replaced the submerged object by an equal volume of fluid (indicated by the dotted lines) and eliminated the spring. As we have said, the buoyant force $B = F_2 - F_1$ acting on this volume of fluid is the same as that acting on our original object. Since this volume of fluid is in equilibrium, the resulting force acting on it must be zero. The buoyant force equals the weight of the fluid in this volume:

Figure 5-18
The situation of Figure 5-17 with the volume of the mass m replaced by fluid. The forces F_1 and F_2 are identical to the corresponding forces on the mass in Figure 5-17b.

$$B = w_f \qquad\qquad 5\text{-}31$$

We have derived Archimedes' principle.

Let ρ_f be the mass per unit volume, called the *density*, of the fluid. A volume V of fluid then has mass $\rho_f V$ and weight $\rho_f g V$. If we submerge an object of volume V, the buoyant force on the object is $\rho_f g V$. The weight of the object can be written $\rho g V$, where ρ is the density of the object. If the density of the object is greater than that of the fluid, the weight will be greater than the buoyant force and the object will sink if not supported. If ρ is less than ρ_f, the buoyant force will be greater than the weight and the object will accelerate up to the top of the fluid unless held down. It will float in equilibrium with a fraction of its volume submerged so that the weight of the displaced fluid equals the weight of the object. Densities of various materials are listed in Appendix B, Table 4.

Density defined

Example 5-10 A 1-lb block of aluminum (density $\rho = 2.7$ gm/cm³) is suspended by a spring scale and submerged in water ($\rho_w = 1.00$ gm/cm³), as in Figure 5-17a. What is the reading on the spring scale? If the block is weighed in air of density $\rho_a = 10^{-3}$ gm/cm³, what is the reading of the scale?

The forces acting on the block are its weight down, the force $\mathbf{F}_s$ up exerted by the spring and the buoyant force $\mathbf{B}$, also up. Since the block is not accelerating, Newton's second law gives

$$\mathbf{F}_s + \mathbf{B} + \mathbf{w} = 0 \qquad \text{or} \qquad F_s + B - w = 0$$

We can write the weight and buoyant force in terms of the volume of the block V: $B = \rho_w g V$ and $w = \rho g V$. Then the spring force is

$$F_s = w - B = \rho g V - \rho_w g V = \rho g V \left(1 - \frac{\rho_w}{\rho}\right) = w \left(1 - \frac{\rho_w}{\rho}\right) \qquad 5\text{-}32$$

But

$$\frac{\rho_w}{\rho} = \frac{1 \text{ gm/cm}^3}{2.7 \text{ gm/cm}^3} = 0.37$$

and so

$$F_s = (1 - 0.37)w = (0.63)(1 \text{ lb}) = 0.63 \text{ lb}$$

If we replace the density of water with that of air in Equation 5-32, we obtain the force exerted by the spring scale when the block is weighed in air. For this case,

$$\frac{\rho_a}{\rho} = \frac{10^{-3}}{2.7} = 3.7 \times 10^{-4}$$

and

$$1 - \frac{\rho_a}{\rho} = 1 - 0.00037 \approx 1$$

showing that we can usually neglect the buoyant force of air.

Ira Rosenberg/Detroit Free Press

The buoyant force of air is not always negligible. Here it equals the weight of the balloon plus passengers, so that the balloon floats in the air. When the air in the balloon is heated more, it expands and the buoyant force is greater, causing the balloon to rise.

Example 5-11 A cork has a density of $\rho = 0.2$ gm/cm³. (a) Find what fraction of the volume of the cork is submerged when the cork floats in water. (b) Find the net force on the cork if it is completely submerged and then released.

(a) Let V be the volume of the cork and V' be the volume that is submerged when it floats on the water. The weight of the cork is $\rho g V$, and the buoyant force is $\rho_w g V'$. Since the cork is in equilibrium, the buoyant force equals the weight. Thus

$$B = w \qquad \rho_w g V' = \rho g V$$

$$\frac{V'}{V} = \frac{\rho}{\rho_w} = \frac{0.2}{1} = \frac{1}{5} \qquad\qquad 5\text{-}33$$

Thus one-fifth of the cork is submerged.

(b) When the cork is held completely submerged, the buoyant force is $\rho_w g V$. This is 5 times the weight of the cork since the density of water is 5 times that of the cork. The net force up is then

$$F = B - w = 5w - w = 4w$$

The net force upward is 4 times the weight of the cork. The upward acceleration of the cork is significantly less than $4g$ because as the cork moves upward an amount of water (which depends on the shape of the cork) must be accelerated to make room for the cork. The detailed calculation of the acceleration of the cork is a complicated problem in hydrodynamics.

We can use Archimedes' principle to find the pressure of a fluid as a function of depth. Consider a slab of fluid of area A and thickness Δh, where h is the depth measured from the top of the water (see Figure 5-19). If P_2 is the pressure at the bottom of the slab and P_1 that at the top, the buoyant force on the slab is $(P_2 - P_1)A = \Delta P \, A$, where ΔP

Figure 5-19
A slab of fluid of area A and thickness Δh. The difference between the forces on the upper and lower surfaces of the slab, $P_2 A - P_1 A$, must equal the weight of the slab.

is the pressure change in the depth change Δh. Setting this equal to the weight of the volume of fluid $A\,\Delta h$, we obtain

$$\Delta P\,A = mg = \rho A\,\Delta h\,g$$

$$\frac{\Delta P}{\Delta h} = g\rho$$

If we let Δh approach zero, the ratio $\Delta P/\Delta h$ becomes the derivative dP/dh

$$\frac{dP}{dh} = \rho g \qquad\qquad\qquad 5\text{-}34$$

Equation 5-34 holds for any fluid. To solve this equation we must know how the density of the fluid depends on the pressure. For water, the density is approximately independent of the pressure; i.e., water is nearly incompressible. Then according to Equation 5-34, $dP/dh =$ constant and the pressure varies linearly with h:

$$P = P_0 + \rho g h \qquad\qquad\qquad 5\text{-}35$$

where P_0 is the pressure at $h = 0$. We can also use this type of analysis to find an expression for the variation of atmospheric air pressure with height y above the ground. Since it is convenient to measure y upward from the ground rather than h downward, Equation 5-34 is replaced by

$$\frac{dP}{dy} = -\rho g \qquad\qquad\qquad 5\text{-}34a$$

However, the density of air is not independent of pressure. Air is compressible; the greater the pressure the greater the density. It is left as a problem to show that if the density is proportional to the pressure, the pressure decreases exponentially with height above the ground (see Problem 20).

Let us now consider an accelerating fluid. In Figure 5-20a a container of water is falling freely with the acceleration of gravity g. The resultant force on any part of the water must equal mg because the water is accelerating with $a = g$. Since this force equals the weight, there can be no buoyant force in this case. This result can be demonstrated by placing a cork at the bottom of a long tube of water and throwing the tube into the air. (Remember that whether the tube is moving up or down, its acceleration is g downward; i.e., it is a projectile.) The cork does not float to the top of the tube but remains where it was when the tube was thrown.

If we submerge a cork by suspending it from the bottom of a container of water with a string and accelerate the container in a horizontal direction (Figure 5-20b), the somewhat surprising result is that the string inclines forward toward the direction of acceleration. Let us first consider an element of water of volume V and mass $m_w = \rho_w V$. Since the water is accelerating to the right, the pressure on the left part of the water must be greater than that on the right, giving a net force to the right on the element equal to $m_w a$, where a is the acceleration. If we now replace this element of water with a cork, the cork will experience the same force to the right, but since the mass of the cork is less than m_w, the acceleration of the cork will be greater than that of the water and the container. The cork will thus accelerate to the right relative to the container. If the cork is attached by a string, as in Figure

(a)

(b)

Figure 5-20
A cork is tied to the bottom of a container of water. (a) When the container is in free fall, $\mathbf{a} = \mathbf{g}$ and there is no buoyant force on the cork. (b) When the container accelerates to the right, the cork is deflected in the direction of the acceleration with the string perpendicular to the water surface.

Buoyant force on a submerged ball in an accelerated frame. The pendulum and water container are on a rotating platform and are therefore accelerating toward the center of rotation, which is toward the left in this photograph. Note that both strings are perpendicular to the water surface. (*Courtesy of Larry Langrill, Oakland University.*)

5-20*b*, the string provides a force to the left, so that the acceleration of the cork and the container are the same. How does this buoyant force to the right arise? If we look at the surface of the water, we see that it is not horizontal. The water piles up at the left, so that at a given distance from the bottom the water is deeper at the left of the cork than at the right. Note that the string holding the cork is perpendicular to the surface of the water.

This interesting behavior can be demonstrated by placing the container of water at the edge of a turntable and securing it so that it cannot fall off. When the table rotates, the acceleration of the container is toward the center and the string holding the cork inclines in that direction.

Questions

9. How might you estimate your average density at a swimming pool?

10. Smoke which usually rises from a smokestack is observed to sink on a very humid day. What can be concluded about the relative densities of humid and dry air?

11. Why is it easier to float in seawater than in fresh water?

12. A certain object has mass density nearly equal to that of water so that it floats almost completely submerged. However, it is much more compressible than water. What happens if the floating object is given a slight push to submerge it?

13. Fish can adjust their volume by varying the amount of oxygen and nitrogen gas (obtained from the blood) in a thin-walled sac under their spinal column called a swim bladder. Explain how this helps them swim.

5-4   Motion with a Retarding Force Proportional to the Speed

When an object moves through a fluid, in addition to the buoyant force there is a retarding force which depends on the velocity of the object. In general the greater the velocity the greater the retarding force. In some cases this retarding force is approximately proportional to the velocity

$$\mathbf{F}_r = -b\mathbf{v} \qquad\qquad 5\text{-}36$$

The proportionality constant b generally depends on the shape of the object and on the fluid. The negative sign in Equation 5-36 indicates that the retarding force is always in the direction opposite the velocity.

Example 5-12   A particle is dropped from rest and falls under the influence of its own weight and a retarding force given by Equation 5-36 (Figure 5-21). Describe its motion.

   For simplicity we shall neglect the buoyant force (we can always include it by replacing the weight by $w\text{-}B$, as given by Equation 5-32). Since the particle falls down due to its weight, the retarding force is up. When the downward direction is taken to be positive, Newton's second law $\Sigma\mathbf{F} = m\mathbf{a}$ gives

$$mg - bv = ma = m\,\frac{dv}{dt}$$

or

$$\frac{dv}{dt} = g - \frac{b}{m}\,v \qquad\qquad 5\text{-}37$$

Figure 5-21
The free-body diagram for a particle falling through a resistive fluid. In this case, the buoyant force is considered to be negligible. This corresponds to the situation of a comparatively heavy mass falling through air.

When the retarding force equals his weight, the sky diver is in equilibrium and falls with constant velocity. The terminal velocity (without parachute) is approximately 120 mi/h.

Andy Keech

Equation 5-37 is a differential equation relating the speed v and its time rate of change dv/dt. It can be solved by standard methods of calculus, but since these methods may not be familiar to you yet, we shall consider the solution of this equation qualitatively. We can sketch the resultant v-versus-t curve from Equation 5-37 knowing only that dv/dt is the slope of this curve. We are given that the initial speed is zero. Thus initially there is no retarding force, and the acceleration is g. As the speed increases, the term bv increases and the acceleration decreases. Thus as time goes on, the speed increases (dv/dt is positive) but the rate of increase dv/dt gets smaller. Eventually, the retarding force bv equals the weight mg, and the acceleration is zero. From this time onward, the particle moves with constant velocity called its *terminal velocity*. An expression relating the terminal velocity to the constant b is obtained by setting $dv/dt = 0$ in Equation 5-37. The result is

$$mg - bv_t = 0$$

$$v_t = \frac{mg}{b} \qquad\qquad 5\text{-}38$$

A sketch of v versus t is shown in Figure 5-22. The function satisfying Equation 5-37 with $v = 0$ at $t = 0$ is

$$v = \frac{mg}{b}(1 - e^{-bt/m}) = v_t(1 - e^{-t/t_c}) \qquad\qquad 5\text{-}39$$

The time $t_c = m/b$ is the time for the particle to reach 63 percent of its terminal velocity.

The larger the constant b the smaller the terminal velocity and the sooner an appreciable fraction of the terminal velocity is reached. We have mentioned that the constant b depends on the shape of the object. For example, a parachute is designed to make b large so that the terminal velocity is small. On the other hand, cars are designed with b small to reduce the effect of wind resistance.

Example 5-13   A particle with initial velocity v_0 moves under the influence of a single force given by Equation 5-36. Describe its motion.
 Newton's second law for this example is

$$-bv = m\frac{dv}{dt}$$

$$\frac{dv}{dt} = -\frac{b}{m}v \qquad\qquad 5\text{-}40$$

Fundamental Photographs

A golf ball and a styrofoam ball falling in air. The air resistance is negligible for the heavier golf ball, which falls with essentially constant acceleration. The styrofoam ball reaches terminal velocity quickly, as indicated by the nearly equal spacing at the bottom.

Figure 5-22
A plot of velocity versus time for an object falling through a resistive fluid; v_t is the maximum, or terminal, velocity attained by the object; t_c, usually called the time constant, is the time required for the object to attain 63 percent of its terminal velocity.

Figure 5-23
A plot of velocity versus time for the particle of Example 5-13. Here, the particle has an initial velocity v_0 and is subject to a single force given by $\mathbf{F} = -b\mathbf{v}$. The velocity decreases exponentially with time, reaching $e^{-1}v_0 = 0.37v_0$ after time t_c.

In this case the acceleration is always negative. The initial speed is v_0. As time goes on, the speed decreases. The slope of the v-versus-t curve is always negative. As v approaches zero, its slope dv/dt also approaches zero. A sketch of v versus t is shown in Figure 5-23. The mathematical function describing this curve is

$$v = v_0 e^{-bt/m} \qquad\qquad\qquad 5\text{-}41$$

We can check that Equation 5-41 is a solution to Equation 5-40 by direct differentiation:

$$\frac{dv}{dt} = \frac{d}{dt}\left(v_0 e^{-bt/m}\right) = v_0 \left(\frac{-b}{m}\right) e^{-bt/m} = -\frac{b}{m} v_0 e^{-bt/m} = -\frac{b}{m} v$$

Questions

14. How does a sky diver vary the value of b?

15. How would you expect the value of b for air resistance to depend on the density of the air?

Review

A. Define, explain, or otherwise identify:

Contact force, 113
Action-at-a-distance force, 113
Free-body diagram, 113
Normal force, 113
Smooth surface, 114
Tension, 114

Constraint, 114
Buoyant force, 125
Archimedes' principle, 125
Pressure, 126
Density, 126
Terminal velocity, 131

B. Write out the steps involved in the general method of attack for solving problems using Newton's laws of motion.

C. True or false:

1. Action-at-a-distance forces can be neglected when determining the acceleration of an object.

2. At any given time, the tension in a string must have the same magnitude at any two points.

3. When the bob of a pendulum swings through its lowest point, the tension in the string has the magnitude mg.

4. The terminal velocity of an object depends on its shape.

5. When an object floats in a fluid, the fraction submerged depends only on the ratio of the densities of the object and fluid.

Exercises

*Unless instructed otherwise, use the approximate value $g = 32$ ft/sec² $= 9.8$ m/sec²
for the acceleration of gravity in Exercises and Problems.*

Section 5-1, Linear Motion with Constant Forces

1. A 10-kg object is subjected to the two forces $\mathbf{F}_1$ and $\mathbf{F}_2$, as shown in Figure
5-24. (*a*) Find the acceleration $\mathbf{a}$ of the object. (*b*) A third force $\mathbf{F}_3$ is applied so
that the object is in static equilibrium. Find $\mathbf{F}_3$.

Figure 5-24
Exercise 1.

2. A 5-kg object is pulled along a frictionless horizontal surface by a horizontal
force of 10 N. (*a*) If the object is at rest at $t = 0$, how fast is it moving after 3
sec? (*b*) How far does it travel from $t = 0$ to $t = 3$ sec? (*c*) Indicate on a diagram
all the forces acting on the object.

3. A 4-kg object is subjected to two forces, $\mathbf{F}_1 = 2\mathbf{i} - 3\mathbf{j}$ N and $\mathbf{F}_2 = 4\mathbf{i} + 11\mathbf{j}$ N.
The object is at rest at the origin at time $t = 0$. (*a*) What is the object's accelera-
tion? (*b*) What is its velocity at time $t = 3$ sec? (*c*) Where is the object at time
$t = 3$ sec?

4. A 3-lb object is suspended 4 ft from the ceiling by two 6-ft wires, as shown
in Figure 5-25. Assuming the wires to have negligible mass, find the tension
in the wires.

Figure 5-25
Exercise 4.

5. A 2-lb picture is hung by two wires of equal length which make an angle θ
with the horizontal, as shown in Figure 5-26. (*a*) If $\theta = 30°$, find the tension in
the wires. (*b*) Find the tension for general θ and weight w of the picture. For
what angle θ is T the least? The greatest?

Figure 5-26
Exercise 5.

6. In Figure 5-27 the masses are attached to spring balances calibrated in newtons. Give the reading of the balances in each case. (The strings are massless, and the incline is smooth.)

Figure 5-27
Exercise 6.

7. One of the first steps in the solution of a problem is drawing a correct diagram. In Figure 5-28a a mass is suspended from a horizontal cable. In Figure 5-28b a mass is suspended from a guy wire. (a) Correct the diagrams shown in this figure. (b) *Prove* that the diagrams are incorrect.

Figure 5-28
Exercise 7.

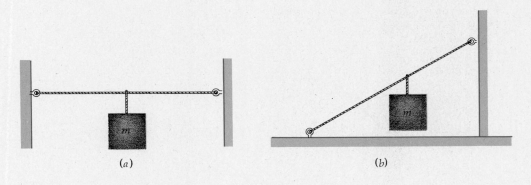

8. A mass is held in position by a cable along a smooth incline (Figure 5-29). (*a*) If $\theta = 60°$ and $m = 50$ kg, find the tension in the cable and the normal force exerted by the incline. (*b*) Find the tension as a function of θ and m and check your result for $\theta = 0$ and $\theta = 90°$.

Figure 5-29
Mass held on smooth incline for Exercise 8.

9. A vertical force T is exerted on a 5-kg mass near the surface of the earth as shown in Figure 5-30. Find the acceleration of the mass if (*a*) $T = 5$ N; (*b*) $T = 10$ N; (*c*) $T = 100$ N.

Figure 5-30
Exercise 9.

10. Two 5-kg masses are connected by a light string as shown in Figure 5-31. The table is smooth, and the string passes over a smooth peg. Find the acceleration of the masses and the tension in the string.

Figure 5-31
Exercise 10.

11. Two masses are connected by a light string as shown in Figure 5-32. The incline and peg are smooth. Find the acceleration of the masses and the tension in the string for $\theta = 30°$ and $m_1 = m_2 = 5$ kg.

Figure 5-32
Exercise 11.

12. Two masses are connected by a light string as shown in Figure 5-33. The string passes over a smooth peg. Find the acceleration of each mass and the tension in the string for $m_1 = 200$ gm and $m_2 = 100$ gm.

Figure 5-33
Exercise 12 and Problem 12.
Atwood's machine.

13. Two masses m_1 and m_2 rest on a smooth horizontal table. A force $\mathbf{F}$ is applied to m_1 (Figure 5-34). For $m_1 = 2$ kg, $m_2 = 4$ kg, and $F = 3$ N, find (a) the acceleration of the masses, (b) the *resultant* force on m_1, (c) the resultant force on m_2, and (d) the magnitude of the contact force exerted by one mass on the other.

Figure 5-34
Exercise 13 and Problem 9.

14. A mass m_1 rests on a mass m_2, which rests on a smooth table. A force $\mathbf{F}$ is exerted on m_2, as shown in Figure 5-35. Consider $m_1 = 2$ kg, $m_2 = 4$ kg, and $F = 3$ N. (a) If the surface between m_1 and m_2 is perfectly smooth, find the acceleration of each mass. (b) If the surface between m_1 and m_2 is rough enough to ensure that m_2 does not slide on m_1, find the acceleration of the two masses. (c) In case (b) what are the resultant forces acting on each mass? What is the magnitude and direction of the contact force exerted by mass m_1 on m_2?

Figure 5-35
Exercise 14 and Problem 10.
The table is assumed to be smooth, but the surface between m_1 and m_2 is rough.

15. A 2-kg mass hangs from a spring balance (calibrated in newtons) attached to the ceiling of an elevator (Figure 5-36). What does the balance read (a) when the elevator is moving up with constant velocity of 30 m/sec, (b) when the elevator is moving down with constant velocity of 30 m/sec, (c) when the elevator is accelerating upward at 10 m/sec²? (d) From $t = 0$ to $t = 2$ sec the elevator moves upward at 10 m/sec. Its velocity is then reduced uniformly to zero in the next 2 sec so that it is at rest at $t = 4$ sec. Describe the reading on the balance during the time $t = 0$ to $t = 4$ sec.

16. A man holding a 10-kg mass on a cord made to withstand 150 N steps into an elevator. When the elevator starts up, the line breaks. What was the minimum acceleration of the elevator?

17. A 2-kg mass rests on a smooth wedge which has an inclination of 60° (Figure 5-37), and an acceleration a to the right such that the mass remains stationary relative to the wedge. Find a. What would happen if the wedge were given a greater acceleration?

Figure 5-37
A 2-kg mass resting on a smooth wedge which is accelerating so that the mass does not move relative to the wedge (Exercise 17).

Figure 5-36
A 2-kg mass hanging from a spring balance in an elevator (Exercise 15).

Elevator

18. In a tug of war, two boys pull on a rope, each trying to pull the other over a line midway between their original positions. According to Newton's third law, the forces exerted by each boy on the other (transmitted by the rope) are equal and opposite. Draw a diagram to show how it is possible for one boy to win despite Newton's third law.

Section 5-2, Circular Motion

19. A 3-lb stone attached to a string is whirled in a horizontal circle of radius 2 ft (as in Figure 5-14). The string makes an angle $\theta = 30°$ with the vertical. (a) Find the magnitude and direction of the resultant force on the stone. (b) What is the tension in the string? (c) What is the speed of the stone?

20. A model airplane of mass 500 gm flies in a circle of radius 6 m attached to a horizontal string. The plane makes 1 rev every 4 sec. What is the tension in the string? (Assume that the only inward force on the plane is the tension in the string.)

21. A 12-in-diameter record rotates at 33.3 rev/min on a turntable. A penny of mass 3 gm rests on the outer edge of the record. What is the frictional force on the penny if it does not slide? By what factor must this force increase if the rotation of the record is increased to 45 rev/min?

22. A 2000-lb car rounds an unbanked curve which has a radius of curvature of 100 ft. The maximum frictional force the road can exert on the car is 800 lb. At what maximum speed (in miles per hour) can the car travel around the curve without skidding?

23. A curve of radius 100 ft is banked as shown in Figure 5-38 so that a car can round the curve at 30 mi/h even if the road is smooth and there is no friction. Show in a force diagram that a component of the normal force exerted by the road on the car can provide the centripetal force necessary if the angle θ is great enough. Find the banking angle θ for these conditions.

Figure 5-38
Car on banked road (Exercise 23).

24. A pail of water is swung in a vertical circle of radius 3 ft. What is the minimum speed at the top of the circle for the water to stay in the pail?

25. A pilot comes out of a vertical dive in a circular arc such that his upward acceleration is 9g. (a) If he weighs 175 lb, what is the magnitude of the force exerted by the airplane seat on him at the bottom of the arc? (b) If the speed of the plane is 200 mi/h, what is the radius of the circular arc?

26. A man stands on a scale at the equator, which rotates once a day in a circle of radius about 4000 mi. (a) By what fraction is the scale reading less than his true weight? (b) If the rotation of the earth were increased such that the scale reading were one-half his true weight, what would be the length of the day (in terms of our present hours)? (Assume that the earth maintains its present shape.)

Section 5-3, Buoyant Forces; Archimedes' Principle

27. A 1-kg piece of copper is submerged in water and suspended from a spring balance (Figure 5-39). The density of copper is 6 times that of water. (a) What force does the balance read? (b) The whole system is dropped out of the window. Describe the initial motion of the copper relative to the jar.

Figure 5-39
A 1-kg mass submerged in water and suspended by a spring balance (Exercise 27).

Water

28. It is sometimes said that only the tip of an iceberg shows and that 90 percent lies beneath the surface. (a) Find the density of ice if this is true. (b) What fraction of an ice cube is beneath the surface in a glass of water on the moon, where the acceleration of gravity is about one-sixth that on earth?

29. A piece of copper (density about 6 gm/cm^3) floats in mercury (density 13.6 gm/cm^3). What fraction of the copper is submerged?

30. The pressure on the surface of a lake is atmospheric pressure $P_a = 1.01 \times 10^5$ N/m². (a) At what depth is the pressure twice atmospheric pressure? (b) If the pressure at the top of a deep pool of mercury is P_a, at what depth is the pressure $2P_a$?

31. A balloon filled with helium floats in air in a car. A string tied to the balloon is held down by a weight resting on the car seat. The car makes a sharp right turn, throwing the passengers to the left (relative to the car). Which way does the balloon move relative to the car? Why?

32. A 10 by 10 ft raft is 4 in thick and made of wood with density 0.6 gm/cm³. How many 150-lb people can stand on the raft without getting their feet wet when the water is calm (1 ft³ of water weighs 62.4 lb)?

Section 5-4, Motion with a Retarding Force Proportional to the Speed

33. If the retarding force is written $F_r = -bv$, what are the dimensions and mks units of the constant b?

34. In Example 5-12 show that the critical time t_c is just the time it would take to reach the terminal velocity v_t if the acceleration were constant and equal to g. Interpret this result on the graph of v versus t (see Figure 5-22).

35. A sky diver can slow himself to a constant speed of 60 mi/h by adjusting his form. If the diver weighs 150 lb, what is the retarding force, and what is the value of the constant b?

36. List some examples of an object moving with terminal velocity.

Problems

1. Your car is stuck in a mudhole. You are alone, but you have a long, strong rope. Having studied physics, you tie the rope taut to a tree and pull on it sideways, as in Figure 5-40. Find the force exerted by the rope on the car when the angle θ is 3° and you are pulling with a force of 100 lb but the car does not move. How strong must the rope be if it takes a force of 150 lb at an angle of $\theta = 3°$ to move the car?

Figure 5-40
Problem 1.

2. A box of mass m_1 is pulled by a force **F** exerted at the end of a rope which has a much smaller mass m_2, as shown in Figure 5-41. The box slides along a smooth horizontal surface. (a) Find the acceleration of the rope and box. (b) Find the tension in the rope at the point where it is attached to the box. (c) The diagram in Figure 5-41 with the rope horizontal is not quite correct for this situation. Correct the diagram and state how this correction affects your solution.

Figure 5-41
Force **F** applied to rope attached to block on smooth table (Problem 2).

3. Two 100-kg boxes are dragged along a smooth surface with a constant acceleration of 1 m/sec². Each of the ropes used has a mass of 1 kg (Figure 5-42). Find the force **F** and the tensions in the ropes at points *A*, *B*, and *C*.

Figure 5-42
Problem 3.

Useful information about a situation can often be obtained by assuming a constant force even though it actually varies greatly with time. In this problem and the next problem, assume that the forces are constant.

4. A rifle bullet of mass 9 gm starts from rest and moves 0.6 m in the rifle barrel. The speed of the bullet as it leaves the barrel is 1200 m/sec. Assuming the force to be constant on the bullet while it is in the barrel, find (*a*) the average speed of the bullet in the barrel and the time it spends in the barrel and (*b*) the change in momentum of the bullet and the force exerted on the bullet.

5. A car traveling 60 mi/h comes to a sudden stop to avoid an accident. Fortunately the driver is wearing a seat belt. Using reasonable values for the mass of the driver and the time it takes to come to a stop, estimate the force (assumed constant) exerted on the driver by the seat belt.

6. Two boxes slide on smooth inclines, as shown in Figure 5-43. (*a*) Find the acceleration and the tension in the rope. (*b*) The two masses are replaced by two other masses m_1 and m_2 such that there is no acceleration. Find whatever information you can about the two masses.

Figure 5-43
Two boxes on inclines
(Problem 6).

7. (*a*) Find the mass *m* in Figure 5-44 such that there is no acceleration. (*b*) Find the mass *m* such that *m* has a downward acceleration of $\frac{1}{2}g$. (*c*) Find *m* such that it has an upward acceleration $\frac{1}{4}g$. (*d*) What is the maximum upward acceleration possible for any mass *m*?

Figure 5-44
Problem 7.

8. A 128-lb girl stands on a 32-lb aluminum platform to paint a house. A rope attached to the platform and passing over an overhead pulley allows the painter to raise herself and the platform (Figure 5-45). (a) To get started, she accelerates herself and the platform at a rate of 2 ft/sec². With what force must she pull on the rope? (b) After 1 sec she pulls so that she and the platform go up at a constant speed of 2 ft/sec. What force must she exert on the rope? (Ignore the mass of the rope.)

Figure 5-45
Painter on platform for
Problem 8.

9. In Figure 5-34 (a) find the acceleration a and the contact force F_c for general masses m_1 and m_2 and applied force F. (b) If $m_2 = nm_1$, show that $F_c = nF/(n + 1)$.

10. For Figure 5-35 find the maximum force F that can be exerted without any slipping of m_1 if the maximum frictional contact force between the masses is $\mu m_1 g$, where μ is a fraction less than 1.

11. In Figure 5-46 find the maximum mass m_3 such that m_1 will not slip on m_2 if the maximum frictional contact force between m_1 and m_2 is $\mu m_1 g$.

Figure 5-46
Problem 11.

12. The arrangement shown in Figure 5-33, called Atwood's machine, is used to measure the acceleration of gravity g by measuring the acceleration of the masses. (a) For general masses m_1 and m_2, find the acceleration a and the tension in the string T. Check your answers for the special cases $m_1 = m_2$ and for one mass much larger than the other. (b) The acceleration is measured by measuring the time t for the larger mass to fall a distance L from rest. Find an equation relating g to m_1, m_2, L, and t. (c) Show that if the time t changes by a small amount dt, there is a corresponding change in the acceleration a of

amount da, which is related to dt by $da/a = -2dt/t$. Show also that an error in the determination of a of the amount da results in an error dg in g related by $dg/g = da/a$. Find two masses m_1 and m_2 each less than 1 kg such that g can be measured to 5 percent with a watch that is accurate to 0.1 sec if $L = 3$ m. Assume that the only important uncertainty in the measurement is in the time of fall.

13. A constant force F is exerted on a smooth peg of mass m_1. Two masses m_2 and m_3 are connected to a string which goes around the peg as shown in Figure 5-47. Assuming that F is greater than $2T$, (a) find the acceleration of each of the masses and the tension in the string if $m_1 = m_2 = m_3$ and (b) the acceleration of each mass if $m_2 = m_1$ and $m_3 = 2m_1$.

Figure 5-47
Atwood's machine for
Problem 13.

14. A 120-lb girl weighs herself by standing on a scale mounted on a skate board which rolls down an incline (Figure 5-48). (The force exerted by the incline on the board is perpendicular to the incline.) What is the reading on the scale if $\theta = 30°$?

Figure 5-48
Girl on scale·mounted on
skate board rolling down incline (Problem 14).

15. A small block of mass m slides on a smooth circular track in a vertical circle of radius R as shown in Figure 5-49. (a) Show that the speed of the block cannot be constant. (b) If the speed of the block at the top of the track is v, find the force exerted on the block by the track and the resultant force on the block. (c) What is the minimum value of v for the block to stay on the track? If the speed is less than this value, describe the path of the block.

16. A mass m_1 is attached to a cord of length L_1, which is fixed at one end. The mass moves in a horizontal circle supported by a smooth table. A second mass m_2 is attached to the first by a cord of length L_2 and also moves in a circle, as

Figure 5-49
Small block sliding on circular
track (Problem 15).

shown in Figure 5-50. If the masses make f rev/sec, find the tension in each of the cords.

Figure 5-50
Two masses connected by a light cord moving in a horizontal circle (Problem 16).

17. A block of gold-aluminum alloy weighs 5 lb. When the block is submerged in water, it weighs 4 lb. How much gold is in the block? (The density of aluminum is 2.7 gm/cm³, and that of gold is 19.3 gm/cm³.)

18. When you weigh yourself in air, the scale reading is less than your weight because of the buoyant force of the air. Estimate the number of ounces you should add to correct for this.

19. A beaker which weighs 1 lb contains 2 lb of water and rests on a scale. A 2-lb block of aluminum (density 2.7 gm/cm³) suspended from a spring scale is submerged in the water. Find the readings of both scales (Figure 5-51).

Figure 5-51
Problem 19.

20. Consider a slab of air of area A and thickness dy, where y is the height of the air above the ground. Show that the difference dP in pressure between the bottom and top of the slab is related to dy by $dP = -\rho g\ dy$, where ρ is the density of air. This equation is equivalent to Equation 5-34 except that y is measured from the ground up (compared with measuring h from the top of a liquid down). However, the density of a gas is not independent of the pressure. For many gases, the density is proportional to the pressure $\rho = KP$, where K is a constant (assuming constant temperature). Show that P and y then obey the differential equation

$$\frac{dP}{P} = -Kg\ dy$$

Find the indefinite integral of both sides of the equation and show that the pressure can be written

$$P = e^{C}e^{-Kgy} = P_0 e^{-Kgy}$$

where C is the constant of integration and $P_0 = e^C$ is the pressure at $y = 0$.

21. (a) Show using the result of Problem 20 that the density of air varies with height y as $\rho = \rho_0 e^{-Kgy}$, where ρ_0 is the density at sea level $y = 0$. (b) Find the mass of a slab of air of area A and thickness dy at a height y above sea level. (c) Integrate your result to find the total mass of an air column of area A. Show that the total weight of the air column is P_0A, where P_0 is the pressure at sea level.

22. A rectangular dam 100 ft wide supports a body of water to a height of 80 ft. (a) Neglecting atmospheric pressure, find the total force due to water pressure acting on a thin strip of height dy located at depth y. (b) Integrate the result in part (a) to find the total horizontal force due to the water acting on the dam. Why is it reasonable to neglect atmospheric pressure?

23. A water tank near the earth's surface is accelerated upward at a constant rate of $5g$. (a) Find the "buoyant force" acting on a 1-kg element of the water in the tank. (b) How does this force compare with the weight of a piece of aluminum which has the same volume as 1 kg of water? Will aluminum float in this tank while the tank is accelerating up? Explain.

CHAPTER 6 Forces in Nature

All the different forces observed in nature can be explained in terms of four basic interactions occurring among elementary atomic particles:

1. Gravitational forces

2. Electromagnetic forces

3. Strong nuclear forces

4. Weak nuclear forces

Most of the everyday forces we observe between macroscopic objects, e.g., contact forces, friction, and the forces exerted by springs and strings, are complicated manifestations of the basic electromagnetic interaction. In this chapter we take a brief look at some of the characteristics of the basic interactions and some empirical descriptions of the common, everyday forces that result from them. We shall study the gravitational and electromagnetic interactions in more detail later.

6-1 Gravity

All particles exert upon each other a gravitational force of attraction. The magnitude of the gravitational force exerted by a particle of mass m_1 on another particle of mass m_2 a distance r_{12} away is given by Newton's law of gravitation:

$$F_{12} = \frac{Gm_1m_2}{r_{12}^2}$$

Law of gravity

where G is a universal constant which has been determined experimentally. The direction of the force on m_2 is toward m_1. We can write this force in vector notation by defining a unit vector $\hat{r}_{12}$. If $\mathbf{r}_{12}$ is the

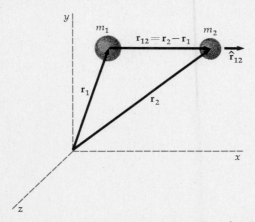

Figure 6-1
Definition of the unit vector,
$\hat{\mathbf{r}}_{12}$; $\hat{\mathbf{r}}_{12}$ is 1 unit in length and
has the direction of $\mathbf{r}_{12} =$
$\mathbf{r}_2 - \mathbf{r}_1$.

vector displacement from m_1 to m_2, the unit vector $\hat{\mathbf{r}}_{12}$ (see Figure 6-1)
is defined to be

$$\hat{\mathbf{r}}_{12} = \frac{\mathbf{r}_{12}}{r_{12}} \qquad\qquad 6\text{-}1$$

In terms of this unit vector, Newton's law of gravitation is written

$$\mathbf{F}_{12} = -\frac{Gm_1m_2}{r_{12}{}^2}\,\hat{\mathbf{r}}_{12} \qquad\qquad 6\text{-}2$$

The minus sign in Equation 6-2 indicates that the force is an attractive
force acting toward m_1. The force is inversely proportional to the
square of the distance between the attracting particles and therefore
decreases rapidly as they are separated. The force is proportional to
the mass of each particle. For this reason, the attraction of a very large
object like the earth is noticeable (as weight) even though the value of
G is so small that the gravitational attractions between everyday objects are too small to be observed except with great difficulty.

We can apply Equation 6-2 to calculate the force exerted *on m_1 by m_2*
by interchanging the subscripts 1 and 2. The result obtained has the
same magnitude as the force exerted on m_2 by m_1 but is in the op-
posite direction. (The unit vector $\hat{\mathbf{r}}_{21}$ is the negative of $\hat{\mathbf{r}}_{12}$.) Thus
Newton's law of gravitation meets the requirements of Newton's third
law.

The inverse-square nature of the gravitational force was suspected
by Hooke and others during Newton's time. Using his laws of motion
and Kepler's laws, the empirical laws describing planetary motion,
Newton deduced the full law. As a check on its validity Newton compared the acceleration of the moon in its orbit with the acceleration of
objects near the surface of the earth (such as the legendary apple),
assuming that both accelerations are due to the same cause, the gravitational attraction of the earth. Let us consider this calculation in some
detail.

Assuming moon and earth to be approximately point masses, the
force exerted by the earth on the moon has the magnitude $GM_Em_m/r_m{}^2$,
where M_E and m_m are the masses of the earth and moon, respectively,
and $r_m = 2.39 \times 10^5$ mi $= 3.84 \times 10^8$ m is the distance from the center
of the earth to the center of the moon. The direction of this force is
toward the center of the earth. The acceleration of the moon, according
to Newton's second law of motion, is

$$a_m = \frac{F}{m_m} = \frac{GM_E}{r_m{}^2} \qquad \text{toward center of earth} \qquad 6\text{-}3$$

Treating the earth and moon as point masses is a reasonable approximation because the distance between them is great compared with their sizes. However, the situation is different for the earth and a body near its surface. After a considerable effort, Newton was able to prove that if his law of gravity is correct, the force the whole earth exerts on a body on or outside its surface is the same as if all the earth's mass were concentrated at its center. The proof involves integral calculus, a tool developed by Newton for this problem, among others. We shall assume the result for now and consider the proof later. The force on a body of mass m near the surface of the earth is then directed toward the center of the earth and has magnitude

$$F = \frac{GM_E m}{R_E^2}$$

where R_E is the radius of the earth. The acceleration of gravity g (in an inertial reference frame) is then

$$g = \frac{F}{m} = \frac{GM_E}{R_E^2} \qquad\qquad 6\text{-}4$$

According to Equations 6-3 and 6-4, if both g and the acceleration of the moon are due to the earth's gravitational attraction, their ratio is just the ratio of the squares of the distance to the moon and the radius of the earth. Dividing Equation 6-4 by Equation 6-3, we obtain

$$\frac{g}{a_m} = \frac{GM_E/R_E^2}{GM_E/r_m^2} = \frac{r_m^2}{R_E^2} = \frac{(3.84 \times 10^8 \text{ m})^2}{(6.38 \times 10^6 \text{ m})^2} = 3.62 \times 10^3 \qquad 6\text{-}5$$

where we have taken $R_E = 6.38 \times 10^6$ m for the radius of the earth.[1] The centripetal acceleration of the moon is easily computed from its period $T = 27.3$ d $= 2.36 \times 10^6$ sec and the radius of its orbit r_m. Since it goes a distance $2\pi r_m$ in time T, its speed is $v = 2\pi r_m/T$ and its acceleration is

$$a_m = \frac{v^2}{r_m} = \frac{(2\pi r_m/T)^2}{r_m} = \frac{4\pi^2 r_m}{T^2}$$

$$= \frac{4\pi^2(3.84 \times 10^8 \text{ m})}{(2.36 \times 10^6 \text{ sec})^2} = 2.72 \times 10^{-3} \text{ m/sec}^2$$

Taking 9.81 m/sec² for g at the equator, we obtain for the ratio of g and the acceleration of the moon

$$\frac{g}{a_m} = \frac{9.81}{2.72 \times 10^{-3}} = 3.61 \times 10^3$$

We see that g/a_m is indeed very nearly equal to r_m^2/R_E^2.

The constant G, called the *universal gravitational constant*, can be determined from either Equation 6-4 or 6-5 if the mass of the earth is known. Newton estimated the value of G from an estimate of the earth's density. The constant was first determined accurately by Cavendish in 1798 by directly measuring the force between two small spheres of known mass and separation. (Details of this measurement are given in Chapter 16.) The value of G is

$$G = 6.67 \times 10^{-11} \text{ N-m}^2/\text{kg}^2 \qquad\qquad 6\text{-}6$$

---

[1] The earth is not quite spherical. The radius 6.38×10^6 m is the distance from the center of the earth to the equator. The corresponding distance at the poles is 6.36×10^6 m. The radius of the sphere of volume equal to that of the earth, 6.37×10^6 m, is often taken as the average radius of the earth.

We can use this value to compute the gravitational attraction between two ordinary objects.

Example 6-1 What is the force of attraction between two balls each of mass 1 kg when their centers are 10 cm apart?

We can treat spheres as if the total mass were at a point at the center. The force exerted on either one by the other is then

$$F = \frac{(6.67 \times 10^{-11})(1)(1)}{(10^{-1})^2} = 6.67 \times 10^{-9} \text{ N}$$

This example demonstrates that the gravitational force exerted by one object of ordinary size on another such object is extremely small. For example, the weight of a 1-gm mass is 9.8×10^{-3} N, more than a million times the force computed in Example 6-1. We can usually neglect the gravitational force between two objects compared with other forces acting on them. The gravitational attraction can be noticed only if the objects are extremely massive, e.g., mountains, or if extreme care is taken to eliminate all other forces on the objects, as in the Cavendish experiment to measure G.

According to Equation 6-2, the weight of an object (and hence its free-fall acceleration) decreases as the object's distance from the center of the earth increases. Consider an object at a height h above the surface of the earth. The distance between the object and the center of the earth is then

$$r = R_E + h$$

and the free-fall acceleration of the object is

$$g(r) = \frac{F}{m} = \frac{GM_E}{r^2} = \frac{GM_E}{(R_E + h)^2} \qquad \text{6-7}$$

If h is small compared with the radius of the earth, we can obtain a useful approximation for this acceleration using the binomial expansion (Equations 1-15 and 1-16). We have

$$(R_E + h)^{-2} = R_E^{-2}\left(1 + \frac{h}{R_E}\right)^{-2} = R_E^{-2}\left(1 - 2\frac{h}{R_E} + \cdots\right)$$

Then

$$g(r) \approx \frac{GM_E}{R_E^2}\left(1 - 2\frac{h}{R_E}\right) = g\left(1 - 2\frac{h}{R_E}\right) \qquad \text{6-8}$$

where $g = GM_E/R_E^2 = 9.8$ m/sec² is the acceleration at the surface of the earth. The change in the acceleration of gravity for a given change h in the distance from the center of the earth is thus approximately

Variation of g with altitude

$$\Delta g = g(r) - g = -2g\frac{h}{R_E}$$

(The minus sign indicates that g decreases as r increases.) If h is only a few miles or less, we can usually neglect the variation in g since R_E is about 4000 mi. For larger heights with h still much less than R_E, we have the useful approximation for the fractional decrease in $g(r)$:

$$\frac{\Delta g}{g} \approx -2\frac{h}{R_E} \qquad \text{6-9}$$

Equation 6-9, found by using the binomial expansion, can also be obtained by using the differential dg to approximate Δg. The rate of change of $g(r)$ with respect to r is

$$\frac{dg}{dr} = \frac{d}{dr}(GM_E r^{-2}) = -2GM_E r^{-3} = \frac{-2}{r}\frac{GM_E}{r^2} = \frac{-2g}{r}$$

Thus when r changes by a small amount dr, the change in g is approximately dg, given by

$$dg = -2g\frac{dr}{r}$$

and the fractional change is

$$\frac{dg}{g} = -2\frac{dr}{r} \qquad\qquad 6\text{-}10$$

Equations 6-9 and 6-10 are the same except for the symbols. The fractional change in $g(r)$ is just twice the fractional change in distance if this change is small.

Example 6-2 What is the acceleration of a satellite in a circular orbit 100 mi above the earth's surface?

Taking 4000 mi for the earth's radius gives a fractional change in r of about

$$\frac{dr}{r} = \frac{h}{R_E} = \frac{100\text{ mi}}{4000\text{ mi}} = \frac{1}{40} = 2\tfrac{1}{2}\%$$

Then

$$\frac{dg}{g} = -2\frac{h}{R_E} = -5\%$$

$$dg = -(5\%)g = -\tfrac{5}{100}(9.8\text{ m/sec}^2) = -0.49\text{ m/sec}^2$$

$$g(r) \approx 9.8\text{ m/sec}^2 - 0.49\text{ m/sec}^2 = 9.3\text{ m/sec}^2$$

Questions

1. The greater the mass of an object the greater the force of gravity acting on it. Why, then, does a heavy body fall no faster than a light one? Why in some cases, e.g., a brick and a paper box of the same shape, does the heavy one fall faster?

2. An astronaut moves from the earth toward the moon. Describe qualitatively how his weight changes during the trip. Describe how his mass changes.

6-2   Electromagnetic Forces

Forces exerted by one particle on another because of the electric charges of the particles are called *electromagnetic forces*. Their description is considerably more complicated than that of the gravitational force. For one thing, the electromagnetic force can be either attractive or repulsive whereas the gravitational force is always attractive. A more serious complication arises because when charges are in motion, part of the electromagnetic force, the magnetic force, depends on both the magnitudes and directions of the velocities of the particles and is not generally along the line joining them. We avoid this complication

Bruce Roberts/Rapho Guillumette

A lightning discharge is a spectacular effect resulting from electromagnetic forces.

here by postponing any discussion of magnetism until Chapter 36. In our present brief survey of forces, we shall consider only the electrostatic force, i.e., the force between electric charges at rest.

There are several important properties of electric charge:

1. There are two kinds of electric charge. Like charges repel each other; unlike charges attract each other. The two kinds are labeled positive and negative, following the suggestion of Benjamin Franklin.

2. Charge is quantized. An electric charge always has the magnitude Ne, where N is an integer and e is a fundamental unit of charge equal in magnitude to the charge of an electron or a proton. All known elementary particles have a charge of $+e$, $-e$, or zero.

3. Charge is conserved. In certain nuclear reactions it is possible to create electrons and other particles. Whenever a particle with charge $-e$ (an electron) is created, a particle with charge $+e$ is created simultaneously or another particle with charge $-e$ is destroyed. The algebraic sum of the charges in an isolated system does not change.

A more detailed discussion of electric forces and charge is postponed until Chapter 29. The law which gives the electrostatic force between two point charges, *Coulomb's law*, is an empirical inverse-square law similar to Newton's law of gravitation. If there are two point charges q_1 and q_2 separated by a distance r_{12}, the force exerted on charge q_2 by charge q_1 is given by

$$\mathbf{F}_{12} = k \frac{q_1 q_2}{r_{12}{}^2} \hat{\mathbf{r}}_{12} \qquad \qquad 6\text{-}11$$

Coulomb's law of electric force

where $\hat{\mathbf{r}}_{12}$ is a unit vector pointing from q_1 to q_2 and k is a constant, known as the coulomb constant. In the international system of units, the unit of charge is the coulomb (C), which is the amount of charge flowing past a point in a wire in one second when the current in the wire is one ampere. The unit of current, the ampere (A), defined in terms of magnetic-force measurement (Chapter 37), is the practical unit of current used in everyday electrical work.

The fact that like charges repel and unlike charges attract is included in Equation 6-11. If both charges have the same sign, the product $q_1 q_2$ is positive and the force on q_2 is directed away from q_1 parallel to $\hat{\mathbf{r}}_{12}$. If the charges have opposite signs, the product $q_1 q_2$ is negative and the force on q_2 is toward q_1 antiparallel to $\hat{\mathbf{r}}_{12}$. The value of k is

$$k = 8.99 \times 10^9 \text{ N-m}^2/\text{C}^2 \approx 9 \times 10^9 \text{ N-m}^2/\text{C}^2 \qquad 6\text{-}12$$

The fundamental unit of charge is

$$e = 1.602 \times 10^{-19} \text{ C} \qquad 6\text{-}13$$

It takes a large number of electrons or protons to produce a charge with a magnitude of 1 C.

Since atoms normally contain an equal number of positively charged protons and negatively charged electrons (and no other charged particles), atoms are electrically neutral, i.e., have no net electric charge. An atom can sometimes lose one of its electrons or gain an additional electron to become a charged particle called an *ion*. Macroscopic objects usually contain a large number of neutral atoms and are therefore electrically neutral. Electrons, however, can often be transferred from one macroscopic object to another, leaving one with an excess positive charge and the other with an excess negative charge. For example, when a glass rod is rubbed with a silk cloth, electrons are transferred from the rod to the cloth. With no knowledge of the process of transfer of charge, Franklin arbitrarily labeled the charge of the glass rod positive and that of the cloth negative. It is for this reason that the electron charge is now taken to be negative and the proton charge positive rather than the other way around. Excess charges of the order of several microcoulombs can be obtained by putting certain objects in intimate contact, often by simply rubbing the surfaces together. Such charges produce relatively large forces, as we shall see in Example 6-3.

Example 6-3 What is the force between two point charges of 1 μC separated by a distance of 1.0 cm?

From Coulomb's law, the magnitude of the force is

$$F = \frac{(9 \times 10^9 \text{ N-m}^2/\text{C}^2)(10^{-6} \text{ C})(10^{-6} \text{ C})}{(10^{-2} \text{ m})^2} = 90 \text{ N} \approx 20 \text{ lb}$$

In metals, some electrons are so weakly attached to their atoms that they are essentially free to move about the whole volume of the metal. Such materials are called *electric conductors.* For example, in copper, about one electron per atom is free. In other materials, e.g., wood or glass, the electrons are tightly bound (by electric forces) to their molecules. These materials are called *insulators.* Even though the electrons in insulators do not leave their molecules, the presence of an external charged object will cause a slight separation of the positive and negative charge in the nearby molecules. For example, suppose that a balloon charged by rubbing against a piece of cloth acquires an excess of electrons and is thus negatively charged. When the balloon is held near an insulating wall, the negative charge in the molecules near the surface of the wall is repelled and the positive charge attracted, causing the slight separation illustrated schematically in Figure 6-2.

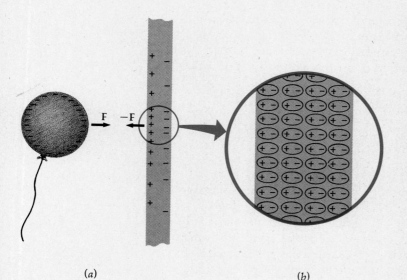

(a)   (b)

Figure 6-2
(*a*) The negative charge on the balloon attracts an excess of positive charge to the surface of the wall. The result is an attractive force between the balloon and the wall, even though the total charge of the wall is neutral. (*b*) An enlargement of the circled section of the wall from (*a*) showing schematically how the molecular charges in the wall are polarized by the proximity of the negatively charged balloon.

The molecules in the insulator are said to be *polarized*. Since the positive charge of these molecules is slightly closer to the negatively charged balloon than the negative charge, the balloon is attracted to the wall. It should be clear that if the balloon were positively charged, it would polarize the atoms in the wall in the opposite sense and again be attracted to the wall. Thus both positively and negatively charged objects are attracted by neutral insulators. In the same way, electrically charged objects attract small neutral objects, the most familiar example being small bits of paper or wood shavings attracted to a comb charged by running it through the hair. When the bits of paper touch the comb, they sometimes acquire some of its excess charge, and then fly off due to the repulsion of like charges.

Because both the electrostatic force and the gravitational force between two particles vary inversely with the square of the separation, the ratio of these forces is independent of the separation of the particles. We can thus compare the relative strengths of these forces for elementary particles, such as two protons, two electrons, or an electron and a proton. Consider the case of two protons. The mass of a proton is 1.67×10^{-27} kg, and its charge is 1.6×10^{-19} C. The ratio of the electrostatic force to the gravitational force between two protons at any separation is

$$\frac{F_e}{F_g} = \frac{kq_1q_2}{Gm_1m_2} = \frac{(9 \times 10^9)(1.6 \times 10^{-19})^2}{(6.67 \times 10^{-11})(1.67 \times 10^{-27})^2} \approx 10^{36} \qquad 6\text{-}14$$

Since electrons have a mass about $\frac{1}{1836}$ times that of protons, the ratio for two electrons is even greater.

The gravitational force between two elementary particles is so much smaller than the electrostatic force that it can be neglected in describing their interaction. It is only because such large masses as the earth contain almost exactly equal numbers of positive and negative charges that the gravitational force is important at all. If the positive and negative charges in bodies did not almost exactly cancel each other, the electric forces between them would be much greater than the gravitational attraction.

Questions

3. How can you tell whether the force acting on a body is gravitational or electric?

4. If all atoms are made up of electrically charged particles, and if electric forces are so much stronger than gravitational forces, why are we so aware of gravity in everyday life and so unfamiliar with electric forces?

5. A charged balloon is also attracted to an uncharged conductor regardless of the charge on the balloon. Explain.

6-3 Nuclear Forces

Besides the gravitational and electromagnetic forces the two other basic forces are the strong nuclear force and the weak nuclear force. It is clear from the stability of atomic nuclei that there must be some strong attractive forces besides electromagnetic and gravitational forces. Consider, for example, the helium nucleus, ^{4}He, which consists of two neutrons and two protons, a total of four particles contained in a volume with a radius of about 10^{-15} m. The repulsive electric force between protons this close together is quite large, and we have seen that by comparison the attractive gravitational force is negligible. Yet ^{4}He is very stable. The force which binds the neutrons and protons together in a nucleus is called the strong nuclear force. It acts between two protons, two neutrons, or a proton and neutron but only if the particles are very close together. When two nucleons[1] are within about 10^{-15} m of each other, the strong nuclear attractive force is about 10 times stronger than the repulsive electric force of two protons at this separation. However, this nuclear force has a short range; i.e., its strength decreases very rapidly with separation, much more rapidly than the inverse-square decrease in the electric force. At a separation greater than about 1.5×10^{-14} m the nuclear force is much less than the electric force and can be neglected.

Thus there is no macroscopic experiment which can be performed to investigate the properties of this force. Instead, information is obtained by bombarding neutrons, protons, and nuclei with neutrons, protons, and other particles and observing the results. Such *scattering experiments* have yielded much information about the nuclear force but have not produced a unique or simple formula like Coulomb's law or Newton's law of gravitation. Some of the known characteristics of the strong nuclear force are:

1. Charge independence: the nuclear force between two neutrons is the same as between two protons or between a neutron and a proton.

Characteristics of the strong nuclear force

2. Saturation: in a nucleus containing many nucleons, each nucleon bonds to only a few of the other nucleons. Thus the force needed to tear a neutron from a nucleus is approximately the same whether the nucleus contains five or six nucleons or one hundred nucleons.

3. Short range: at a distance of about 10^{-15} m, the strong nuclear force is attractive and about 10 times the electric force between two protons. The force decreases rapidly with increasing distance, becoming completely negligible at about 15 times this separation.

4. Repulsive at very short range: since at distances of about 0.4×10^{-15} m the nuclear force is repulsive, nuclei do not collapse.

A large class of particles, called *hadrons,* interact with one another via the strong nuclear force. Hadrons include *mesons* of many types and *baryons,* which in turn include nucleons and other particles. Particles in a much smaller class, the *leptons,* do not participate in the strong nuclear force at all. Leptons include electrons, positrons, muons, and neutrinos.

The *weak nuclear force* acts between all leptons and hadrons. It is also a short-range force. Its effect is to produce a degree of instability in nuclei and elementary particles. It is responsible for the type of radioactivity known as *beta decay,* and it explains, for example, why ^{12}C, a carbon nucleus with six protons and six neutrons, is stable while ^{11}C, a carbon nucleus with six protons and five neutrons, is not.

---

[1] A nucleon is either a proton or a neutron.

6-4   Molecular Forces

The forces which bind two or more atoms together to make a molecule are electromagnetic in origin, but the details of this bonding are extremely complicated. Consider one of the simpler cases, the NaCl molecule. When neutral sodium and chlorine atoms come close to each other, the sodium atom has a tendency to give up one of its electrons to the chlorine atom because of the structure of these atoms. We then have two ions, Na^+ with a net charge of $+e$ and Cl^- with a net charge of $-e$. These ions attract each other (much like point charges), but at a certain separation the force of attraction becomes zero, and at smaller separations the ions repel each other. This repulsion is a complicated phenomenon which cannot be understood even approximately in terms of classical mechanics or electromagnetism but only in terms of quantum mechanics.[1] We can, however, give a qualitative sketch of the force between the ions as a function of separation, as in Figure 6-3, where repulsive forces are indicated as positive and attractive forces as negative. At the distance $r = r_0$ in this figure, the force is zero. This is called the *equilibrium separation* for the atoms, and for NaCl it is of the order of 10^{-10} m, the same order as the distance from the center of the atom to its outermost electrons. For small displacements from equilibrium (between points A and B in the figure) the force curve is linear

Figure 6-3
Force exerted by one ion on another as a function of separation r. At $r = r_0$ the force is zero. At greater separation the force is negative, indicating attraction. At separation less than r_0 the force is positive, indicating repulsion. In the range from A to B near the equilibrium separation r_0 the curve $F(r)$ versus r is approximately linear, similar to that for a spring (see Figure 6-5).

and resembles the force exerted by a spring when compressed or extended (see Figure 6-5). In its solid state, NaCl exists in a regular array of Na^+ and Cl^- ions, each ion bound by ions of the other type into a lattice, as illustrated in Figure 6-4. Such a structure, called a *crystal*, is quite rigid. When we try to deform the solid by pushing or pulling on it, in an effort to change the separation distances between the ions, the strong forces between the ions resist compression or extension.

A more common type of molecular bonding, called *covalent bonding*, occurs, for example, between two hydrogen atoms in the H_2 molecule, between the carbon and oxygen atoms in CO, or between two carbon atoms in many organic compounds. In this type of bonding, the atoms do not give up or accept electrons to form ions; instead, some of the outer atomic electrons are shared by the atoms. In covalent bonding,

[1] Early in this century it became clear that newtonian mechanics is inadequate for treating the motions of particles within atoms. By 1926 a new and more general theory of mechanics, known as *quantum mechanics,* was developed which successfully describes the details of subatomic motions. Quantum mechanics applied on a macroscopic scale reduces to newtonian mechanics.

Figure 6-4
Arrangement of Na$^+$ and Cl$^-$
ions in an NaCl crystal.

both the attraction and the repulsion of the atoms are complicated quantum-mechanical phenomena. As with ionic bonding, the force-versus-separation curve looks like Figure 6-3.

There are other kinds of molecular bonds, e.g., metallic bonds, responsible, say, for the bonding of copper atoms in a solid piece of copper. In general, all forces between atoms and molecules are complex manifestations of the basic electromagnetic interaction, the details of which can be understood only within the framework of quantum mechanics. Nevertheless, we can often find empirical descriptions of these forces which are quite useful in determining the motion of macroscopic objects. At this level we must be content with such empirical descriptions.

6-5   Springs and Strings

A coil spring is made by winding a piece of stiff wire into a helix. If a spring is compressed or extended and released, it returns to its original, or natural, length provided the displacement is not too great. There is a limit to such displacements, beyond which the spring does not return to its original length but remains permanently deformed. If we allow only displacements below this limit, we can calibrate the extension or compression Δx in terms of the force needed to produce this extension or compression, as outlined in the beginning of Chapter 4. A typical calibration curve is shown in Figure 6-5. The sudden change in the slope of this curve at large compressions is at the point where the coils are completely collapsed so that adjacent turns are touching. Beyond this point it takes a very large force to produce any noticeable compression. We see from this curve that for small Δx the force exerted by the spring is approximately proportional to Δx. This result, known as *Hooke's law,* can be written

$$F_x = -k(x - x_0) = -k\,\Delta x \qquad\qquad 6\text{-}15$$

Hooke's law

where the empirically determined constant k is called the *force constant* of the spring. It is equal to the negative of the slope of the straight-line portion of the curve in Figure 6-5. The distance x is the coordinate of the free end of the spring or of any object attached to that end of the

Figure 6-5
The force F_x exerted by the spring plotted versus the length x of the spring. x_0 is the natural or unextended length. The change in length is $\Delta x = x - x_0$, and $F_x \approx -k\,\Delta x$ in the linear portion of the curve near $x = x_0$. For compression, Δx is negative and F_x is positive (to the right); for extension, Δx is positive and F_x is negative (to the left).

spring. The constant x_0 is the value of this coordinate when the spring is unstretched from its equilibrium position.

If we attach our spring to a mass m on a smooth table, as in Figure 6-6, and extend the spring, there will be a resultant force on the mass to the left whether Equation 6-15 holds for this extension or not. If we release the mass from rest, it will accelerate to the left until $x = x_0$, when the spring has its natural length. At this point the force, and therefore the acceleration, is zero, but the mass is moving to the left and therefore continues. The spring then becomes compressed and exerts a force on the mass to the right tending to reduce its speed. Eventually the speed reaches zero at some point $x < x_0$, and the resultant force in the positive x direction now causes the speed to increase in the positive direction. The mass again overshoots the equilibrium position $x = x_0$, this time going to the right, and comes momentarily to rest at its original position. The motion then repeats. The mass oscillates back and forth.

The curve in Figure 6-5 is similar to the one we sketched for the force between two atoms in a molecule (Figure 6-4). It is often useful to visualize the atoms in a molecule as being connected by springs. For example, if we slightly increased the separation of the atoms in the molecule and released them, we would expect the atoms to oscillate back and forth as if they were two masses connected by a spring.

If we pull on a flexible string, the string stretches slightly and pulls back with an equal but opposite force (unless the string breaks). We can think of a string as a spring with such a large force constant that the extension of the string is negligible. If the string is flexible, however, we cannot exert a force of compression on it. When we push on a string, it merely flexes or bends.

Figure 6-6
(a) A mass m on a smooth table subject to the force of a spring. (b) When the displacement is to the right (positive), the force is to the left (negative). When the displacement is to the left (negative), the force is to the right (positive). Hence, the mass oscillates about x_0.

(a)

(b)

6-6   Contact Forces and Friction

Consider a block resting on a horizontal table. The weight of the block pulls the block downward, pressing it against the table. Because the molecules in the table have a great resistance to compression, as discussed previously, the table exerts a force upward on the block perpendicular, or normal, to the surface with no noticeable compression of the table. (Careful measurement would show that the supporting surface always does bend slightly in response to a load.) Similarly, the block exerts a downward force on the table.

Let us now exert a horizontal force on the block. The block does not move if the horizontal force is not too large. The table evidently exerts a horizontal force equal and opposite to the force we exert as long as the force is small enough. This force parallel to the surface of the table is called a *frictional force*. The block of course exerts an equal and opposite frictional force on the table, tending to drag it in the direction of the horizontal force we exert. This frictional force is due to the bonding of the molecules of the block and the table at the places where the surfaces are in very close contact.

We might expect the maximum force of friction to be proportional to the area of contact between the two surfaces. However, experimentally, to a good approximation it is independent of this area and simply proportional to the normal force exerted by one surface on the other. Figure 6-7, an enlarged picture of the contact between the block and the table, shows that the actual microscopic area of contact at which the molecules can bond together is just a small fraction of the macroscopic area. A possible model of static friction consistent with our intuition and with the empirical results is the following. The maximum force of friction *is* proportional to this microscopic area of contact, as expected, but this microscopic area is proportional to the total area and to the force per unit area exerted between the surfaces. Thus it does not depend on the total area of contact. Consider, for example, a 1-lb block with a side area of 30 in² and an end area of 10 in². When it is on its side on the table, a small fraction of the total 30 in² is actually in microscopic contact. When it is placed on end, the fraction of the

Figure 6-7
The microscopic area of contact between block and table. The microscopic contact is only a small fraction of the macroscopic area of the block. As the normal force on the block is increased, there is an approximately proportionate increase in the microscopic contact.

Leonardo da Vinci understood that the frictional force is independent of the macroscopic area of contact, as this drawing from one of his notebooks shows. (*Courtesy of the Deutsches Museum, Munich.*)

Average global winds for the two hemispheres and for the summer and winter half years are shown in Figure 2. This representation does not include average north-south winds, which are considerably smaller than the zonal winds (east-west) in middle latitudes. The jet stream is shown as a high-speed core at about 200 millibars and between latitudes 30 and 45 north or south.

In order to understand the horizontal pressure forces, we must discuss the vertical balance of the atmosphere. Since pressure decreases from about 1 atm at the surface to zero in space, there is a large upwardly directed pressure force which is approximately balanced by the large gravitational force.

Figure 3
Balance of forces on a horizontal atmospheric slab of unit area.

Consider the atmospheric slab shown in Figure 3 contained between the levels z and $z + dz$ (pressures p and $p - dp$). Since pressure is expressed as force per unit area, the upward force is dp. The downward force is mass $\rho\, dz$, where ρ is the density, multiplied by g. Since pressure must decrease as height increases, the balance of forces is expressed by

$$dp = -\rho g\; dz \qquad\qquad\qquad 1$$

But, according to the gas laws (Chapter 17),

$$p = \frac{k}{m}\,\rho T$$

where k is Boltzmann's constant, m the mass of a molecule of "air," and T the temperature in kelvins. If we eliminate ρ, we find

$$\frac{dp}{p} = -\frac{dz}{H} \qquad\qquad\qquad 2$$

where $H = kT/mg$ is the *scale height* of the atmosphere. For the earth's atmosphere at 288 K, the scale height is 8.4 km.

To clarify the issues, consider the idealized case of constant scale height. Equation 2 can then be integrated from the ground ($p = p_0$, $z = 0$) upward:

$$p = p_0 e^{-z/H} \qquad\qquad\qquad 3$$

The pressure at the surface p_0 is approximately the same over the globe. The pressure at a height z then depends mainly on a ratio z/H: the pressure will be high when H is large, i.e., when the temperature is high. Thus, in hot regions of the globe the pressure a few kilometers above the ground will exceed that in cooler regions. Since, on the average, the temperature decreases from equator to poles, at high altitudes there must be pressure forces directed from the equator toward the poles. At these altitudes, both hemispheres should behave like huge cyclones, and the geostrophic wind will be toward the east (Figure 1). We therefore anticipate a westerly wind circling the globe with its greatest intensity away from the ground, corresponding to the observations.

Review

A. List the four basic interactions.

B. Assign a letter to each basic interaction in your list in part A. After each term below, write the letter of the basic interaction (if any). If there is no associated basic interaction, explain.

1. Molecular forces
2. Centrifugal force
3. Coriolis force
4. Force holding the nucleus together
5. Beta decay

6. Friction
7. Force of a spring
8. Force holding a planet in orbit
9. Your weight

C. List three properties of electric charge.

D. List three properties of the strong nuclear force.

E. True or false:

1. The force of gravity is always attractive.

2. A proton and an electron have charges of equal magnitude.

3. Two protons always repel each other.

4. An example of the strong nuclear force is the force between the two oxygen nuclei in the O_2 molecule.

5. Contact forces and friction are related to molecular forces.

6. Pseudo forces appear only in accelerated reference frames.

Exercises

Unless instructed otherwise, use the approximate value $g = 32$ ft/sec² $= 9.8$ m/sec² for the acceleration of gravity in Exercises and Problems.

Section 6-1, Gravity

1. Using the values $G = 6.67 \times 10^{-11}$ N-m²/kg², $g = 9.8$ m/sec², and the radius of the earth $R_E = 6.37 \times 10^6$ m, calculate the mass of the earth.

2. From the known acceleration of the earth, calculate the mass of the sun.

3. Find the gravitational force which attracts a 140-lb boy to a 120-lb girl when they are 2 ft apart. (Assume that they are point masses.)

4. A particle is dropped from a height of 4000 mi above sea level. What is its initial acceleration?

5. Three 100-kg masses lie at the vertices of an equilateral triangle with 20-cm sides. Find the resultant gravitational force acting on one of the masses. (Indicate the direction of the force on your diagram.)

6. At what altitude above the earth's surface is the acceleration of gravity half its value at sea level?

7. Use Equation 6-9 to find the percentage decrease in the acceleration of gravity on top of a 14,000-ft mountain compared with that at sea level.

Section 6-2, Electromagnetic Forces

8. Two small spheres with charge of -1 μC each are 20 cm apart. (*a*) What is the minimum number of electrons on each sphere? (*b*) Find the magnitude of the electric force exerted by one sphere on the other.

9. Two small electrified objects separated by 5 cm attract each other with a force of 4 N. If their separation is increased to 7 cm, what force does one exert on the other?

10. Two small spheres each of mass $m = 10$ gm are suspended from a common point by threads of length $L = 50$ cm. When each carries a charge q, they come to equilibrium, each thread making an angle $\theta = 10°$ with the vertical, as shown in Figure 6-15. Find q.

11. Four equal charges $q = 5 \times 10^{-8}$ C are situated at the corners of a square of length $L = 4$ cm. Find the resultant electric force exerted on any one of the charges by the other three charges. (Indicate the direction of the force in your diagram.)

12. The most probable distance between the proton and the electron in the hydrogen atom is 0.53×10^{-10} m. Find the electric force of attraction between the electron and proton at this distance.

Figure 6-15
Exercise 10.

13. A penny has a mass of about 3 gm; 64 gm of copper contains Avogadro's number of atoms ($N_A = 6.02 \times 10^{23}$). Each copper atom contains 29 electrons. (*a*) Find the number of atoms, the number of electrons, and the total amount of negative charge in coulombs of the electrons in a penny. (*b*) How long would it take for this much charge to flow through a wire at a rate of 1 C/sec? (*c*) If 10 percent of the negative charge on one penny could be transferred to another penny, calculate the electrostatic force exerted by one penny on the other if they were separated by 20 cm. (Assume them to be point charges.)

Section 6-3, Nuclear Forces, and Section 6-4, Molecular Forces

14. Calculate the magnitude of the strong nuclear force between two protons separated by a distance of 10^{-15} m assuming that this force is 10 times the electric force between the protons. Compare this force with that between the electron and proton in the hydrogen atom.

15. The equilibrium separation of the Na^+ and Cl^- ions in NaCl is about 2.4×10^{-10} m. Find the electric force of attraction between the ions at this separation assuming that they are point charges. Compare your result with the results of Exercise 12 for atomic forces and those of Exercise 14 for nuclear forces.

Section 6-5, Springs and Strings

16. A spring has a force constant $k = 2.0$ N/cm. A 5-kg mass is suspended motionless from the spring. Find (*a*) the numerical values of all the forces acting on the mass and (*b*) the extension of the spring from its equilibrium position.

17. A 100-kg mass is pulled with acceleration 0.5 m/sec² along a smooth table by a cable. The cable stretches 0.3 cm. Assuming that the cable is a spring that obeys Hooke's law, find its force constant.

18. A 2-kg mass rests on a smooth incline of angle $\theta = 30°$ supported by a spring (Figure 6-16). The spring stretches 3 cm. (*a*) Find the force constant of the spring. (*b*) If the mass is pulled down the incline 3 cm from its equilibrium position and released, what will its initial acceleration be?

Figure 6-16
Exercise 18.

19. A mass m is attached to two springs along a line as shown in Figure 6-17. Each spring is stretched from its equilibrium position. The force constants of the springs are k_1 and k_2. (a) Find the ratio of the amount of stretching of the springs. (b) Show that if the mass is displaced a small distance x from equilibrium, the net restoring force is the same as if the mass were attached to a single spring of force constant $k = k_1 + k_2$.

Figure 6-17
Exercise 19.

Section 6-6, Contact Forces and Friction

20. The coefficient of friction between the tires of a car and the road is 0.5. (a) If the resultant force on the car is the frictional force, what is the acceleration of the car? (b) What is the least distance in which the car can stop if it is initially traveling at 88 ft/sec?

21. The force which accelerates a car along a flat road is the frictional force between the road and the car tires. (a) Explain why the acceleration is greater when the tires do not spin. (b) If a car is to accelerate from 0 to 60 mi/h in 12 sec at constant acceleration, what is the minimum coefficient of friction between the tires and the road?

22. The coefficient of static friction between a car's tires and the road is 0.6. What is the greatest speed with which the car can turn a corner of radius 200 ft if the road is flat and the car does not skid?

23. The coefficient of static friction between the floor of a truck and a box resting on it is 0.3. The truck is traveling at 50 mi/h. What is the least distance in which the truck can stop if the box is not to slide?

24. A chair slides across a polished floor. Its initial speed is 4 ft/sec. It comes to rest after sliding 4 ft. What is the coefficient of kinetic friction between the floor and the chair?

25. A 100-lb box must be moved across a level floor. The coefficient of static friction between the box and the floor is 0.6. One method is to push down on the box at an angle θ with the horizontal. Another method is to pull up on the box at an angle θ with the horizontal. (a) Explain why one method is better than the other. (b) Calculate the force necessary to move the box by each method if $\theta = 30°$ and compare these results with that for $\theta = 0°$.

26. The coefficient of friction between box A and the cart in Figure 6-18 is 0.6. The box has a mass of 2 kg. (a) Find the minimum acceleration a of the cart and box such that the box will not fall. (b) What is the magnitude of the frictional force in this case? (c) If the acceleration is greater than this minimum, will the frictional force be greater than in part (b)? Explain. (d) Show in general that for a box of any mass, the box will not fall if the acceleration is $a \geq g/\mu_s$, where μ_s is the coefficient of static friction.

Figure 6-18
Exercise 26.

Section 6-7, Pseudo Forces

In Exercises 27 to 31, the situations described take place in a box car which has initial velocity $\mathbf{v} = 0$ *but an acceleration* $\mathbf{a} = (5 \text{ m/sec}^2)\mathbf{i}$ *(Figure 6-19). Work the exercises in the frame of the box car using pseudo forces and in an inertial frame using only real forces. Assume* $g = 10 \text{ m/sec}^2$.

Figure 6-19
Box car initially at rest with acceleration 5 m/sec² to the right for Exercises 27 to 31.

27. A 2-kg object is slid along the smooth floor with initial velocity of (10 m/sec)$\mathbf{i}$. (*a*) Describe the motion of the object. (*b*) When does the object reach its original position relative to the box car?

28. A 2-kg object is slid along the smooth floor with initial transverse velocity of (10 m/sec)$\mathbf{k}$. Describe the motion.

29. A 2-kg object is slid along a rough floor (coefficient of sliding friction 0.3) with initial velocity (10 m/sec)$\mathbf{i}$. Describe the motion of the object. (Assume that the coefficient of static friction is greater than 0.5.)

30. A 2-kg object is suspended from the ceiling by a massless unstretchable string. (*a*) What angle does the string make with the vertical? (*b*) Indicate all the forces acting on the object in each frame.

31. A 6-kg mass is attached to the ceiling by a (massless) spring of unstretched length 0.5 m. The spring constant is 10 N/cm. By how much is the spring stretched?

Problems

1. Both the sun and the moon exert gravitational forces on the oceans of the earth, causing tides. (*a*) Show that the ratio of the force exerted by the sun to that exerted by the moon is $M_s R_m{}^2 / M_m R_s{}^2$, where M_s and M_m are the mass of the sun and moon and R_s and R_m are the distance from the earth to the sun and the moon. Evaluate this ratio using the values given in Appendix B. (*b*) Even though the sun exerts a much greater force on the ocean than the moon, the moon has a greater effect on the tides because it is the *change* in the force when the distance changes (due to rotation of the earth) that is important. Differentiate the expression $F = Gm_1 m_2 / r^2$ to calculate the change in F due to a small change in r. Show that $dF/F = -2\,dr/r$. (*c*) The largest change in distance due to rotation is twice the radius of the earth. Show that for a given small change in distance the change in the force exerted by the sun is related to the change in the force exerted by the moon by

$$\frac{\Delta F_s}{\Delta F_m} \approx \frac{M_s R_m{}^3}{M_m R_s{}^3}$$

and calculate this ratio.

2. Use Newton's law of gravitation along with the second law of motion to show that the period T of a planet moving in a circular orbit is related to the radius of the orbit by Kepler's law $T^2 = Cr^3$ and find the constant C.

3. Kepler's law $T^2 = Cr^3$ also applies to satellites in circular orbits around the earth. (*a*) Show that for this case, the constant C can be determined from the radius of the earth and the acceleration of gravity g without knowing the mass

of the earth or the constant G. (b) Calculate the period of a satellite orbiting near the surface of the earth. (c) Use your result in part (b) and Kepler's law to find the height above the earth for a satellite which appears to be stationary, i.e., which has a period of 24 h.

4. The planet Mars has a satellite orbiting at a distance $r = 9.4 \times 10^6$ m from the center of Mars with a period of 460 min. Use these data to calculate the mass of Mars.

5. A plumb bob near a large mountain is slightly deflected from the vertical by the gravitational attraction of the mountain. Estimate the order of magnitude of the angle of deflection using any assumptions you like. (Assuming the mountain to be a sphere of diameter equal to its height would allow the mountain to be treated as a point mass a distance r from the plumb bob.)

6. Show with a force diagram how a motorcycle can ride in a circle on a vertical wall. Assume reasonable parameters (coefficient of friction, radius of the circle, mass of the motorcycle, or whatever required) and calculate the minimum speed needed.

7. In Figure 6-20 the mass $m_2 = 10$ kg slides on a smooth table. The coefficients of static and kinetic friction between m_2 and the mass $m_1 = 5$ kg are $\mu_s = 0.6$ and $\mu_k = 0.4$. (a) What is the maximum acceleration of m_1? (b) What is the maximum value of the mass m_3 if m_1 moves with m_2 without slipping? (c) If $m_3 = 30$ kg, find the acceleration of each mass and the tension in the string.

Figure 6-20
There is no friction between m_2 and the table, but there is friction between m_1 and m_2 (Problem 7).

8. A 100-lb box rests on a horizontal table. The coefficient of static friction is 0.6. The box is pulled by a massless rope with a force $\mathbf{F}$ at an angle θ, as shown in Figure 6-21. The minimum value of the force needed to move the box depends on the angle θ. Discuss qualitatively how you would expect this force to depend on θ. Compute the force for the angles $\theta = 0$, 10, 20, 30, 40, 50, and $60°$ and make a plot of F versus θ. From your plot, at what angle is it most efficient to apply the force to move the box?

Figure 6-21
Box pulled along rough horizontal surface by force $\mathbf{F}$ making angle θ with horizontal (Problem 8).

9. A box of mass m rests on a horizontal table. The coefficient of friction is μ. A force $\mathbf{F}$ is applied at an angle θ, as in Figure 6-21. (a) Find the force F needed to move the box as a function of angle θ. (b) At the angle θ for which this force is minimum, the slope $dF/d\theta$ of the curve F versus θ is zero. Compute $dF/d\theta$ and show that this derivative is zero at the angle θ which obeys $\tan \theta = \mu$. Compare this general result with that obtained in Problem 8.

10. A mass m is attached to a spring of force constant k_1, which in turn is connected to a second spring of force constant k_2, as shown in Figure 6-22. When the springs are unstretched, the mass is at point x_0. Show that when the mass is at point x, the force on the mass is $F_x = -k(x - x_0)$, where k is related to k_1 and k_2 by $1/k = 1/k_1 + 1/k_2$.

Figure 6-22
Problem 10.

11. A block of metal of mass m and density ρ is submerged in water and suspended by a spring of force constant k in an elevator. The water not only provides a buoyant force but also damps out oscillations of the metal so that it quickly comes to rest at its equilibrium position. The elevator accelerates upward with acceleration a for a short time, moves up at constant speed for a time, and then decelerates again with magnitude a until it stops at the top floor. The length of the spring is x_0 when the elevator is at rest. Describe the equilibrium position of the block of metal during the various parts of the ascent in terms of the given variables.

12. A 10-kg mass is suspended from the middle of a spring of natural length 30 cm and force constant 100 N/cm (Figure 6-23). By how much does the spring sag?

Figure 6-23
Problem 12.

13. A student wishing to find the density of a block of wood submerges it in water and attaches a spring (of negligible volume) to the wood and to the bottom of the tank to hold the block under. He observes that the water rises 2 cm in his 20 by 40 cm tank and that his spring of force constant 4.9 N/cm stretches 1.6 cm. Find the density of the wood.

14. A 2-kg mass is attached to a spring having a natural length of 30 cm and a force constant of 2000 N/m. The mass rotates in a circle (supported by a smooth horizontal surface) at $v = 4$ m/sec (Figure 6-24). (a) Write an exact equation for the amount x that the spring stretches in terms of the mass m, the force constant k, the natural length x_0, and the speed v. (b) Solve this quadratic equation for x for the values given. (c) Show that if the change in the radius of the circle because of the stretching of the spring is neglected, the stretching is given approximately by $x = mv^2/kx_0$. Find x for the values given in this approximation, and compare your result with the exact value found in part (b). (d) A better approximate value can be found by correcting the radius of the circle using the first approximation for x. Compute $x = mv^2/k(x_0 + x_1)$, where x_1 is the value found in part (c), and compare your result with the exact value.

4 m/sec

2 kg

Figure 6-24
Problem 14.

15. A block is on an incline whose angle can be varied. The angle is gradually increased from 0°. At 30°, the block starts to slide down the incline. It slides 3 m in 2 sec. Calculate the coefficients of static and kinetic friction between the block and incline.

16. Atoms are electrically neutral because they contain an equal number of positively charged protons and negatively charged electrons and because the magnitudes of the electron charge and proton charge are exactly equal. Suppose that each atom contained an equal number Z of electrons and protons but that the charge of the electron were slightly greater in magnitude than that of the proton so that the atom has a net charge $-fZe$, where f is the fractional charge difference. Estimate the order of magnitude of the fractional difference in charge that would cause the electric repulsion between the earth and the sun to equal the gravitational attraction, so that there would be no net force exerted on the earth by the sun. [This is not as difficult as it may seem at first because the mass and charge of either body is just proportional to the number of atoms. Let the mass of a typical atom be $2Zm_p$, where m_p is the mass of the proton (Appendix B) and the factor 2 is used because of the equal number of neutrons with approximately equal mass. Then find f so that the electrical repulsion of the charges fZe equals the gravitational attraction of the masses for two such atoms.]

17. A 2-kg block sits on a 4-kg block which rests on a smooth table (Figure 6-25). The coefficient of friction (both static and kinetic) between the blocks is 0.2. A force **F** is applied to the 4-kg block as shown. (a) What is the maximum F that can be applied if the 2-kg block is not to slide on the 4-kg block? (b) If F is twice this maximum, find the acceleration of each block. (c) If F is half this maximum, find the acceleration of each block and the friction force acting on each block.

Figure 6-25
Problem 17.

18. A road is banked so that a car traveling 50 mi/h can round a curve of radius 100 ft even if the road is so icy that the coefficient of friction is approximately zero. Find the range of speeds at which a car can travel around this curve without skidding if the coefficient of friction between the road and the tires is 0.3.

19. In an amusement-park ride participants are held against the walls of a spinning cylinder as the floor falls away. If the radius of the cylinder is 10 ft, find the minimum number of revolutions per minute necessary if the coefficient of friction between a rider and the wall is 0.4.

20. A 4-kg mass rests on a 30° incline attached to a cord which passes over a smooth peg and is attached to a second mass m, as shown in Figure 6-26. The coefficient of static friction between the mass and the incline is 0.4. (a) Find the range of possible values of m such that the system will be in static equilibrium. (b) If $m = 1$ kg, the system will be in static equilibrium. What is the frictional force on the 4-kg mass in this case?

Figure 6-26
Problem 20.

21. A smooth platform rotates counterclockwise (as seen from above) with angular velocity ω. A small object of mass m rests on the platform at a distance r from the center. The object is at rest relative to an inertial frame. (The smooth platform rotates under the mass.) (a) Describe the motion of the object relative to the platform. What are the magnitude and direction of the resultant pseudo force acting on the mass in the frame of the platform? (b) Show that in this case the coriolis force has twice the magnitude of the centrifugal force and is oppositely directed.

22. A space station has two compartments, as shown in Figure 6-27. The station rotates at B rev/min. (a) A mass m rests on the floor of one of the compartments a distance r from the center of rotation as shown. What is the normal force exerted by the floor on the mass? (b) The mass is now dropped from the ceiling of the compartment. Describe its motion relative to the compartment. What forces (including pseudo forces) act on the mass while it is falling? (c) Explain qualitatively why the mass falls to the floor from the point of view of an inertial reference frame in which there are no forces acting on the mass.

Figure 6-27
Rotating space platform
(Problem 22).

CHAPTER 7   Work and Energy

In most of our illustrations applying the laws of motion, we chose situations in which the forces are constant in magnitude in order to simplify the analysis. For one-dimensional motion with a constant force, for example, the position and velocity functions are determined by the constant-acceleration formulas 2-11 and 2-12, once the acceleration is determined by applying Newton's second law. If the force on a particle is a known function of time $F(t)$, determining the velocity and position functions is not much more difficult. Since $dv/dt = a(t) = F(t)/m$, the velocity function can be found by direct integration. In most physical situations, however, the force is neither constant nor a known function of time. It is more common to know the force on a particle as a function of the particle's position. For example, both the law of gravitation and Coulomb's law give the force exerted by one particle on another as an inverse-square function of the separation of the particles. Thus in the planetary problem we know the force on the planet exerted by the sun as a function of the distance from the planet to the sun. This distance varies as the planet moves along its elliptical orbit, and the force varies in both magnitude and direction. Similarly, in the empirical description of complex forces, we often find the force on a particle given as a function of position, such as $F = -k(x - x_0)$ for the force on a body attached to a spring which obeys Hooke's law.

In this chapter, we develop general methods for the solution of problems in which the force depends on the position of the particle. In the process we introduce the concept of the *work* done by a force as the particle on which it acts moves from one place to another. We shall see that this concept is closely related to the concept of *energy*, which plays a central role in our lives and in the description of the physical universe. In succeeding chapters we shall investigate the concept of energy more fully and see how to apply the law of conservation of energy to various problems.

7-1 Work in One Dimension

We define the work done on a particle by a force F_x as the particle moves from x_1 to x_2 to be the area under the curve F_x versus x between x_1 and x_2. That is, the work done by the force F_x is

$$W = \int_{x_1}^{x_2} F_x \, dx = \text{area under } F_x\text{-versus-}x \text{ curve} \qquad 7\text{-}1$$

Definition of work in one dimension

This definition is equivalent to saying that the work dW done over a very short interval dx is

$$dW = F_x \, dx \qquad 7\text{-}1a$$

The work dW is positive if the motion is in the same direction as the force and negative if it is in the opposite direction. The total work done over a finite displacement, calculated using Equation 7-1, may be either positive or negative, depending on the direction of the force during that interval, i.e., predominantly with the motion or against it.

The dimensions of work are those of force times distance. In the international system, the unit of work is the *joule* (J):

$$1 \text{ J} = 1 \text{ N-m} = 1 \text{ kg-m}^2/\text{sec}^2 \qquad 7\text{-}2$$

The joule defined

where we have used the fact that $1 \text{ N} = 1 \text{ kg-m/sec}^2$. In the British engineering system the unit of work is the foot-pound. The relation between these units is easily found using the relations between pounds and newtons and between meters and feet:

$$1 \text{ J} = 0.738 \text{ ft-lb} \qquad 7\text{-}3$$

Example 7-1 A block resting on a smooth table (Figure 7-1*a*) is attached to a horizontal spring which obeys Hooke's law and exerts a force $F_x = -kx$, where x is measured from the equilibrium length of the spring and the force constant is $k = 400$ N/m. The spring is compressed to

Jane Latta/Photo Researchers

Work is being done by these horses because they exert a force through a distance as they pull the harrow. Despite the fact that the Amish farm boy shown in this photograph is working according to the everyday use of the word, he does very little work according to the scientific definition because he exerts little force on the harrow; rather he guides its direction by use of the reins.

(a)

(b)

Figure 7-1
(a) Mass on a spring for Example 7-1. The spring is compressed 5 cm from equilibrium and released. (b) F_x versus x for mass on spring. The work done by the spring as the mass moves from $x_1 = -5$ cm to $x_2 = 0$ is the shaded area.

$x_1 = -5$ cm. Find the work done by the spring as the block moves from $x_1 = -5$ cm to its equilibrium position $x_2 = 0$.

Figure 7-1b is a sketch of this force versus distance. The work done as the block moves from x_1 to x_2 is by definition equal to the area under this curve between these limits, as indicated in the figure. This area is one-half the base times the height of the triangle. The base is 5 cm = 0.05 m, and the height is the value of the force at x_1, which is $F_x = -(400 \text{ N/m})(-0.05 \text{ m}) = +20$ N. The work done is thus $W = \frac{1}{2}(0.05 \text{ m})(20 \text{ N}) = 0.500$ N-m = 0.500 J. This work is positive because the force is in the direction of motion. This is indicated in the figure by the fact that the area is above the x axis.

7-2   Work Done by the Resultant Force; Kinetic Energy

If several forces are acting on a particle, we can compute the work done by each from the definition in Equation 7-1. The total work done on the particle by all forces acting on it is just the algebraic sum of the work done by each of the individual forces. (Work is a scalar quantity.) This total work is just the work done by the resultant force. For example, if there are three forces F_{x1}, F_{x2}, F_{x3}, the total work done when the particle moves a small distance dx is

$$dW_{net} = F_{x1}\, dx + F_{x2}\, dx + F_{x3}\, dx = (F_{x1} + F_{x2} + F_{x3})\, dx$$
$$= \Sigma F_x\, dx \qquad\qquad\qquad 7\text{-}4$$

The net work done as the particle moves from point x_1 to x_2 is

$$W_{net} = \int_{x_1}^{x_2} \Sigma F_x\, dx \qquad\qquad\qquad 7\text{-}5$$

There is an important relation between the net work done on a particle and the speed of the particle at the original and final positions. This relation is obtained by using Newton's second law relating the resultant force to the acceleration of the particle $\Sigma F_x = ma$. We shall first consider the case in which the resultant force is constant and then show that the relation obtained is true for any force.

If the resultant force is constant, as in Figure 7-2, the area under the force-versus-x curve is just the force times the distance. The net work is thus

$$W_{net} = \int_{x_1}^{x_2} \Sigma F_x \, dx = \Sigma F_x (x_2 - x_1) = \Sigma F_x \, \Delta x = ma \, \Delta x \qquad \text{7-6}$$

Figure 7-2
Constant resultant force ΣF_x versus x. The work done as the particle moves from x_1 to x_2 is indicated by the shaded area $W = \Sigma F_x(x_2 - x_1)$

Since the acceleration is constant, we can relate the distance moved to the initial and final speeds by the constant-acceleration formula 2-13:

$$v_2^2 - v_1^2 = 2a \, \Delta x$$

Thus

$$W_{net} = ma \, \Delta x = \tfrac{1}{2}mv_2^2 - \tfrac{1}{2}mv_1^2 \qquad \text{7-7}$$

The quantity $\tfrac{1}{2}mv^2$, called the *kinetic energy E_k* of the particle, is a scalar quantity which depends on the particle's mass and speed. We can also write the kinetic energy in terms of the momentum of the particle, $p = mv$:

$$E_k = \tfrac{1}{2}mv^2 = \frac{(mv)^2}{2m} = \frac{p^2}{2m} \qquad \text{7-8}$$

Kinetic energy defined

The quantity on the right side of Equation 7-7 is the change in the kinetic energy of the particle, i.e., the kinetic energy $\tfrac{1}{2}mv_2^2$ at the end of the interval when the particle is at x_2 minus its kinetic energy $\tfrac{1}{2}mv_1^2$ at the beginning of the interval when the particle was at x_1. The work done by the resultant force equals the change in the kinetic energy of the particle:

$$W_{net} = \tfrac{1}{2}mv_2^2 - \tfrac{1}{2}mv_1^2 = \Delta E_k \qquad \text{7-9}$$

Work-energy theorem

We shall now show that this result, derived for the special case of a constant resultant force, is true for a general force which may vary with position. Consider a resultant force which varies with x as shown in Figure 7-3. The work done by this force as the particle moves from position x_1 to position x_2 is the area under this curve, i.e., the shaded region in the figure. In Figure 7-4 we have approximated this area by a series of rectangles. By choosing a large number of narrow rectangles, we can approximate the area to any desired accuracy. (In fact, the area under the original curve is defined to be the area of the rectangles in the limit as the number of the rectangles goes to infinity and the width

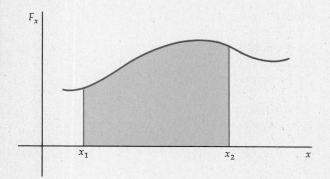

Figure 7-3
A general force F_x versus x.
The work done as the particle
moves from x_1 to x_2 is the
area under the curve in-
dicated.

Figure 7-4
The shaded area from Figure
7-3 is broken up into a series
of rectangles. Their sum
approximates the area under
the curve. The approximation
is improved as the number of
rectangles is increased and
the width of each is de-
creased.

of each goes to zero.) Since for each rectangle the force is constant, we
can apply Equation 7-9. The area of each rectangle equals the change
in kinetic energy for that interval. For example, the area of the first
rectangle for the interval $\Delta x_1 = x' - x_1$ equals $\frac{1}{2}mv'^2 - \frac{1}{2}mv_1^2$, where v'
is the speed of the particle at position x'. Similarly, the area of the sec-
ond rectangle for the interval $\Delta x_2 = x'' - x'$ equals $\frac{1}{2}mv''^2 - \frac{1}{2}mv'^2$. The
sum of these two areas is $\frac{1}{2}mv''^2 - \frac{1}{2}mv_1^2$, the sum of the changes in
kinetic energy, which is just the net change for the interval from x_1 to
x''. The total area under the curve equals the sum of the changes in
kinetic energy for each subinterval, or the net change in the kinetic
energy $\frac{1}{2}mv_2^2 - \frac{1}{2}mv_1^2$.

An alternative proof of the validity of Equation 7-9 for a general
force in one dimension makes use of the chain rule for derivatives (see
Appendix Table E-1, rule 3). Combining Newton's second law with
Equation 7-5 gives

$$W_{\text{net}} = \int_{x_1}^{x_2} \Sigma F_x \, dx = \int_{x_1}^{x_2} m \, \frac{dv}{dt} \, dx \qquad\qquad 7\text{-}10$$

Since the force is a function of x, the acceleration and speed are also
functions of x. Then

$$\frac{dv}{dt} = \frac{dv}{dx} \frac{dx}{dt} = v \, \frac{dv}{dx}$$

since $dx/dt = v$. Substituting this into Equation 7-10, we have

$$W_{\text{net}} = \int_{x_1}^{x_2} mv \, \frac{dv}{dx} \, dx = \int_{v_1}^{v_2} mv \, dv = \frac{1}{2}mv_2^2 - \frac{1}{2}mv_1^2$$

In one dimension, the work done by the resultant force equals the
change in kinetic energy whether the force is constant or not.

Example 7-2 A 3-kg block initially at rest is pulled with a constant horizontal force of 6 N for a distance of 5 m along a smooth horizontal
surface (Figure 7-5). Find the work done and the final speed of the
block.

Figure 7-5
Example 7-2. The 3-kg block is accelerated from rest by a constant horizontal force of 6 N. Since the vertical forces cancel, this is the resultant force. The work done by the resultant force, 6 N × 5 m = 30 J, equals the change in kinetic energy of the block.

Since the weight of the block is balanced by the normal force of the table and there is no friction, the resultant force is just the applied force $F = 6$ N. The work done by this constant force is

$$W = F \, \Delta x = (6 \text{ N})(5 \text{ m}) = 30 \text{ N-m} = 30 \text{ J}$$

The initial kinetic energy is zero since the initial speed is zero. The final kinetic energy is $\frac{1}{2}mv^2$. Thus

$$W = \Delta E_k = \tfrac{1}{2}mv^2 - 0 = 30 \text{ J}$$

$$v^2 = \frac{60 \text{ J}}{3 \text{ kg}} = 20 \text{ m}^2/\text{sec}^2 \qquad v = 4.47 \text{ m/sec}$$

Example 7-3 A 4-kg block is attached to the spring of Example 7-1. The spring is compressed 5 cm from equilibrium and released from rest. Find the speed of the block when the spring is at its equilibrium position.

The work done by the spring from $x_1 = -5$ cm to $x_2 = 0$ is 0.500 J, as computed in Example 7-1. Since the force exerted by the spring is the resultant force, this work equals the change in kinetic energy from 0 to $\frac{1}{2}mv^2$. Therefore

$$W = 0.500 \text{ J} = \tfrac{1}{2}mv^2 = \tfrac{1}{2}(4.00)v^2$$

$$v^2 = 0.250 \text{ m}^2/\text{sec}^2$$

$$v = 0.50 \text{ m/sec} = 50 \text{ cm/sec}$$

Example 7-4 Find the speed of the block in Example 7-3 when the spring is at its equilibrium position if the coefficient of kinetic friction between the table and block is 0.200.

In this case the work done by the spring is not the net work done on the block because the frictional force also does (negative) work. Since the frictional force is constant, the work done by it is just the force times the distance. This work is negative because the force $f_x = -\mu_k N = -\mu_k mg$ is opposite the direction of motion. The work done by the frictional force is

$$W_f = -\mu_k mgx = -(0.200)(4.00)(9.81)(0.050) = -0.392 \text{ J}$$

The net work done on the block is then

$$W_{net} = 0.500 \text{ J} - 0.392 \text{ J} = 0.108 \text{ J}$$

The net work equals the change in kinetic energy, which is $\frac{1}{2}mv^2$:

$$W_{net} = 0.108 \text{ J} = \tfrac{1}{2}mv^2 = \tfrac{1}{2}(4.00)v^2$$

$$v^2 = 0.054 \text{ m}^2/\text{sec}^2$$

$$v = 0.232 \text{ m/sec} = 23.2 \text{ cm/sec}$$

Questions

1. A block is pulled up an inclined plane a certain distance. Then it is pulled down the same distance. How does the work done by the friction as the block moves up compare with that done by friction as the block moves down?

2. How does the work done by gravity as the block in Question 1 moves up compare with the work done by gravity as it moves down?

3. Is it possible to exert a force which does work on a body without increasing its kinetic energy? If so, give an example.

4. How does the kinetic energy of a car change when its speed is doubled?

7-3   Work and Energy in Three Dimensions

The definition of work in one dimension given by Equation 7-1 is useful because the net work done by all the forces acting on a particle equals the change in kinetic energy of the particle. This result can be carried over to the motion of a particle in three dimensions if we modify the definition of work slightly to recognize that in general the resultant force is not parallel to the direction of motion of the particle, as indicated in Figure 7-6b. In general, the component of the force perpendicular to the velocity of the particle does not affect the speed of the particle. Instead, this component changes the direction of the velocity. (For example, if there is no component of the force along the instantaneous line of motion, i.e., if the resultant force is perpendicular to the velocity, the particle moves in a circle with constant speed. In this case the acceleration produced by the force is the centripetal acceleration, which is associated completely with the change in direction of the velocity.) On the other hand, the component of the force tangential to the curve (parallel or antiparallel to the velocity) produces a tangential acceleration which is just the time rate of change of the speed. It is this component which affects the kinetic energy of the particle.

Consider a particle moving along a curve as in Figure 7-6a. Let s be the distance traveled by the particle as measured along the curve. The work done by a force $\mathbf{F}$ acting on the particle as it moves a small distance ds is defined to be the product of the component of the force along a line tangent to the curve F_s and the distance ds:

$$dW = F_s \, ds \qquad\qquad 7\text{-}11$$

Work in three dimensions defined

(a)   (b)

Figure 7-6
(a) Particle moving along a curve in space. (b) The component of the force perpendicular to the motion $F_\perp = F \sin \phi$ affects the direction of motion but not the speed. The component parallel to the motion $F_s = F \cos \phi$ equals the mass times the tangential acceleration, which is dv/dt. The work done by this force during the displacement ds is defined by $dW = F_s \, ds$.

The work done by the rope equals the force times the distance raised. (*Courtesy of the Museum of Modern Art/Film Archives, New York.*)

To find the total work done by the force as the particle moves from point 1 to point 2 we compute the product $F_s \, ds$ for each element of the path and sum:

$$W = \int F_s \, ds \qquad\qquad 7\text{-}12$$

As with motion in one dimension, the net work done by the resultant force equals the change in kinetic energy. This is most easily seen by noting that the component of the resulting force tangential to the curve equals the mass times the tangential acceleration, which is the rate of change of the speed

$$\Sigma F_s = ma_t = m \frac{dv}{dt}$$

We can now think of the speed as a function of the distance s measured along the curve and apply the chain rule for derivatives:

$$\frac{dv}{dt} = \frac{dv}{ds}\frac{ds}{dt} = v\frac{dv}{ds}$$

where we have used the fact that ds/dt is just the speed v. Thus the work done by the resultant force is

$$W_{\text{net}} = \int_{s_1}^{s_2} \Sigma F_s \, ds = \int_{s_1}^{s_2} m\frac{dv}{dt}\, ds$$

$$= \int_{s_1}^{s_2} mv\frac{dv}{ds}\, ds = \int_{v_1}^{v_2} mv \, dv = \tfrac{1}{2}mv_2{}^2 - \tfrac{1}{2}mv_1{}^2 \qquad 7\text{-}13$$

Work-energy theorem in three dimensions

Equation 7-13 (along with its one-dimensional counterpart, Equation 7-9) is known as the *work-energy theorem:*

The net work done by the resultant force equals the change in the kinetic energy of the particle.

The theorem follows directly from the definition of work ($dW = F_s\,ds$) and kinetic energy ($E_k = \tfrac{1}{2}mv^2$) and from Newton's second law of motion ($\Sigma \mathbf{F} = m\,d\mathbf{v}/dt$).

If ϕ is the angle between the force $\mathbf{F}$ and the element of displacement $d\mathbf{s}$, the component of the force parallel to ds is $F_s = F \cos \phi$, as can be seen from Figure 7-6. Therefore Equation 7-12 for the work done by a force $\mathbf{F}$ can be written

$$W = \int F_s\,ds = \int F \cos \phi\,ds \qquad\qquad 7\text{-}14$$

In general both F and ϕ vary as the particle moves along a curve in three dimensions. Note that $\cos \phi\,ds$ is the component of the displacement ds on a line parallel to the force. Thus we may think of the element of work $dW = F \cos \phi\,ds$ either as the product of the displacement ds and the parallel component of the force $F \cos \phi$ or as the product of the force F and the parallel component of the displacement $ds \cos \phi$. The second interpretation is sometimes useful when the force is constant in direction.

Example 7-5 A particle of mass m starts from rest and slides down a smooth plane inclined at angle θ from the horizontal. Find the work done by all the forces and the speed of the particle after it slides a distance s measured along the plane.

The forces acting on the particle are the weight $m\mathbf{g}$ and the contact force $\mathbf{N}$ exerted by the plane, which is perpendicular to the plane because the plane is smooth. These are indicated in Figure 7-7. Since the normal force $\mathbf{N}$ is perpendicular to the motion, it does no work. The only force that does work is the weight $m\mathbf{g}$, which has the component $mg \sin \theta$ in the direction of motion. (Note that the angle ϕ between the weight and the direction of motion is the complement of the angle of inclination θ. Thus the element of work done by the weight is $dW = mg \cos \phi\,ds = mg \sin \theta\,ds$.) Since the weight is constant, the work done over the distance s is merely $mg \sin \theta\,s$. This is the net work done by all the forces, and therefore it equals the change in kinetic energy, which is just $\tfrac{1}{2}mv^2$ because the particle begins from rest. Thus the work-energy theorem gives

$$W_{\text{net}} = mg \sin \theta\,s = \tfrac{1}{2}mv^2$$

or

$$v^2 = 2s \sin \theta\,g = 2gh$$

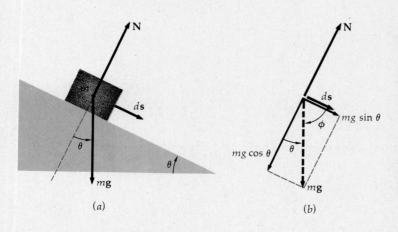

(a)   (b)

Figure 7-7
(a) Block on an inclined plane for Example 7-5. (b) The free-body diagram for the block. The resultant force is $mg \sin \theta$ down the incline. The work done by the resultant force is $mg \sin \theta\,s = mgh$, where s is the total distance traveled and $h = s \sin \theta$ is the vertical distance the block descends.

where $h = s \sin \theta$ is the total vertical height through which the particle descended. The work done by the earth on the particle is mgh, independent of the angle of the incline. If the angle θ were increased, the particle would travel a smaller distance s to drop the same vertical distance h but the component of the weight parallel to the motion $mg \cdot \sin \theta$ would be greater, making the work done $mg \sin \theta \, s$ the same.

The results of Example 7-5 can be generalized. Consider a particle sliding down a curve of any shape under the influence of gravity. Figure 7-8 shows a small displacement ds parallel to the curve. The work done by the earth during this displacement is $mg \cos \phi \, ds$, where ϕ is the angle between the displacement and the downward force of gravity. The quantity $ds \cos \phi$ is just dh, the vertical distance dropped. As the particle slides down the curve, the angle ϕ varies, but for each displacement ds, the downward component of displacement parallel to the weight is $ds \cos \phi = dh$ and the work done by the earth is $mg \, ds \cdot \cos \phi = mg \, dh$. Thus the total work done by the earth is mgh, where h is the total vertical distance the particle descends. If the curve is smooth (frictionless), the weight is the only force that does work. In this case the speed of the particle after descending a vertical distance h is obtained from $\frac{1}{2}mv^2 - \frac{1}{2}mv_0^2 = mgh$, where v_0 is the initial speed. If the curve is not smooth, the frictional force will do work (this work will be negative because the frictional force is in the direction opposite the motion). The work done by the friction force depends on the length and shape of the curve and on the coefficient of friction.

Figure 7-8
Particle of mass m sliding down a smooth curve of arbitrary shape. The work done by gravity for a displacement ds is $mg \cos \phi \, ds = mg \, dh$, where $dh = \cos \phi \, ds$ is the vertical component of the displacement. The total work done by gravity is mgh, where h is the total vertical distance descended.

Questions

5. A body moves in a circle at constant speed. Does the force that accounts for its acceleration do work on it? Explain.

6. When a body moves along some surface, what work does the normal force exerted by the surface do?

7. A heavy box is dragged across the floor from point A to point B. Will the work done by friction differ if the box is pulled along a zigzag path instead of along the shortest path from A to B? How?

8. The net force acting on a body does no work. Can the body be moving along a straight line?

9. How can a man who can exert a force of 100 lb raise a 200-lb box from the ground to a shelf a height 4 ft above the ground? Could a boy who can exert only 50 lb raise the box to the shelf? How much work would each have to do?

7-4   Potential Energy

Often the work done by a force applied to an object produces no increase in the kinetic energy of the object because other forces do an equal amount of negative work. For example, consider a block being pulled slowly up a smooth incline with constant velocity by an applied force F_{app} which just balances the component of the weight of the block parallel to the incline, $F_{app} = mg \sin \theta$.

The work done by the applied force in moving the block a distance s is

$$W = F_{app}s = mg \sin \theta \, s = mgh$$

where $h = s \sin \theta$ is the height the block has been raised above its initial level. In this case there is no increase in kinetic energy of the block because the weight does an equal but negative amount of work:

$$W_{earth} = -mg \sin \theta \, s = -mgh$$

However, we can convert the work done by the applied force into a change in kinetic energy by merely releasing the block and letting it slide back down the incline. The weight will then do a positive amount of work $mg \sin \theta \, s = mgh$, which equals the increase in kinetic energy because it is the only work done on the block.

We can use the gravitational attraction of the earth for the block to store the work we do on the block for later use in giving the block kinetic energy. We say that the block at the height h has *potential energy mgh* relative to the original position. The work done by the applied force increases the potential energy of the block. When the block slides back down under the influence of its weight alone, the work done by the earth decreases the potential energy while increasing the kinetic energy by an equal amount. Here potential energy is converted into kinetic energy. Since the loss of potential energy equals the gain in kinetic energy for each part of the downward motion, the sum of potential energy and kinetic energy is constant as the block slides down the incline. This is an example of the *conservation of energy*.

If we project an object up a smooth incline with initial velocity v_0, it will travel until the negative work done by the earth decreases the kinetic energy to zero. Since this negative work equals the increase in potential energy mgh, the maximum height attained by the object is given by $mgh = \frac{1}{2}mv_0^2$ (Figure 7-9). (Again, this height is independent of the angle of inclination of the plane.) The object stops momentarily at this height and then slides back down, gaining kinetic energy and losing potential energy. When it reaches its starting point its kinetic energy is again $\frac{1}{2}mv_0^2$.

Jen and Des Bartlett/Photo Researchers

These climbers do work in increasing their gravitational potential energy.

Figure 7-9
A particle projected up a smooth inclined plane with initial speed v_0. (*a*) Initially its kinetic energy is $\frac{1}{2}mv_0^2$, and its potential energy is zero. (*b*) When the particle comes momentarily to rest, it has potential energy $mgh = \frac{1}{2}mv_0^2$ and zero kinetic energy. (*c*) It then slides back down the incline and has its original kinetic energy when it reaches its starting point.

$v = 0$

v_0

h

v_0

K.E. $= \frac{1}{2}mv_0^2$
P.E. $= 0$

P.E. $= mgh = \frac{1}{2}mv_0^2$
K.E. $= 0$

K.E. $= \frac{1}{2}mv_0^2$
P.E. $= 0$

(*a*)   (*b*)   (*c*)

There are many other kinds of potential energy. Suppose we have a mass on a spring at its equilibrium position. If we extend the spring by applying a force equal to that exerted by the spring (after we give the mass a slight start), the spring does negative work equal in magnitude to that done by the applied force and the kinetic energy does not change. In the extended position, the spring has potential energy equal to the magnitude of the (negative) work done by the spring. When the mass is released, the spring does positive work on the mass. This increases the kinetic energy of the mass and decreases the potential energy. We shall investigate this situation and other examples of potential energy in detail in the next chapter.

7-5   Work and Energy

Let us compare the scientific definition of work with our everyday use of the word. Consider a person holding a weight a distance h off the floor, as in Figure 7-10. In everyday usage, we say that it takes work to do this: we have to exert a force, which is tiring to our muscles; but in our scientific definition, no work is done by a force acting on a stationary object. We could eliminate the effort of holding the weight by merely tying the string to some fixed object and the block would be supported with no help from us. It is useful to think of work, as we have defined it, as a quantity which has to be paid for in some way. The payment is in some kind of energy loss by whatever exerts the force. For example, we cannot lift the weight in Figure 7-10 to a greater height unless we supply energy in some form or another. If we attach a slightly greater weight to the string and lift our original weight by letting the second weight fall, we pay in the loss of potential energy of our second weight. If we merely lift the weight with our muscles, we pay for the work done in the loss of internal chemical energy of our body. In order to continue to do work with our muscles, we must eventually replenish this energy by taking in nourishment. If we attach the string to an electric motor to raise the weight, we spend electric energy to perform this work.

Atlas. There is no work done without motion.

Figure 7-10
No work is done by the man holding the weight at a fixed height. The same task could be accomplished by tying the rope to a fixed point.

Energy Resources

Laurent Hodges
Iowa State University

Directly or indirectly, energy is essential for everything that exists or is done in modern society: coal in extracting metals from their ores, petroleum fuels for ground and air transportation, natural gas or fuel oil for heating buildings, electricity for industrial machinery and home appliances.

Primary energy resources, i.e., resources from the environment which are the ultimate sources of our energy, include the fossil fuels (coal, oil, and gas) and three types of electricity: hydroelectricity generated by falling water, electricity from nuclear power plants (ultimately from the heat of fission of ^{235}U), and electricity generated by geothermal power (the heat of steam and hot water from beneath the earth). These are really only the so-called *commercial* energy sources. Although such energy sources as wood, peat, and cow or camel dung are absent from international trade and account for perhaps only 3 percent of world energy consumption, they may represent up to about half the energy consumption in certain developing countries. Wood was the leading energy source in the United States throughout most of the nineteenth century, but coal displaced it in the 1880s and the fossil fuels have been predominant ever since.

Figure 1 shows the consumption of commercial energy by the world and the United States in the years 1950 and 1970. During that period coal declined in relative importance while crude oil and natural gas grew in popularity because of their greater convenience in transportation and use and their lesser environmental problems. Nuclear power was first used during that period but still made only a small contribution in the early 1970s. Nuclear energy and natural gas are relatively sophisticated fuels used mainly in the developed countries.

Figure 1
Commercial energy consumption in the United States and the world in 1950 and 1970.

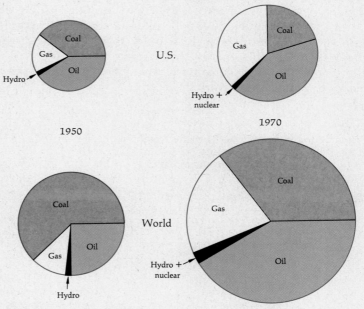

The energy actually used is often in a modified form, referred to as a *secondary energy resource*. For example, about 80 percent of the electricity used in the United States is generated by the combustion of fossil fuels; in this case the fossil fuel is the primary energy resource and the electricity is a secondary resource. Similarly the hydrogen fuel of any future "hydrogen economy" will be a secondary resource obtained from one or more primary resources via the electrolysis of water.

Figure 2 shows the per capita energy consumption in the world and different parts of the world. United States per capita consumption is about $2\frac{1}{2}$ times that in the other developed countries (Canada, Europe, Australia, New Zealand, Japan, Israel, Soviet Russia) and 25 to 30 times that in the developing countries. It is often stated that the United States cannot cut its energy consumption significantly without returning to some unspecified "dark age." Actually a drastic 60 percent cut would only put United States per capita energy consumption at the level of that in the other developed countries, where the standard of living is certainly decent and civilized. A less drastic but supposedly intolerable cut of 30 percent would return us to consumption levels of about 10 years ago, which few of us remember as a dark age.

Annual increases in United States per capita consumption in recent years have about equaled the total per capita consumption in developing countries.

Figure 2
Per capita energy consumption in 1970.

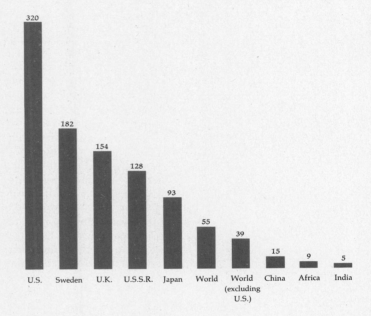

This is an unfortunate trend. It would be more equitable for the consumption increases to come in the developing countries, especially since they are providing most of the world's energy production increases. In the early 1950s both the United States and Great Britain were producing approximately as much energy as they consumed, but by the early 1970s they were importing about 15 and 50 percent, respectively, of the energy they consumed, most of the imports being produced in developing countries.

About 40 percent of United States energy consumption is by the industrial sector, 25 percent is by ground, air, and water transportation, 20 percent by residences, and 15 percent by commercial establishments (stores, offices, restaurants, etc.). Figure 3 shows the breakdown into end uses. All the small electrical appliances in use — clocks, radios, televisions, power tools, hair dryers — account for much less than 1 percent of total energy consumption in the United States.

The fossil fuels that constitute the bulk of our energy sources are a finite nonrenewable resource and cannot meet our energy needs forever. Although the recoverable reserves of these fuels can be estimated only imperfectly and future energy demands are uncertain, it seems clear that oil and gas can continue to be a major resource for only a few more decades at most and coal only a few centuries. Nuclear energy in the form of ^{238}U or ^{232}Th used in breeder reactors or deuterium or other light isotopes used in controlled thermonuclear fusion reactors (should they prove feasible) could supply projected energy needs for much longer — thousands or even millions of years assuming a leveling off of the growth of energy consumption.

Figure 3
Approximate energy use in
the United States as of the
early 1970s.

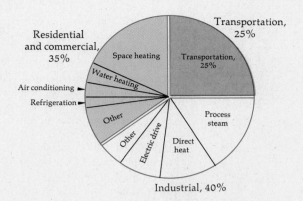

Residential
and commercial,
35%

Space heating

Water heating

Air conditioning ►

Refrigeration ►

Other

Other

Electric drive

Transportation,
25%

Transportation,
25%

Process
steam

Direct
heat

Industrial, 40%

Other renewable or continuously available energy resources which are of negligible importance today may make significant contributions to our energy supply in the future: e.g., solar energy, wind power, organic wastes, tidal energy. Solar energy is especially abundant, though its low power density may make necessary the collection of solar radiation over large land areas.

Extensive use of renewable energy resources may be required if society is to have abundant and environmentally tolerable energy. Society has become increasingly concerned with the environmental costs of energy production and use. Some of the major environmental costs are land devastation by the strip mining of coal, high acid concentrations in the streams of coal mining areas, particulate matter and sulfur oxide air pollution from coal combustion, water pollution from oil-field operations, air pollution from petroleum refining, sulfur oxide pollution from petroleum combustion, carbon monoxide and hydrocarbon air pollution from the use of gasoline in motor vehicles, nitrogen oxide air pollution from any high-temperature combustion process, and radiation releases from uranium mining and from nuclear power plants.

Unfortunately much of the energy used today is wasted. For this reason energy conservation has become an important policy to implement. If we can use energy more efficiently, if we can devise new products with lower energy requirements (think of pocket calculators!), if we can change our life styles to reduce energy consumption, we can slow the rate of depletion of our energy resources and simultaneously decrease the adverse environmental effects of energy production and consumption. It will be especially advantageous to increase the use of renewable resources and thereby conserve fossil fuels for their other valuable uses, such as the manufacture of chemicals and drugs.

7-6   Power

The rate at which a force does work is called the *power input P* of the force. Consider a particle with instantaneous velocity **v**. In a short time interval dt, the particle has a displacement $d\mathbf{s} = \mathbf{v}\,dt$. The work done by a force **F** acting on the particle during this time interval is

$$dW = F \cos \phi \, ds = F \cos \phi \, v \, dt$$

where ϕ is the angle between **F** and **v**. The power input is

$$P = \frac{dW}{dt} = F \cos \phi \, v \qquad\qquad 7\text{-}15 \qquad \textit{Power defined}$$

The SI unit of power, one joule per second, is called a watt (W):

$$1 \text{ W} = 1 \text{ J/sec} \qquad\qquad 7\text{-}16 \qquad \textit{Watt defined}$$

When you buy energy from a power company, you are usually charged by the kilowatt-hour (kWh). A kilowatt-hour of energy is

$$1 \text{ kWh} = 10^3 \text{ W} \times 3600 \text{ sec} = 3.6 \times 10^6 \text{ W-sec} = 3.6 \times 10^6 \text{ J} \qquad 7\text{-}17$$

In the British engineering system, the unit for energy is the foot-pound and for power is the foot-pound per second. A more common multiple of this unit is called a horsepower:

$$1 \text{ horsepower} = 550 \text{ ft-lb/sec} = 746 \text{ W} \qquad 7\text{-}18$$

Example 7-6 A 1-ton automobile travels at a steady speed of 60 mi/h (= 88 ft/sec) along a road which gains altitude at a constant rate of 100 ft in every mile traveled. What power must be expended by the motor to do this?

The automobile is moving along a plane inclined at an angle θ given by

$$\sin \theta = \frac{100 \text{ ft}}{5280 \text{ ft}} = 0.0189$$

Since the car moves at constant speed, its motor must supply a force up along the incline which just balances the component of the car's weight down the incline. This applied force must be

$$F_{\text{app}} = mg \sin \theta = (2000 \text{ lb})(0.0189) = 37.9 \text{ lb}$$

Since $\mathbf{F}_{\text{app}}$ and $\mathbf{v}$ are parallel, the power required is

$$P = F_{\text{app}} v = (37.9 \text{ lb})(88 \text{ ft/sec}) = 3.3 \times 10^3 \text{ ft-lb/sec}$$
$$= 6.06 \text{ horsepower}$$

Actually additional power is needed to do work against friction in the moving parts of the car and against a considerable air resistance.

7-7   Scalar, or Dot, Product of Two Vectors

The scalar quantities work and power, defined by Equations 7-14 and 7-15, each involve the product of the magnitudes of two vectors and the cosine of the angle between them; the vectors are the force $\mathbf{F}$ and the displacement $d\mathbf{s}$ for work and the force $\mathbf{F}$ and the velocity $\mathbf{v}$ for power. A scalar function of two vectors occurs often in physics and is called the *scalar product*. The scalar product of two vectors $\mathbf{A}$ and $\mathbf{B}$ is written $\mathbf{A} \cdot \mathbf{B}$ and defined

---

$$\mathbf{A} \cdot \mathbf{B} = AB \cos \phi \qquad 7\text{-}19$$

Scalar, or dot, product defined

where ϕ is the angle between $\mathbf{A}$ and $\mathbf{B}$. Because of this notation, the scalar product is also called the *dot product*.[1] With this notation, the element of work dW is written

---

$$dW = \mathbf{F} \cdot d\mathbf{s} \qquad 7\text{-}20$$

---

[1] A vector function of two vectors, the vector product or cross product, written $\mathbf{A} \times \mathbf{B}$, will be defined in Chapter 13.

Figure 7-11
The geometric interpretation of the dot product $\mathbf{A} \cdot \mathbf{B}$. It can be thought of as the magnitude of $\mathbf{A}$ times the component of $\mathbf{B}$ in the direction of $\mathbf{A}$, or the magnitude of $\mathbf{B}$ times the component of $\mathbf{A}$ in the direction of $\mathbf{B}$; that is, $\mathbf{A} \cdot \mathbf{B} = A(B \cos \phi) = B(A \cos \phi)$.

and the power is written

$$P = \mathbf{F} \cdot \mathbf{v} \qquad\qquad 7\text{-}21$$

The dot product $\mathbf{A} \cdot \mathbf{B}$ can be thought of as the product of A and the component $B \cos \phi$ in the direction of $\mathbf{A}$ or as the product of B and the component $A \cos \phi$ in the direction of $\mathbf{B}$ (Figure 7-11). We have already discussed these interpretations applied to the dot product of $\mathbf{F}$ and $d\mathbf{s}$.

If $\mathbf{A}$ and $\mathbf{B}$ are perpendicular, their dot product is zero because $\phi = 90°$. Conversely, if $\mathbf{A} \cdot \mathbf{B} = 0$, either $\mathbf{A} = 0$, or $\mathbf{B} = 0$, or $\mathbf{A}$ and $\mathbf{B}$ are mutually perpendicular. If $\mathbf{A}$ and $\mathbf{B}$ are parallel vectors, the dot product is just the product of their magnitudes. The dot product of a vector with itself is the square of the magnitude of the vector:

$$\mathbf{A} \cdot \mathbf{A} = A^2$$

It follows from the definition that the scalar product is independent of the order of multiplication $\mathbf{A} \cdot \mathbf{B} = \mathbf{B} \cdot \mathbf{A}$. This is known as the *commutative rule of multiplication*. The scalar product also obeys the distributive rule of multiplication:

$$(\mathbf{A} + \mathbf{B}) \cdot \mathbf{C} = \mathbf{A} \cdot \mathbf{C} + \mathbf{B} \cdot \mathbf{C}$$

(The proof of this rule is given in Section 7-8.) We can use this result to write the dot product of two vectors in terms of their rectangular components:

$$
\begin{aligned}
\mathbf{A} \cdot \mathbf{B} =\ & (A_x\mathbf{i} + A_y\mathbf{j} + A_z\mathbf{k}) \cdot (B_x\mathbf{i} + B_y\mathbf{j} + B_z\mathbf{k}) \\
=\ & A_xB_x\mathbf{i} \cdot \mathbf{i} + A_xB_y\mathbf{i} \cdot \mathbf{j} + A_xB_z\mathbf{i} \cdot \mathbf{k} \\
& + A_yB_x\mathbf{j} \cdot \mathbf{i} + A_yB_y\mathbf{j} \cdot \mathbf{j} + A_yB_z\mathbf{j} \cdot \mathbf{k} \\
& + A_zB_x\mathbf{k} \cdot \mathbf{i} + A_zB_y\mathbf{k} \cdot \mathbf{j} + A_zB_z\mathbf{k} \cdot \mathbf{k}
\end{aligned}
$$

Since the unit vectors $\mathbf{i}$, $\mathbf{j}$, and $\mathbf{k}$ are mutually perpendicular, all the dot products of two different unit vectors in the expression above are zero. Thus six of the nine terms vanish. Each of the remaining terms contains the product of a unit vector with itself. Since each of these vectors has magnitude 1, these remaining dot products have just the value 1. The result for $\mathbf{A} \cdot \mathbf{B}$ thus reduces to

$$\mathbf{A} \cdot \mathbf{B} = A_xB_x + A_yB_y + A_zB_z \qquad\qquad 7\text{-}22$$

If the vectors $\mathbf{A}$ and $\mathbf{B}$ are given in terms of their rectangular components, we can use Equation 7-22 to find the angle between them.

Example 7-7 Find the angle between the vectors $\mathbf{A} = 2\mathbf{i} + 2\mathbf{j} + 4\mathbf{k}$ and $\mathbf{B} = -2\mathbf{i} + 5\mathbf{j} + 5\mathbf{k}$.

We have that $\mathbf{A} \cdot \mathbf{B} = AB \cos \phi = A_xB_x + A_yB_y + A_zB_z = (2)(-2) + (2)(5) + (4)(5) = -4 + 10 + 20 = 26$. The magnitudes of the vectors are

$$A = \sqrt{A_x^2 + A_y^2 + A_z^2} = \sqrt{4 + 4 + 16} = \sqrt{24}$$

$$B = \sqrt{B_x^2 + B_y^2 + B_z^2} = \sqrt{4 + 25 + 25} = \sqrt{54}$$

Thus

$$\cos \phi = \frac{\mathbf{A} \cdot \mathbf{B}}{AB} = \frac{26}{\sqrt{24} \ \sqrt{54}} = \frac{26}{36} = 0.72$$

$$\phi = 44°$$

If the vectors $\mathbf{A}$ and $\mathbf{B}$ are functions of time, we compute the derivative of $\mathbf{A} \cdot \mathbf{B}$ by applying the product rule for derivatives:

$$\frac{d(\mathbf{A} \cdot \mathbf{B})}{dt} = \mathbf{A} \cdot \frac{d\mathbf{B}}{dt} + \mathbf{B} \cdot \frac{d\mathbf{A}}{dt} \qquad 7\text{-}23$$

This result can be obtained by taking the derivative of the right side of Equation 7-22. Since A_x and B_x are scalar functions of time, the product rule applies. Thus $d(A_x B_x)/dt = A_x \ dB_x/dt + B_x \ dA_x/dt$, with similar results for the other products. The six terms thus obtained are the same as the six terms obtained by writing out the right side of Equation 7-23 in terms of the components.

Example 7-8 Show that if the magnitude of a vector is constant in time, the rate of change of the vector is perpendicular to the vector.

We apply Equation 7-23 to the dot product of $\mathbf{A}$ with itself:

$$\mathbf{A} \cdot \mathbf{A} = A^2 = \text{constant}$$

$$\frac{d(\mathbf{A} \cdot \mathbf{A})}{dt} = \mathbf{A} \cdot \frac{d\mathbf{A}}{dt} + \mathbf{A} \cdot \frac{d\mathbf{A}}{dt} = 2\mathbf{A} \cdot \frac{d\mathbf{A}}{dt} = 0$$

Since the dot product of $\mathbf{A}$ and $d\mathbf{A}/dt$ is zero, they must be perpendicular (unless either $\mathbf{A}$ or $d\mathbf{A}/dt$ is zero). We have seen examples of this result in circular motion. Since the position vector $\mathbf{r}$ is constant in magnitude, the velocity $\mathbf{v} = d\mathbf{r}/dt$ is perpendicular to $\mathbf{r}$. If the motion is at constant speed, the acceleration $\mathbf{a} = d\mathbf{v}/dt$ is perpendicular to $\mathbf{v}$.

If we write the force and displacement in terms of their rectangular components, the element of work becomes

$$dW = \mathbf{F} \cdot d\mathbf{s} = (F_x \mathbf{i} + F_y \mathbf{j} + F_z \mathbf{k}) \cdot (dx \ \mathbf{i} + dy \ \mathbf{j} + dz \ \mathbf{k})$$
$$= F_x \ dx + F_y \ dy + F_z \ dz$$

The net work done by the resultant force can then be written

$$W_{\text{net}} = \int \Sigma F_x \ dx + \int \Sigma F_y \ dy + \int \Sigma F_z \ dz$$

The work-energy theorem in three dimensions can be derived from this equation by considering each term on the right side separately as a one-dimensional problem and using Newton's second law in component form ($\Sigma F_x = ma_x$). Then the first term can be written as the change in the quantity $\frac{1}{2}mv_x^2$, with similar expressions for the other two terms. The net work is thus the change in the quantity

$$\tfrac{1}{2}mv_x^2 + \tfrac{1}{2}mv_y^2 + \tfrac{1}{2}mv_z^2 = \tfrac{1}{2}m(v_x^2 + v_y^2 + v_z^2) = \tfrac{1}{2}m\mathbf{v} \cdot \mathbf{v} = \tfrac{1}{2}mv^2 = E_k$$

Questions

10. Can the scalar product of two vectors be negative? If so, how?

11. If the scalar product of two vectors is zero, does it follow that one of the vectors is zero?

Optional

7-8   Proof of the Distributive Law for the Dot Product

Figure 7-12 shows the vectors **A**, **B**, and **A + B** along with their projections on vector **C**. ϕ_A is the angle between **A** and **C**, ϕ_B the angle between **B** and **C**, and ϕ_{AB} the angle between **A + B** and **C**. From the figure it is clear that

$$|A + B| \cos \phi_{AB} = A \cos \phi_A + B \cos \phi_B$$

This multiplied by the magnitude of **C** is

$$|A + B|C \cos \phi_{AB} = AC \cos \phi_A + BC \cos \phi_B$$

But, by definition, the quantity on the left is $(A + B) \cdot C$, and the two terms on the right are $A \cdot C$ and $B \cdot C$. Hence, the last equation is the same as

$$(A + B) \cdot C = A \cdot C + B \cdot C$$

Figure 7-12
Diagram to show that
$(A + B) \cdot C = A \cdot C + B \cdot C$.

Review

A. Define, explain, or otherwise identify:

Work, 175
Joule, 175
Kinetic energy, 177
Work-energy theorem, 177
Power, 188

Watt, 188
Horsepower, 189
Scalar product, 189
Dot product, 189

B. True or false:

1. Work is the area under the force-versus-time curve.

2. Only the resultant force acting on an object can do work.

3. No work is done on a particle which remains at rest.

4. A force which is always perpendicular to the velocity of a particle does no work on the particle.

5. A kilowatt-hour is a unit of power.

6. If **A** and **B** are in opposite directions, $A \cdot B$ is zero.

7. No net work is done in carrying a heavy box at constant speed across a horizontal surface.

Exercises

Unless instructed otherwise, use the approximate value $g = 32$ ft/sec^2 = 9.8 m/sec^2 for the acceleration of gravity in Exercises and Problems.

Section 7-1, Work in One Dimension

1. A 5-kg mass is raised at constant velocity a distance of 10 m by a force F_0. Find the work done on the mass (*a*) by the force F_0 and (*b*) by the earth.

2. A force F_x varies with x as shown in Figure 7-13. Find the work done by the force acting on a particle as the particle moves from $x = 1$ m to $x = 4$ m.

Figure 7-13
F_x versus x for Exercises 2 and 15.

3. A force F_x varies as shown in Figure 7-14. (*a*) Find the work done by the force acting on the particle as the particle moves from $x = 0$ to $x = 3$ m. (*b*) Find the work done by F_x as the particle moves from $x = 3$ m to $x = 6$ m. (*c*) Find the total work done by F_x over the distance $x = 0$ to $x = 6$ m.

Figure 7-14
F_x versus x for Exercises 3 and 16.

4. A 10-kg box rests on a horizontal table. The coefficient of friction between the box and table is 0.4. A force F_x pulls the box at constant velocity a distance of 5 m. Find the work done (*a*) by F_x and (*b*) by friction.

5. The box described in Exercise 4 is pulled by a force F_x so that the box has an acceleration of 2 m/sec^2. (*a*) Find the work done by F_x while the box is pulled a distance of 5 m. (*b*) What is the work done by the frictional force in this case ($\mu = 0.4$)?

6. From the conversion factors for newtons to pounds and meters to feet derive the relation between the joule and the foot-pound expressed in Equation 7-3.

7. The unit of force in the cgs system is the dyne, defined as the force which produces an acceleration of 1 cm/sec^2 when acting on a 1-gm mass. The cgs

unit of work is the dyne-centimeter, called an erg. Find the number of ergs in a joule.

8. A force F_x is related to position by the formula $F_x = Cx^2$, where C is a constant. Find the work done by this force acting on a particle when the particle moves from $x = 0$ to $x = 3$ m.

Section 7-2, Work Done by the Resultant Force; Kinetic Energy

9. A 10-gm bullet has a velocity of 1000 m/sec. (*a*) What is its kinetic energy in joules? (*b*) If the speed is halved, what is its kinetic energy?

10. A 2-lb block moves with speed 10 ft/sec. (*a*) What is its kinetic energy in foot-pounds? (*b*) What is its kinetic energy in joules?

11. A 2-kg mass and a 200-kg mass have equal momenta of 40 kg-m/sec. Find the kinetic energy of each mass.

12. A 5-kg box initially at rest on a smooth table is pulled by a constant horizontal force of 10 N for a distance of 6 m. Find (*a*) the final kinetic energy of the box and (*b*) the final speed of the box.

13. A 5-kg mass is raised a distance of 4 m by a vertical force of 80 N. Find (*a*) the work done by the force and the work done by the earth and (*b*) the final kinetic energy of the mass if it was originally at rest.

14. A 2-kg box is initially at rest on a horizontal table. The coefficient of friction between the box and table is 0.4. The box is pulled along the table a distance of 3 m by a horizontal applied force of 10 N. (*a*) Find the work done by the applied force. (*b*) Find the work done by friction. (*c*) Find the change in kinetic energy of the box. (*d*) Find the speed of the box after it has traveled 3 m.

15. A particle of mass 2 kg is subjected to a single force F_x, which varies with x as shown in Figure 7-13. When the particle is at position $x = 1$ m, it has a velocity of 3 m/sec. (*a*) What is its kinetic energy at $x = 1$ m? (*b*) What is its kinetic energy at $x = 4$ m? (See Exercise 2.) (*c*) What is the speed of the particle when it is at $x = 4$ m?

16. A particle of mass 4 kg is subjected to a single force F_x shown in Figure 7-14. The particle is initially at rest at $x = 0$. Find the kinetic energy and speed of the particle (*a*) when it is at $x = 3$ m and (*b*) when it is at $x = 6$ m.

17. A 5-kg object is lifted by a rope exerting a force T so that it accelerates upward at 5 m/sec². The object is lifted 3 m. Find (*a*) the tension T, (*b*) the work done by T, (*c*) the work done by the earth, (*d*) the final kinetic energy of the object after being lifted 3 m if it is originally at rest.

18. A 4000-lb car moves with initial speed of 80 ft/sec. It is stopped in 200 ft by a constant frictional force. (*a*) What is the initial kinetic energy of the car? (*b*) How much work is done by the frictional force in stopping the car? (*c*) What is the coefficient of friction?

Section 7-3, Work and Energy in Three Dimensions

19. A 5-kg box is pulled a distance of 6 m along a smooth horizontal surface by a 20-N force which makes an angle of 30° with the horizontal. Find (*a*) the work done by the force and (*b*) the change in kinetic energy of the box and the final speed if the box is initially at rest.

20. A block of mass 6 kg slides down a rough incline starting from rest. The coefficient of friction is 0.2, and the angle of the incline is 60°. (*a*) List all the forces acting on the block and find the work done by each force when the block slides 2 m (measured along the incline). (*b*) What is the net work done on the block? (*c*) What is the velocity of the block after it has slid 2 m?

21. A 2-kg mass attached to a string moves on a smooth horizontal surface in a circle of radius 3 m. The speed of the mass is 1.5 m/sec. (a) Find the tension in the string. (b) List the forces acting on the mass and find the work done by each force during 1 rev.

22. A 200-lb cart is lifted up a 2-ft step by rolling the cart up an incline formed when a plank of length L is laid from the lower level to the top of the step. (Assume the rolling is equivalent to sliding without friction.) (a) Find the force parallel to the incline needed to push the cart up without acceleration for values of L of 3, 4, and 5 ft. (b) Calculate directly from Equation 7-12 the work needed to push the cart up the incline for each of these values of L. (c) Since the work found in (b) is the same for each value of L, what advantage if any is there in choosing one length over another?

23. A 2-kg box slides down a rough incline of length 10 m and angle of inclination 30°. The coefficient of friction is 0.3. (a) List all the forces acting on the box and find the work done by each. (b) Find the kinetic energy of the box at the bottom of the incline assuming that it began at the top with speed $v = 2$ m/sec.

24. A 2-kg mass is released from rest at point A on a smooth circular track of radius 50 cm (Figure 7-15). (a) Using the generalization of Example 7-4, find the work done by the earth while the mass slides from point A to the bottom of the track. (b) What is the velocity of the mass at the bottom of the track? (c) The mass slides past the bottom and up the right side of the track until the negative work done by the earth equals the kinetic energy of the mass at the bottom. At what point on the track will the mass come to rest momentarily? (d) Describe the subsequent motion of the mass on the track.

Figure 7-15
Particle on a smooth vertical circular track for Exercise 24.

Section 7-4, Potential Energy

25. A man of mass 80 kg climbs up a stairway of height 5 m. (a) What is the increase in potential energy of the man? (b) What is the least amount of work the man must do to climb the stairway? (c) Explain why the work done by the man may be more than this minimum amount.

26. List some situations in which work done by some applied force is not stored; i.e., it cannot be recovered and changed into kinetic energy.

27. A man raises a 50-lb weight from the ground overhead to a resting position 7.5 ft above the ground. (a) Find the work done by the man and the work done by the earth. (b) What is the net work done by all the forces acting on the weight? (c) The weight is now released and allowed to fall to the ground. What is the kinetic energy of the weight just as it hits the ground? (d) Find the total work done by the man and the total work done by the earth during the complete cycle of moving the weight from the ground up to the height of 7.5 ft and back to the ground.

28. A 2-kg mass is held at a height of 20 m above the ground and released at time $t = 0$. (a) What is the original potential energy of the mass relative to the ground? (b) From Newton's laws, find the distance the mass falls after 1 sec and the velocity of the mass at this time. (c) Find the potential energy and kinetic energy of the mass at time $t = 1$ sec. What is the sum of the potential energy and kinetic energy at this time? (d) At time $t = 2$ sec, find the height of the mass, its potential energy, and its kinetic energy. What is the sum of kinetic and potential energy at this time?

29. A 2-kg box slides along a long smooth incline of angle 30°. It starts from rest at time $t = 0$ at the top of the incline a height of 20 m above the ground. (a) What is the initial potential energy of the mass? Find (b) the acceleration of the mass and (c) its position and speed after 2 sec. (d) At time $t = 2$ sec, find the potential energy of the mass, its kinetic energy, and the sum of the potential and kinetic energy. (e) What is the kinetic energy of the mass when it reaches the bottom of the incline?

Section 7-5, Work and Energy

There are no exercises for this section.

Section 7-6, Power

30. A 4-kg mass is lifted by a force F_0 equal to the weight of the mass. The mass moves upward at a constant velocity of 2 m/sec. (*a*) What is the power input of the force F_0? (*b*) What is the power input of the force exerted by the earth? (*c*) How much work is done by the force F_0 in 2 sec?

31. A constant horizontal force $F_0 = 3$ N drags a box along a rough horizontal surface at a constant velocity v_0. The force does work at the rate of 5 W. (*a*) What is the velocity v_0? (*b*) How much work is done by F_0 in 3 sec?

32. A single force of 5 N acts in the x direction on a 10-kg mass. (*a*) If the mass starts at rest at position $x = 0$ at time $t = 0$, find the velocity v and position x as a function of time t. (*b*) What is the power input of the force at time $t = 2$ sec? (*c*) Write an expression for the power input of the force as a function of time t.

33. A constant force of 4 N acts at an angle of 30° above the horizontal on a box of mass 2 kg resting on a rough horizontal surface. The box is dragged with a constant speed of 50 cm/sec. (*a*) Find the normal force exerted by the table on the box and the coefficient of friction. (*b*) What is the power input of the applied force? (*c*) How much work is done by the frictional force in 3 sec?

34. An engine is rated at 400 horsepower. How much work is done by it operating at full power for 1 min? Express your answer in foot-pounds and in kilowatt-hours.

35. A 4000-lb car drives up a road inclined at 2° to the horizontal at a rate of 60 mi/h (88 ft/sec). (*a*) What is the minimum force exerted by the road on the car tangent to the road? (*b*) At what rate (in horsepower) does the potential energy of the car increase? (*c*) Why must the car engine develop a greater horsepower than this?

Section 7-7, Scalar, or Dot, Product of Two Vectors

36. Two vectors **A** and **B** have magnitudes 6 ft and make an angle of 60° with each other. Find **A** · **B**.

37. The scalar product of two vectors, **A** and **B**, is 4 units. The magnitudes of the vectors are $A = 4$ and $B = 8$. Find the angle between the vectors.

38. Find **A** · **B** for the following vectors: (*a*) **A** $= 2\mathbf{i} - 6\mathbf{j}$, **B** $= -3\mathbf{i} + 2\mathbf{j}$; (*b*) **A** $= 4\mathbf{i} + 4\mathbf{j}$, **B** $= 2\mathbf{i} - 3\mathbf{j}$; (*c*) **A** $= 3\mathbf{i} + 4\mathbf{j}$, **B** $= 4\mathbf{i} - 3\mathbf{j}$.

39. Find the angle θ between the vectors **A** and **B** given in Exercise 38.

40. Find the power input of a force **F** acting on a particle which moves with velocity **v** for (*a*) **F** $= 3\mathbf{i} + 4\mathbf{k}$ N, **v** $= 2\mathbf{i}$ m/sec; (*b*) **F** $= 5\mathbf{i} - 6\mathbf{j}$ N, **v** $= -5\mathbf{i} + 4\mathbf{j}$ m/sec; (*c*) **F** $= 2\mathbf{i} - 4\mathbf{j}$ N, **v** $= 6\mathbf{i} + 3\mathbf{j}$ m/sec.

41. If **A** · **B** $= 0$ and **A** $= 2\mathbf{i} - 3\mathbf{j}$, what can be said about **B**?

Problems

1. Derive the expression

$$W_{net} = \int \Sigma F_x \, dx = \int \frac{p}{m} \, dp$$

by using Newton's second law in the form $F_x = dp/dt$ and applying the chain rule to dp/dt. Consider the momentum p to be a function of x.

Figure 7-16
F_x versus x for Problem 2.

2. A 3-kg mass is moving with speed 1.00 m/sec in the x direction. When it passes the origin, it is acted on by a single force F_x, which varies with x as shown in Figure 7-16. (a) Find the work done by the force from $x = 0$ to $x = 2$ m. (b) What is the kinetic energy of the mass at $x = 2$ m? (c) What is the speed of the particle at $x = 2$ m? (d) Find the work done on the particle from $x = 0$ to $x = 4$ m. (e) What is the velocity of the particle at $x = 4$ m?

3. When you walk along a horizontal surface, you lift part of your weight a small amount in each step and therefore do work against the force of gravity. (a) Estimate the work done in each step and the total work you do in lifting yourself when you walk 1 mi along a horizontal surface. (b) If you walk 1 mi in 20 min, what is your horsepower output?

4. A 5-kg block is held against a spring of force constant 20 N/cm, compressing it 3 cm. The block is released, and the spring expands, pushing the block along a rough horizontal surface. The coefficient of friction between the surface and the block is 0.2. (a) Find the work done on the block by the spring as it extends from its compressed position to its equilibrium position. (b) Find the work done on the block by friction while it moves the 3 cm to the equilibrium position of the spring. (c) What is the speed of the block when the spring is at its equilibrium position? (d) If the block is not attached to the spring, how far will it slide along the rough surface before coming to rest? (e) Suppose the block is attached to the spring so that the spring is extended when the block slides past the equilibrium point. By how much will the spring be extended before the block comes momentarily to rest? Describe the subsequent motion.

5. Figure 7-17 shows a pendulum bob making an angle θ with the vertical. (a) Indicate all the forces acting on the bob at angle θ. Write the tangential component of the force as a function of θ. (b) Show that the work done by the earth when the angle increases by $d\theta$ is $-mgL \sin \theta \, d\theta$. Hint: Write the path length ds in terms of θ. (c) Find the total work done by the earth when the bob moves from $\theta = 0$ to $\theta = \theta_0$. Express your result in terms of the vertical distance H the bob is lifted from $\theta = 0$ to $\theta = \theta_0$.

Figure 7-17
Problem 5.

6. A pendulum bob of mass m is raised to $\theta = 90°$ and released. (a) Find the work done by all forces acting on the bob while it swings from $\theta = 90°$ to $\theta = 0$. (b) Find the kinetic energy of the bob at $\theta = 0°$. (c) Show that the tension in the string at $\theta = 0°$ is 3 times the weight of the bob.

7. A particle of mass m moves in a horizontal circle of radius r on a rough table. It is attached to a string fixed at the center of the circle. The speed of the particle is initially v_0. After completing one full trip around the circle, the speed of the particle is $\frac{1}{2}v_0$. (a) Find the work done by friction during that 1 rev in terms of m, v_0, and r. (b) What is the coefficient of sliding friction? (c) How many more revolutions will the particle make before coming to rest?

8. A 2-kg box is projected with initial speed of 3 m/sec up a rough plane inclined at 60° to the horizontal. The coefficient of friction is 0.3. (a) List all the forces acting on the box and find the work done by each as the box slides up the plane. (b) How far does the box slide along the plane before it stops momentarily? (c) Find the work done by each force acting on the box as it slides back down the plane. (d) Find its speed when it reaches its initial position.

9. Vectors **A**, **B**, and **C** form a triangle, as shown in Figure 7-18. The angle between **A** and **B** is θ; the vectors are related by $\mathbf{C} = \mathbf{A} - \mathbf{B}$. Compute $\mathbf{C} \cdot \mathbf{C}$ in terms of A, B, and θ and derive the law of cosines $C^2 = A^2 + B^2 - 2AB \cos \theta$.

Figure 7-18
Problem 9.

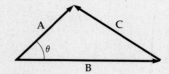

CHAPTER 8   Potential Energy and
Conservative Forces

We saw in Chapter 7 that in some cases work can be stored in the form
of potential energy. For example, the work needed to lift an object of
mass m a vertical distance h is mgh. At the height h, the object is said
to have potential energy mgh relative to its original position $h = 0$.
When the object moves back to its original position, the work done by
the force of gravity is mgh no matter what path the object follows. In
this chapter we investigate the concept of potential energy in detail.
We shall see that potential energy is associated with the work done by
a certain class of forces called *conservative forces*. Examples of conservative forces are the force of gravity, the force exerted by an elastic
spring, and the electrostatic force. For each conservative force we
define a potential-energy function U such that the work done by the
force equals the decrease in the potential energy. If the conservative
force is the only force acting on a particle or the only force that does
work, the work done also equals the increase in the kinetic energy, as
discussed in Chapter 7. Then the sum of the kinetic energy and the
potential energy, called the *total mechanical energy*, remains constant
because the decrease in potential energy is balanced by an increase in
kinetic energy. (If the work done by the conservative force is negative,
the potential energy increases and the kinetic energy decreases by an
equal amount.) The total mechanical energy is said to be conserved.

8-1   Conservative Forces

The criterion for a force to be conservative can be simply stated. *A*
force is conservative if the total work it does on a particle is zero when the
particle moves around any closed path returning to its initial position. We
have already seen that the force of gravity has this property. If we
project an object up an inclined plane with some initial speed, the
force of gravity does work $-mgh$ while the object moves up and $+mgh$
while it moves down, where h is the maximum vertical distance the

Conservative force defined

The waterfall in this 1961 lithograph by the Swiss artist M. C. Escher violates the law of the conservation of energy. When the water falls, part of its potential energy is converted into the kinetic energy of the waterwheel. How does the water get back to the top of the waterfall? (*Courtesy of the Escher Foundation, Haags Gemeentemuseum, The Hague.*)

object rises. If this conservative force is the only force acting, the object has the same kinetic energy when it arrives back at its starting point that it had originally.

An example of a nonconservative force is that of sliding friction. Since this force is always opposite to the direction of motion, it always does negative work. When an object makes a round trip ending at its original position, the total work done by sliding friction on it is negative. For example, if we project an object up a rough inclined plane with some initial speed, the frictional force does work $-\mu_k Ns$ on the way up and $-\mu_k Ns$ on the way down, where μ_k is the coefficient of friction, N is the normal force, and s is the distance traveled up the plane. When a nonconservative force such as friction acts on an object, the object does not have its original kinetic energy when it arrives back at its original position. In this example the kinetic energy is less by an amount $2\mu_k Ns$.

An alternative statement of the criterion for a force to be conservative is that *the work done on a particle by a conservative force is independent of how the particle moves from one point to another.* Figure 8-1 shows several paths connecting points P_1 and P_2. If the work done by a conservative force is W when the particle moves from P_2 to P_1 along one of the paths, it must be $-W$ when the particle returns along any of the paths because the total round-trip work must be zero.

Alternative definition of conservative force

Figure 8-1
Several paths connecting
points P_1 and P_2. By definition, the work done by a conservative force is zero for any
round-trip path ending at its
starting point. If a conservative force does work W on a
particle moving from P_2 to P_1
along path 2, it must then do
work $-W$ on the particle as it
moves back along any return
path such as path 1 or 3. It
follows that the work done by
a conservative force on a particle moving from point P_1 to
point P_2 is the same for all
paths connecting the points.

The work done on a particle by a force $\mathbf{F}$ as the particle moves from point P_1 to P_2 along some path can be written

$$W = \int_1^2 \mathbf{F} \cdot d\mathbf{s} \qquad\qquad 8\text{-}1$$

The integral in this equation, called a *line integral*, is computed by taking the dot product of the force $\mathbf{F}$ and the displacement $d\mathbf{s}$ for each element along the path and summing. If the force is conservative, the work does not depend on which path is taken between the points or on the particle's speed. The work done by a conservative force depends only on the end points P_1 and P_2. It is therefore just a function of the positions P_1 and P_2. We define the potential-energy function U so that the work done equals the decrease in the potential energy:

$$W = \int_1^2 \mathbf{F} \cdot d\mathbf{s} = U_1 - U_2 = -\Delta U \qquad\qquad 8\text{-}2a$$

where

$$\Delta U = U_2 - U_1 = -\int_1^2 \mathbf{F} \cdot d\mathbf{s} \qquad\qquad 8\text{-}2b$$

For very small displacements $d\mathbf{s}$ we can write this definition of potential energy in differential form:

$$dU = -\mathbf{F} \cdot d\mathbf{s} \qquad\qquad 8\text{-}3$$

Definition of potential energy

Since only the change in the potential energy is defined, the value of the function U at any point is not specified by the definition. We are free to choose the value of U at any one point arbitrarily. We usually choose U to be zero at some reference point. The potential energy at any other point is then the difference between the potential energy at that point and at the reference point.

The work done by a nonconservative force acting on a particle which moves from point P_1 to point P_2 can also be written as a line integral, as in Equation 8-1, but this work may depend on the path followed by the particle, on the speed of the particle, or on other quantities. Since this work is not just a function of the initial and final positions of the particle, there is no potential-energy function associated with a nonconservative force.

8-2 The Conservation of Mechanical Energy

The negative sign in the definition of potential energy in Equations 8-2 and 8-3 is introduced so that the work done by a conservative force equals the *decrease* in potential energy. If this force is the only force acting, or if it is the only force that does work on the particle, the work done by the force also equals the *increase* in *kinetic energy*, i.e.,

$$W = \int \mathbf{F} \cdot d\mathbf{s} = -\Delta U = +\Delta E_k$$

Hence

$$\Delta E_k + \Delta U = \Delta(E_k + U) = 0 \qquad \text{8-4}$$

Conservation of mechanical energy

This is an example of the conservation of energy, which we discuss more fully in the next chapter. We call the sum of the potential energy and kinetic energy the *total mechanical energy of the particle:*

$$E_{\text{total}} = E_k + U \qquad \text{8-5}$$

Equation 8-4 states that the total mechanical energy is constant if the only force that does work is a conservative force. (This is the origin of the expression conservative force.) When only such forces do work, the total mechanical energy is conserved.

8-3 Conservative Forces and Potential Energy in One Dimension

For one-dimensional motion, a necessary and sufficient condition for a force to be conservative is that the force be constant or depend only on the position of the particle. The work done by a force $\mathbf{F}$ acting on a particle moving along the x axis from point x_1 to point x_2 is

$$W = \int_{x_1}^{x_2} \mathbf{F} \cdot dx \, \mathbf{i} = \int_{x_1}^{x_2} F_x \, dx \qquad \text{8-6}$$

where F_x can be either positive or negative. In general, the force may depend on the position of the particle, the velocity of the particle, or other quantities. If the force is constant or depends only on the position x, the work done depends only on the initial and final positions x_1 and x_2 and the force is conservative. The potential-energy function $U(x)$ is defined by the one-dimensional equivalents of Equations 8-2 and 8-3,

$$\Delta U = U(x_2) - U(x_1) = -\int_{x_1}^{x_2} F_x \, dx \qquad \text{8-7}$$

or in differential form,

$$dU = -F_x \, dx \qquad \text{8-8}$$

An example of a conservative force in one dimension which we have already discussed is the force of gravity. (This force is also conservative for general three-dimensional motion, as we shall see later.) Let us consider motion near the surface of the earth along a vertical line which we take to be the y axis. The force of gravity on a particle of mass m is constant and directed downward. If we choose up for the positive direction of y, this force is

$$\mathbf{F} = F_y\mathbf{j} = -mg\mathbf{j}$$

The work done by gravity when the particle is displaced from point y_1 to point y_2 is

$$W = \int_{y_1}^{y_2} -mg\ (\mathbf{j} \cdot d\mathbf{s}) = \int_{y_1}^{y_2} -mg\ dy = -mg(y_2 - y_1)$$

Setting this work equal to the decrease in potential energy, we have

$$-mg(y_2 - y_1) = -\Delta U = U(y_1) - U(y_2)$$

or

$$\Delta U = U(y_2) - U(y_1) = mgy_2 - mgy_1$$

If we choose the potential energy equal to zero at the reference height $y = 0$, the potential energy at any height y relative to $y = 0$ is

$$U(y) = mgy \qquad\qquad 8\text{-}9$$

Gravitational potential energy near earth's surface

This potential-energy function can also be determined from the differential form, Equation 8-8 (using y instead of x since we are considering vertical motion),

$$dU = -F_y\ dy = -(-mg)\ dy = +mg\ dy$$

Integrating gives

$$U(y) = mgy + C$$

where C is an arbitrary constant of integration. This constant is related to the choice of zero potential energy. If we choose $U = 0$ at $y = 0$, the constant C is zero.

Example 8-1 A 2-kg mass is raised from height $y_1 = 0$ to $y_3 = 10$ m and then lowered to its final height $y_2 = 8$ m. Find the work done by the force of gravity and the change in potential energy.

The weight of the mass is $mg = (2\text{ kg})(9.81\text{ m/sec}^2) = 19.6$ N. The work done by gravity when the mass is raised is negative because the force is opposed to the motion:

$$W_1 = -mg(y_3 - y_1) = -(19.6\text{ N})(10\text{ m}) = -196\text{ J}$$

When the mass is lowered from 10 to 8 m, the force of gravity does positive work equal to

$$W_2 = (19.6\text{ N})(2\text{ m}) = 39.2\text{ J}$$

The total, or net, work done by the force of gravity is the sum of these:

$$W_{\text{total}} = W_1 + W_2 = -196\text{ J} + 39.2\text{ J} = -157\text{ J}$$

The negative of this work is $+157$ J, which is the change in the potential energy of the mass:

$$U = mg(y_2 - y_1) = (19.6\text{ N})(8\text{ m}) = 157\text{ J}$$

This work is the same as if the mass were just raised from $y = 0$ to $y = 8$ m. It does not depend on how the mass moves but only on its initial and final positions.

Joe Monroe/Photo Researchers

This boulder, located in the Arches National Park in Utah, has gravitational potential energy relative to ground level.

Culver Pictures

A slingshot is an example of elastic potential energy. The work done in stretching the rubber is stored as potential energy and then converted into kinetic energy of the missile.

Example 8-2 Find the potential-energy function associated with a spring which exerts a force $F_x = -kx$.

Here we have chosen the origin $x = 0$ at the equilibrium length of the spring. In this example, the force is not constant, but since it is a one-dimensional force which is a function of position only, it must be conservative. The potential-energy function $U(x)$ can be calculated from the differential form (Equation 8-8) or from Equation 8-7. Equation 8-8 gives

$$dU = -F_x\, dx = -(-kx)\, dx = +kx\, dx$$

Integrating gives

$$U = \tfrac{1}{2}kx^2 + C$$

where again the constant of integration C depends on our arbitrary choice of the position of zero potential energy. In this case, C is the value of the potential-energy function at the equilibrium length $x = 0$. If we choose the potential energy to be zero at this point, $C = 0$. The potential energy relative to $x = 0$ is then

$$U = \tfrac{1}{2}kx^2 \qquad\qquad\qquad\qquad 8\text{-}10$$

Potential energy of a spring

The potential-energy function can also be calculated from the integral form (Equation 8-7). If the spring is stretched from $x = 0$ to some distance x, the work done by the spring is

$$W = \int_0^x -kx\, dx = -\tfrac{1}{2}kx^2$$

This work is just the area under the F_x-versus-x curve in Figure 8-2.

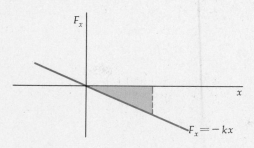

Figure 8-2
Work done by a spring when it is stretched from its equilibrium length. The force F_x exerted by the spring is plotted versus extension x, where $x = 0$ is chosen at the equilibrium length. The work indicated by the shaded area is negative when the spring is stretched because the force opposes the motion.

The work is negative because the force opposes the motion. The negative of this work is the change in potential energy of the spring

$$\Delta U = U(x) - U(0) = +\tfrac{1}{2}kx^2$$

or

$$U(x) = \tfrac{1}{2}kx^2 + U(0)$$

This result is the same as Equation 8-10 when the potential energy at $x = 0$ is chosen to be zero.

By our definition of potential energy, when a conservative force does positive work, the potential energy decreases. The force is thus in the direction of decreasing potential energy. A particle under the influence of a single conservative force accelerates in the direction of decreasing potential energy; with gravity the acceleration is downward; with a mass on a spring, the mass accelerates toward the equilibrium position $x = 0$.

If we apply a force equal and opposite to a conservative force so that the particle moves (without acceleration) in the direction opposite the conservative force, the conservative force does negative work and we do positive work equal to the increase in potential energy. Thus to lift a mass through a vertical distance y without acceleration the work we do is mgh; to stretch a spring from its equilibrium length $x = 0$ to some length x the work we do is $\tfrac{1}{2}kx^2$.

Linda Cronquist

Another example of elastic potential energy. As the ball is dropped, gravitational potential energy is converted into kinetic energy, which is greatest just before the ball strikes the floor. Some of the kinetic energy is then stored momentarily as elastic potential energy of deformation. This potential energy is quickly converted into kinetic energy, which is again changed into gravitational potential energy as the ball rises.

Questions

1. A mass moves along a vertical line. Must two observers (in the same reference frame) studying its motion agree on the value of its kinetic energy at any instant? Must they agree on the value of its potential energy?

2. A mass rests on a table 4 ft above the floor. Where would you choose the reference point for potential energy to be so that the gravitational potential energy for the mass will be (*a*) positive, (*b*) zero, (*c*) negative?

3. Estimate the amount by which your gravitational potential energy changes when you walk up a flight of stairs.

4. The force exerted by a spring which obeys Hooke's law is a conservative force. Would the force of a spring which is stretched beyond its elastic limit be conservative?

5. If a spring did not obey Hooke's law for large displacements but did obey the law $F_x = -kx + bx^3$, where b is a constant, would the force be conservative?

8-4   Nonconservative Forces in One Dimension

It is important to realize that a potential-energy function $U(x)$ can be defined by Equations 8-7 and 8-8 only if the force **F** is conservative, i.e., if **F** is constant or a function of position only. The reason for this restriction can be seen by considering forces which depend on quantities other than position, e.g., the speed of the particle. In this case, the work done on a particle as it travels from point x_1 to x_2 depends on how fast the particle travels. Since we cannot write this work as a function of the points x_1 and x_2, we cannot define a potential energy $U(x)$ by Equation 8-7. An example of such a nonconservative force is viscous drag, which increases in magnitude with increasing speed and is in the direction opposite the velocity of the particle.

Another example of a nonconservative force, already mentioned, is sliding friction. Consider a box sliding on a rough plane from point x_1 to x_2. The frictional force depends on the *velocity* of the box and cannot be written as a function of the position of the box. For example, if the box is at rest with no applied force, the frictional force is zero. If the box moves to the right, the frictional force is to the left; if the box moves to the left, the frictional force is to the right. Even if the magnitude of the frictional force is approximately independent of speed, the direction of the force depends on the direction of the velocity. Therefore, we cannot write the work done by this force as a function of the initial and final positions, and we cannot define a potential-energy function associated with this force. If we move the box from $x_1 = 0$ to $x_2 = 5$ m, the work done by friction is negative, but we cannot get this work back when we release the box. If the box is moved from $x_1 = 0$ to $x_3 = 10$ m and then back to $x_2 = 5$ m, the frictional force does 3 times as much work as when we move it directly from 0 to 5 m (assuming constant magnitude of the frictional force). The work done by this force depends on how the object is moved from one point to another.

Another common example of a nonconservative force is a force applied by a human agent like a push or a pull. Suppose you decide to lift a weight through a vertical distance h. You may apply a vertical force equal to the weight, just balancing the force of gravity so that the weight does not accelerate. Or you may apply a force greater than the weight so that the weight is accelerated. The force you apply clearly does not depend merely on position and is thus nonconservative.

Questions

6. Is the work done by a nonconservative force always negative?

7. When you jump into the air, the forces exerted by your leg muscles do work on your body. Are these forces conservative?

8-5   Conservative Forces and Potential Energy in Three Dimensions

The problem of determining whether a given force is conservative is more complicated in three-dimensional motion. The work done by a force as a particle moves from one point to another is the line integral given in Equation 8-1. As in one dimension, if the force depends on velocity or any quantity other than position, the work done is not just a function of the initial and final positions and a potential-energy function of position cannot be defined by this work. Thus it is still necessary that the force not depend on any quantity other than position if it is to be conservative. However, in three-dimensional motion, even if a force is a function of position only, the work done by the force may depend on the path taken by the particle between the initial and final positions, in which case this force is nonconservative and a potential-energy function cannot be defined. We shall illustrate such a nonconservative force in Example 8-6.

If we can show that the work done by a force along two different paths connecting the same initial and final positions is different, we know immediately that the force is not conservative. Alternatively, we can show that a force is nonconservative if we can show that the work it does is not zero when a particle moves in a closed path ending at its initial position. To show that a given force is conservative, we must show that the work done is the same along *every* path connecting the initial and final positions. Surprisingly, this can be done rather easily for any given force using the properties of partial derivatives of a function of two or more variables. (We discuss this briefly in Section 8-10 for students familiar with this part of calculus.) Fortunately, for many forces of interest, we can show that the force is conservative by calculating the work done along a general path in space and showing that this work depends only on the initial and final positions.

The simplest example of a conservative force in three dimensions is a constant or uniform force. A force which has the same magnitude and direction at every point in space is called a *uniform force*. An example is the force of gravity near the surface of the earth. If we choose the y axis parallel to the direction of the force, such a force can be written

$$\mathbf{F} = F_0 \mathbf{j}$$

where F_0 is the magnitude of the force and $\mathbf{j}$ is the unit vector in the y direction. A general displacement in three dimensions can be written

$$d\mathbf{s} = dx\,\mathbf{i} + dy\,\mathbf{j} + dz\,\mathbf{k}$$

The work done by the force $\mathbf{F}$ for this displacement is

$$dW = \mathbf{F} \cdot d\mathbf{s} = (F_0 \mathbf{j}) \cdot (dx\,\mathbf{i} + dy\,\mathbf{j} + dz\,\mathbf{k}) = F_0\,dy$$

The work done by the force when a particle moves from initial position (x_1, y_1, z_1) to final position (x_2, y_2, z_2) is

$$W = \int_{y_1}^{y_2} F_0\,dy = F_0(y_2 - y_1)$$

This work depends only on the initial and final positions, and so the force is conservative. If $\mathbf{F}$ is the force of gravity near the surface of the earth, $F_0 = -mg$ (assuming y to be positive upward). This result for W agrees with our result (discussed in Chapter 7) that the work done by the force of gravity when a particle moves from height y_1 to height y_2 is $-mg(y_2 - y_1) = mg(y_1 - y_2)$ no matter what path the particle follows (see Figure 7-8). The potential-energy function associated with the force of gravity near the surface of the earth is given by Equation 8-9.

In another important class of forces in three-dimensional motion are forces directed toward or away from the origin. Such a force is called a

William Vandivert

As the tree falls, potential energy is converted into kinetic energy. When it hits, the kinetic energy is lost as heat and sound.

central force. If the magnitude of the force depends only on the distance from the origin, the force is conservative. We can represent such a force in general by

$$\mathbf{F} = F_r\hat{\mathbf{r}} = f(r)\hat{\mathbf{r}}$$ 8-11

where $f(r)$ is any function of r and $\hat{\mathbf{r}}$ is a unit vector pointing in the radial direction away from the origin. This general case includes the force of gravity, for which $f(r) = -Gm_1m_2/r^2$, and the electrostatic force, for which $f(r) = kq_1q_2/r^2$. Central forces of this type are conservative no matter what the function $f(r)$ may be.

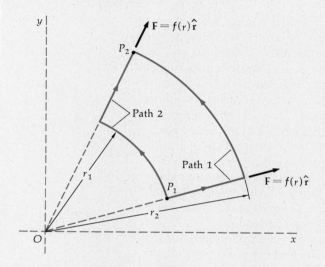

Figure 8-3
Two paths connecting points P_1 and P_2 in a radial force field $\mathbf{F} = f(r)\hat{\mathbf{r}}$. When a particle moves along either arc segment, the work done by the force is zero because the force is perpendicular to the motion. The work done by the force on a particle moving from r_1 to r_2 is the same along either radial segment because the magnitude of the force depends only on r. It follows that the work done by the force is the same for each of the paths connecting P_1 and P_2.

Consider the two simple paths between points P_1 and P_2 shown in Figure 8-3. Each path consists of a straight radial segment and a circular arc segment at a constant distance from the origin. The work done by the force $\mathbf{F}$ along a radial segment is

$$W = \int_{r_1}^{r_2} \mathbf{F} \cdot d\mathbf{s} = \int_{r_1}^{r_2} F_r\, dr = \int_{r_1}^{r_2} f(r)\, dr$$ 8-12

This work is the same for the radial segments of each path because the magnitude of the force $F_r = f(r)$ depends only on r and not on θ. The work is in fact the same for all radial paths beginning at a distance r_1 and ending at a distance r_2. Along a circular arc segment, the displacement $d\mathbf{s}$ is always perpendicular to the force $\mathbf{F}$, so that the work done by the force is zero. Thus the work done by the force is the same along each of the paths shown between points P_1 and P_2.

We now consider a general path connecting these points shown in Figure 8-4. We can approximate this path by a series of radial segments and circular arc segments. The work done by the force along any radial segment is $dW = f(r)\, dr$. Along any circular arc segment the work is zero because $d\mathbf{s}$ is perpendicular to $\mathbf{F}$. Hence the total work done is just the sum of the work done along the radial segments, which is

$$W = \int_{r_1}^{r_2} f(r)\, dr$$

This is the same for all paths connecting P_1 and P_2. Thus the force given by Equation 8-11 is conservative. We shall calculate the potential-energy functions for the gravitational and electrostatic forces of this type in Examples 8-3 and 8-4.

Figure 8-4
Any path from P_1 to P_2 can be approximated by a series of radial segments and arc segments of constant radius. Since a radial force $\mathbf{F} = f(r)\hat{\mathbf{r}}$ does work only along the radial segments, the total work is the sum of the work along these segments. The total work is the same for all paths connecting P_1 and P_2.

Example 8-3 Find the potential-energy function $U(r)$ associated with the gravitational force exerted by the earth on a particle which is not necessarily near the surface of the earth.

The gravitational force exerted by the earth on a particle of mass m at a distance r from the center of the earth is given by

$$\mathbf{F} = -\frac{GM_E m}{r^2}\,\hat{\mathbf{r}} \qquad\qquad 8\text{-}13$$

where M_E is the mass of the earth, r is the distance from the center of the earth to the mass, and $\hat{\mathbf{r}}$ is the unit vector pointing away from the center of the earth. This force is a conservative central force with $f(r) = -GM_E m/r^2$, as discussed above. The potential-energy function is most easily computed from the differential definition, Equation 8-3. For any displacement $d\mathbf{s}$, we have

$$dU = -\mathbf{F} \cdot d\mathbf{s} = -F_r\, dr = -\frac{-GM_E m}{r^2}\, dr = +\frac{GM_E m}{r^2}\, dr$$

Integrating gives

$$U = -\frac{GM_E m}{r} + C$$

where C is a constant of integration. The potential energy $U(r)$ increases as r increases to a maximum value $U = C$ at infinite distance. For this case the reference point for zero potential energy is customarily chosen to be at infinite distance so that the constant C is zero. Then

$$U = -\frac{GM_E m}{r} \qquad\qquad 8\text{-}14$$

Gravitational potential energy

With this choice of zero potential energy, the potential energy is always negative. Since only changes in U enter into its definition, the actual value at any one point is unimportant. This potential-energy function is shown in Figure 8-5. At $r = R_E$, the radius of the earth, the

(a)

(b)

Figure 8-5
(a) Graph of the gravitational potential-energy function $U = -GM_E m/r$ versus r. At the surface of the earth ($r = R_E$) the potential energy has the value $-GM_E m/R_E$, and it increases to zero at infinite r. Near the surface of the earth the curve is approximately linear. (b) The same potential-energy function near the surface of the earth with the zero chosen at $r = R_E$. The function U' is related to U by $U' = U + GM_E m/R_E$. If $y = r - R_E$ is small compared with R_E, U' is approximately *mgy*.

potential energy is $U = -GM_Em/R_E$. At values of r less than R_E Equation 8-13 does not hold, and so the potential-energy function (Equation 8-14) does not hold either.

We can relate this potential-energy function to the one obtained previously for positions near the surface of the earth. Let U' be the potential-energy function which is defined to be zero at $r = R_E$. From Figure 8-5 we see that U' and U are related by

$$U' = U + \frac{GM_Em}{R_E} = -\frac{GM_Em}{r} + \frac{GM_Em}{R_E}$$

$$= \frac{GM_Em}{rR_E}(r - R_E)$$

But $r - R_E = y$, the height above the surface of the earth, and $GM_E/R_E^2 = g$, the free-fall acceleration of gravity. Then

$$U' = mgy\frac{R_E}{r} \qquad \text{8-15}$$

Near the surface of the earth, r and R_E are approximately equal, and Equations 8-15 and 8-9 are the same.

Example 8-4 Electrostatic Potential Energy According to Coulomb's law, the force exerted by a charge q_1 at the origin on another charge q_2 at position **r** is

$$\mathbf{F} = \frac{kq_1q_2}{r^2}\hat{\mathbf{r}}$$

where q_1 and q_2 are the magnitudes of the respective charges and k is the coulomb constant. This expression is similar to the gravitational force except that GM_Em is replaced by kq_1q_2 and there is no negative sign. That is, if q_1 and q_2 have the same sign, the force is repulsive, unlike the gravitational force, which is always attractive. The potential-energy function can be found as in the previous example. If q_2 is given displacement $d\mathbf{s}$, we have

$$dU = -\mathbf{F} \cdot d\mathbf{s} = -F_r\, dr = -\frac{kq_1q_2}{r^2}\, dr$$

and

$$U = \frac{kq_1q_2}{r} + C$$

Again, it is convenient to choose the potential energy to be zero at an infinite separation so that the constant C is zero. Then

$$U = +\frac{kq_1q_2}{r} \qquad \text{8-16}$$

Electrostatic potential energy

In this case the potential energy is positive if the charges have the same signs and negative if they have different signs. The magnitude decreases as r increases.

Example 8-5 Find the potential energy for an electron and proton at their most likely separation in the hydrogen atom, which is $r = 0.529 \times 10^{-10}$ m. The charges are

$$q_e = -e = 1.6 \times 10^{-19} \text{ C}$$

$$q_p = +e = 1.6 \times 10^{-19} \text{ C}$$

and the coulomb constant is $k = 9 \times 10^9$ N-m²/C². The potential energy is then

$$U = \frac{(9 \times 10^9 \text{ N-m}^2/\text{C}^2)(-1.6 \times 10^{-19} \text{ C})(+1.6 \times 10^{-19} \text{ C})}{0.529 \times 10^{-10} \text{ m}}$$

$$= -4.36 \times 10^{-18} \text{ N-m} = -4.36 \times 10^{-18} \text{ J}$$

Example 8-6 Show that the force $\mathbf{F} = f(r)\hat{\boldsymbol{\theta}}$ is nonconservative, where $f(r)$ is any function of r and $\hat{\boldsymbol{\theta}}$ is the unit vector perpendicular to $\mathbf{r}$.

At any distance r from the origin, this force is tangent to the circle of radius r and in the direction of increasing θ as in Figure 8-6a. This kind of force is exerted on a charge moving between the poles of an electromagnet when the magnetic field is changing. An example of its application is the betatron, a device for accelerating electrons to high energy for producing x-rays. We can show that the force is nonconservative by showing that the work done by the force when a particle makes a round trip is not zero.

Consider a particle moving in a circle of radius r in the direction of the force. Since the force is constant and in the direction of motion, the work done is just the force $f(r)$ times the distance $s = 2\pi r$

$$W = f(r)2\pi r$$

Since this work is not zero when the particle has returned to its initial position, the force is not conservative. Alternatively, we can show that the work done by the force on a particle which moves from one point to another is different for different paths. Consider points P_1 and P_2 equidistant from the origin, as in Figure 8-6b. When the particle moves along the circular arc from point P_1 to point P_2, the work done is $f(r)s$, where s is the distance measured along the arc. If the particle first moves from point P_1 to the origin along a radial line and then back out to P_2 along another radial line, the force does no work because it is always perpendicular to the displacement for this path.

Figure 8-6
(a) The force $\mathbf{F} = f(r)\hat{\boldsymbol{\theta}}$ for Example 8-6. At distance r from the origin the force is tangent to the circle of radius r and in the direction of increasing θ. If a particle moves around the circle and returns to its original position, the work done by the force is not zero. The force is therefore not conservative. (b) Two paths connecting points P_1 and P_2. The work done by the force in (a) along path 1 is $f(r)s$, where s is the distance measured along the arc. Along path 2 the work done by the force is zero because it is perpendicular to the motion.

Questions

8. When you climb a mountain, is the work done on you by gravity different if you take a short steep trail instead of a long gentle trail? If not, why would you find one trail easier than the other?

9. What are the advantages or disadvantages in choosing the gravitational and electrostatic potential-energy functions to be zero at $r = \infty$?

8-6   The Electron Volt Energy Unit

The electrostatic potential energy of a particle divided by the charge of the particle is called the *electrostatic potential* of the particle. We shall study this concept in detail in Chapter 32; now we are interested only in the SI unit of potential, which is the joule per coulomb, called a *volt* (V):

$$1 \text{ V} = 1 \text{ J/C}$$

Energies in atomic physics are usually given in units of the fundamental electric charge e times 1 V. This unit, called the *electron volt* (eV), is related to the joule by

Electron volt defined

$$1 \text{ eV} = 1.6 \times 10^{-19} \text{ C-V} = 1.6 \times 10^{-19} \text{ J} \qquad \text{8-17}$$

For example, the potential energy found in Example 8-5, for the electron in the hydrogen atom, expressed in electron volts, is

$$U = -4.36 \times 10^{-18} \text{ J} \times \frac{1 \text{ eV}}{1.6 \times 10^{-19} \text{ J}} = -27.2 \text{ eV}$$

Common multiples are the kiloelectron volt (1 keV $= 10^3$ eV) and the megaelectron volt (1 MeV $= 10^6$ eV).

8-7   Force from Potential Energy

So far we have been finding the potential-energy function from a given force. We now consider the inverse problem, finding the force from a given potential-energy function. For most cases of interest to us (one-dimensional motion and central forces) the force has only one component, and the potential energy is a function of just one variable. In these cases the force is just the negative derivative of the potential energy. According to Equation 8-8, the force and potential-energy function for one dimension are related by

$$dU = -F_x \, dx$$

If we divide both sides by dx, we obtain

$$F_x = -\frac{dU}{dx} \qquad \text{8-18}$$

The force is thus the negative derivative of U with respect to x. For central forces, e.g., those of gravity and electrostatics, we found in Examples 8-3 and 8-4 that

$$dU = -F_r \, dr$$

In this case the force has only a radial component F_r, which is the negative derivative of U with respect to r:

$$F_r = -\frac{dU}{dr} \qquad \text{8-19}$$

Example 8-7 Given $U(x) = Cx^2$, where C is a constant, what is the force corresponding to this potential energy?

We have $dU/dx = 2Cx$; therefore, $F_x = -dU/dx = -2Cx$. We see that this is the same as for a spring of force constant $k = 2C$, with $x = 0$ at the equilibrium point.

Example 8-8 Given $U(x) = C(1/\sqrt{x^2 + a^2})$ with C and a constant, find F_x.

We have

$$\frac{dU}{dx} = -\tfrac{1}{2}C(x^2 + a^2)^{-3/2}2x = -Cx(x^2 + a^2)^{-3/2}$$

Thus the force is

$$F_x = -\frac{dU}{dx} = +\frac{Cx}{(x^2 + a^2)^{3/2}}$$

The general relation between force and potential energy is given by

$$dU = -\mathbf{F} \cdot d\mathbf{s}$$

Let us consider various displacements of magnitude ds but with different directions. If $d\mathbf{s}$ is perpendicular to $\mathbf{F}$, the potential-energy change is zero. The greatest change in U occurs when $d\mathbf{s}$ is parallel or antiparallel to the force. When $d\mathbf{s}$ is parallel to the force, we can write

$$F = -\frac{dU}{ds} \qquad d\mathbf{s} \parallel \mathbf{F} \qquad\qquad 8\text{-}20$$

A vector which points in the direction of the greatest change in a scalar function and whose magnitude equals the derivative of the function with respect to distance in that direction is called the *gradient* of the function. Thus in general, the force is the negative gradient of the potential energy.

8-8 Equilibrium and Potential Energy in One Dimension

Figure 8-7 shows a plot of potential energy versus x for a mass on a spring. The potential-energy function, from Equation 8-10, is

$$U(x) = \tfrac{1}{2}kx^2$$

The force is given by the negative slope of this curve,

$$F_x = -\frac{dU}{dx}$$

At the position where the slope is zero, the force is zero and the particle is in equilibrium. By equilibrium we mean that if F_x is the only force acting on it, the particle will remain at rest in this position if it is placed there at rest. This occurs at $x = 0$ when the spring is un-

Figure 8-7
Potential energy U versus displacement from equilibrium x for a mass on a spring. The force F_x is the negative slope $-dU/dx$ of this curve. For x positive, the slope is positive, indicating that F_x is negative. For x negative, the slope is negative, indicating that F_x is positive. The slope is zero at $x = 0$, indicating zero force. A minimum point in the potential-energy curve is a point of stable equilibrium because for displacements on either side of this point the force is toward the equilibrium position.

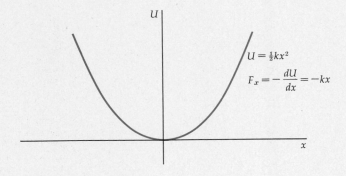

$U = \tfrac{1}{2}kx^2$

$F_x = -\dfrac{dU}{dx} = -kx$

stretched. For x slightly greater than zero the slope is positive; thus F_x is negative and the particle would accelerate toward the equilibrium point $x = 0$. For x slightly less than zero the slope is negative; thus F_x is positive, and the particle again would accelerate toward $x = 0$. The equilibrium is thus stable; i.e., if a particle at rest at the equilibrium point $x = 0$ is displaced slightly, the force then accelerates it back toward the equilibrium point.

Stable equilibrium defined

Figure 8-8 shows the potential-energy curve from Example 8-8. At $x = 0$, the slope is zero. Thus $F_x = 0$ at $x = 0$, and the particle is in equilibrium. However, this equilibrium is unstable. For x slightly greater than zero, the slope is negative and $F_x = -dU/dx$ is positive. Thus if a particle in equilibrium is given a small positive displacement, it will experience a positive force F_x and will accelerate away from the equilibrium position. Similarly, for x slightly less than zero, the slope is positive, indicating that F_x is negative. If the particle is displaced slightly to the left of its equilibrium position, it will accelerate to the left, away from equilibrium. Both maximum and minimum points on a potential-energy curve are positions of equilibrium; at minimum points the equilibrium is stable, and at maximum points it is unstable. We also note that force always urges a particle toward lower potential energy.

Figure 8-8
The potential energy $U(x) = C/\sqrt{x^2 + a^2}$ versus x for Example 8-8. The maximum at $x = 0$ is a position of equilibrium because the slope is zero and $F_x = -dU/dx = 0$. However, this equilibrium is unstable because for displacements in either direction the force is away from the equilibrium position.

Questions

10. You are shown a graph of $U(x)$ versus x. At some places the curve $U(x)$ is steep and at others not so steep. There are maximum and minimum points. At what points is the force associated with $U(x)$ large? Small? Zero?

11. For a certain range of x the potential energy is constant. What is the force in this range?

8-9   Potential Energy of a System of Particles

In our examples we have considered one particle in situations where there is assumed to be an external force which depends on position, e.g., the force due to gravity or a spring. We thus spoke of the potential energy of a particle in a given situation. This description is sufficient for many macroscopic problems in which we concentrate on one particle and treat the surroundings as merely an agent supplying a force F.

Let us now look at a more fundamental situation, a system consisting of two interacting particles. As an example, consider the special case of two charged particles, say protons. Let the particles be a distance r apart, as shown in Figure 8-9. The force on each is the electrostatic force of magnitude $F = kq_1q_2/r^2$ directed away from the other particle (assuming like charges and of course neglecting gravity). We cannot choose a coordinate system fixed on one particle and use Newton's laws because each particle accelerates. Let us instead choose an inertial frame with the origin on the line joining the particles. Let Δr_1 and Δr_2 be the distance moved by particles 1 and 2, respectively, in a short time interval Δt. Since the separation distance is $r = r_1 + r_2$, the change in separation is

$$\Delta r = \Delta r_1 + \Delta r_2$$

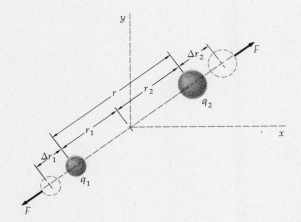

Figure 8-9
Two charges separated by a distance $r = r_1 + r_2$ are given displacements Δr_1 and Δr_2. The total work done on both charges by the electrostatic force of interaction equals the decrease in the electrostatic potential energy of the two-particle system.

If we choose Δt small enough, these distances will be so small that we can neglect the variation in the force during the motion. The work done on particle 1 is $F\,\Delta r_1$, and that done on particle 2 is $F\,\Delta r_2$. Since for each particle F is the resultant force, we can set this work done equal to the change in kinetic energy:

$$\Delta E_{k1} = F\,\Delta r_1 = \frac{kq_1q_2}{r^2}\,\Delta r_1$$

$$\Delta E_{k2} = F\,\Delta r_2 = \frac{kq_1q_2}{r^2}\,\Delta r_2$$

The total increase in kinetic energy of the system is

$$\Delta(E_{k1} + E_{k2}) = \frac{kq_1q_2}{r^2}\,(\Delta r_1 + \Delta r_2) = \frac{kq_1q_2}{r^2}\,\Delta r$$

We define the potential energy of the *system* by

$$U(r) = \frac{kq_1q_2}{r} \qquad\qquad 8\text{-}21$$

For a small change in r, we have

$$\Delta U(r) \approx \frac{dU}{dr}\,\Delta r = \frac{d}{dr}\left(\frac{kq_1q_2}{r}\right)\Delta r = \frac{-kq_1q_2}{r^2}\,\Delta r \qquad\qquad 8\text{-}22$$

Thus

$$\Delta(E_{k1} + E_{k2}) = -\Delta U \qquad \text{8-23}$$

or

$$\Delta(E_{k1} + E_{k2} + U) = 0 \qquad \text{8-24}$$

When we consider the total system, particle plus surroundings, the potential energy is a quantity associated with the configuration of the system rather than with a single particle. Equation 8-21 defines the electrostatic potential energy for a two-particle system. In general when two particles interact via any conservative force,

The potential energy of a two-particle system is the negative of the work done on both particles by the forces of interaction when the particles are brought from some reference separation to a given configuration.

We can think of this in a slightly different way. If we push the two protons together with zero acceleration, we must exert an applied force on each that is equal and opposite to the force of interaction. Thus the work done by the applied force is just the negative of the work done by the interaction forces. The potential energy of the system equals the work done by an applied force which brings the particles from infinite separation to their final configuration without acceleration.

Questions

12. Two particles interact through a conservative force. The potential energy of the system is U. Would you think it possible to divide U into two parts U_1 and U_2 ($U = U_1 + U_2$) which would be the potential energies of m_1 and m_2?

13. When you consider your own interaction with the earth, you ordinarily think of the potential energy as being yours rather than the earth's. Why is this possible?

14. The electrostatic force between an electron and a proton is attractive. Does their mutual potential energy increase or decrease as they move toward each other? Answer the same question for two protons, which repel each other.

Optional

8-10   General Test for Conservative Forces in Three Dimensions

In general the potential energy can be a function of all three coordinates x, y, and z, and the force has components F_x, F_y, and F_z. The potential-energy function $U(x,y,z)$ is related to a conservative force **F** by

$$dU = -\mathbf{F} \cdot d\mathbf{s} = -(F_x \, dx + F_y \, dy + F_z \, dz) \qquad \text{8-25}$$

where we have written out the dot product in rectangular coordinates for a general displacement $d\mathbf{s} = dx \, \mathbf{i} + dy \, \mathbf{j} + dz \, \mathbf{k}$. We can relate any one of these components, say F_x, to the change in $U(x,y,z)$ when y and z are held fixed. Consider a displacement $d\mathbf{s} = dx \, \mathbf{i}$. Then

$$dU(x,y,z) = -\mathbf{F} \cdot d\mathbf{s} = -F_x \, dx \qquad y, z \text{ held fixed} \qquad \text{8-26}$$

Thus F_x is the negative derivative of U with respect to x with y and z held constant. Such a derivative is called a partial derivative. It is written $\partial U/\partial x$. Thus in general, the components of the force are related to the potential energy by

$$F_x = -\frac{\partial U}{\partial x} \qquad F_y = -\frac{\partial U}{\partial y} \qquad F_z = -\frac{\partial U}{\partial z} \qquad \text{8-27}$$

If we take the derivative of a function with respect to x and then with respect to y, we get the same result as when we take the derivative first with respect to y and then x (assuming these second partial derivatives exist). Thus

$$\frac{\partial}{\partial y}\left(\frac{\partial U}{\partial x}\right) = \frac{\partial}{\partial x}\left(\frac{\partial U}{\partial y}\right)$$

Applying this to Equation 8-27, we have as a condition that $\mathbf{F}$ be conservative

$$\frac{\partial F_x}{\partial y} = \frac{\partial F_y}{\partial x} \qquad \text{8-28a}$$

Similarly

$$\frac{\partial F_y}{\partial z} = \frac{\partial F_z}{\partial y} \qquad \text{and} \qquad \frac{\partial F_x}{\partial z} = \frac{\partial F_z}{\partial x} \qquad \text{8-28b,c}$$

Equations 8-28 are a necessary and sufficient condition that the force $\mathbf{F}$ be conservative.

Example 8-9 A force is given by $\mathbf{F} = C(-y\mathbf{i} + x\mathbf{j})$, where C is a constant. Is this force conservative?

Applying the test, we have

$$\frac{\partial F_x}{\partial y} = \frac{\partial(-Cy)}{\partial y} = -C$$

$$\frac{\partial F_y}{\partial x} = \frac{\partial(+Cx)}{\partial x} = +C \neq \frac{\partial F_y}{\partial x}$$

Thus this force is not conservative. It is in fact the type of force discussed in Example 8-6. If we change to polar coordinates, we have $x = r\cos\theta$, $y = r\sin\theta$; then

$$\mathbf{F} = C(-r\sin\theta\,\mathbf{i} + r\cos\theta\,\mathbf{j}) = rC(-\sin\theta\,\mathbf{i} + \cos\theta\,\mathbf{j}) = rC\hat{\boldsymbol{\theta}}$$

where $\hat{\boldsymbol{\theta}} = -\sin\theta\,\mathbf{i} + \cos\theta\,\mathbf{j}$ is a unit vector tangent to the circle around the origin.

Review

A. Define, explain, or otherwise identify:

Conservative force, 199
Potential energy, 201
Total mechanical energy, 202
Central force, 208

Electron volt, 212
Stable equilibrium, 214
Unstable equilibrium, 214

B. State the criterion for a force to be conservative.

C. Derive the law of conservation of mechanical energy.

D. True or false:

1. Only conservative forces do work.

2. There is a potential-energy function associated with every force.

3. If only conservative forces act, the kinetic energy of a particle does not change.

4. When a particle makes a round trip, the total work done by each conservative force is zero.

5. The work done by a conservative force decreases the potential energy associated with that force.

6. The total mechanical energy of a particle must be greater than zero.

Exercises

Section 8-1, Conservative Forces

1. A 2-kg ball moves from an initial position $x = 0$, $y = 4$ m to the final position $x = 4$ m, $y = 0$. (a) Calculate the work done by gravity along the segments AB and BC in Figure 8-10 and the total work done along this path (I in the figure). (b) Calculate the work done by gravity along the segments AD, DE, and EC and the total work done along path II. (c) Calculate directly the work done by gravity along the direct path AC (path III).

2. A particle is acted on by a force $\mathbf{F} = 4\mathbf{i} + 3\mathbf{j}$ N. The particle moves from the origin to point $x = 8$ m, $y = 6$ m. (a) Find the work done on the particle if it moves along the straight line from the origin to its final position (note that the force acts parallel to this line). (b) If the particle moves along the x axis to the point (8 m, 0) and then perpendicular to the x axis to its final position, find the work done by the force along each part of the path and the total work. (c) If the particle moves first along the y axis to the point (0, 6 m) and then parallel to the x axis to its final position, find the work done along each part of the path and the total work.

3. A particle is acted on by a force $\mathbf{F} = 4y\mathbf{i} + 5\mathbf{j}$, where $\mathbf{F}$ is in newtons and y is in meters. Show that this force is not conservative by computing the work done by the force in moving from the origin to the point ($x = 2$ m, $y = 2$ m) along two paths. (a) The first path is along the x axis to point (2 m, 0) and then parallel to the y axis along the line $x = 2$ m to the final point (2 m, 2 m). Find the component of the force parallel to the displacement for each of these parts of the path, the work done along each part of this path, and the total work. (b) The second path is first along the y axis to the point $x = 0$, $y = 2$ m and then parallel to the x axis. Find the work done along each part of this path and the total work.

Section 8-2, The Conservation of Mechanical Energy

4. List some situations in which the total mechanical energy of a particle is not conserved.

5. A particle is acted upon by a single conservative force which increases its kinetic energy by 10 J. (a) What is the change in the potential energy of the particle? (b) What is the change in the total energy of the particle?

6. A particle of mass 2 kg moves under the influence of a single conservative force which decreases its velocity from 20 to 10 m/sec. (a) Find the change in kinetic energy, the change in potential energy, and the change in total mechanical energy of the particle. (b) If the original potential energy of the particle was 100 J (when traveling at 20 m/sec), find the potential energy and the total energy when the speed is 10 m/sec.

7. A 0.5-kg ball is thrown straight up with initial speed of 10 m/sec. (a) Find the initial kinetic energy of the ball and total mechanical energy, assuming that the initial potential energy is zero. (b) Find the kinetic energy, potential energy, and total mechanical energy of the ball at the top of its flight. (c) Use the law of conservation of total mechanical energy to find the maximum height of the ball. (Take $g = 10$ m/sec² for convenience.) (d) Compare this method of

Figure 8-10
Exercise 1.

finding the maximum height of the ball with that in Chapter 2 using the constant-acceleration formulas. Can you find the time needed for the ball to reach its maximum height from the conservation of mechanical energy?

8. A particle moves under the influence of a single conservative force. Under what conditions (if any) is it possible for the potential energy to increase?

9. A conservative force does 25 J of work on a particle in moving it from point x_1 to x_2. (a) Find the change in potential energy of the particle when it moves from x_1 to x_2. (b) If the potential energy of the particle is zero at x_1, what is it at x_2? (c) If the mass of the particle is 5 gm and it starts from rest at x_1 and moves under the influence of this force only, what is its velocity at point x_2?

10. A particle moves under the influence of a single conservative force. In doing so the speed of the particle first decreases, then becomes zero momentarily, and then increases. (a) Describe the change in potential energy of the particle during this motion. (b) Suggest a physical situation corresponding to these conditions.

11. During its motion, the potential energy of a 10-kg mass increases by 200 J. (a) How much work was done on the mass by conservative forces? (b) If the particle travels at constant speed, how much work was done by nonconservative forces?

Section 8-3, Conservative Forces and Potential Energy in One Dimension

12. (a) Make a plot of the potential energy of a 10-lb weight versus its height above the ground for heights ranging from 0 to 50 ft. Use the ground as the reference level at which $U = 0$. (b) On the same graph plot the potential energy of the weight, using the height 25 ft as the point of zero potential energy.

13. How high must a mass be lifted to gain an amount of potential energy equal to the kinetic energy it has when moving at speed 60 mi/h?

14. A constant force acts in the negative x direction $F_x = -6$ N. Find the potential-energy function associated with this conservative force (a) if $U = 0$ at $x = 0$, (b) if $U = 0$ at $x = 5$ m, (c) if $U = 50$ J at $x = 0$.

15. A constant force is given by $F_x = 4$ N. (a) Find the potential-energy function associated with this force for arbitrary choice of zero potential energy. (b) Find $U(x)$ such that $U(x)$ is zero at $x = 6$ m. (c) Find $U(x)$ such that $U = 12$ J at $x = 6$ m.

16. A man places a 2-lb block against a horizontal spring of force constant $k = 20$ lb/ft and compresses it 9 in. (a) Find the work done by the man and the work done by the spring. (b) The spring is released from its compression of 9 in. and returns to its original position. Find the work done by the spring and the kinetic energy of the block at this point (assuming that only the spring does work on the block).

17. A spring obeys Hooke's law with force constant $k = 10^4$ N/m. How far must it be stretched for its potential energy to be (a) 100 J and (b) 50 J?

18. A spring is stretched so that its potential energy is 25 J and the force it exerts is 500 N. (a) By how much is the spring stretched from its natural length? (b) What is the force constant k?

Section 8-4, Nonconservative Forces in One Dimension

19. Which of the following forces are conservative, and which are nonconservative? (a) Frictional force exerted on a sliding box, (b) force exerted by a linear spring obeying Hooke's law, (c) force of gravity, (d) wind resistance on a moving car, (e) force exerted by a nonlinear spring obeying $F_x = -kx + Cx^2$, (f) force exerted by boy on ball when throwing the ball, (g) force exerted by floor on a dropped egg.

20. A man lifts a 100-lb weight from the floor to a shelf a height of 4 ft. The weight is at rest initially and finally. (*a*) What is the change in the potential energy of the weight? (*b*) List the forces acting on the weight as it is lifted and label them conservative or nonconservative.

Section 8-5, Conservative Forces and Potential Energy in Three Dimensions

21. Find the potential-energy function associated with the constant force $\mathbf{F} = F_0\mathbf{k}$ (**k** is a unit vector in the *z* direction) such that the potential energy is zero at (*a*) $z = 0$, (*b*) $z = -15$ m, and (*c*) $z = 15$ m.

22. (*a*) Show that Equation 8-14 for the gravitational potential energy can be written

$$U = -\frac{mgR_E^2}{r}$$

where *g* is the free-fall acceleration of gravity at the earth's surface and R_E is the radius of the earth. (*b*) Use this result to calculate the potential energy in joules of a 1-kg mass at the positions $r = R_E$, $r = 2R_E$, and $r = 3R_E$. (Take R_E to be 6.37×10^6 m.)

23. A 1-kg mass is lifted at constant velocity by an applied force which just balances the gravitational force. (*a*) From your results of Exercise 22, calculate the work done by the applied force to raise the mass from $r = R_E$ to $r = 2R_E$. (*b*) Compare your result with that obtained assuming that the gravitational force had the constant value *mg*. (*c*) What are the minimum and maximum values of the magnitude of the applied force during this procedure?

24. A force similar to that discussed in Example 8-6 is given by

$$\mathbf{F} = (10 \text{ N})\hat{\theta}$$

Find the work done by the force on a particle which moves from the initial position $x = 5$ m, $y = 0$, $z = 0$ to the final position $x = -5$ m, $y = 0$, $z = 0$ if (*a*) the particle moves along a circular arc of radius 5 m in the direction of the force, and (*b*) the particle moves along the *x* axis. (*c*) Find a path between the initial and final positions such that the work done by the force is half that found in part (*a*).

Section 8-6, The Electron Volt Energy Unit

25. Convert the following energies in joules to electron volts, kiloelectron volts, or megaelectron volts: (*a*) 3×10^{-19} J; (*b*) 10^{-16} J; (*c*) 1.5×10^{-7} J; (*d*) 8.16×10^{-14} J.

26. A nucleus contains a positive electric charge of $50e$, where *e* is the magnitude of the electron charge. An electron is a distance of 2×10^{-10} m from the nucleus. Find the potential energy of the electron in electron volts and in joules.

27. The energy released in the fission of one uranium nucleus is about 200 MeV. (*a*) Convert this energy into joules. (*b*) Find the energy in joules released if 1 gm of uranium undergoes fission [1 gm contains about $(6.02 \times 10^{23})/235$ uranium nuclei].

Section 8-7, Force from Potential Energy, and Section 8-8, Equilibrium and Potential Energy in One Dimension

28. Figure 8-11 shows a potential-energy function $U(x)$ versus *x*. (*a*) At each point indicated, state whether the force F_x is positive, negative, or zero. (*b*) At which point does the force have the greatest magnitude? (*c*) Identify any equilibrium points and state whether the equilibrium is stable or unstable.

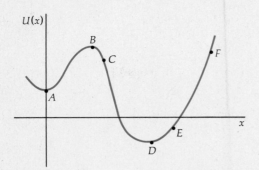

Figure 8-11
Exercise 28.

29. Repeat Exercise 28 for the potential-energy function $U(x)$ shown in Figure 8-12.

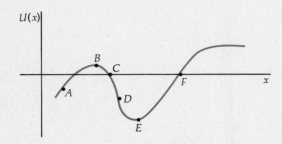

Figure 8-12
Exercise 29.

30. (a) Find the force F_x associated with the potential-energy function $U(x) = Ax^4$, where A is a constant. (b) At what point or points is the force zero?

31. A potential-energy function is given by $U(x) = U_0 \ln (x/x_0)$, where U_0 and x_0 are constants. (a) Find the force F_x. (b) Are there any points of equilibrium?

32. In the potential-energy curve $U(y)$ shown in Figure 8-13 the segments AB and CD are straight lines. Sketch the force F_y versus y.

Figure 8-13
Exercise 32.

33. A potential-energy function is given by $U(r) = C/r$, where C is a positive constant. (a) Find the radial force F_r as a function of r. (b) Is this force toward the origin or away from it; i.e., is F_r negative or positive? (c) Does the potential energy increase or decrease as r increases? (d) Answer parts (b) and (c) if C is a negative constant.

Section 8-9, Potential Energy of a System of Particles

34. Calculate the electrostatic potential energy in electron volts of two protons separated by a distance of 10^{-15} m. This is a typical separation of protons in an atomic nucleus.

35. When ^{235}U fissions, the energy first appears as electrostatic potential energy of the two fission fragments. The fragments then fly apart as the potential energy is converted into kinetic energy of the fragments. Estimate the energy released in fission by assuming the $^{235}_{92}$U nucleus is split into two equal nuclei (not usually true in practice), each carrying a charge of $+46e$ and separated by

15×10^{-15} m (this is about twice the radius of a nucleus of mass number 118), and calculating the electrostatic potential energy for these two particles. Express your answer in megaelectron volts.

36. Two bodies have masses 5 and 10 kg. They are 2 m apart and 2 m above the ground. (a) Calculate their potential energy because of their mutual gravitational attraction. (b) Compare this potential energy with the total potential energy relative to the ground level they have because of the gravitational attraction of the earth.

Section 8-10, General Test for Conservative Forces in Three Dimensions

37. Apply the general test (Equation 8-28) to determine whether the following forces are conservative: (a) $\mathbf{F} = y^3\mathbf{i} + 3xy^2\mathbf{j}$, (b) $\mathbf{F} = x\mathbf{i} + y\mathbf{j}$, (c) $\mathbf{F} = x^2y\mathbf{i} + x^2y\mathbf{j}$, (d) $\mathbf{F} = x^2\mathbf{i} + xy\mathbf{j}$.

38. A potential-energy function is given by $U(x,y,z) = C(1/\sqrt{x^2 + y^2 + z^2})$, where C is a constant. (a) Find the rectangular components of the force F_x, F_y, and F_z and show explicitly that Equation 8-28 is satisfied by these components. (b) Show that the force found in part (a) is a central force.

Problems

1. Figure 8-14 gives the force F_x on a particle as a function of its distance x from the origin. (a) Calculate from the graph the work done by the force when the particle moves from $x = 0$ to the following values of x: $-4, -3, -2, -1, 0, 1, 2, 3$, and 4 m. (b) How do you know that this force is conservative? (c) Plot the potential energy versus x for the range of x from -4 m to $+4$ m assuming that $U = 0$ at $x = 0$.

Figure 8-14
Problem 1.

2. Repeat Problem 1 for the force F_x shown in Figure 8-15.

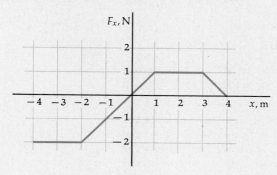

Figure 8-15
Problem 2.

3. The force on a particle moving along the x axis is given by $F_x = -ax^2$, where a is a constant. (a) Calculate the potential energy $U(x)$ relative to $U = 0$ at $x = 0$. (b) Sketch a graph of $U(x)$ versus x.

4. A force is given by $F_x = +A/x^3$, where $A = 8$ N-m³. (a) For positive x, does the potential energy associated with this force increase or decrease with increasing x? Convince yourself of the correct answer to this question by imagining a particle placed at rest at some point x and released. When it moves, its kinetic energy will increase and its potential energy therefore must decrease. (b) Find the potential-energy function $U(x)$ associated with this force such that U approaches zero as x approaches infinity. Sketch $U(x)$ versus x.

5. Figure 8-16 shows the potential-energy function $U(r)$ versus r for a diatomic molecule, where r is the separation of the atoms. (a) Indicate the equilibrium point on the graph and discuss its stability. (b) From this graph, sketch a graph of the force F_r exerted by one atom on the other versus separation distance r.

Figure 8-16
Problem 5.

6. Figure 8-17 shows the potential-energy function $U(r)$ versus r associated with the nuclear force between two protons, two neutrons, or a neutron and proton, where r is the separation distance. From this graph sketch the force F_r versus r.

Figure 8-17
Problem 6.

7. A force acting in the xy plane is given by $\mathbf{F} = 10\mathbf{i} + 3x\mathbf{j}$, where $\mathbf{F}$ is in newtons and x is in meters. Suppose the force acts on a particle as it moves from initial position $x = 4$ m, $y = 1$ m to a final position $x = 4$ m, $y = 4$ m. (a) Show that this force is not conservative by computing the work done by the force for at least two different paths. (b) Find a path for which the work done by the force is zero.

8. A straight rod of negligible mass is mounted on a frictionless pivot, as shown in Figure 8-18. Masses m_1 and m_2 are suspended at distances l_1 and l_2 as shown. (a) Write the gravitational potential energy of the masses as a function of the angle θ made by the rod and the horizontal. (b) For what angle θ is the potential energy a minimum? Is the statement "systems tend to move toward minimum potential energy" consistent with your result? (c) Show that if $m_1 l_1 = m_2 l_2$, the potential energy is the same for all values of θ. (When this holds, the system will balance at any angle θ. This result is known as *Archimedes' law of the lever.*)

Figure 8-18
Problem 8.

9. The force between two atoms in a diatomic molecule can be represented approximately by the potential-energy function

$$U(r) = U_0 \left[\left(\frac{r_0}{r} \right)^{12} - 2 \left(\frac{r_0}{r} \right)^6 \right]$$

where r_0 and U_0 are constants. (a) Find the force F_r. (b) At what value of r is the potential energy zero? At what value of r is the force zero? (c) At what value of r is the potential energy a minimum? What is the value of this minimum potential energy? (This minimum potential energy is approximately equal to the dissociation energy of the molecule.) (d) Sketch $U(r)$ versus r.

10. A theoretical form for the potential energy associated with the nuclear force between two protons, two neutrons, or a neutron and proton is the Yukawa potential

$$U = -U_0 \left(\frac{a}{r} \right) e^{-r/a}$$

where U_0 and a are constants. (a) Sketch U versus r using the parameters $U_0 = 23$ MeV and $a = 2.5 \times 10^{-15}$ m. (b) Find the force F_r. (c) Compare the magnitudes of the forces at the separations $r = a$, $r = 2a$, and $r = 5a$.

CHAPTER 9   Conservation of Energy

The potential energy of a particle is defined so that the work done on the particle by conservative forces equals the decrease in the potential energy. When only conservative forces do work, the total mechanical energy of the particle remains constant because the increase in kinetic energy equals the decrease in potential energy. This principle of conservation of energy is one of the most important in physics.

In the macroscopic world, nonconservative forces are always present, the most common being frictional forces. Another type of nonconservative force is involved in large deformations of bodies. For example, if a spring is stretched beyond its elastic limit, it becomes permanently deformed and the work done in the stretching is not recovered when the spring is released. When nonconservative forces do work on a particle, the sum of kinetic and potential energies of the particle is not constant. Because some kind of frictional force is nearly always present in the motion of a macroscopic body, the importance of energy and its conservation was not realized until the nineteenth century. Then it was discovered that the disappearance of *macroscopic mechanical energy* is accompanied by the appearance of *internal energy,* usually indicated by an increase in temperature. We now know that, on the microscopic scale, this internal energy of the surroundings consists of kinetic and potential energy of molecular motion. When the concept of energy is generalized to include this internal energy, the total energy of an object plus its surroundings does not change even when friction is present.

If we carefully define a system, e.g., several bodies and their local surroundings (as we did in solving force and acceleration problems in Chapter 5), we find that even when internal energy is included, the total energy of the system does not always remain constant. However, we are always able to account for the increase or decrease in the system energy by the appearance or disappearance of energy somewhere else. For example, energy of a system is often decreased because of some form of radiation, e.g., sound waves from a collision of two objects, water waves produced by a ship, or electromagnetic waves

The action of a pole vaulter demonstrates several kinds of energy. First he converts internal chemical energy into kinetic energy when he begins to run. Some of this energy is then converted into elastic potential energy of deformation of the pole and eventually into gravitational potential energy, which in turn changes into kinetic energy as he drops. The mechanical energy is finally lost as heat when he reaches the ground. (*Courtesy of Harold E. Edgerton.*)

produced by accelerated charges in a radio antenna. We can write a generalized statement of the conservation of energy in the following way. Let E_{sys} be the total energy of a given system and P_{in} be the power input, i.e., the rate at which energy is put into the system. Then

$$P_{in} = \frac{dE_{sys}}{dt} \qquad 9\text{-}1$$

where P_{in} is negative if energy is flowing out of the system. The significance of this statement is that if the energy concept is sufficiently generalized, changes in the total energy of the system are always precisely accounted for by energy flow into or out of the system. Energy is never created or destroyed in the system, though it may change from one form to another.

In this chapter, we consider only *mechanical energy*, the kinetic energy of a particle, $\frac{1}{2}mv^2$, and the various potential-energy functions associated with the forces acting on a particle. Consider a body acted on by a nonconservative force F_{nc} and several conservative forces F_i so that the resultant force is

$$\Sigma F = F_{nc} + F_1 + F_2 + \cdots$$

The work done by the resultant force, according to the general work-energy theorem, equals the increase in kinetic energy of the particle

$$W_{net} = \int \Sigma F \cdot ds = \int F_{nc} \cdot ds + \int F_1 \cdot ds + \int F_2 \cdot ds + \cdots = \Delta E_k$$
$$9\text{-}2$$

For each conservative force $\mathbf{F}_i$ we define a potential-energy function U_i in the usual way:

$$\int \mathbf{F}_i \cdot d\mathbf{s} = -\Delta U_i$$

Then Equation 9-2 can be written

$$\int \mathbf{F}_{nc} \cdot d\mathbf{s} - \Delta U_1 - \Delta U_2 + \cdots = \Delta E_k$$

or

$$\int \mathbf{F}_{nc} \cdot d\mathbf{s} = \Delta(E_k + U_1 + U_2 + \cdots) = \Delta E_{\text{total}} \qquad 9\text{-}3$$

Work-energy theorem modified to include potential energy

where the total mechanical energy of the particle is

$$E_{\text{total}} = E_k + U_1 + U_2 + \cdots \qquad 9\text{-}4$$

The work done by nonconservative forces equals the change in the total mechanical energy of the particle. This modified form of the work-energy theorem is the most convenient in many applications since explicit calculation of work done along the path is required only for the nonconservative forces. When the only forces that do work are conservative, the left side of Equation 9-3 is zero. Then there is no change in the total mechanical energy of the particle:

$$E_{\text{total}} = E_k + U_1 + U_2 + \cdots = \text{constant} \qquad 9\text{-}5$$

In this chapter we consider various examples of the use of the work-energy theorem and the conservation of energy expressed in Equations 9-3 and 9-5. Since we derived these equations from Newton's laws, we can never obtain more information about a mechanics problem than is contained in Newton's laws. Any problem that can be solved by using conservation of energy can also be solved directly from Newton's laws. In spite of this, energy conservation and the work-energy theorem are extremely useful tools for the analysis of problems. Since the kinetic energy is $\frac{1}{2}mv^2$ and the potential-energy functions are functions of position, Equation 9-5 relates the speed of a particle to its position. In any problem in which one of these quantities is to be found, the energy-conservation equation is generally simpler to use than a direct application of $\Sigma \mathbf{F} = m\mathbf{a}$. We shall illustrate this in Section 9-1. In many cases, examining the potential-energy function offers a qualitative understanding of the possible motion of a system without a detailed solution of the equations of motion.

9-1   Some Illustrative Examples

Example 9-1 Block on a Rough Incline Consider a block of mass m which is drawn up a rough incline by a constant applied force $\mathbf{T}$ parallel to the incline. The angle of the incline is θ. The block starts from rest at the bottom of the incline. Find its speed when it has moved a distance s up along the incline.

This problem is readily solved by the direct application of Newton's laws of motion, i.e., by analyzing the forces, finding the acceleration (which is constant), and then using the kinematic relationships for constant acceleration. We shall use the work-energy theorem instead to illustrate this method of analyzing a problem.

Figure 9-1
Block drawn up rough incline
by force **T** (Example 9-1).

There are four forces which act on the block as it moves up the incline (see Figure 9-1). The normal force **N**, which prevents the block from moving down into the incline, does no work during the motion because it is always perpendicular to the motion. The weight $m\mathbf{g}$ is a conservative force. As we have already seen, the increase in gravitational potential energy as the block ascends through the vertical distance $h = s \sin \theta$ is $U = mgh = mgs \sin \theta$.

The frictional force **f** is, of course, a nonconservative force. We must calculate the work it does as the block moves up the distance s along the incline. Since f is constant, and opposed to the motion, this work is just

$$W_f = -fs$$

Finally, the applied force **T** is a nonconservative force. (It depends on the action of whatever agency exerts it and not merely on the position of the block.) Hence we must compute its work. **T** is a constant force in the same direction as the motion; therefore the work is positive

$$W_T = +Ts$$

According to the work-energy theorem (Equation 9-3), the total work of the nonconservative forces equals the increase in total mechanical energy. The latter consists of the increase in gravitational potential energy plus the increase in the kinetic energy. Since the kinetic energy is zero at the bottom of the incline (the block starts from rest), the increase in kinetic energy is just the kinetic energy at the top, $\frac{1}{2}mv^2$.

Combining these facts gives

$$+Ts - fs = \tfrac{1}{2}mv^2 + mgs \sin \theta$$

The left side of this equation is the total work of the nonconservative forces. The right-side contains the increase in kinetic energy plus the increase in potential energy. Solving for the speed v gives

$$v = \sqrt{\frac{2s}{m} \, (T - f - mg \sin \theta)} \qquad\qquad 9\text{-}6$$

The quantity under the radical sign must be positive for its square root to have a meaningful value for the speed v. This requires that T be greater than $f + mg \sin \theta$. That, of course, means only that the applied force **T** must overbalance the sum of the opposing frictional force **f** and the component of the weight down the plane.

Equation 9-6 can also be obtained from the constant-acceleration formula $v^2 = 2as$, where the acceleration is the resultant force divided by the mass.

Example 9-2 The Simple Pendulum A mass m is suspended on a light string of length L. It is pulled aside so that the string makes an angle θ_0 with the vertical and is then released from rest. What is the speed v at the bottom of the swing, and what is the tension in the string there?

There are only two forces acting on m as it moves (neglecting air resistance). One is the tension $\mathbf{T}$ in the string, which is always perpendicular to the motion and therefore does no work. The other is the weight $m\mathbf{g}$, which is a conservative force. Here only conservative forces do work, and so the total mechanical energy of the mass is conserved.

Let us choose the gravitational potential energy to be zero at the bottom of the swing. At its original position a height h above the bottom the mass has potential energy mgh and no kinetic energy because it is at rest. As it swings down, the potential energy is converted into kinetic energy. Conservation of energy gives us for the speed v at the bottom,

$$\tfrac{1}{2}mv^2 = mgh$$

According to Figure 9-2, the distance h is related to the original angle θ_0 and the length of the pendulum L by

$$h = L - L \cos \theta_0 = L(1 - \cos \theta_0)$$

Thus

$$v^2 = 2gL(1 - \cos \theta_0) \qquad\qquad 9\text{-}7$$

The tension at the bottom is found as in Example 5-8. At this point the mass has centripetal acceleration $v^2/r = v^2/L$. The forces acting are

Multiflash photograph of a simple pendulum. As the bob descends, gravitational potential energy is converted into kinetic energy and the speed increases, as indicated by the increased spacing of the recorded positions. The speed decreases as the bob moves up, and the kinetic energy is changed into potential energy.

Figure 9-2
Simple pendulum for Example 9-2. The initial height above the bottom of the swing is related to the initial angle θ_0 by $h = L - L \cos \theta_0$. After the pendulum is released from rest, the speed of the bob at the bottom can be found from conservation of energy: $\tfrac{1}{2}mv^2 = mgh = mgL(1 - \cos \theta_0)$.

Berenice Abbott/Photo Researchers

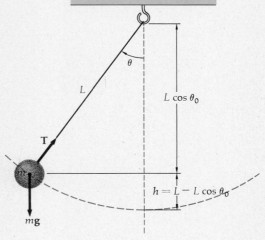

T up and *mg* down. Setting the resultant force equal to the mass times the acceleration gives

$$T - mg = \frac{mv^2}{r} = \frac{mv^2}{L} = 2mg(1 - \cos\theta_0)$$

$$T = mg + 2mg(1 - \cos\theta_0) \qquad\qquad 9\text{-}8$$

We now obtain Equation 9-7 directly from Newton's laws of motion to show how this method differs from the method of conservation of energy, just used. In Figure 9-3 the mass is at a point where the string makes some angle θ with the vertical. The mass has a velocity **v** tangent to the circular arc of motion. We can relate the speed v to the angle θ as follows. The distance s measured along the path length is related to θ by $s = L\theta$. Then the speed is

$$v = \frac{ds}{dt} = \frac{d(L\theta)}{dt} = L\frac{d\theta}{dt} \qquad\qquad 9\text{-}9$$

The tangential acceleration is just the rate of change of the speed:

$$a_t = \frac{dv}{dt} = L\frac{d^2\theta}{dt^2}$$

The only tangential force is the component of the weight $-mg\sin\theta$, where the minus sign indicates that this force component is in the direction of decreasing θ. The tangential component of $\Sigma\mathbf{F} = m\mathbf{a}$ is thus

$$-mg\sin\theta = ma_t = m\frac{dv}{dt} = mL\frac{d^2\theta}{dt^2} \qquad\qquad 9\text{-}10$$

or

$$L\frac{d^2\theta}{dt^2} = -g\sin\theta \qquad\qquad 9\text{-}11$$

A complete solution of Equation 9-11 for $\theta(t)$ is difficult. We shall consider an approximate solution (valid if θ is small) in Chapter 14, but we can obtain an exact solution for the speed $v = L\,d\theta/dt$. From Equation 9-10 we have

$$\frac{dv}{dt} = -g\sin\theta$$

Figure 9-3
Forces on the pendulum bob when the string makes angle θ with the vertical and the bob moves with speed v. The resultant inward radial force $T - mg\cos\theta$ produces the centripetal acceleration v^2/L, while the resultant tangential force $mg\sin\theta$ produces the tangential acceleration dv/dt.

We can eliminate the time t by noting that since θ is a function of t, v must be a function of θ. Using the chain rule for derivatives, we have

$$\frac{dv}{dt} = \frac{dv}{d\theta}\frac{d\theta}{dt} = \frac{dv}{d\theta}\frac{1}{L}\left(L\frac{d\theta}{dt}\right) = \frac{v}{L}\frac{dv}{d\theta}$$

Then

$$\frac{v}{L}\frac{dv}{d\theta} = -g\sin\theta$$

or

$$v\,dv = -gL\sin\theta\,d\theta \qquad\qquad 9\text{-}12$$

Integrating θ from θ_0 to 0 and v from 0 to v gives

$$\int_0^v v\,dv = \int_{\theta_0}^0 -gL\sin\theta\,d\theta$$

$$\tfrac{1}{2}v^2\Big]_0^v = +gL\cos\theta\Big]_{\theta_0}^0$$

$$\tfrac{1}{2}v^2 - 0 = (gL\cos 0) - (gL\cos\theta_0)$$

$$v^2 = 2gL(1 - \cos\theta_0)$$

This is the same as the result we obtained using conservation of energy. The steps we have carried out here are essentially the same as those carried out in deriving the work-energy theorem. The integration on the right above is equivalent to calculating the work done by the component of the weight along the path. The integration on the left is essentially a calculation of the increase in kinetic energy similar to that carried out in our earlier derivation.

Example 9-3 A skier skis down a smooth hill of height H of arbitrary shape (see Figure 9-4). Find his speed at the bottom of the hill.

We have already considered this type of problem in Chapter 7. We repeat it here to contrast it with the pendulum problem. We have only one force that does work, i.e., gravity, which is conservative. The normal force exerted by the snow on the skis acts to constrain the skier to follow a certain path but does no work. Taking the potential energy to be zero at the bottom of the hill and assuming the initial speed at the top of the hill to be zero, we obtain from conservation of energy,

$$(E_k + U)_{\text{top}} = (E_k + U)_{\text{bottom}}$$

$$0 + mgH = \tfrac{1}{2}mv^2 + 0$$

$$v^2 = 2gH$$

$v_0 = 0$
Mass $= m$

H

$v = ?$

Figure 9-4
Skier and smooth hill of arbitrary shape for Example 9-3. The total energy at the top of the hill is mgH assuming zero potential energy at the bottom. At the bottom of the hill the total energy is $\tfrac{1}{2}mv^2$. Conservation of energy gives $v^2 = 2gH$.

Helmut Gritscher/DPI

If there were no friction, the kinetic energy of the skier would equal the decrease in gravitational potential energy and his speed after descending through a given vertical distance would be the same as if he had fallen through that distance. In practice, frictional forces decrease the mechanical energy.

This example illustrates the great power of the principle of conservation of energy. To calculate v by direct application of Newton's second law would be impossible in this case because lacking a precise description of the curve along which the particle moves we cannot compute the tangential component of the weight at each point. Even if we had the equation of the curve, the direct application of $\Sigma\mathbf{F} = m\mathbf{a}$ would be very complex. On the other hand, a straightforward use of the conservation-of-energy principle enables us to obtain v quite easily.

Example 9-4 Atwood's Machine Figure 9-5 shows a device developed in the eighteenth century to make the first accurate determinations of the acceleration of gravity g. *Atwood's machine* consists of two masses m_1 and m_2 connected by a light string passing over a light pulley with negligible friction in its bearings. If the two masses are equal, they remain at rest at any position, each balancing the other. If m_2 is greater than m_1, m_2 accelerates downward and m_1 upward. The acceleration is constant, and if m_2 is only slightly greater than m_1, the acceleration is small and readily measured. From the measured acceleration it is possible to calculate g. We wish to find the equation to be used for this purpose. (This method was necessary because the acceleration g is too great to be measured directly with the instruments available 250 years ago. Direct measurement of g had to await the development of precise clocks capable of measuring times to accuracies of at least 0.01 sec.)

If friction in the pulley bearings is negligible and the pulley mass is so small that the work done to speed it up is negligible, the tension in the string is uniform. That is, the tension acting upward on m_1 equals the tension acting upward on m_2. The net work done by the tension on the masses is zero because when m_1 moves upward in the direction of T, m_2 moves downward the same distance in the direction opposite T. The only force that does net work on the two-mass system is gravity, and therefore the total kinetic plus gravitational potential energy of the two masses is conserved.

Figure 9-5
Atwood's machine (Example 9-4). When released from rest in the position shown, the larger mass m_2 falls and the smaller mass m_1 rises. After some time the masses are at the positions indicated by the dashed lines and moving with some speed v. The speed can be related to the distance moved by conservation of energy.

Let us choose the potential energy to be zero at the initial position of the masses. Since they are at rest at this position, the total energy is zero. Let v be the speed of m_1 after it has moved up a distance y. Then its kinetic energy is $\frac{1}{2}m_1v^2$, and its potential energy is m_1gy. Since the connecting string does not stretch, m_2 must move down the same distance y and acquire the same speed v. Then its kinetic energy is $\frac{1}{2}m_2v^2$, and its potential energy is $-m_2gy$. Conservation of energy gives

$$E = \tfrac{1}{2}m_1v^2 + m_1gy + \tfrac{1}{2}m_2v^2 - m_2gy = 0$$

or

$$\tfrac{1}{2}(m_1 + m_2)v^2 = (m_2 - m_1)gy \qquad\qquad 9\text{-}13$$

Solving this equation for v^2 gives

$$v^2 = \frac{2(m_2 - m_1)}{m_1 + m_2}\, gy \qquad\qquad 9\text{-}14$$

which relates the speed of either mass to the distance it moves. Comparing this with the constant-acceleration equation $v^2 = 2ay$, we see that the acceleration is

$$a = \frac{m_2 - m_1}{m_1 + m_2}\, g \qquad\qquad 9\text{-}15$$

In Example 9-4 we found the acceleration from the expression for v^2 using the constant-acceleration equation. In general, when a single conservative force acts, we can find the acceleration from the conservation-of-energy equation by differentiation. Consider such a one-dimensional problem in which a particle has initial energy E_0. At some time later it has kinetic energy $\frac{1}{2}mv^2$ and potential energy $U(x)$. Conservation of energy gives us

$$\tfrac{1}{2}mv^2 + U(x) = E_0 \qquad\qquad 9\text{-}16$$

We can obtain the acceleration from Equation 9-16 by differentiating with respect to time and using the chain rule:

$$\tfrac{1}{2}m2v\,\frac{dv}{dt} + \frac{dU}{dx}\frac{dx}{dt} = 0$$

Since dx/dt is just the speed v, we can divide out these terms. Then

$$m\,\frac{dv}{dt} = -\frac{dU}{dx} \qquad\qquad 9\text{-}17$$

This is just Newton's second law, since the negative derivative of U with respect to x is the force F_x. We could have obtained Equation 9-15 by differentiating Equation 9-14 (using $dy/dt = v$) without using the fact that the acceleration is constant.

Example 9-5 A Mass on a Horizontal Spring A mass m is placed on a smooth horizontal table and attached to a light spring of constant k. It is displaced a distance A from equilibrium and released (Figure 9-6a). Describe its motion.

The total mechanical energy is conserved since the only force that does work is the conservative force of the spring. If we choose $x = 0$ at the natural length of the spring, the potential energy of the spring is

$$U = \tfrac{1}{2}kx^2$$

Figure 9-6b shows a plot of $U(x)$ versus x. The minimum value of U occurs at $x = 0$, the equilibrium point where the slope $dU/dx = -F_x$ is

(a)

(b)

Figure 9-6
Mass on horizontal spring for
Example 9-5. (*a*) The mass is
displaced a distance A from
equilibrium and released. (*b*)
The potential-energy function
$U(x) = \frac{1}{2}kx^2$ for the mass on
the spring. The total energy
$E = \frac{1}{2}kA^2$ is indicated by the
horizontal line. The kinetic
energy $E_k = E - U(x)$ is represented by the vertical distance between the total energy line and $U(x)$. The points
P_1 and P_2 are the intersections
of E and $U(x)$. At these points
the kinetic energy is zero, and
the velocity of the particle reverses.

zero. Since the mass begins at $x = A$ with zero velocity, its total energy
at this point is potential energy:

$$E = \tfrac{1}{2}kA^2$$

This total energy, which is constant, is represented in Figure 9-6*b* by a
horizontal line. The speed v of the particle is related to its position x
through the conservation-of-energy equation,

$$\tfrac{1}{2}mv^2 + \tfrac{1}{2}kx^2 = E = \tfrac{1}{2}kA^2 \qquad\qquad 9\text{-}18$$

For any value of x, the kinetic energy $\frac{1}{2}mv^2 = E_k = E - U(x)$ is represented by the vertical distance between the total-energy line and the
potential-energy curve U, as shown in the figure. Since the kinetic
energy cannot be negative, the total-energy line must be above the potential-energy curve for physically possible motions. In Figure 9-6*b* the
curve $U(x)$ and the total-energy line intersect at $x = A$ (point P_1) and
$x = -A$ (point P_2). For this value of total energy, the motion is confined to the values of x between these points.

The points $x = +A$ and $x = -A$ are called *turning points* for the motion of the mass. At these points the velocity of the mass decreases to
zero and reverses. In this example, we start the mass from rest at
$x = +A$. The slope of $U(x)$ at this point is positive. The force $F_x =
-dU/dx$ is negative, and the particle accelerates to the left, decreasing
its potential energy and increasing its kinetic energy. When it reaches
the equilibrium point $x = 0$, its potential energy is zero and its kinetic
energy equals its total energy. Therefore its speed is maximum at this
point. After it passes the equilibrium point, the slope of $U(x)$ is negative, indicating a positive force. This force decreases the speed since it
is in the direction opposite the motion. The mass continues to the left

with its potential energy increasing and its kinetic energy decreasing until it reaches point P_2 at $x = -A$. Here it has no kinetic energy and is momentarily at rest. The force is still to the right, and so the particle turns and moves back toward the equilibrium point $x = 0$. Again, when it reaches this point, its kinetic energy is maximum and it continues moving to the right, until it comes momentarily to rest at the starting point P_1. After a full cycle of motion is completed, the mass begins a new identical cycle.

The symmetry of the potential-energy curve in Figure 9-6b makes the turning points equidistant from the equilibrium point. This distance A, called the *amplitude of the motion*, depends only on the total energy. It is also clear from the symmetry of $U(x)$ that the motion from $x = 0$ to $x = A$ and back to $x = 0$ is exactly like the motion from $x = 0$ to $x = -A$ and back except for reversal in direction; i.e., these two parts of the cycle of motion must take the same time.

We have been able to describe most of the features of the motion of a mass on a spring by using the energy diagram of Figure 9-6b. We shall use this type of analysis often in the next section. The length of time required for each oscillation (called the *period*) will be discussed in Chapter 14.

Example 9-6 A particle of mass m is dropped from a height h which is not necessarily small compared with the radius of the earth R_E. Find its speed when it reaches the surface of the earth assuming that air resistance can be neglected.

Gravity is the only force acting on the particle, and so its total mechanical energy is constant. Since the mass is not necessarily near the surface of the earth, we must use the general potential-energy function (Equation 8-14) rather than mgh. The initial kinetic energy of the particle is zero, and its initial potential energy is $-GM_E m/r_1$, where $r_1 = R_E + h$ is the initial distance from the center of the earth. When the particle reaches the surface of the earth, it has kinetic energy $\frac{1}{2}mv^2$ and potential energy $-GM_E m/R_E$. Conservation of energy gives

$$\tfrac{1}{2}mv^2 - \frac{GM_E m}{R_E} = -\frac{GM_E m}{r_1} \qquad\qquad 9\text{-}19$$

or

$$\tfrac{1}{2}mv^2 = \frac{GM_E m}{R_E} - \frac{GM_E m}{r_1} = \frac{GM_E m}{R_E r_1}\,(r_1 - R_E)$$

To simplify the calculation we write GM_E in terms of the free-fall acceleration near the surface of the earth, $g = GM_E/R_E^2$. Substituting gR_E^2 for GM_E gives

$$\tfrac{1}{2}mv^2 = \frac{mgR_E}{r_1}\,(r_1 - R_E)$$

or

$$v^2 = \frac{2gR_E}{r_1}\,(r_1 - R_E) = 2gh\,\frac{R_E}{r_1} = 2gh\,\frac{R_E}{R_E + h} \qquad\qquad 9\text{-}20$$

where we have written h for $r_1 - R_E$. The speed is smaller than the result $v^2 = 2gh$ obtained by neglecting the decrease in the force of gravity with distance.

In practice, the speed will be less than that given by Equation 9-20 because of air resistance.

Questions

1. Suggest two forces that may be important in skiing which are neglected in Example 9-3. Are these forces conservative? Is the work they do positive or negative? How would their inclusion affect the result $v^2 = 2gH$?

2. If the mass of the pulley in Atwood's machine is not negligible, the pulley has kinetic energy of rotation (to be studied in Chapter 12). Do you expect the inclusion of this kinetic energy to increase or decrease the value of the speed v for a given distance y?

3. Discuss the advantages and disadvantages of solving mechanics problems by energy methods compared with using Newton's laws.

9-2   Escape Velocity and Binding Energy

In the example of a mass oscillating on a spring we found that the mass is confined to a certain region of space bounded by turning points $x = \pm A$, where the amplitude A is related to the total energy by $A = \sqrt{2E/k}$. If we increase the total energy by initially pulling the mass out farther (and thus doing a greater amount of work on it), the turning points change. However, for this system, with potential energy given by Figure 9-6b, no matter how great the energy, the mass is confined because the total-energy line always intersects the potential energy at two values of x. Such a system is called a *bound system*. In this section we consider systems which are bound for values of the total energy below some critical value. For values of the total energy above this critical value the particles are not bound in any region of space.

Example 9-7 Escape Velocity Consider a particle of mass m a distance r from the center of the earth, where r is greater than the earth's radius R_E. The general gravitational potential-energy function is

$$U(r) = -\frac{GM_E m}{r} \qquad 9\text{-}21$$

As in Example 9-6, it simplifies calculation to write GM_E as gR_E^2, where g is the free-fall acceleration near the surface of the earth. The gravitational potential energy is then

$$U(r) = -\frac{mgR_E^2}{r} \qquad 9\text{-}22$$

At the surface of the earth $r = R_E$, and the gravitational potential energy is

$$U(R_E) = -\frac{mgR_E^2}{R_E} = -mgR_E \qquad 9\text{-}23$$

If we project the mass upward with some initial speed, it moves up with decreasing speed until the increase in potential energy equals the initial kinetic energy. It then stops and falls back toward the earth, losing potential energy and gaining kinetic energy. At an infinite distance from the earth, the potential energy is zero. For a particle initially at the surface of the earth with potential energy $-mgR_E$, the greatest possible increase in potential energy is mgR_E. This greatest possible increase in potential energy equals the greatest possible decrease in kinetic energy. If the initial kinetic energy of the particle at the surface of the earth is greater than mgR_E, the particle will never stop and fall back to the earth but escapes into outer space. The escape velocity is defined by

$$\tfrac{1}{2}mv_e^2 = mgR_E \qquad\qquad 9\text{-}24$$

or

$$v_e = \sqrt{2gR_E} \qquad\qquad 9\text{-}25$$

Using $g = 32.2$ ft/sec^2 = 32.2/5280 mi/sec^2 and $R_E = 3960$ mi, we obtain

$$v_e = \sqrt{2\,\frac{32.2}{5280}\,3960} = 6.95 \text{ mi/sec} = 2.50 \times 10^4 \text{ mi/h}$$

$$= 11.2 \text{ km/sec}$$

The potential-energy function $U(r)$ is sketched in Figure 9-7. The shaded region $r < R_E$ is inside the earth.

The total energy of a particle is the sum of the kinetic energy and the potential energy

$$E = E_k + U(r) = \tfrac{1}{2}mv^2 - \frac{mgR_E^2}{r} \qquad\qquad 9\text{-}26$$

If v_0 is the speed of the particle at the earth's surface, the total energy is

$$E = \tfrac{1}{2}mv_0^2 - \frac{mgR_E^2}{R_E} = \tfrac{1}{2}mv_0^2 - mgR_E \qquad\qquad 9\text{-}27$$

From Equation 9-24 we see that if v_0 equals the escape velocity v_e, the total energy is zero. If v_0 is greater than v_e, the total energy is positive; if v_0 is less than v_e, the total energy is negative. In terms of energy, the minimum kinetic energy needed by a particle to escape from the earth is that which makes the total energy zero.

In Figure 9-7, a horizontal line is drawn for total energy $E = E_1$ which is negative. The kinetic energy of a particle with total energy E_1 is $E_k = E_1 - U(r)$ represented by the vertical distance on the graph between the total energy and the potential energy. The kinetic energy

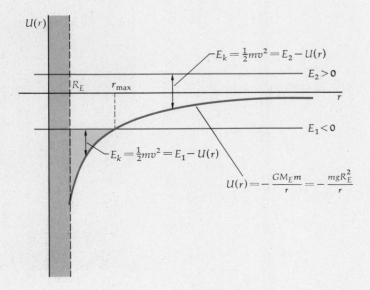

Figure 9-7
The potential-energy function $U(r) = -GM_E m/r = -mgR_E^2/r$ for a mass a distance r from the center of the earth, where r is greater than the radius of the earth R_E. If the particle has total energy E_1 less than zero, it is confined between R_E and r_{max}, where E_1 intersects $U(r)$. The kinetic energy $E_k = E_1 - U(r)$ is represented by the vertical distance between E_1 and $U(r)$. If the total energy is E_2, greater than zero, the particle is not confined. A positive total-energy line does not intersect the potential-energy curve.

238   CHAPTER 9   Conservation of Energy

decreases with increasing r and is zero at $r = r_{max}$, where the total-energy line E_1 intersects the potential-energy curve $U(r)$. The distance $r = r_{max}$ is the maximum distance from the center of the earth that can be reached by a particle with total energy E_1. The motion of a particle with total energy E_1 is therefore confined to the region between R_E and r_{max}, as indicated in the figure.

The horizontal line $E = E_2$ in Figure 9-7 indicates a total energy greater than zero. Again, the kinetic energy of a particle with this total energy is represented by the vertical distance between the total-energy line and the potential-energy curve. As r increases, the kinetic energy decreases, but it never reaches zero if E is positive. The positive total-energy line does not intersect the potential-energy curve. As r approaches infinity, the potential energy approaches zero and the kinetic energy approaches the total energy E_2. The motion of a particle with total energy greater or equal to zero is not confined; i.e., the particle is not bound to the earth. If a particle is projected away from the earth's surface with velocity greater than the escape velocity, it will escape whether its velocity is radial or at some angle, because the work done by gravity depends only on the radial distance traveled.

Example 9-8 Energy of an Orbiting Satellite Consider a particle of mass m orbiting the earth in a circular orbit above the surface of the earth. Its total energy is greater than $-GM_Em/r$ because it already has some kinetic energy. From Newton's law $\Sigma \mathbf{F} = m\mathbf{a}$ for circular motion we have

$$\frac{GM_Em}{r^2} = ma = \frac{mv^2}{r} \qquad 9\text{-}28$$

Thus the kinetic energy for a circular orbit is

$$\tfrac{1}{2}mv^2 = \frac{\tfrac{1}{2}GM_Em}{r} = \tfrac{1}{2}|U(r)| \qquad 9\text{-}29$$

This result (that the kinetic energy is half the magnitude of the potential energy) holds for any circular orbit in an inverse-square force field. On the energy diagram of Figure 9-7 the total energy of an orbiting satellite is thus halfway between $-GM_Em/r$ and zero. The minimum additional energy an orbiting satellite must be given to escape from the earth is just $\tfrac{1}{2}GM_Em/r$. The kinetic energy of the orbiting satellite must be doubled.

Example 9-9 Flight of Apollo 11 As a practical example of escape from the earth, consider the flight of Apollo 11, July 1969, during which man first set foot on the moon. The spacecraft was launched from the earth into a nearly circular orbit around the earth at an altitude of 119 mi and speed of 17,427 mi/h. From this orbit, the engine of the craft was fired to give it a speed of 24,245 mi/h. This speed, which nearly doubled the kinetic energy of the craft, is less than the escape velocity we calculated because the moon exerts a gravitational attraction which we have neglected. The spacecraft then traveled toward the moon, with its speed decreasing, to a point 23,800 mi from the moon, where the attraction of the moon equals the attraction of the earth. Beyond this point the craft accelerated toward the moon. As the craft passed the moon, its kinetic energy was greater than that needed to escape from the moon. On the far side of the moon, retarding rockets were fired to slow it down and put it into an orbit around the moon. (This

Blast-off of Saturn V rocket July 16, 1969, carrying Apollo 11 astronauts on man's first voyage to the moon.

NASA

was an elliptical orbit of maximum altitude of 195 mi and minimum altitude of 70 mi.) From this orbit, the lunar module Eagle, containing astronauts Armstrong and Aldrin, separated from the main craft and dropped into an orbit of about 50,000 ft altitude. From this orbit the module was flown to a landing on the surface of the moon.

Example 9-10 Ionization of the Hydrogen Atom In the Bohr model of the hydrogen atom, the electron follows a circular orbit around the proton. In the lowest energy state (called the *ground state*) the radius of the orbit is 0.529×10^{-10} m. We calculated the electrostatic potential energy for this distance in Example 8-5. The result is $U = -kq_1q_2/r = -4.36 \times 10^{-18}$ J $= -27.2$ eV. The energy diagram for this system has the same form as that for a satellite orbiting the earth. The kinetic energy of the electron in its circular orbit is

$$\tfrac{1}{2}mv^2 = \tfrac{1}{2}|U| = 13.6 \text{ eV}$$

The total energy of the electron is thus

$$E = \tfrac{1}{2}mv^2 + U = 13.6 \text{ eV} - 27.2 \text{ eV} = -13.6 \text{ eV} \qquad 9\text{-}30$$

To escape from the proton, the electron must have a total energy greater than or equal to zero. Thus to remove the electron, we must give it an additional energy of 13.6 eV, called the *binding energy* of the atom. Since removing an electron from an atom is called *ionization*, the binding energy is also called the *ionization energy*.

Example 9-11 Molecular Oscillations and Dissociation The force between two atoms or ions in a molecule, discussed briefly in Chapter 6 (see Figure 6-3), is similar to that exerted by a spring connecting the two atoms except that at great separation distances the force becomes zero. The potential energy U as a function of separation distance r is shown in Figure 9-8. This curve might apply to the two hydrogen atoms in the H_2 molecule or to the Na^+ and Cl^- ions in an NaCl molecule. At the point $r = r_0$, the slope of the potential-energy curve is zero, and hence the force is zero. This is a stable equilibrium point, since $U(r)$

Figure 9-8
Potential energy versus separation for a diatomic molecule. E_1, E_2, and E_3 are successively greater total energies for the system. E_1 and E_2 are negative, and the system is bound between the maximum and minimum separations where the total-energy line intersects the potential-energy curve. E_3 is positive, and the system is not bound; i.e., the atoms or ions of the molecule are dissociated. The minimum energy for dissociation D is also called the binding energy.

increases on either side of this point. Very near this point the curve is similar to that for a mass on a spring. If the total energy is E_1, as shown in Figure 9-8, the atoms will oscillate about the equilibrium point like two masses joined by a spring. If the total energy is the larger value E_2, the motion will be an oscillation but not the simple, symmetric oscillation of two masses connected by a spring. The two turning points at r_1 and r_2 are different distances from the equilibrium point r_0. The two "halves" of the oscillation would take different times. Also, the average separation for this energy is slightly greater than r_0.

If the total energy is positive, e.g., the value E_3 in Figure 9-8, there is only one turning point. In this case the two particles are not bound. If initially the two particles were approaching, their separation would decrease until this single turning point was reached. Then they would move apart. Since there is no other turning point, they would continue to move apart.

The normal state of a molecule is for its parts to be nearly at rest relative to each other at the equilibrium separation r_0. If the molecule is given a greater energy, such as E_1, an oscillating motion ensues. This occurs, for example, when the body of which the molecule is a part is heated. If the heating is enough to increase the molecular energy to a value like E_2, the average separation of the particles is greater than r_0. In fact, the greater E_2 is, the greater the average separation. If the molecules are in a solid, this requires the solid to expand as E_2 is increased. In fact, this model accounts for the familiar phenomenon of the thermal expansion of solids.

We also can see from Figure 9-8 that there is a minimum energy that must be supplied to the molecule to make its parts separate completely. This energy, called the *binding* or *dissociation energy,* is evidently equal to the magnitude of the potential energy at the equilibrium separation r_0. (It is actually slightly less because the atoms are always oscillating with some total energy slightly greater than the minimum potential energy.)

Questions

4. If the gravitational potential energy of a mass m is chosen to be zero at the surface of the earth, what is its value when the mass is an infinite distance from the earth?

5. Two equal particles are separately projected with their escape velocities, but one is projected radially and the other tangentially to the surface of the earth. After 1 sec, how do their distances from the surface of the earth compare? (Neglect air resistance.) How do their speeds compare? When the particle projected tangentially is at a height $h = R_E$ above the earth's surface, how does its speed compare with that of the other particle at the same height?

6. In Example 9-9 it is stated that when Apollo 11 approached the moon, its kinetic energy was greater than that needed to escape from the moon. Explain why this must be true.

7. A comet enters the solar system, orbits around the sun, and leaves again. When it is near the sun, its gravitational potential energy (relative to infinity) plus its kinetic energy is found to be less than zero. Will the comet ever return?

Atmospheric Evaporation

Richard Goody
Harvard University

The expression for escape velocity of a particle near the earth's surface (Equation 9-25) can be generalized to apply to the escape of a particle from the surface of any planet or the moon. If R is the radius of the planet and g the acceleration of gravity at the surface, the escape velocity is given by

$$v_e = \sqrt{2gR}$$

This result is independent of the mass of the particle and therefore equally valid for a spacecraft, a projectile, or a molecule. The application to the escape of molecules from the surface of a planet leads to an important concept in planetary physics: using this equation and some results from the kinetic theory of gases, we can understand why some planets have atmospheres and others do not. We look to this mechanism to explain, for example, why the earth appears to have lost hydrogen to space following decomposition of water molecules, leaving an oxygen-rich atmosphere while, to a first approximation, Jupiter is a gigantic ball of hydrogen.

Several conditions must be met before a molecule (or atom) can escape from the surface of a planet. First, the magnitude of the molecule's velocity must be greater than the escape velocity v_e for the planet. Table 9-1 lists escape velocities for the moon and planets in the solar system. A second condition is that the direction of the velocity of the molecule must be away from the planet rather than toward it. Finally, the molecule must not collide with other molecules on its outward journey.

The chance that a molecule will collide with another in a particular region of space depends on the density of molecules in that region. The molecular density falls off rapidly with height above the surface of the planet (see Problems 20 and 21 in Chapter 5). There must therefore be a level, called the *escape level*, which varies with the planet and depends upon the atmospheric temperature, above which the collision probability is so small that a molecule heading away from a planet with velocity greater than v_e leaves the planet never to return. Figure 1 shows the trajectories of molecules above the escape level. Molecules with speeds greater than v_e escape, while those with speeds less than v_e fall back toward earth. These trajectories differ greatly from those

Table 9-1
Escape velocities for the moon and planets

Planet	Gravitational acceleration, m/sec²	Radius, km	Escape velocity v_e, km/sec
Mercury	3.76	2,439	4.3
Venus	8.88	6,049	10.3
Earth	9.81	6,371	11.2
Moon	1.62	1,738	2.3
Mars	3.73	3,390	5.0
Jupiter	26.2	69,500	60
Saturn	11.2	58,100	36
Uranus	9.75	24,500	22
Neptune	11.34	24,600	24

Figure 1
Molecules or atoms whose velocities exceed the escape velocity v_e can escape from the planet. These may form only a minute fraction of the total number at the critical level.

Figure 2
The Maxwell-Boltzmann speed distribution. The fraction of molecules having speeds in some interval dv equals the area under the curve for that interval. The speed v_0 for which $f(v)$ is maximum is the most probable speed. The mean speed $\bar{v}$ and the root-mean-square speed v_{rms} differ slightly from the most probable speed.

of gas molecules near the earth's surface, where a molecule can travel only a short distance before colliding with another. For earth, the escape level averages about 500 km above the ground with considerable diurnal and seasonal variation because of atmospheric temperature changes. For Venus, the escape level is about 200 km above the surface.

Although escape velocity does not depend on the mass of the molecule, the distribution of molecular speeds depends strongly on the mass of the molecule and on the temperature: in thermal equilibrium it is given by the Maxwell-Boltzmann distribution (Figure 2). In this figure, $f(v)\,dv$ is the fraction of all the molecules which have speeds in some interval dv. This fraction for an interval dv centered about some speed v is indicated by the shaded area in the figure. The most probable speed is related to the mass of the molecule m and the absolute temperature T by

$$v_0 = \sqrt{\frac{2kT}{m}}$$

where k is a constant called Boltzmann's constant.[1]

Some typical values of v_0 are shown in Table 9-2. Comparing Tables 9-1 and 9-2, we see that v_0 is greater than v_e only for hydrogen on the surface of the moon at temperatures greater than 300 K. Since lunar daytime temperatures exceed 300 K, any hydrogen would evaporate into space almost instantaneously.

Even when the escape speed v_e is much greater than the most probable speed v_0, there will be some molecules or atoms which have speeds greater than v_e and therefore have a chance of escaping. From Figure 1 we discern that most molecules have speeds not much different from v_0 but a few have speeds $2v_0$, $3v_0$, or even $100v_0$, though the fraction with speeds much greater than v_0 is very small and decreases rapidly with increasing v. Whether a certain type of molecule or atom is likely to be found in the atmosphere of a planet depends on the rate of escape of these molecules, which in turn depends crit-

Table 9-2
Most probable velocities in kilometers per second

Atom	Atomic weight, μ	Temperature, K		
		300	600	900
H	1	2.24	3.16	3.87
He	4	1.12	1.58	1.94
O	16	0.56	0.79	0.97

[1] Because of the asymmetry of the curve for $f(v)$, the most probable speed v_0, the mean speed $\bar{v}$, and the root-mean-square speed v_{rms} are slightly different, though they all have the same dependence on the temperature and molecular mass. In Chapter 17, it will be shown that the root-mean-square speed is given by $v_{rms} = \sqrt{3kT/m}$.

Figure 3
The fraction of atoms or molecules with velocities greater than v_e in terms of the ratio v_e/v_0. The two parts of the figure differ only in scale.

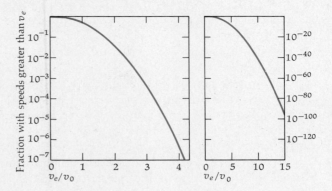

ically on the fraction of molecules or atoms above the escape level with speeds greater than v_e. This fraction is shown in Figure 3 as a function of the ratio v_e/v_0. When this ratio is greater than about 2, this fraction is given approximately by

$$f_{v>v_e} = \frac{4}{\pi} \frac{v_e}{v_0} e^{-(v_e/v_0)^2}$$

The temperature of the escape level on earth is close to 600 K, and v_0 is therefore 0.79 km/sec for atomic oxygen and about 3.16 km/sec for atomic hydrogen. Using $v_e = 11.2$ km/sec, we obtain for the fraction of hydrogen atoms with speeds greater than the escape speed:

$$f_{v>v_e}(\text{H}) = \frac{4}{\pi} \frac{11.2}{3.16} e^{-(11.2/3.16)^2} \approx 1.6 \times 10^{-5}$$

This result tells us that out of every million hydrogen atoms at the escape level about 16 will have speeds greater than v_e, and since half, on the average, will be moving away from the earth, 8 will escape. This fraction, seemingly small, is large enough to account for the almost complete absence of hydrogen from the earth's atmosphere now, approximately 4×10^9 years after formation of the earth.

For atomic oxygen, on the other hand, the fraction with speeds greater than v_e is

$$f_{v>v_e}(\text{O}) = \frac{4}{\pi} \frac{11.2}{0.79} e^{-(11.2/0.79)^2} \approx 9.3 \times 10^{-87}$$

This fraction for oxygen atoms is much smaller than for hydrogen atoms. If we want to evaluate the evaporation rates of hydrogen and oxygen numerically, our model of the escape process must be elaborated; nevertheless, the ratio of the numbers of hydrogen and oxygen atoms with velocities high enough for escape (more than 10^{81} to 1) is so large that the simultaneous retention of oxygen and escape of hydrogen is plausible. Because of the huge mass of Jupiter, its escape velocity of 60 km/sec enables it to retain hydrogen as easily as oxygen is retained on earth. We can therefore see in a general way why the two planets have such markedly different compositions.

9-3   Bernoulli's Equation

To illustrate the wide range of application of the work-energy theorem, we now apply it to the flow of fluids. Consider a fluid flowing steadily through a pipe that is not level. The pressure will change from point to point along the pipe, and work must be done to make the fluid flow up. If the cross-sectional area of the pipe varies, the speed of the fluid will vary and so will the pressure. The fundamental relationship which relates the pressure, flow speed, and height was first obtained in 1738 by Daniel Bernoulli and is named for him. It is in effect just the work-energy theorem applied to this situation. We shall derive Bernoulli's equation for the restricted case of an incompressible fluid (most liquids) which is nonviscous (no internal friction) and which flows steadily and without turbulence in a closed pipe. The result can be shown to hold in somewhat more general circumstances.

Figure 9-9a shows a sectional view of a length of pipe. We apply the work-energy theorem to the fluid contained initially between points 1 and 2. After a short time Δt, this fluid will have moved along the pipe and will be contained between points 1' and 2', as shown in Figure 9-9b.

If the flow is steady, the only change between Figure 9-9a and b is for the heavily shaded portions of the fluid mass. The fluid in the intermediate, lightly shaded region is different fluid, but the physical conditions of its location, pressure, speed, and energy are exactly the same as those of the fluid initially occupying this same position. The net change in time Δt is equivalent to lifting the fluid in the heavily shaded portion of Figure 9-9a to the position of the heavily shaded portion of Figure 9-9b and of changing its speed from v_1 at point 1 to v_2 at point 2.

Let Δm be the mass of this heavily shaded portion of the fluid. The mass can be written in terms of the density ρ and the volume ΔV

$$\Delta m = \rho \, \Delta V \tag{9-31}$$

The Granger Collection

Daniel Bernoulli (1700–1782).

(a)

(b)

Figure 9-9
Fluid moving in a pipe for the derivation of Bernoulli's principle. The net work done by the forces P_1A_1 and P_2A_2 has the effect of raising the part of the fluid indicated by heavy shading from height y_1 to y_2 and changing its speed from v_1 to v_2. Bernoulli's equation is a statement of the work-energy theorem applied to the fluid.

If the fluid is incompressible, the density and volume of this part of the fluid will be the same at position 2 as at position 1. The volume at position 1 is $A_1 \, \Delta x_1$, where A_1 is the cross-sectional area of the pipe at this position. Similarly, the volume at position 2 is $A_2 \, \Delta x_2$. Thus for an incompressible fluid we have

$$A_2 \, \Delta x_2 = A_1 \, \Delta x_1 \qquad\qquad 9\text{-}32$$

But $\Delta x_1 = v_1 \, \Delta t$, where v_1 is the speed at position 1, and $\Delta x_2 = v_2 \, \Delta t$. Substituting these into Equation 9-32 and canceling out the common factor Δt, we obtain a simple relation for the speeds of an incompressible fluid:

$$A_2 v_2 = A_1 v_1 \qquad\qquad 9\text{-}33$$

Velocity-area product is constant for incompressible fluid

As the entire body of fluid we are considering moves in time Δt, the fluid following it in the pipe exerts a force on it of magnitude $F_1 = P_1 A_1$, where P_1 is the pressure at point 1. This force does work $W_1 = F_1 \, \Delta x_1 = P_1 A_1 \, \Delta x_1 = P_1 \, \Delta V$, where ΔV is just the volume of the heavily shaded mass Δm. At the same time, the fluid preceding that under consideration exerts a force $F_2 = P_2 A_2$ to the left in the figure. This force does negative work (since it opposes the motion) $W_2 = -F_2 \, \Delta x_2 = -P_2 A_2 \, \Delta x_2 = -P_2 \, \Delta V$. Thus the net work done by these forces is

$$W = P_1 \, \Delta V - P_2 \, \Delta V = (P_1 - P_2) \, \Delta V \qquad\qquad 9\text{-}34$$

This work equals the change in the kinetic energy and gravitational potential energy of the fluid under consideration, i.e., just the change in energy of the portion of mass $\Delta m = \rho \, \Delta V$. The change in potential energy of this mass is

$$\Delta U = \Delta m \, g y_2 - \Delta m \, g y_1$$

The change in kinetic energy is

$$\Delta E_k = \tfrac{1}{2}(\Delta m) v_2{}^2 - \tfrac{1}{2}(\Delta m) v_1{}^2$$

Thus the work-energy theorem gives

$$(P_1 - P_2) \, \Delta V = \Delta m \, g y_2 - \Delta m \, g y_1 + \tfrac{1}{2}(\Delta m) v_2{}^2 - \tfrac{1}{2}(\Delta m) v_1{}^2$$

If we divide each term by ΔV and write the density $\rho = \Delta m / \Delta V$, we obtain

$$P_1 - P_2 = \tfrac{1}{2}\rho v_2{}^2 - \tfrac{1}{2}\rho v_1{}^2 + \rho g y_2 - \rho g y_1$$

When we collect all the quantities with subscript 2 on one side and those with subscript 1 on the other side, this equation becomes

$$P_1 + \rho g y_1 + \tfrac{1}{2}\rho v_1{}^2 = P_2 + \rho g y_2 + \tfrac{1}{2}\rho v_2{}^2 \qquad\qquad 9\text{-}35$$

This result can be restated as

$$P + \rho g y + \tfrac{1}{2}\rho v^2 = \text{constant} \qquad\qquad 9\text{-}36$$

Bernoulli's equation

meaning that this combination of quantities evaluated at any point along the pipe has the same value as at any other point. Equation 9-36 is known as *Bernoulli's equation* for steady, nonviscous flow of an incompressible fluid. To a considerable extent Bernoulli's equation also applies to compressible fluids like gases.

A special application of Bernoulli's equation occurs for a fluid at rest. Then $v_1 = v_2 = 0$, and we obtain

$$P_1 - P_2 = \rho g (y_2 - y_1) = \rho g h$$

where $h = y_2 - y_1$ is the difference in height between points 2 and 1.

This is just the result we obtained from Archimedes' principle, derived in Chapter 5 from Newton's laws. We now give some examples of the use of Bernoulli's equation in nonstatic situations.

Example 9-12 An incompressible fluid such as water flows through a horizontal pipe which has a constricted section as shown in Figure 9-10. Show that the pressure is *reduced* in the constriction.

Since both sections of the pipe are at the same elevation, we take $y_1 = y_2$ in Equation 9-35. We then have

$$P_1 + \tfrac{1}{2}\rho v_1{}^2 = P_2 + \tfrac{1}{2}\rho v_2{}^2 \qquad\qquad 9\text{-}37$$

But, from Equation 9-33,

$$A_1 v_1 = A_2 v_2 \qquad \text{or} \qquad v_2 = \frac{A_1}{A_2}\, v_1$$

Substituting this result in Equation 9-37 gives

$$P_1 + \tfrac{1}{2}\rho v_1{}^2 = P_2 + \tfrac{1}{2}\rho\, \frac{A_1{}^2 v_1{}^2}{A_2{}^2}$$

or

$$P_1 - P_2 = \tfrac{1}{2}\rho \left(\frac{A_1{}^2}{A_2{}^2} - 1 \right) v_1{}^2 \qquad\qquad 9\text{-}38$$

Since A_1 is larger than A_2, the quantity on the right is positive. Hence P_2 is less than P_1. Note that the only circumstance in which P_2 and P_1 can be equal, according to Equation 9-38, is when $v_1 = 0$, that is, when the fluid is at rest in the pipe.

Figure 9-10
Constriction in a pipe carrying a moving fluid. The pressure is smaller in the narrow section of the pipe, in which the fluid is moving faster.

Example 9-13 A large water tower (Figure 9-11) is drained by a pipe of cross section A through a valve a distance h below the surface of the water in the tower. Show that the pressure in the pipe is reduced when the valve is opened.

In applying Equation 9-35 we take point 1 to be the top surface of the water in the tower, where the pressure is atmospheric pressure P_a. We also let $y_1 = h$. Point 2 is in the pipe just before the valve, and $y_2 = 0$. Because the surface area A_1 of the tower is so large compared to the area of the pipe, the speed v_1 with which the surface drops as the tower is drained can be neglected. Then, according to Equation 9-35,

$$P_a + \rho g h = P_2 + \tfrac{1}{2}\rho v_2{}^2$$

or

$$P_2 = P_a + \rho g h - \tfrac{1}{2}\rho v_2{}^2 \qquad\qquad 9\text{-}39$$

If the valve is closed, the water is at rest and $v_2 = 0$. Then the pressure in the pipe at the valve is, according to Equation 9-34, just $P_2 = P_a + \rho g h$. When the valve is opened, the water will move and v_2 will not be zero. Then, according to Equation 9-39, the pressure in the pipe will decrease by $\tfrac{1}{2}\rho v_2{}^2$.

Example 9-14 Calculate the pressure P_2 in Example 9-13 in pounds per square inch if $h = 40$ ft, $P_a = 14.6$ lb/in², and $v_2 = 48$ ft/sec with the valve open.

The density of water is 1 gm/cm³ = 1.94 slugs/ft³. In the British engineering system it is usually convenient to work with ρg in pounds per cubic foot rather than the density ρ. Using $g = 32.2$ ft/sec², we have for water,

$$\rho g = (1.94 \text{ slugs/ft}^3)(32.2 \text{ ft/sec}^2) = 62.5 \text{ lb/ft}^3$$

The quantity $\rho g h$ in Equation 9-39 is then

$$\rho g h = (62.5 \text{ lb/ft}^3)(40 \text{ ft}) = 2.50 \times 10^3 \text{ lb/ft}^2 = 17.4 \text{ lb/in}^2$$

The quantity $\frac{1}{2}\rho v_2{}^2$ is

$$\frac{1}{2}\rho v_2{}^2 = \frac{\frac{1}{2}\rho g v_2{}^2}{g} = \frac{\frac{1}{2}(62.5 \text{ lb/ft}^3)(48 \text{ ft/sec})^2}{32.2 \text{ ft/sec}^2}$$

$$= 2.24 \times 10^3 \text{ lb/ft}^2 = 15.5 \text{ lb/in}^2$$

Then with the valve closed and $v_2 = 0$ the pressure is

$$P_2 = P_a + \rho g h = 14.6 \text{ lb/in}^2 + 17.4 \text{ lb/in}^2 = 32.0 \text{ lb/in}^2$$

and with the valve open

$$P_2 = P_a + \rho g h - \frac{\frac{1}{2}\rho g v_2{}^2}{g}$$

$$= 14.6 \text{ lb/in}^2 + 17.4 \text{ lb/in}^2 - 15.5 \text{ lb/in}^2 = 16.5 \text{ lb/in}^2$$

Question

8. In Figure 9-10 the water entering the narrow part of the pipe is accelerated to a greater speed. What forces act on this water to produce this acceleration?

Review

A. Define, explain, or otherwise identify:

Work-energy theorem, 226   Ionization energy, 239
Escape velocity, 236   Dissociation energy, 240
Binding energy, 239   Bernoulli's equation, 245

B. True or false:

1. The total mechanical energy of a particle is always conserved.

2. When only conservative forces do work on a particle, its kinetic energy depends only on its position.

3. The time it takes a particle to move from one point to another can be found directly from the energy-conservation equation.

4. The kinetic energy needed to escape from the earth depends on the choice of reference point for the zero of potential energy.

5. Archimedes' principle can be derived from Bernoulli's equation.

Exercises

Section 9-1, Some Illustrative Examples

1. A 5-kg block is pushed along a horizontal rough surface by a constant horizontal force $F_0 = 25$ N. The coefficient of friction is 0.2. The block is pushed 3 m. (a) What is the work done on the block by the force F_0? (b) How much work is done on the block by friction? (c) What is the net increase in kinetic energy of the block? (d) What is the speed of the block after it has traveled 3 m?

2. A block is projected along a horizontal surface with initial velocity of 10 m/sec. The coefficient of friction between the block and the surface is 0.2. How far does the block slide before coming to rest?

3. A 2-kg block slides down a smooth curved ramp from rest at a height of 1 m (Figure 9-12). It slides 6 m on a rough horizontal surface before coming to rest. (a) What is the speed of the block at the bottom of the ramp? (b) How much work is done by friction on the block? (c) What is the coefficient of friction between the block and the horizontal surface?

Figure 9-12
Block slides down smooth curve onto a rough surface for Exercise 3.

4. A 1-kg mass is released from rest at a height of 5 m on a curved smooth ramp. At the foot of the ramp is a spring of spring constant 400 N/m (Figure 9-13). The mass slides down the ramp and onto the spring, compressing it a distance x before coming momentarily to rest. (a) Find x. (b) What happens to the mass after it comes to rest?

Figure 9-13
Exercise 4.

5. A 3-kg mass slides along a smooth horizontal surface with speed 5 m/sec and encounters a smooth ramp inclined at an angle of 30° to the horizontal. How far up the incline does the mass slide before coming momentarily to rest?

6. A 2-kg mass is pushed against a spring of force constant 500 N/m, compressing it 20 cm. It is released, and the spring projects the mass along a smooth horizontal surface and then up a smooth incline of angle 45°, as shown in Figure 9-14. (a) What is the speed of the mass when it leaves the spring? (b) How far up the incline does the mass travel?

Figure 9-14
Exercise 6.

7. A 6-kg block slides down a 30° incline starting from rest. After sliding 10 m along the incline, its speed is 7 m/sec. (a) What work did gravity do on the block in this descent? (b) What was the increase in kinetic energy of the block? (c) By how much did the total energy of the block increase or decrease? (d) How much work was done by friction on the block?

Figure 9-15
Exercise 8.

8. For the Atwood's machine shown in Figure 9-15 find the velocity of each mass when all masses are at the same height. The system is at rest when the lower string is cut.

9. A 0.5-lb ball is thrown with initial speed of 80 ft/sec at an angle of 53° above the horizontal. (a) What is the total mechanical energy initially? (b) Write the initial kinetic energy in terms of the velocity components v_x and v_y. What is the minimum kinetic energy during the flight of the ball? At what point does the ball have this minimum kinetic energy? (c) What is the maximum potential energy of the ball during its flight? (d) Find the maximum height of the ball.

10. Two men stand at the edge of a 50-m cliff. Simultaneously they throw balls at initial speed of 10 m/sec, one straight up and the other straight down. (a) If air resistance is neglected, how do the speeds of the balls compare when they reach the bottom of the cliff? What are their speeds there? (b) How much later does one ball reach the bottom than the other? (c) Discuss qualitatively how your answers would differ if air resistance were taken in account.

11. In Figure 9-16, $m_1 = 4$ kg, $m_2 = 2$ kg, and there is no friction. Find the speed of the masses when m_2 has fallen 2 m.

Figure 9-16
Exercise 11 and Problem 7.

12. A mass slides along the frictionless track shown in Figure 9-17. Initially it is at point P headed downhill with speed v_0. Describe the motion in as much detail as you can if (a) $v_0 = 7$ m/sec and (b) $v_0 = 12$ m/sec. (c) What is the least speed needed by the mass to get past point Q?

Figure 9-17
Exercise 12.

13. A pendulum of length L has a bob of mass m. It is released from some angle θ. The string hits a peg at a distance x directly below the pivot itself (Figure 9-18) and wraps itself around the peg, shortening the length of the pendulum. Show that the maximum height that the pendulum reaches equals its initial height. (Assume that initially the bob is below the height of the peg.)

Figure 9-18
Exercise 13 and Problem 3.

14. A mass m is attached to a spring of force constant k on a horizontal smooth surface. Its equilibrium position is $x = 0$. The mass is given a displacement $x = A$ and released. (a) What is the initial potential energy of the system? (b) Show that when the mass is at position x at any later time, its speed is given by $v = \sqrt{k/m}\ \sqrt{A^2 - x^2}$.

15. (a) Find the potential energy (relative to zero at infinity) of a 100-kg mass at the surface of the earth. (Take the radius of the earth to be $R_E = 6.4 \times 10^6$ m.) (b) Find the potential energy of the same mass at a height above the earth's surface equal to the earth's radius. (c) If the mass is dropped from this height, find its speed when it hits the surface of the earth. (Neglect air resistance; in practice, air resistance is of primary importance in this type of problem.)

Section 9-2, Escape Velocity and Binding Energy

16. A particle is projected from the surface of the earth with velocity equal to twice the escape velocity. When the particle is very far from the earth, what is its speed?

17. Find the escape velocity for a rocket leaving the moon. (The acceleration of gravity on the moon is 0.166 times that on earth, and the moon's radius is 0.273 R_E.)

18. The planet Saturn has mass of 95.2 times that of the earth and radius of 9.47 times that of the earth. Find the escape velocity for Saturn.

19. A space probe is to be sent from the earth so that it has a velocity of 50 km/sec when it is very far from the earth. What velocity is needed for the probe at the surface of the earth?

20. (a) Calculate the energy in joules necessary to send a 1-kg mass away from the earth with the escape velocity. (b) Convert this energy to kilowatt-hours. (c) If energy can be obtained at 3 cents per kilowatt-hour, what is the minimum cost of giving an 80-kg astronaut enough energy to escape the earth's gravitational field?

21. A satellite orbits the earth in a circular orbit. The orbit is then changed to another circular one of larger radius. Discuss the change in potential energy, total energy, and kinetic energy, i.e., whether each increases, decreases, or remains constant.

22. In the Bohr model of the hydrogen atom, the electron, with charge $-e$, moves in a circular orbit of radius r about the proton, with charge $+e$. Show that the kinetic energy of the electron is $E_k = \frac{1}{2}ke^2/r$ and the total energy is $E = -\frac{1}{2}ke^2/r$, where k is the coulomb constant.

Section 9-3, Bernoulli's Equation

23. Water flows through a 1-in-diameter hose with speed 2 ft/sec. The diameter of the nozzle is $\frac{1}{8}$ in. (a) At what speed does the water pass through the nozzle? (b) If the pump at one end and the nozzle at the other end are at the same height and the pressure at the nozzle is atmospheric, what is the pressure at the pump?

24. A large tank of water is tapped a distance h below the water surface by a small pipe, as shown in Figure 9-19. (a) Why is the pressure the same at points a and b? (b) Show that the speed of the water emerging at point b is $\sqrt{2gh}$ in the approximation that the speed at point a is negligible. (This is known as *Torricelli's law.*) Why is this a good approximation?

Figure 9-19
Exercise 24 and Problem 16.

25. Water is flowing at 3 m/sec in a horizontal pipe under a pressure of 2×10^5 N/m², which is about twice atmospheric pressure. The pipe narrows to half its original diameter. (a) What is the speed of flow in the narrow section? (b) What is the pressure in the narrower section of pipe? (c) How does the number of kilograms of water flowing through the narrow section each second compare with that flowing through the wider section?

26. The pressure in a section of 1-in-diameter horizontal pipe is 20.6 lb/in². Water flows through the pipe at 0.1 ft³/sec. What should the diameter of a constricted section of the pipe be for the pressure to be atmospheric pressure (14.6 lb/in²).

Problems

1. A small mass m slides without friction along the loop-the-loop track shown in Figure 9-20. The circular loop has radius R. The mass starts from rest at point P a distance h above the bottom of the loop. (a) What is the kinetic energy of m when it reaches the top of the loop? (b) What is its acceleration at the top of the loop assuming that it stays on the track? (c) What is the least value of h if m is to reach the top of the loop without leaving the track? (d) Assuming that h is greater than this least value, write an expression for the normal force exerted by the track on the mass.

Figure 9-20
Problem 1.

2. The rate of energy loss of a certain system at a given time is directly proportional to the total energy of the system at that time. (a) Write a differential
equation relating the energy E to the rate of change of energy dE/dt expressing
the above property. Let the proportionality constant be C. (b) Solve your equation to obtain a general relationship for the energy of the system E as a function of time t. (c) Find the constant C in your result when 10 percent of the
energy is lost in 10 sec. (d) How long does it take for half the energy of the
system to be lost when C has the value found in part (c)?

3. In the problem of the pendulum string hitting a peg (Exercise 13) the
pendulum is released from rest at $\theta = 90°$. (a) Find the speed of the bob in
terms of g, L, and x when it is directly above the peg and moving in a circle of
radius $L - x$. (b) What is the least value of its acceleration at that point if the
string is not to go slack? (c) Show that the bob will not reach this point with
the string still taut unless x is greater than or equal to $3L/5$.

4. A particle moves under the influence of a conservative force along the x axis
with total energy E. The potential energy associated with the force is $U(x)$. (a)
Show that the speed of the particle is given by $v = \sqrt{2/m}\ \sqrt{E - U}$. (b) Show
that the distance dx traveled during the time interval dt is given by

$$\frac{dx}{\sqrt{E - U(x)}} = \sqrt{\frac{2}{m}}\ dt$$

(c) For a mass on a spring the potential energy is $U = \frac{1}{2}kx^2$, where k is the force
constant, and the total energy is $E = \frac{1}{2}kA^2$, where A is the maximum displacement. By integrating your result in part (b) find the total time taken for a mass
on a spring to move from $x = -A$ to $x = +A$.

5. A 2-kg mass is released on a smooth incline 4 m from a spring of constant
$k = 100$ N/m. The spring is fixed along the plane inclined at $\theta = 30°$ (Figure
9-21). (a) Find the maximum compression of the spring, assumed to be
massless. (b) If the incline is not smooth but the coefficient of friction between
it and the mass is 0.2, find the maximum compression. (c) For the rough
incline, how far up the incline will the mass travel after leaving the spring? (d)
Describe the subsequent motion of the mass for the rough incline.

Figure 9-21
Problem 5.

6. A Superball can bounce to 90 percent of its original height. (a) How much
energy is lost after a 30-gm ball is bounced once from an initial height of 3 m?
(b) A ball dropped from an original height of H makes N bounces. Find a general expression for the maximum height of the ball after N bounces for a ball of
mass m dropped from height H. (c) About how many bounces are required if
the maximum height after the Nth bounce is 1 percent of the original height?

7. For the arrangement in Figure 9-16 with general masses m_1 and m_2, (a) find
an expression for the speed of the masses after m_2 has fallen a distance y. (b)
Differentiate this expression to obtain an expression for the acceleration of the
masses.

8. A space probe launched from the surface of the earth accelerates for a short
distance Δr and then moves under the influence of gravity only. Since it is

already a short distance Δr above the surface of the earth, its escape velocity is slightly less than that at the earth's surface by amount Δv. (a) Find Δv in terms of Δr using the differential approximation $\Delta v \approx dv$ and $\Delta r \approx dr$. (b) Find the escape velocity for $\Delta r = 200$ mi.

9. (a) Show that the total energy of a satellite in a circular orbit of radius r is given by $E = -GM_E m/2r$, where M_E is the mass of the earth and m the mass of the satellite, and that the speed v is given by $v = \sqrt{GM_E/r}$. (b) If you wish to decrease the radius of the circular orbit of a satellite, must you increase or decrease the kinetic energy of the satellite? How do the potential energy and total energy change if the radius is decreased? (c) Using the differential approximation $\Delta v \approx dv$ and $\Delta r \approx dr$, show that a small change in radius must be accompanied by a small change in speed given by

$$\frac{\Delta v}{v} = -\frac{1}{2}\frac{\Delta r}{r}$$

10. In the Bohr model of the hydrogen atom the electron moves in a circular orbit around the proton. Only certain orbits are allowed, given by $r = N^2 r_0$, where N is a positive integer and $r_0 = 0.529 \times 10^{-10}$ m is the radius of the smallest allowed orbit. (a) Show that the allowed total energies of the hydrogen atom are given by $E_N = -|E_1|/N^2$, where $E_1 = -\frac{1}{2}ke^2/r_0 = -13.6$ eV is the lowest energy (see Exercise 22). Make a diagram to scale of the allowed energies by labeling them on a vertical energy line for $N = 1, 2, 3, 4, 10$, and ∞. (b) Normally the hydrogen atom is in its lowest energy state $N = 1$, the ground state. If it absorbs just the right amount of energy, it can be excited to a higher energy state. Calculate the amount of energy needed to raise the hydrogen atom from its ground state $N = 1$ to its first excited state $N = 2$. Do the same for $N = 1$ to the second excited state $N = 3$. (c) When the hydrogen atom changes from an excited state to the ground state or an excited state of lower total energy, the excess energy is given off, usually as electromagnetic radiation. Calculate the energy given off when the atom makes the following changes: $N = 3$ to $N = 1$, $N = 2$ to $N = 1$, $N = 3$ to $N = 2$.

11. (a) With the following information, graph the potential-energy curve of the NaCl molecule versus separation distance r of the ions Na$^+$ and Cl$^-$:

1. The equilibrium separation is 2.4×10^{-10} m.
2. The dissociation energy is 4.2 eV.
3. When the potential energy is -1.0 eV, the separation is either 1.5×10^{-10} m or 7.0×10^{-10} m.
4. When the potential energy is $+5.0$ eV, the separation is 1.0×10^{-10} m.
5. When the potential energy is -3.0 eV, the separation is either 1.8×10^{-10} m or 3.5×10^{-10} m.
6. At infinite separation the energy of the Na$^+$ and Cl$^-$ ions is $+1.3$ eV. (This is not zero because it takes 1.3 eV to make ions from the original atoms. The dissociation energy is measured from the minimum potential energy to zero.)

(b) From your graph find the maximum and minimum separation of the ions when the total energy is -2 eV.

12. A fountain designed to spray a column of water 36 ft into the air has a $\frac{1}{2}$-in-diameter nozzle at ground level. The water pump is 10 ft below the ground. The pipe to the fountain has a diameter of 1 in. Find the necessary pump pressure.

13. In an aspirator pump water is pumped through a pipe at pressure 30 lb/in^2 and a speed of 10 ft/sec. The pipe narrows at the same level, so that the pressure drops. A tube connects the narrow part of the pipe to a vacuum chamber, in which the pressure is to be 1 lb/in^2. What is the ratio of the areas of the pipe?

14. A large beer keg of height H and area A_1 is filled with beer. The top is open to atmospheric pressure. At the bottom is a spigot opening of area A_2, much smaller than A_1. (a) Show that the velocity of beer leaving the spigot is

approximately $\sqrt{2gh}$ when the height of the beer is h. (b) Show that in the approximation A_2 much less than A_1, the rate of change of height h of the beer is given by $dh/dt = -(A_2/A_1)\sqrt{2gh}$. (c) Show that the result of part (b) can be written $-dh/\sqrt{h} = (A_2/A_1)\sqrt{2g}\ dt$ and integrate to obtain an expression for h as a function of time. Take $h = H$ at $t = 0$ to determine the constant of integration. (d) Find the total time needed to drain the keg if $H = 2$ m, $A_1 = 0.8$ m^2, and $A_2 = 10^{-4}\ A_1$.

15. In calculating the escape velocity in Example 9-7 the rotation of the earth was neglected. The velocity that must be given to a body relative to the ground will be less if the body is launched in the direction of the earth's rotation or more if it is launched away from it. Take the earth's rotation into account for a body launched on the equator in the direction of motion of the earth's surface (horizontally eastward). (a) What is the speed relative to the center of the earth of an object at rest on the equator? (b) Relative to the earth's surface, what speed must be given to a body for it to escape the earth? (c) By what percentage is the work required to accelerate the body reduced because of the earth's rotation?

16. (a) For Figure 9-19 find the distance x at which the water strikes the ground. Express your result in terms of h and H. (b) Show that there are two values of h equidistant from the point $h = \frac{1}{2}H$ which give the same distance x. (c) Show that x is a maximum when $h = \frac{1}{2}H$. What is the value of the maximum distance x?

CHAPTER 10   Many-Particle Systems

So far we have been concentrating on the motion of a single particle. We now turn to more complicated problems dealing with two or more particles. Although the detailed description of the complete motion is quite complicated, some general methods, which follow directly from Newton's laws, are useful in dealing with a wide variety of problems.

We begin by defining the center of mass for a system of particles. We then show that the motion of this point is quite simple, no matter how complicated the motions of all the individual particles in the system. Figure 10-1 is a multiflash photograph of a baton thrown into the air. Although the motion of the baton is complicated, the motion of one point, the center of mass, is simple. While the baton is in the air, the center of mass follows a parabolic path. We shall show in general that the acceleration of the center of mass of a system of particles equals the resultant external force divided by the total mass of the system. For the baton thrown into the air, the acceleration of the center of mass is g downward.

Figure 10-1
Multiflash photograph of a baton. One point on the baton, the center of mass, follows the same simple parabolic path as if it were a single point particle. (*Courtesy of Harold E. Edgerton.*)

10-1   Center of Mass

Let us first consider a simple system of two particles in one dimension. Let x_1 and x_2 be the coordinates of the particles relative to some arbitrary origin. The center-of-mass coordinate x_{CM} is then defined by

$$Mx_{CM} = m_1x_1 + m_2x_2 \qquad\qquad \text{10-1}$$

Center of mass

where $M = m_1 + m_2$ is the total mass of the system. For this case of just two particles, the center of mass lies on the line joining the particles at some point between them (Figure 10-2a). This is easily seen if we choose our origin on one of the particles, say m_1 (Figure 10-2b). Then x_2 is the distance d between the two particles. The center-of-mass coordinate for this choice of origin is, from Equation 10-1,

$$Mx_{CM} = m_1x_1 + m_2x_2 = m_1(0) + m_2d$$

$$x_{CM} = \frac{m_2}{M}d = \frac{m_2}{m_1 + m_2}d \qquad\qquad \text{10-2}$$

For equal masses, the center of mass is halfway between the particles. Otherwise, the center of mass is closer to the particle of greater mass (Figure 10-2c). For example if $m_1 = 4$ kg and $m_2 = 1$ kg, the center of mass is a distance $\frac{1}{5}d$ from m_1.

We obtain the velocity of the center of mass v_{CM} by differentiating Equation 10-1:

$$M\frac{dx_{CM}}{dt} = m_1\frac{dx_1}{dt} + m_2\frac{dx_2}{dt}$$

or

$$Mv_{CM} = m_1v_1 + m_2v_2 \qquad\qquad \text{10-3}$$

Velocity of the center of mass

The right side of Equation 10-3 is just the total momentum of our two-particle system. Thus

The velocity of the center of mass times the total mass equals the total momentum of the system.

Figure 10-2
The center of mass of a two-particle system. (*a*) If the particles have equal mass, the center of mass is midway between them. (*b*) If the origin is chosen at m_1, the position of the center of mass is given by $x_{CM} = m_2d/(m_1 + m_2)$. (*c*) If the particles have unequal mass, the center of mass is closer to the more massive particle.

We obtain the acceleration of the center of mass by differentiating Equation 10-3:

$$M \frac{dv_{CM}}{dt} = m_1 \frac{dv_1}{dt} + m_2 \frac{dv_2}{dt}$$

or

$$Ma_{CM} = m_1 a_1 + m_2 a_2 = \Sigma F_{x1} + \Sigma F_{x2} = \Sigma F_x \qquad \text{10-4}$$

where $\Sigma F_{x1} = m_1 a_1$ is the resultant force acting on particle 1, $\Sigma F_{x2} = m_2 a_2$ is the resultant force acting on m_2, and $\Sigma F_x = \Sigma F_{x1} + \Sigma F_{x2}$ is the resultant force acting on the two-particle system. The forces acting on the system can be put in two categories, internal forces and external forces. The *internal forces* are the forces of interaction between the two particles: their mutual gravitational attraction, electrostatic attraction or repulsion, contact forces, and forces exerted by strings or springs which connect the particles. *External forces* are any forces exerted by agents outside the system. Figure 10-3 shows two particles connected by a spring and resting on a table. Our system is defined by the shading in this figure. The internal forces are those exerted by the spring, the gravitational attraction of the two bodies (which is so small that we can usually neglect it), and electrostatic attraction or repulsion if the bodies are charged. These forces are all exerted by agents within the system so defined. The external forces in this example are the weights of the bodies, exerted by the earth; the normal forces, exerted upward by the table; the frictional forces exerted by the table; and the tension T. According to Newton's third law, for each force exerted by m_1 on m_2 there is an equal but opposite force exerted by m_2 on m_1. Thus the internal forces occur in pairs. When we sum all the forces acting on the two-particle system, the internal forces cancel out. Thus the total force ΣF_x acting on the system is just the total external force $\Sigma F_{x,\text{ext}}$. Equation 10-4 can thus be written

$$\Sigma F_{x,\text{ext}} = Ma_{CM} = M \frac{dv_{CM}}{dt} = \frac{dP}{dt} \qquad \text{10-5}$$

where $P = Mv_{CM} = m_1 v_1 + m_2 v_2$ is the total momentum. Equation 10-5 states that the resultant (external) force on the system equals the total mass times the acceleration of the center of the mass of the system. This has the same form as Newton's second law for a *single particle* of mass M located at the center of mass and under the influence of resultant force $\Sigma F_{x,\text{ext}}$.

The center of mass moves like a particle of mass $M = m_1 + m_2$ under the influence of the resultant external force on the system.

Motion of the center of mass

Figure 10-3
A system consisting of two masses connected by a spring on a table. The shaded region indicates the system. The forces external to this system are **T**, the normal and frictional forces exerted by the table, and the weights of the masses.

We can easily generalize from our special case of two particles in one dimension to many particles in three dimensions. If we have N particles, the x coordinate of the center of mass is defined by

$$Mx_{CM} = m_1x_1 + m_2x_2 + m_3x_3 + \cdots = \Sigma m_i x_i \qquad \text{10-6}$$

where again, $M = \Sigma m_i$ is the total mass of the system. Similar equations define the y and z coordinates:

$$My_{CM} = \Sigma m_i y_i \qquad \text{10-7}$$

and

$$Mz_{CM} = \Sigma m_i z_i \qquad \text{10-8}$$

It is convenient to locate the center of mass by its *position vector* $\mathbf{r}_{CM}$, whose components are the rectangular coordinates x_{CM}, y_{CM}, and z_{CM}:

$$\mathbf{r}_{CM} = x_{CM}\mathbf{i} + y_{CM}\mathbf{j} + z_{CM}\mathbf{k}$$

If we use the definitions given in Equations 10-6 to 10-8, we have

$$\mathbf{r}_{CM} = \frac{\Sigma m_i x_i}{M}\,\mathbf{i} + \frac{\Sigma m_i y_i}{M}\,\mathbf{j} + \frac{\Sigma m_i z_i}{M}\,\mathbf{k}$$

$$M\mathbf{r}_{CM} = \Sigma m_i(x_i\mathbf{i} + y_i\mathbf{j} + z_i\mathbf{k})$$

But since the quantity in parentheses is just the position vector $\mathbf{r}_i$ of particle m_i,

$$M\mathbf{r}_{CM} = \Sigma m_i \mathbf{r}_i \qquad \text{10-9}$$

Equation 10-9 is the three-dimensional many-particle extension of Equation 10-1. We obtain the extension of Equation 10-3 for the total momentum of the system by differentiating Equation 10-9:

$$M\mathbf{v}_{CM} = \Sigma m_i \mathbf{v}_i = \mathbf{P} \qquad \text{10-10}$$

where, as before, the total momentum $\mathbf{P}$ is just the sum of the momenta of the particles. Differentiating again, we obtain

$$M\mathbf{a}_{CM} = \Sigma m_i \mathbf{a}_i = \frac{d\mathbf{P}}{dt} \qquad \text{10-11}$$

This is written in the form of Equation 10-5 by noting that $m_i\mathbf{a}_i = \Sigma\mathbf{F}_i$, where $\Sigma\mathbf{F}_i$ is the net force on the ith particle, and that in the sum $\Sigma\mathbf{F}_i$ the internal forces add to zero so that the sum is just the resultant external force on the system. Thus

$$\Sigma\mathbf{F}_{i,\text{ext}} = \frac{d\mathbf{P}}{dt} = M\mathbf{a}_{CM} \qquad \text{10-12}$$

Again

The center of mass of a system of particles moves like a single particle of mass $M = \Sigma m_i$ under the influence of the resultant external force acting on the system.

This theorem is important because it shows us how to describe the motion of one point, the center of mass, for any system of particles, no matter how extensive the system may be. The center of mass of the system behaves just like a single particle subject to the external forces only. The individual motions of the members of the system generally are much more complex. For example, even if air resistance is negligible, the motion of something like a pair of masses connected by a spring and thrown into the air is quite involved. The masses tumble and turn as they move and oscillate along the line joining them. But the center of mass of the system, which lies between the two masses, moves just as if it were a single particle: it follows a simple parabolic trajectory.

The justification for our earlier treatment of large objects as point particles is actually this theorem on center-of-mass motion. All large objects should be considered to be made up of many small masses whose motions are governed by Newton's three laws. The motion of such a system generally includes rotations and oscillations relative to the center of mass. To work out all details of the motion would be very difficult, but often we are satisfied with solving the motion of the center of mass. Our theorem states that this can be treated as a problem of the motion of a single point particle.

For the baton thrown into the air (Figure 10-1) the only external force acting on the object is its weight. Thus the center of mass follows the parabolic path of a particle in projectile motion predicted by Equation 10-12. This equation does not give a complete description of the complicated motion of the baton. We have described, so far, only the motion of one point, the center of mass of the system.

Some of the various methods of locating the center of mass of a system of particles are discussed in Section 10-5. In particular we shall see that the center of mass of a regular uniform object is at the geometric center of the object; the center of mass of a uniform disk is at the center of the disk, that of a uniform cylinder is on the axis of the cylinder, halfway between the faces, etc.

Example 10-1 A projectile explodes into two equal pieces, each of mass *m*, at the top of its flight. One of the pieces drops straight down while the other moves off horizontally so that they land simultaneously. Where does the second piece land?

Considering the projectile to be the system (whether it is in one piece or two), the only external force before the masses hit the ground is that due to gravity. The forces exerted in the explosion are internal forces, which do not affect the motion of the center of mass. After the explosion the center of mass traces out the rest of the parabola just as if there had been no explosion. Since the center of mass is halfway between equal masses and we know that one mass drops straight down, the other must land at an equal distance from the center of mass, as shown in Figure 10-4.

Figure 10-4
A projectile explodes into two equal fragments at the top of its flight so that the fragments land simultaneously. The internal forces of the explosion do not affect the motion of the center of mass. It follows the same parabolic path it would have followed if there had been no explosion. The center of mass is midway between the two equal fragments.

Example 10-2 Two equal masses connected by a spring rest on a smooth table with an external force **T** applied to one of the masses. Describe the motion. This situation is the same as that in Figure 10-3 except that there is no friction.

We cannot describe the detailed motion of each mass unless we know the spring constant. Even then, the problem is complicated. However, the motion of the center of mass is simple. Its acceleration is given by

$$\mathbf{a}_{CM} = \frac{\mathbf{T}}{m + m}$$

assuming the mass of the spring to be negligible. The forces exerted by the spring are internal to the system and do not affect the motion of the center of mass. (We can think of the spring as allowing each mass to exert a force on the other.) Although the motion of each mass may be quite complicated, the motion of the center of mass, which again is halfway between the equal masses, is that of uniform acceleration in the direction of the external tension $\mathbf{T}$.

Example 10-3 Consider the same example with no spring; i.e., just two equal masses on a smooth table with a force $\mathbf{T}$ exerted on one of them. It is of course easy to describe the motion of each separately. One remains at rest, and the other has acceleration $\mathbf{a}_2 = \mathbf{T}/m$. However, the center-of-mass motion is the same as in the previous example, $\mathbf{a}_{CM} = \mathbf{T}/(m + m) = \mathbf{T}/2m$. We include this simple example to show that the particles of a system need not be interacting and that external forces may be acting on only some of the particles in the system. Remember that the motion of the center of mass is only part of the description of the motion of a system of particles. Equation 10-12 says nothing about the motion of the particles relative to the center of mass. In this example the motion is quite different from that in the previous one, though the motion of the center of mass is the same.

Example 10-4 Consider a cylinder of mass M resting on a rough piece of paper on a table. A force $\mathbf{f}$ is applied to the cylinder by pulling the paper to the right, as in Figure 10-5. Which way does the cylinder move?

We shall show (Section 10-5) that the center of mass of a uniform cylinder is at its geometric center, i.e., on the axis, halfway between the faces. Taking the cylinder as our system, we have

$$\mathbf{f} = M\mathbf{a}_{CM}$$

The acceleration of the center of mass of the cylinder is in the direction of the force $\mathbf{f}$ and has the magnitude f/M. Since $\mathbf{f}$ is in the direction the paper is pulled, $\mathbf{a}_{CM}$ is to the right for the case illustrated in Figure 10-5. This result may be somewhat surprising at first because the paper also accelerates and the cylinder appears to move back in the

Figure 10-5
Cylinder rolling on a paper pulled to the right. Since the net external force on the cylinder is the frictional force to the right, the cylinder accelerates to the right. The cylinder rolls backward relative to the paper because the acceleration of the paper is greater than that of the cylinder.

direction opposite **f**. The forward acceleration of the cylinder is easily
demonstrated, however, with a piece of chalk if the initial position of
the chalk is marked on the *table*. The chalk accelerates back *relative to
the paper*, because the acceleration of the paper is greater than that of
the chalk. Relative to the table, the chalk accelerates forward in the
direction of **f**. Note again that Equation 10-12 does not describe the rotation of the cylinder but only the motion of its center of mass.

Questions

1. Two masses are connected by a light string which passes over a
pulley to form an Atwood's machine. Consider the two masses and the
string as a system. What are the external forces? What are the internal
forces?

2. A self-made man is said to have pulled himself up by his boot-
straps. Discuss this from the point of view of internal and external
forces and the motion of the center of mass of a system.

3. If only external forces can cause the center of mass of a system to
accelerate, how can an automobile be accelerated by its motor?

4. A man is at rest at the center of a large, frictionless ice rink. Can he
get off it? How?

5. A rocket ship initially is at rest (relative to the distant stars) in
empty space when its engines are turned on. What happens to the center of mass of the rocket and its original contents? How can the rocket
move?

10-2 Conservation of Linear Momentum

In an important special case of Equation 10-12 the resultant external
force is zero. Then

$$\frac{d\mathbf{P}}{dt} = M\mathbf{a}_{CM} = 0$$

and

$$\mathbf{P} = M\mathbf{v}_{CM} = \Sigma m_i \mathbf{v}_i = \text{constant} \qquad 10\text{-}13$$

The total momentum of the system and the velocity of the center of
mass are constant. If a system is isolated from its surroundings so that
no external forces are acting on it, the total momentum of the system
does not change in time. This important result is known as the law of
conservation of linear momentum. (The quantity $\mathbf{p} = m\mathbf{v}$, which we have
been calling momentum, is often also called linear momentum to distinguish it from angular momentum, defined in Chapter 13.) This
result is the generalization to many-particle systems of the conservation-of-momentum law for two particles discussed in Chapter 4.
(The conservation of momentum for two particles with no external
forces was, of course, the original experimental observation from
which Newton postulated his third law.) This law is one of the most
important in physics. It is more generally applicable than the law of
conservation of mechanical energy because internal forces exerted by
one particle in the system on another are often not conservative. Thus
they can change the total mechanical energy of the system, but since

Conservation of momentum

these internal forces always occur in pairs, they cannot change the total linear momentum of the system. The conservation of momentum is particularly useful in studying collisions (Chapter 11).

Example 10-5 A man weighing 150 lb and a boy weighing 75 lb are standing together on a smooth ice surface for which friction is negligible. If after they push each other apart, the man moves away with speed 1 ft/sec, relative to the ice, how far apart are they after 5 sec (Figure 10-6)?

Figure 10-6
Man and boy on smooth ice push each other (Example 10-5). Since there are no external horizontal forces on the man-boy system, the total horizontal momentum which is zero initially does not change. The center of mass remains at its original position.

We take the man and boy together as the system. The weight of each is balanced by a corresponding normal force of the ice. Since there is no friction, the resultant force on the system is zero. The force exerted by the man on the boy is equal and opposite to that exerted by the boy on the man. The total momentum of the system is zero since they are standing at rest initially. Therefore, after they push each other, they must have equal and opposite momentum. Since the man has twice the mass of the boy, the boy must have twice the speed of the man. Since the man moves in one direction with speed 1 ft/sec, the boy moves in the opposite direction with speed 2 ft/sec. After 5 sec the man has moved 5 ft and the boy 10 ft and they are 15 ft apart. The center of mass of this system remains at rest in its original position, the point where they originally stood. Note that the mechanical energy of this system is not conserved. The force exerted by each on the other is not conservative. In this case the mechanical energy is increased, since the kinetic energy was initially zero and the potential energy did not change.

Example 10-6 A bullet of mass 10 gm moves horizontally with speed 400 m/sec and embeds itself in a block of mass 390 gm initially at rest on a smooth table. What is the final velocity of the bullet and block (Figure 10-7)?

Figure 10-7
Example 10-6. Collision of bullet and block resting on smooth surface. There are no external horizontal forces on the bullet-block system so the horizontal momentum is conserved. After the collision the bullet and block move together with velocity v_x given by conservation of momentum $(m_1 + m_2)v_x = m_1 v_{1x}$.

Before impact: $P_{ix} = m_1 v_{1x}$ After impact: $P_{fx} = (m_1 + m_2)v_x$

Since there are no horizontal forces on the bullet-block system, the horizontal component of the total momentum of the system is conserved. (There is a small vertical resultant force on the system, the weight of the bullet before it strikes the block. The bullet accelerates toward the earth before it strikes the block. We shall ignore this slight vertical motion.)

The total initial horizontal momentum P_{ix} before the bullet strikes the block is just that of the bullet:

$$P_{ix} = m_1 v_{1x} = (10 \text{ gm})(400 \text{ m/sec}) = 4000 \text{ gm-m/sec} = 4 \text{ kg-m/sec}$$

Afterward the bullet and block move together with a common velocity v_x. The total final momentum P_{fx} is

$$P_{fx} = (m_1 + m_2)v_x = (10 \text{ gm} + 390 \text{ gm})v_x = (0.4 \text{ kg})v_x$$

Since the total momentum is conserved, the final momentum equals the initial momentum.

$$(0.4 \text{ kg})v_x = 4 \text{ kg-m/sec}$$

$$v_x = 10 \text{ m/sec}$$

Since the bullet and block both move together with this velocity, the center of mass must move with this velocity. We could have found the velocity of the center of mass (which is constant) before the collision from Equation 10-10:

$$Mv_{CM,x} = \Sigma m_i v_{ix} = m_1 v_{1x} + m_2(0)$$

$$v_{CM,x} = \frac{m_1 v_{1x}}{m_1 + m_2} = \frac{4 \text{ kg-m/sec}}{0.4 \text{ kg}} = 10 \text{ m/sec}$$

This is the same calculation used to find v_x. A simple computation of the initial and final energies shows that again mechanical energy is not conserved. The original kinetic energy is $\frac{1}{2}m_1 v_{1x}^2 = \frac{1}{2}(0.01 \text{ kg})(400 \text{ m/sec})^2 = 800 \text{ J}$, and the final energy is $\frac{1}{2}(0.4 \text{ kg})(10 \text{ m/sec})^2 = 20 \text{ J}$. In this case most of the original kinetic energy (780 J out of 800 J) is lost because large nonconservative forces between the bullet and the block deform the bodies.

10-3   The Center-of-Mass Reference Frame

As we have seen, when the resultant external force on a system is zero, the velocity of the center of mass is constant. It is often convenient to choose a coordinate system with the origin at the center of mass. Then relative to the original coordinate system, this coordinate system moves with constant velocity $\mathbf{v}_{CM}$. If the original coordinate system is in an inertial reference frame, the one with origin at the center of mass is also. The reference frame with the origin at the center of mass is called the *center-of-mass reference frame*. Relative to this frame the velocity of the center of mass is of course zero. Since the total momentum of a system of particles equals the total mass times the velocity of the center of mass, the total momentum is zero in the center-of-mass reference frame. This frame is also called the *zero-momentum reference frame*. In the analysis of many problems it is convenient to transform from a given frame to the center-of-mass frame and back.

The laboratory reference frame.   The CM reference frame.

(a)

(b)

For example, the analysis of most collisions is easiest in the center-of-mass reference frame, as we shall see in the next chapter. However, many collisions are observed in other frames; e.g., one particle at rest initially is struck by another. The transformation between the center-of-mass frame and another frame is not difficult. Consider a simple two-particle system with one particle of mass m_1 moving with velocity $\mathbf{v}_1$ and the second of mass m_2 moving with velocity $\mathbf{v}_2$ (Figure 10-8a). The total momentum and velocity of the center of mass are given by Equation 10-10:

$$\mathbf{P} = m\mathbf{v}_{CM} = m_1\mathbf{v}_1 + m_2\mathbf{v}_2$$

We transform to the center-of-mass reference frame by subtracting the velocity $\mathbf{v}_{CM}$ from each particle, as illustrated in Figure 10-8. Let $\mathbf{u}_1$ and $\mathbf{u}_2$ be the velocities of the particles relative to the center of mass. Then

$$\mathbf{u}_1 = \mathbf{v}_1 - \mathbf{v}_{CM} \quad \text{and} \quad \mathbf{u}_2 = \mathbf{v}_2 - \mathbf{v}_{CM} \qquad \text{10-14}$$

Velocity relative to center of mass

We can check that the total momentum is zero in the center-of-mass frame by computing the total momentum using the transformation Equation 10-14. We have

$$m_1\mathbf{u}_1 + m_2\mathbf{u}_2 = m_1(\mathbf{v}_1 - \mathbf{v}_{CM}) + m_2(\mathbf{v}_2 - \mathbf{v}_{CM})$$
$$= m_1\mathbf{v}_1 + m_2\mathbf{v}_2 - (m_1 + m_2)\mathbf{v}_{CM} = 0$$

since, by Equation 10-10, $(m_1 + m_2)\mathbf{v}_{CM}$ equals $m_1\mathbf{v}_1 + m_2\mathbf{v}_2$.

If the particles interact, as in a collision, their velocities will change; but if there is no resultant external force, the center of mass will remain at rest and the total momentum will not change. We can transform from the center-of-mass frame to any other frame in which the center of mass moves by adding the velocity $\mathbf{v}_{CM}$ to each velocity $\mathbf{u}_1$ and $\mathbf{u}_2$.

Example 10-7 Find the velocities and the total kinetic energy of the bullet and block of Example 10-6 in the center-of-mass reference frame (Figure 10-9).

In that example the initial velocity of the 10-gm bullet was 400 m/sec and the 390-gm block was initially at rest. We found the velocity of the center of mass to be 10 m/sec. If u_{1x} is the velocity of the bullet and u_{2x} the velocity of the block in the center-of-mass frame, we have

$$u_{1x} = 400 - 10 = 390 \text{ m/sec}$$

and

$$u_{2x} = 0 - 10 = -10 \text{ m/sec}$$

Before impact: $P_{ix} = m_1 u_{1x} - m_2 u_{2x} = 0$ After impact: $P_{fx} = 0$

Figure 10-8
(a) Two particles moving in a general reference frame. In this frame the center of mass has velocity $\mathbf{v}_{CM} = (m_1\mathbf{v}_1 + m_2\mathbf{v}_2)/(m_1 + m_2)$. (b) In the center-of-mass, or zero-momentum, reference frame the center of mass is at rest, and the total momentum is zero. The velocities in the two frames are related by $\mathbf{u}_1 = \mathbf{v}_1 - \mathbf{v}_{CM}$ and $\mathbf{u}_2 = \mathbf{v}_2 - \mathbf{v}_{CM}$.

Figure 10-9
Example 10-7. Collision of bullet and block of Example 10-6 viewed in the center-of-mass frame. After the collision the bullet and block are at rest in this frame.

The velocities after the collision are zero in this reference frame. The kinetic energies of the bullet and block before the collision are

$$\tfrac{1}{2}(0.01 \text{ kg})(390 \text{ m/sec})^2 + \tfrac{1}{2}(0.39 \text{ kg})(10 \text{ m/sec})^2$$
$$= 760.5 \text{ J} + 19.5 \text{ J} = 780 \text{ J}$$

After the collision the energy is zero in the center-of-mass frame because the particles are at rest. The energy lost, 780 J, is the same as that calculated in the original frame. We shall show in the next section that this is a general result.

Questions

6. Describe how the center-of-mass frame can be at rest even though both bodies in a collision are moving.

7. Can the center of mass have a greater speed than both bodies in a collision?

10-4   Kinetic Energy of a System of Particles

Although the total momentum of a system of particles must be constant if the resultant external force on the system is zero, the total mechanical energy of the system may change. Internal forces, which cannot change the total momentum, may be nonconservative and thus change the total mechanical energy. In Example 10-6 the forces exerted by the bullet and block on each other were evidently nonconservative since the energy of the system decreased. In such a case, some of the mechanical energy goes into thermal energy of the system, some of it goes into producing permanent deformation of the block and bullet, and a small amount goes into sound waves produced when the bullet strikes the block. Sometimes the total mechanical energy of a system will *increase* even if there is no external force on the system. This happened in Example 10-5 with the man and boy pushing each other. Another example is the explosion of a bomb, in which internal chemical energy is converted into kinetic energy of the fragments.

When the 10-gm bullet collided with the 390-gm block, the kinetic energy lost was 780 J. In the center-of-mass reference frame this was the total kinetic energy. In the original frame with the block initially at rest the 780-J energy loss was only part of the original energy. In that frame all the kinetic energy could not be lost because then the objects would be at rest and momentum would not be conserved. The kinetic energy remaining in that frame was just $\tfrac{1}{2}Mv_{CM}{}^2 = \tfrac{1}{2}(0.4)(10)^2 = 20$ J, where M was the total mass of the system. This example is a special case of a general theorem which we shall now derive.

The kinetic energy of a system of particles can be written as the sum of two terms: (1) the energy associated with center of mass motion $\tfrac{1}{2}Mv_{CM}{}^2$, where M is the total mass of the system, and (2) the energy of motion relative to the center of mass $\Sigma\tfrac{1}{2}m_i\mathbf{u}_i{}^2$, where $\mathbf{u}_i$ is the velocity of the ith particle relative to the center of mass.

Consider a two-particle system in the center-of-mass reference frame and let $\mathbf{u}_1$ and $\mathbf{u}_2$ be the velocities of the two particles relative to the center of mass, which is at rest in this frame. Since the total momentum is zero in this frame, we have

$$m_1\mathbf{u}_1 + m_2\mathbf{u}_2 = 0 \qquad\qquad 10\text{-}15$$

The kinetic energy in this frame is

$$E_{kr} = \tfrac{1}{2}m_1u_1{}^2 + \tfrac{1}{2}m_2u_2{}^2 \qquad\qquad 10\text{-}16$$

(We use the subscript r to indicate that this energy is relative to the center of mass.) We now consider the system in another reference frame in which the center of mass is moving with velocity $\mathbf{v}_{CM}$. We transform to this frame by adding the velocity $\mathbf{v}_{CM}$ to the velocity of each particle according to Equation 10-14. In this frame the particles move with velocity $\mathbf{v}_1$ and $\mathbf{v}_2$, given by

$$\mathbf{v}_1 = \mathbf{u}_1 + \mathbf{v}_{CM} \qquad \mathbf{v}_2 = \mathbf{u}_2 + \mathbf{v}_{CM}$$

The kinetic energy in this frame is

$$
\begin{aligned}
E_k &= \tfrac{1}{2}m_1v_1{}^2 + \tfrac{1}{2}m_2v_2{}^2 \\
&= \tfrac{1}{2}m_1(\mathbf{u}_1 + \mathbf{v}_{CM})^2 + \tfrac{1}{2}m_2(\mathbf{u}_2 + \mathbf{v}_{CM})^2 \\
&= \tfrac{1}{2}m_1(u_1{}^2 + v_{CM}{}^2 + 2\mathbf{v}_{CM}\cdot\mathbf{u}_1) + \tfrac{1}{2}m_2(u_2{}^2 + v_{CM}{}^2 + 2\mathbf{v}_{CM}\cdot\mathbf{u}_2) \\
&= \tfrac{1}{2}m_1u_1{}^2 + \tfrac{1}{2}m_2u_2{}^2 + \tfrac{1}{2}(m_1+m_2)v_{CM}{}^2 + \mathbf{v}_{CM}\cdot(m_1\mathbf{u}_1 + m_2\mathbf{u}_2)
\end{aligned}
$$

The first two terms are just the kinetic energy relative to the center of mass. The third term is $\tfrac{1}{2}Mv_{CM}{}^2$, where M is the total mass of the system. The last term is zero by Equation 10-15. Thus the kinetic energy in this frame is

$$E_k = \tfrac{1}{2}Mv_{CM}{}^2 + E_{kr}$$

where E_{kr} is the kinetic energy relative to the center of mass given by Equation 10-16. This result is easily generalized to a system of many particles:

$$E_k = \tfrac{1}{2}Mv_{CM}{}^2 + E_{kr} \qquad\qquad 10\text{-}17$$

where $M = \Sigma m_i$ is the total mass and $E_{kr} = \Sigma \tfrac{1}{2}m_iu_i{}^2$ is the kinetic energy of motion relative to the center of mass. We shall find many occasions to use this result in the following chapters.

If there are no external forces acting on the system, $\mathbf{v}_{CM}$ is constant. Then the first term in Equation 10-17 does not change; only the relative energy can increase or decrease. Since the relative energy is the same in all reference frames, the change in energy produced by internal forces is the same in all frames. This result is particularly useful in the analysis of collisions (Chapter 11).

10-5   Finding the Center of Mass

In this section we discuss methods of locating the center of mass for various systems of particles. Often the center of mass can be found by intuitive methods or by a simple experiment, avoiding involved calculations.

For a discrete system of particles the x coordinate of the center of mass is given by Equation 10-6:

$$Mx_{CM} = \Sigma m_i x_i$$

with similar equations for the y and z coordinates. If the system is a continuous body, we replace the sum by an integral:

$$Mx_{CM} = \int x \, dm$$

where dm is an element of mass. Let us consider again the simple system of two point masses. As we have seen, the center of mass lies between the masses. If we choose our origin at the center of mass, so that $x_{CM} = 0$, the coordinates of the particles are related by

$$m_1 x_1 + m_2 x_2 = 0$$

or

$$\frac{|x_1|}{|x_2|} = \frac{m_2}{m_1} \qquad\qquad 10\text{-}18$$

(One of the coordinates x_1 or x_2 must be negative since the origin is between the two particles.)

If the two point masses are connected by a light rod of negligible mass, the system balances at any orientation if pivoted at the center of mass (Figure 10-10*a*). This follows from the fact that the potential energy of a system of particles is the same as if the total mass were at the center of mass. Let y_i be the height above the earth of the ith particle in a general system. The potential energy of the system is

$$U = \Sigma m_i g y_i = g \Sigma m_i y_i$$

But $\Sigma m_i y_i = M y_{CM}$, and so

$$U = M g y_{CM} \qquad\qquad 10\text{-}19$$

If we try to balance our two particles on a light rod at some point other than the center of mass, the system will rotate until the potential energy is a minimum. This occurs when the center of mass is at its lowest point consistent with the restraint of the pivot. This point is directly below the pivot. Thus the system will rotate until the center of mass lies below the pivot (Figure 10-10*b*). However, if the pivot is at the center of mass, all orientations have the same potential energy and the system will balance.

This bird looks symmetrical, but evidently its mass distribution is not. Where is its center of mass? (*Courtesy of Larry Langrill, Oakland University.*)

Example 10-8 Center of Mass of an Irregularly Shaped Plane Figure A simple experimental method based on the above analysis can be used to find the center of mass of any plane figure, e.g., a board or metal sheet. If we suspend the object from a frictionless pivot at any point on the object, it will hang in equilibrium with its center of mass directly below the pivot. If we draw a vertical line from the pivot (this can be done with the aid of a plumb bob), the center of mass must lie

Figure 10-10
(*a*) Two masses connected by a light rod pivoted at the center of mass. The gravitational potential energy depends only on the height of the center of mass, which is at the pivot for any orientation. The system balances at any orientation. (*b*) If the pivot is not at the center of mass, the potential energy is least when the center of mass is directly below the pivot.

(*a*)

(*b*)

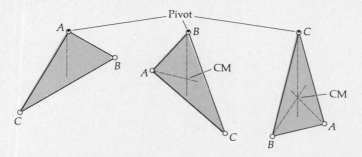

Figure 10-11
The center of mass of an irregularly shaped object lies
directly below any point
about which it is pivoted.
This property can be used to
locate the center of mass.

on this line. We can then suspend the object from another point and
draw a second line, as shown in Figure 10-11. The center of mass will
lie on the intersection of the two lines. The third suspension shown in
Figure 10-11c confirms this result.

Example 10-9 Three Point Masses The center-of-mass position vector
for three point masses is given by

$$M\mathbf{r}_{CM} = \Sigma m_i \mathbf{r}_i = m_1 \mathbf{r}_1 + m_2 \mathbf{r}_2 + m_3 \mathbf{r}_3 \qquad 10\text{-}20$$

where $M = m_1 + m_2 + m_3$ is the sum of the masses. A method useful
for three point masses and many other systems is to break this sum
into two or more parts. For example, the first two terms in the sum are
related to the center of mass of the first two masses by

$$m_1 \mathbf{r}_1 + m_2 \mathbf{r}_2 = (m_1 + m_2)\mathbf{r}'_{CM}$$

where $\mathbf{r}'_{CM}$ is the center-of-mass position vector for masses m_1 and m_2
alone. Thus we can write Equation 10-20 as

$$M\mathbf{r}_{CM} = (m_1 + m_2)\mathbf{r}'_{CM} + m_3 \mathbf{r}_3$$

We have reduced the problem to finding first the center of mass for
the two particles m_1 and m_2 and then finding the center of mass for
two particles, m_3 and the system $m_1 + m_2$. This solution is illustrated
in Figure 10-12. The center of mass for the masses m_1 and m_2 is at
point P_{12}. It lies on the line joining m_1 and m_2 with distances given by
Equation 10-18. The center of mass for the three-particle system is then
on the line joining mass m_3 and point P_{12}. The distance d_3 from m_3 is
related to the distance d_{12} from P_{12} by Equation 10-18

$$\frac{d_3}{d_{12}} = \frac{m_1 + m_2}{m_3}$$

We can see from this analysis that the center of mass for three equal
masses lies at the intersection of the medians of the triangle formed by
the three masses.

The technique used in Example 10-9 can be used for many systems
consisting of several bodies. Consider, for example, two uniform
sticks. The center-of-mass position vector for this system $\mathbf{r}_{CM}$ is defined by

$$M\mathbf{r}_{CM} = \sum_{\substack{\text{both}\\ \text{sticks}}} m_i \mathbf{r}_i$$

where the sum is over all the mass elements of the two sticks. We can
write this sum in two parts:

$$\sum_{\substack{\text{both}\\ \text{sticks}}} m_i \mathbf{r}_i = \sum_{\text{stick 1}} m_i \mathbf{r}_i + \sum_{\text{stick 2}} m_i \mathbf{r}_i$$

The first sum on the right is just $M_1 \mathbf{r}_{CM1}$, where M_1 is the mass of stick

Figure 10-12
Center of mass of three point
particles. Point P_{12} is the
center of mass of the two-particle system $m_1 + m_2$. These
two particles can be replaced
by a single particle of mass
$m_1 + m_2$ at P_{12} for the calculation of the center of mass of
the three particles. The distances d_3 and d_{12} are related
by $m_3 d_3 = (m_1 + m_2)d_{12}$.

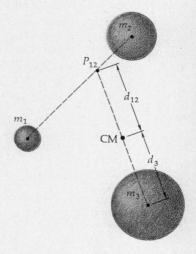

1 and r_{CM1} is the position vector to its center of mass, which is at the center of the stick since it is uniform. Similarly the second term is $M_2 r_{CM2}$, and

$$M r_{CM} = M_1 r_{CM1} + M_2 r_{CM2}$$

The center of mass of the two-stick system lies on the line joining the centers of mass of the separate sticks, as shown in Figure 10-13. We see from this type of reasoning that we can treat any part of a complicated system as a point mass located at the center of mass of the part.

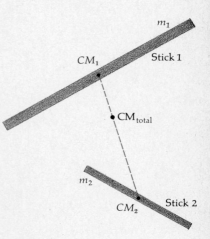

Figure 10-13
The center of mass of a system of two sticks can be found by treating each stick as a point particle at its individual center of mass.

Example 10-10 Symmetrical Bodies It is clear from our arguments about balance that the center of mass of a regular object must lie on any line of symmetry the object may have. For example, the center of mass of a uniform stick lies on the axis of the stick halfway between the ends. The center of mass of a uniform cylinder lies on its axis midway between the faces. We can prove this as follows. Consider first a thin uniform disk. The center of mass of the disk is clearly at the center, as can be seen by balancing or by the method of Example 10-8. If we have two parallel disks of equal mass, we can use the result discussed above. The center of mass of the two disks is on the line joining their individual centers of mass midway between the disks. A cylinder can be thought of as a set of uniform disks; thus its center of mass lies on the axis in the middle of the cylinder. This type of argument can be used to find the center of mass of other solid objects such as blocks.

Since any line through the diameter of a uniform sphere is a line of symmetry, the center of mass of the sphere is at its center.

10-6   Using Integration to Find the Center of Mass

If the center-of-mass coordinates of a continuous body are to be calculated, the sum $\Sigma m_i x_i$ must be replaced by the integral $\int x \, dm$, where dm is an element of mass. We then have

$$M x_{CM} = \int x \, dm \qquad \text{10-21}$$

In most cases, one or more of the coordinates can be found by symmetry without calculation. We give two examples here of finding the center of mass of a continuous body.

Example 10-11 Center of Mass of a Uniform Stick of Mass M and Length L (Figure 10-14) This very simple example, in which the result is known from symmetry beforehand, illustrates the technique of setting up the integration indicated in Equation 10-21. Let us call the linear density, or mass per unit length, λ. Since the density is uniform, $\lambda = M/L$. In

Figure 10-14
Calculation of the center of mass of a uniform stick. The mass element $dm = \lambda \, dx$ at distance x from the end is treated as a point particle.

Figure 10-14 we have chosen the origin at one end of the stick. We need only compute x_{CM}. A mass element of length dx is indicated. Its mass is $dm = \lambda\, dx$, and it is a distance x from the origin. Thus

$$Mx_{CM} = \int x\, dm = \int_0^L x\lambda\, dx = \frac{\lambda x^2}{2}\bigg]_0^L = \frac{\lambda L^2}{2}$$

Using $\lambda = M/L$, we obtain the expected result:

$$x_{CM} = \frac{\lambda L^2}{2M} = \frac{M}{L}\frac{L^2}{2M} = \tfrac{1}{2}L$$

Example 10-12 Center of Mass of a Semicircular Hoop Figure 10-15 shows our choice of coordinate system for this calculation. We have chosen the origin to be on a line of symmetry of the figure. Clearly, $x_{CM} = 0$ because for every mass element at $+x$ there is an equal one at $-x$. However, y_{CM} is not zero. The center of mass is not at the origin, which is at the center of curvature of the hoop. All the mass is at positive y; thus $\int y\, dm$ cannot be zero. In the figure we have indicated a mass element of length $R\, d\theta$ at height $R\sin\theta$. The mass of this element is $dm = \lambda R\, d\theta$, where $\lambda = M/\pi R$ is the mass per unit length. We thus have

$$My_{CM} = \int y\, dm = \int_0^\pi R\sin\theta\, \lambda R\, d\theta = R^2\lambda \int_0^\pi \sin\theta\, d\theta = 2R^2\lambda$$

since

$$\int_0^\pi \sin\theta\, d\theta = -\cos\theta\bigg]_0^\pi = +2$$

Using $\lambda = M/\pi R$, we have

$$My_{CM} = 2R^2\frac{M}{\pi R} \qquad \text{or} \qquad y_{CM} = \frac{2R}{\pi}$$

The center of mass is not within the body in this case. Figure 10-16 shows how to locate the center of mass by suspending a semicircular hoop from one end and then from another point.

Figure 10-15
Calculation of the center of mass of a semicircular hoop. The center of mass lies on the y axis.

Questions

8. Must there be mass at the center of mass of a system? Explain.

9. Must the center of mass of a solid body be in the interior of the body? If not, give examples.

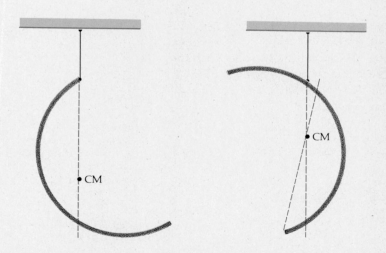

Figure 10-16
The center of mass of a semicircular hoop found experimentally by suspending it from two points.

Review

A. Define, explain, or otherwise identify:

Center of mass, 256
Internal forces, 257
External forces, 257
Conservation of momentum, 261

Center-of-mass reference frame, 263
Zero-momentum reference frame, 263
Relative kinetic energy, 265
Center-of-mass kinetic energy, 265

B. True or false:

1. The center of mass of a two-particle system is always closer to the more massive particle.

2. The total mass of a system times the velocity of the center of mass equals the total momentum of the system.

3. The momentum of a system can be conserved even if the mechanical energy is not.

4. Internal forces do not affect the motion of the center of mass of a system.

5. In the center-of-mass reference frame, the total momentum is zero.

6. The kinetic energy of a system of particles is different in different reference frames.

Exercises

Section 10-1, Center of Mass

1. A 2-kg mass is on the x axis at $x = 3$ m, and a 4-kg mass is on the x axis at $x = 6$ m. Find the center of mass of this system.

2. In Exercise 1 the 2-kg mass is moving to the right at 4 m/sec, and the 4-kg mass is moving to the left at 3 m/sec. (a) What is the velocity of the center of mass? (b) What is the total momentum of the system?

3. Three point masses are located in the xy plane as follows: a 1-kg mass is at the origin, a second 1-kg mass is at $x = 4$ m on the x axis, and a 2-kg mass is at the point $x = 2$ m, $y = 2$ m. Find the center of mass.

4. Three point masses have the following velocities along the x axis: a 1-kg mass is moving to the right with $v_x = 5$ m/sec, a 2-kg mass is moving to the left with $v_x = -3$ m/sec, and a 4-kg mass is moving to the right with $v_x = 4$ m/sec. Find (a) the total momentum of the system and (b) the velocity of the center of mass.

5. Two 3-kg masses have velocities $\mathbf{v}_1 = 2\mathbf{i} + 3\mathbf{j}$ m/sec and $\mathbf{v}_2 = 4\mathbf{i} - 6\mathbf{j}$ m/sec. Find (a) the velocity of the center of mass and (b) the total momentum of the system.

6. A 5-kg mass is at rest at the origin, and a second 5-kg mass is initially at rest at $x = 0$ and $y = 4$ m. A constant force $\mathbf{F} = (10 \text{ N})\mathbf{i}$ is applied to this second mass while no force acts on the first mass. (a) Find the acceleration of the second mass and its position at the times $t = 0, 1, 2,$ and 3 sec. (b) On a diagram, indicate these positions and the position of the center of mass at these times. (c) Find the acceleration of the center of mass and from it the position of the center of mass at these times.

7. A frictional force of 500 lb acts on the surface of each of the rear tires of a 3000-lb car. (a) Draw a diagram indicating these forces and any others acting on the car on a level road at low speed. (b) Find the acceleration of the car neglecting wind resistance.

8. A wheel of mass 3 kg rolls down a plane inclined at $\theta = 30°$. The plane exerts a frictional force on the wheel up the plane of magnitude 4.9 N to keep the wheel from sliding. Find the acceleration of the center of mass of the wheel.

9. A 150-lb man stands at one end of a 60-ft-long log weighing 1500 lb. The log is floating in a millpond at right angles to the shore, the end opposite the man just touching the shore. The man walks along the log toward the shore. Assume that the water exerts no tangential force on the log. (a) On a drawing, indicate the initial position of the center of mass of the man-log system. (b) On a second drawing, directly below the first, indicate the position of the man, the log, and the center of mass when the man is at the middle of the log. (c) On a third drawing below the second, indicate the position of the man, the log, and the center of mass when the man is at the other end of the log. How far is he from shore at this time?

10. Two bodies have masses $m_1 = 1$ gm and $m_2 = 5$ gm. Initially they are at rest 10 cm apart on a frictionless surface. They are electrically charged so that they attract each other. They accelerate toward each other and collide. How far are they from the original position of m_1 when they meet?

11. A 10-gm mass and a 25-gm mass are compressed against opposite ends of a spring which rests on a horizontal table. The masses are not attached to the spring. The spring is released with both masses initially together at $x = 0$ at rest. At some time t after the masses leave the spring the 10-gm mass is observed at $x_1 = 20$ cm traveling at 5 cm/sec. (a) Where is the center of mass initially? (b) Where is the 25-gm mass, and how fast is it traveling at time t?

12. Some physics students find themselves in the middle of a box car teetering on the edge of a cliff (Figure 10-17). The car is on level ground and free to roll, but near the edge the ground is crumbling away. Which way should the students run to save themselves? (The ground is hard except just at the edge of the cliff.)

Figure 10-17
Exercise 12.

Section 10-2, Conservation of Linear Momentum

13. A cart of mass 10 kg is rolling along a level floor at a speed of 5 m/sec. A 4-kg mass dropped from rest lands in the cart. (a) What was the momentum of the cart before the mass was dropped? (b) What is the momentum of the cart and mass after the mass was dropped into the cart? (c) What is the speed of the cart and mass?

14. Two railroad cars have masses of 6×10^4 and 4×10^4 kg. They are initially rolling along the track in the same direction with the lighter car in front moving at 0.5 m/sec and the heavier car trailing but moving at 1.0 m/sec. They collide and couple. (a) What is the total momentum of the two-car system before the collision? (b) What is the total momentum of the two-car system after the collision? (c) What is the speed of the two cars after the collision? (d) Find the total kinetic energy before and after the collision.

15. An open-topped freight car weighing 20 tons is rolling along a track at 5 ft/sec. Rain is falling vertically downward into the car. After the car has collected 2 tons of water, what is its speed? *Hint:* You need not convert these weights to masses if you write mass as w/g.

16. A small 2000-lb automobile traveling north at 50 mi/h collides at an intersection with a 6000-lb truck traveling east at 40 mi/h. The car and truck stick together. (a) What is the total momentum of the car-truck system before the collision? (b) Find the magnitude and direction of the velocity of the combined wreckage just after the collision.

17. A 20-gm bullet is fired horizontally with velocity 250 m/sec from a 1.5-kg gun. If the gun were held loosely in the hand, what would be its recoil velocity?

18. Two masses are held at rest initially on a horizontal frictionless surface. They are pushed together, compressing a small spring between them which is not attached to either mass. When the masses are released the spring accelerates each, giving mass m_1 a velocity 5 m/sec to the left and m_2 a velocity 15 m/sec to the right. (a) What is the total momentum of the system before the masses are released? After they are released? (b) What is the ratio m_1/m_2?

Section 10-3, The Center-of-Mass Reference Frame, and Section 10-4, Kinetic Energy of a System of Particles

19. (a) In Exercise 14 find the velocity of the center of mass of the two-railroad-car system. (b) Find the velocity of each car relative to the center of mass before the collision. What are their velocities relative to the center of mass after the collision? (c) Find the kinetic energies of the cars relative to the center of mass before and after the collision.

20. In Exercise 18 let m_1 be 12 kg and m_2 be 4 kg. (a) Find the kinetic energy of the masses after they are released from the spring. (b) Find the velocity of each mass in a reference frame in which the center of mass is moving to the right with velocity 3 m/sec. (c) Find the total kinetic energy before and after the masses are released in the reference frame of part (b). How much energy do the masses gain from the spring in this frame?

21. A 3-kg mass moves at 5 m/sec to the right. It is chasing a second 3-kg mass moving at 1 m/sec also to the right. (a) Find the total kinetic energy of the two masses in this frame. (b) Find the velocity of the center of mass. (c) Find the velocities of the masses in the center-of-mass frame. (d) Find the kinetic energy of the masses in the center-of-mass frame. (e) Show that your answer for part (a) is greater than that for part (d) by the amount $\frac{1}{2}Mv_{CM}^2$, where v_{CM} is the velocity of the center of mass in the original frame and M is the total mass.

22. A 2-kg mass is moving to the right with a speed of 5 m/sec toward a stationary mass of 3 kg. (a) What is the kinetic energy of this system in this frame? (b) Find the velocity of the center of mass in this frame and the center-of-mass energy $\frac{1}{2}Mv_{CM}^2$. (c) Find the velocity of each mass in the center-of-mass reference frame. (d) Find the total kinetic energy of the two masses in the center-of-mass reference frame.

23. Two equal masses are connected by a light rigid rod. (a) How can they move so that their total kinetic energy is just the energy of center-of-mass motion? (b) How can they move so that their total kinetic energy is entirely energy of motion relative to the center of mass?

24. Describe how a solid ball can move so that (a) its total kinetic energy is just the energy of center-of-mass motion and (b) its total kinetic energy is energy of motion relative to the center of mass.

25. Two masses are connected by a spring. Describe how the masses can move so that (a) the total kinetic energy is just energy of center-of-mass motion and (b) the kinetic energy is entirely energy of motion relative to the center of mass.

Section 10-5, Finding the Center of Mass

26. Find the center of mass of the system shown in Figure 10-18.

27. Find the potential energy for the system in Exercise 26 directly by summing mgy_i over all the particles and show that the result equals Mgy_{CM}.

28. Each of the objects shown in Figure 10-19 is suspended from a ceiling by a thread attached to the point marked x on the object. Describe with a diagram the orientation of each suspended object.

Figure 10-18
Exercise 26.

Figure 10-19
Exercise 28.

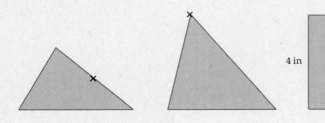

29. An equilateral triangle is made of three uniform sticks of equal length L (Figure 10-20). Find the center of mass of this system (a) by using symmetry arguments and (b) by first finding the center of mass of two of the sticks and then combining this system with the third stick.

30. Find the center-of-mass coordinates x_{CM} and y_{CM} for the figure shown in Figure 10-21. *Hint:* Consider the figure to be three squares and replace each square by a point mass at the center of mass of the square.

Figure 10-20
Exercise 29.

Figure 10-21
Exercise 30.

10 in

10 in

10-6, Using Integration to Find the Center of Mass

31. A nonuniform thin rod of length L lies along the x axis with one end at the origin. It has a linear mass density λ kg/m, given by $\lambda = \lambda_0(1 + x/L)$. The density is thus twice as great at one end as at the other. (a) Use $M = \int dm$ to find the total mass. (b) Find the center of mass of the rod.

Problems

1. The ratio of the mass of the earth to the mass of the moon is $M_E/m_m = 81.3$. The radius of the earth is about 4000 mi, and the distance to the moon is about 240,000 mi. (a) Locate the center of mass of the earth-moon system relative to the surface of the earth. (b) What external forces act on the earth-moon system? In what direction is the acceleration of the center of mass of this system? (c) Assume that the center of mass of this system moves in a circular orbit around the sun. How far must the center of the earth move in the radial direction (toward or away from the sun) during the 14 d between the time the moon is farthest from the sun (full moon) and when it is closest to the sun (new moon)?

2. A projectile is launched at 20 m/sec at an angle of 30° with the horizontal. In the course of its flight it explodes, breaking into two parts, one of which has twice the mass of the other. The two fragments land simultaneously. The lighter fragment lands 20 m from the launch point in the direction the projectile was fired. Where does the other fragment land?

3. A man of mass 80 kg is riding on a small cart of mass 40 kg which is rolling along a level floor at speed of 2 m/sec. He jumps off the back of the cart so that his speed relative to the ground is 1 m/sec in the direction opposite to the motion of the cart. (a) What is the speed of the center of mass of the man-cart system before and after he jumps? (b) What is the speed of the cart after the man jumps? (c) What is the speed of the center of mass after the man hits the ground and comes to rest? (d) What force is responsible for the change in the velocity of the center of mass? (e) Transform all velocities to the center-of-mass reference frame and indicate on a diagram the initial and final velocities of the man and cart in this frame. How much energy was expended by the man in jumping?

4. Use integration to find the center of mass of a uniform plate of material cut in the shape of a half circle.

5. A circular plate of radius r has a circular hole cut out with radius $\frac{1}{2}r$ (Figure 10-22). Find the center of mass of the plate. *Hint:* The hole can be represented by two disks superimposed; one of mass m and the other of mass $-m$.

Figure 10-22
Problem 5.

6. Using the hint from Problem 5, find the center of mass of a solid sphere of radius r which has a spherical hole of radius $\frac{1}{2}r$, as shown in Figure 10-23.

Figure 10-23
Problem 6.

7. A massless spring of force constant 1000 N/m is compressed a distance of 20 cm between masses of 8 and 2 kg. The spring is released on a smooth table. Since the masses are not attached to the spring, they move away with speeds v_1 and v_2. (a) Show that the kinetic energy of the masses when they leave the spring can be written $E_k = \frac{1}{2}p^2(1/m_1 + 1/m_2)$, where p is the momentum of either mass. Use conservation of energy to find p. (b) Find the velocity of each mass as it leaves the spring. (c) Find the velocity of each mass if the system is given an initial velocity of 4 m/sec perpendicular to the spring, as shown in Figure 10-24a. (d) What is the energy of center-of-mass motion in this case? What is the energy of motion relative to the center of mass? (e) Find the velocity of each mass if the system is given an initial velocity of 4 m/sec in the direction along the spring, as shown in Figure 10-24b. What is the energy of center-of-mass motion in this case? What is the energy of motion relative to the center of mass?

(a)   (b)

Figure 10-24
Problem 7.

8. An 80-lb boy gets on his 20-lb wagon on level ground along with two 10-lb bricks. He throws the bricks horizontally off the back of the wagon one at a time at a speed of 20 ft/sec relative to himself. How fast does he finally go?

9. Use integration to find the center of mass of the right isosceles triangle shown in Figure 10-25.

Figure 10-25
Problem 9.

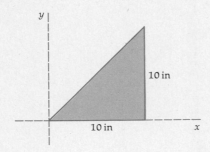

CHAPTER 11   Collisions and Reactions

When two bodies come together and interact strongly for a short time, the event is called a *collision*. Often the forces exerted by one body on the other are much stronger than any other external forces present, and the time of the collision is so short that the bodies do not move appreciably during the interaction.

When the physical or chemical nature of the bodies is changed by the collision, the event is called a *reaction,* e.g., if a proton collides with a hydrogen atom so that the atom is ionized, i.e., the electron is removed, leaving two protons and a free electron after the collision. We consider some of the general properties of collisions and reactions in this chapter and apply our results to some useful examples.

11-1   Impulse

When a golf club hits a ball, the force **F** on the ball is zero just as contact is made. It then increases to a very large value and finally decreases to zero as the ball leaves the club (Figure 11-1). The total time of contact Δt is very small, perhaps only about 0.001 sec. The quantity of interest is not the instantaneous acceleration of the ball, which also varies with time (see Figure 11-1), but the velocity of the ball $\mathbf{v}_f$ or the momentum of the ball just as it leaves the club $\mathbf{p}_f = m\mathbf{v}_f$. These are related to the impulse **I** of the force **F** for the time interval Δt. The impulse of a force for the time interval from t_i to t_f is a vector defined by

$$\mathbf{I} = \int_{t_i}^{t_f} \mathbf{F}\, dt \qquad\qquad 11\text{-}1$$

Figure 11-1
The force exerted by the club on a golf ball plotted as a function of time. The impulse exerted on the ball for the interval from t_i to t_f is the area below the F-versus-t curve for that interval. It equals the change in momentum of the ball.

Impulse defined

The magnitude of the impulse is just the area under the F-versus-t curve. Assuming that **F** is the resultant force and using Newton's law $\mathbf{F} = d\mathbf{p}/dt$, we see that the impulse equals the total change in momentum during the time interval $t_f - t_i$:

$$I = \int_{t_i}^{t_f} \mathbf{F}\, dt = \int_{t_i}^{t_f} \frac{d\mathbf{p}}{dt}\, dt = \mathbf{p}_f - \mathbf{p}_i = \Delta\mathbf{p} \qquad \text{11-2}$$

Impulse equals change in momentum

From Equation 11-2 the units of impulse are newton-seconds or kilogram-meters per second.

For a general force **F**, the impulse given by Equations 11-1 and 11-2 depends on the choice of times t_i and t_f. But the forces which occur in collisions are zero except during a small time interval, as shown in Figure 11-1. For these forces, the impulse does not depend on the time interval as long as t_i is any time before the force occurs and t_f is any time after the force has decreased to zero. It is for this type of force that the concept of impulse is most useful.

For the golf club hitting a ball initially at rest, the change in momentum of the ball is just its final momentum,

$$\Delta\mathbf{p} = \mathbf{I} = \mathbf{p}_f$$

The impulse exerted by the ball on the club is equal in magnitude and opposite in direction to that exerted by the club on the ball since the forces are equal and opposite according to Newton's third law.

Example 11-1 Find the impulse exerted by the block on the bullet for Example 10-6, in which a 10-gm bullet traveling at 400 m/sec embeds itself in a 390-gm block initially at rest.

In that example we found the final speed of the bullet and block to be $v_{CM} = 10$ m/sec. The change in momentum of the bullet is thus

$$\Delta p = p_f - p_i = (10^{-2}\ \text{kg})(10\ \text{m/sec}) - (10^{-2}\ \text{kg})(400\ \text{m/sec})$$
$$= -3.9\ \text{kg-m/sec} = -3.9\ \text{N-sec}$$

The impulse exerted on the bullet is thus 3.9 N-sec to the left. The bullet exerts an equal and opposite impulse on the block, as can be seen from its change in momentum:

$$\Delta p_{\text{block}} = (0.39\ \text{kg})(10\ \text{m/sec}) - 0 = 3.9\ \text{kg-m/sec} = 3.9\ \text{N-sec}$$

Golf club hitting a golf ball. Note the deformation of the golf ball due to the large force exerted by the club during the brief time of contact. As the ball leaves the club, it springs back to its original shape, converting the elastic potential energy of deformation into kinetic energy. (*Courtesy of Harold E. Edgerton.*)

11-2   Time Average of a Force

The time-average force over the interval $\Delta t = t_f - t_i$ is defined by

$$\mathbf{F}_{av} = \frac{1}{\Delta t} \int_{t_i}^{t_f} \mathbf{F}\, dt = \frac{\mathbf{I}}{\Delta t} \qquad \text{11-3}$$

$\mathbf{F}_{av}$ is the constant force which gives the same impulse in the time interval Δt. F_{av} is indicated in Figure 11-2. It is often useful to compute the average force in a collision in order to compare it to such other forces as frictional forces or the force of gravity.

Example 11-2 What are reasonable magnitudes for the impulse I, average force F_{av}, and collision time Δt for a golf club hitting a golf ball?

Let us take the mass of a typical golf ball as $m = 45$ gm. The velocity of the ball when it leaves the club is related to the range by

$$R = \frac{v_0{}^2}{g} \sin 2\theta_0$$

where θ_0 is the angle of the projectile and air resistance is neglected. Taking $\theta_0 = 45°$ for simplicity (corresponding to the maximum range)

Figure 11-2
The average force F_{av} for some time interval is the constant force which gives the same impulse during that interval. The rectangular area $F_{av}\,\Delta t$ is the same as that under the F-versus-t curve.

and $R = 160$ m as a reasonable range (this is about 173 yd), we find

$$v_0^2 = Rg \approx 160 \times 10 = 1600$$

$$v_0 = 40 \text{ m/sec}$$

using $g \approx 10$ m/sec² to simplify the calculation. The magnitude of the impulse is thus

$$I = \int F \, dt = \Delta p = mv_0 = (45 \times 10^{-3} \text{ kg})(40 \text{ m/sec})$$
$$= 1.8 \text{ kg-m/sec} = 1.8 \text{ N-sec}$$

We can estimate the time of the collision as follows. The magnitude of the average acceleration is

$$a_{av} = \frac{F_{av}}{m} = \frac{I}{m \, \Delta t}$$

If the acceleration were constant and equal to the average acceleration, the velocity v_0 would be related to the distance traveled by the ball *during the collision* by the constant-acceleration expression

$$v_0^2 = 2a_{av}x$$

A reasonable estimate for the distance traveled by the ball while it is in contact with the golf club is the radius of the golf ball, about $x = 2$ cm. Then the average acceleration is

$$a_{av} = \frac{v_0^2}{2x} = \frac{1600}{2(0.02)} = 40{,}000 \text{ m/sec}^2$$

The average force is thus estimated to be

$$F_{av} = ma_{av} = (0.045 \text{ kg})(40{,}000 \text{ m/sec}^2) = 1800 \text{ N}$$

The estimated collision time is then

$$\Delta t = \frac{I}{F_{av}} = \frac{1.8 \text{ N-sec}}{1800 \text{ N}} = 0.001 \text{ sec}$$

We could also have estimated Δt from $v_0 = a_{av} \, \Delta t$. Then

$$\Delta t = \frac{v_0}{a_{av}} = \frac{40 \text{ m/sec}}{40{,}000 \text{ m/sec}^2} = 0.001 \text{ sec}$$

We see that the average force exerted by the club, 1800 N, is much larger than any other forces acting on the ball. For example, the weight of the ball is only about 0.45 N, and the frictional forces exerted by the grass or tee on the ball are even less, assuming the coefficient of friction to be less than 1.

Example 11-3 A machine gun fires R bullets per second. Each bullet has mass m and speed v. The bullets strike a fixed target, where they stop. What is the average force exerted on the target over a time long compared to the time between bullets?

Figure 11-3 shows a graph of the instantaneous force on the target. The average force is also indicated. The area under each impulse curve equals the change in momentum of each bullet. This change is just the initial momentum mv since the final momentum is zero. In time Δt, the number of bullets that hit the target is $R \, \Delta t$. Each bullet exerts an impulse mv on the target. The total impulse exerted in time Δt by the $R \, \Delta t$ bullets is consequently $R \, \Delta t \, mv$. The average force is thus

$$F_{av} = \frac{R \, \Delta t \, mv}{\Delta t} = Rmv$$

11-4

Figure 11-3
Instantaneous and average
force exerted by bullets
striking target.

Equation 11-4 also gives the average recoil force exerted by the bullets on the gun. Each bullet receives an impulse of magnitude mv from the gun, and, by Newton's third law, each bullet exerts an impulse back on the gun of magnitude mv. Since in time Δt, $R\,\Delta t$ bullets leave the gun, the total impulse exerted on the gun in time Δt is $mvR\,\Delta t$ and the average recoil force is Rmv.

Questions

1. A ball is dropped from a second-story window, and an identical ball is simultaneously thrown up from the ground so that it just reaches the window. Compare the impulses of gravity on the two balls as they travel between the ground and the window.

2. Could two forces deliver the same impulse in a given time even though one reverses its direction during that time? Explain.

3. Can a force of large magnitude give a body a smaller impulse than a force of smaller magnitude? How?

4. How would the average of a force which fluctuates above and below a value F_0 compare with the average of a force that stays nearly steady at value F_0?

5. If a particle is under the influence of a single force which has an average value of zero during some time, must the acceleration of the particle be zero?

11-3 Pressure of a Gas

The force exerted by the bullets on the target in Example 11-3 is similar to the force exerted by gas molecules on the walls of a container. In the gas there are usually so many molecules that their individual impulses overlap in time and only the average force is observable. Another important difference is that the molecules do not stop when they hit the wall of the container but bounce back with their component of momentum perpendicular to the wall reversed. Let m be the mass of each molecule. If we take the x axis to be perpendicular to the wall, the x component of momentum of a molecule is $+mv_x$ before it hits the wall and $-mv_x$ afterward. The change in momentum during the collision with the wall is the final momentum minus the initial momentum:

$$\Delta p_x = -mv_x - (+mv_x) = -2mv_x$$

the minus sign indicating that the change in momentum is to the left, away from the wall. The magnitude of the momentum change is thus $2mv_x$. The total change in the momentum of all the molecules in some time interval Δt is $2mv_x$ times the number that hit the wall in this time interval. Let us consider a rectangular container of volume V with the right wall having area A (Figure 11-4). Let N_i be the number of gas molecules with x component of velocity v_{xi}. The number of these molecules hitting the right wall in time Δt is the number within a distance $v_{xi} \Delta t$ and traveling to the right. Since there are N_i such molecules in volume V, the number in volume $v_{xi} \Delta t A$ is just $(N_i/V)(v_{xi} \Delta t A)$. If we assume for the moment that v_{xi} is positive, the number that hit the right wall in time Δt is

$$\frac{N_i}{V} v_{xi} \Delta t A$$

The impulse exerted by the wall on these molecules equals the total change in momentum of these molecules, which is $2mv_{xi}$ times the number that hit:

$$I_i = \left(\frac{N_i v_{xi} \Delta t A}{V}\right) 2mv_{xi} = \frac{2N_i m v_{xi}^2 A \Delta t}{V}$$

This also equals the magnitude of the impulse exerted by these molecules *on* the wall. We obtain the average force exerted by these molecules by dividing the impulse by the time interval Δt. The pressure is this average force divided by the area A. The pressure exerted by these molecules is thus

$$P_i = \frac{I_i}{\Delta t A} = \frac{2N_i m v_{xi}^2}{V}$$

The total pressure exerted by all the molecules is obtained by summing over all the x components of velocity v_{xi} that are positive. Since on the average, at any time half the molecules will be moving to the right (positive v_{xi}) and half to the left (negative v_{xi}), we can sum over all the molecules and multiply by $\frac{1}{2}$.

$$P = \tfrac{1}{2}\Sigma P_i = \tfrac{1}{2}\Sigma\frac{2N_i m v_{xi}^2}{V} = \frac{m}{V} \Sigma N_i v_{xi}^2$$

We can write this in terms of the average value of v_x^2, defined to be

$$(v_x^2)_{av} = \frac{1}{N} \Sigma N_i v_{xi}^2$$

where $N = \Sigma N_i$ is the total number of molecules. Thus we can write for the pressure,

$$P = \frac{Nm}{V} (v_x^2)_{av} \qquad\qquad 11\text{-}5$$

If there is no preferred direction for the molecules to move, $(v_x^2)_{av}$ must be the same as $(v_y^2)_{av}$ and $(v_z^2)_{av}$. The square of the speed is

$$v^2 = v_x^2 + v_y^2 + v_z^2$$

Hence

$$(v^2)_{av} = (v_x^2)_{av} + (v_y^2)_{av} + (v_z^2)_{av} = 3(v_x^2)_{av}$$

Thus we can write the pressure in terms of the average square speed:

$$P = \frac{1}{3}\frac{N}{V} m(v^2)_{av} = \frac{2}{3}\frac{N}{V} (\tfrac{1}{2}mv^2)_{av} \qquad\qquad 11\text{-}6$$

Pressure of a gas

showing that the pressure is proportional to the number of molecules per unit volume and to the average kinetic energy of the molecules.

Figure 11-4
Gas molecules in a rectangular container. If a molecule has velocity component v_{xi}, it will hit the right face in the time interval Δt if it is within the distance $v_{xi} \Delta t$ of the face and if v_{xi} is positive. The number of molecules within this distance of the face is proportional to v_{xi} and to the number of molecules per unit volume.

Example 11-4 If 1 mole of a gas occupies 22.4 liters $(\ell) = 22.4 \times 10^{-3}$ m^3 at standard temperature and pressure of 1 atmosphere (atm) $= 1.01 \times 10^5$ N/m^2, find the average square speed of oxygen molecules under standard conditions.

The number N of molecules in a mole times the mass m of each molecule is the *molecular weight*, which for oxygen gas is 32 gm/mole. According to Equation 11-6, the average square speed is

$$(v^2)_{av} = \frac{3PV}{Nm} = \frac{3(1.01 \times 10^5)(22.4 \times 10^{-3})}{32 \times 10^{-3}} = 2.12 \times 10^5 \text{ (m/sec)}^2$$

The square root of $(v^2)_{av}$ is called the root-mean-square (rms) speed v_{rms},

$$v_{rms} = \sqrt{(v^2)_{av}} = 460 \text{ m/sec}$$

This is slightly greater than the speed of sound in air (about 331 m/sec) but of the same order of magnitude.

11-4 The Impulse Approximation

According to Equation 11-3, the impulse for some time interval is related to the average force by

$$\mathbf{I} = \mathbf{F}_{av}\, \Delta t$$

In many collisions the average force exerted by one body on the other is very large, and the time of the collision is very small. We can then neglect other forces which act on the bodies and to a good approximation assume that the momentum of the two-body system is conserved during the collision. We can also neglect the motion of the bodies during the collision if Δt is very small. For example, the average force exerted by the golf club on the ball in Example 11-2 was 1800 N, much larger than the weight of the ball or frictional forces exerted by the grass or the tee on the ball. During the collision time of 0.001 sec in that example, the ball moved only 2 cm, which is a small distance compared with the total horizontal range of 160 m. Neglecting this motion, we assume that the ball is at rest during the collision and then projected with an initial speed $v = I/m$ (40 m/sec in that example). The approximation that F_{av} is very much larger than any other force and Δt is so small that there is essentially no motion during the collision is called the *impulse approximation*.

Example 11-5 For the 10-gm bullet moving with speed 400 m/sec and embedding itself in a 390-gm block initially at rest, estimate the collision time and check the validity of the impulse approximation, assuming that the bullet travels 5 cm into the block.

We first neglect the motion of the block. We estimate the collision time by assuming the acceleration to be constant. The easiest way to do this is to realize that the average velocity for constant acceleration is just the mean between the initial and final velocity. Since the bullet has initial velocity 400 m/sec and final velocity $v_{CM} = 10$ m/sec, as calculated in previous examples, its average velocity during the collision is 205 m/sec. To travel 5 cm $= 0.05$ m at 205 m/sec requires a time $\Delta t = (0.05 \text{ m})/(205 \text{ m/sec}) = 2.44 \times 10^{-4}$ sec. This is our estimate of the collision time. Since the block accelerates from rest to a final velocity of 10 m/sec, its average velocity is 5 m/sec during this time, assuming

constant acceleration. It thus moves a distance of only (5 m/sec)(2.44 ×
10^{-4} sec) = 1.22×10^{-3} m = 0.122 cm. In the impulse approximation,
we neglect this small distance compared with the 5 cm moved by the
bullet in the time of the collision. We could also estimate the distance
moved by the block by viewing the collision in the center-of-mass reference frame. Since the block has 39 times the mass of the bullet, in
this frame it travels with one-thirty-ninth the velocity. In a given time
it thus travels $\frac{1}{39}$ times the distance traveled by the bullet. Thus if the
bullet travels 5 cm, the block travels $\frac{1}{39}$(5 cm) = 0.128 cm. These two
estimates differ slightly because in the first we assumed that the bullet
traveled a total distance of 5 cm into the block while in the second we
assumed that it traveled slightly farther, 5 + 0.128 cm.

Question

6. Name several situations in which the impulse approximation applies.

11-5   Energy Changes in Collisions; Reference Frames

In Chapter 10 we saw that the kinetic energy of a system of particles
can be written as the sum of the kinetic energy associated with the
motion of the center of mass and the kinetic energy of motion relative
to the center of mass

$$E_k = \tfrac{1}{2}Mv_{CM}^2 + E_{kr}$$

where M is the total mass of the system, v_{CM} is the velocity of the
center of mass, and $E_{kr} = \Sigma\frac{1}{2}m_iu_i^2$ is the energy of motion relative to the
center of mass. As we have seen in this chapter, external forces are
usually negligible compared with the internal forces the bodies exert
on each other in a collision. Thus the total momentum of the two-body
system is conserved, the velocity of the center of mass is constant, and
the part of the kinetic energy associated with center-of-mass motion
$\frac{1}{2}Mv_{CM}^2$ does not change. However, since the internal forces may be
nonconservative, E_{kr} may change. The kinetic energy of center of mass
motion $\frac{1}{2}Mv_{CM}^2$ is constant in any collision. If the kinetic energy of relative motion E_{kr} is also constant, the total kinetic energy remains
unchanged in the collision and the collision is said to be *perfectly
elastic*. On the other hand, if all the energy of relative motion is lost in
the collision, the collision is said to be *perfectly inelastic*. Since there is
no motion relative to the center of mass after a perfectly inelastic
collision, the bodies move together after the collision with velocity
v_{CM}. The bullet embedding itself in a block is a typical example of a
perfectly inelastic collision. In many collisions only part of the kinetic-
energy motion relative to the center of mass is lost; these collisions are
neither perfectly elastic nor perfectly inelastic.

Many collisions are more easily analyzed in the center-of-mass, or
zero-momentum, reference frame. For example, in an inelastic collision
in this frame, the two bodies are at rest after the collision. As we shall
see in the next section, in an elastic collision in one dimension, the
velocities of the bodies are merely turned around in the center-of-mass
frame. Although this frame may be more convenient for analysis,
experiments are more often done in a reference frame in which one of

the particles is initially at rest, called the *laboratory frame*. For example, in the famous alpha-particle scattering experiment from which Rutherford deduced the existence of the atomic nucleus, gold nuclei at rest in a thin gold foil were bombarded with alpha particles from a radioactive source. In a typical modern nuclear-physics experiment, nuclei at rest in a target in the laboratory are bombarded by particles accelerated in some type of nuclear accelerator. It is therefore important to know how to transform results obtained in the center-of-mass frame to the laboratory frame and vice versa. We accomplish these transformations using Equations 10-14. Let m_1 be the mass of the incident particle, $\mathbf{v}_1$ its velocity in the laboratory frame, and m_2 the mass of the stationary particle. The velocity of the center of mass in this frame is thus $\mathbf{v}_{CM} = m_1\mathbf{v}_1/(m_1 + m_2)$. The velocities of the particles in the center-of-mass frame are

Laboratory frame

$$\mathbf{u}_1 = \mathbf{v}_1 - \mathbf{v}_{CM} = \mathbf{v}_1 - \frac{m_1\mathbf{v}_1}{m_1 + m_2} = \frac{m_2\mathbf{v}_1}{m_1 + m_2}$$

11-7

$$\mathbf{u}_2 = -\mathbf{v}_{CM} = -\frac{m_1\mathbf{v}_1}{m_1 + m_2}$$

On the other hand, if we know the velocities $\mathbf{u}_1$ and $\mathbf{u}_2$ in the center-of-mass frame, we transform to the laboratory frame by adding $\mathbf{v}_{CM} = -\mathbf{u}_2$ to each velocity so that particle 2 is at rest.

11-6 Perfectly Elastic Collisions in One Dimension

Let us consider the collision in the center-of-mass reference frame first. We assume that the bodies are moving along the x axis. Let $\mathbf{u}_{1i}$ and $\mathbf{u}_{2i}$ be the initial velocities of the bodies. Their initial momenta are then $\mathbf{p}_{1i} = m_1\mathbf{u}_{1i}$ and $\mathbf{p}_{2i} = m_2\mathbf{u}_{2i}$. (We are using vector notation even though we are considering only one-dimensional collisions here in order to keep track of the signs. Of course if $\mathbf{u}_{1i}$ is to the right, $\mathbf{u}_{2i}$ must be to the left because the total momentum is zero in this frame.) Since the total momentum is zero in this frame, $\mathbf{p}_{1i} = -\mathbf{p}_{2i}$, and the magnitudes p_{1i} and p_{2i} are equal. The total kinetic energy E_{ri} is

$$E_{ri} = \tfrac{1}{2}m_1 u_{1i}^2 + \tfrac{1}{2}m_2 u_{2i}^2 = \frac{p_{1i}^2}{2m_1} + \frac{p_{2i}^2}{2m_2} = p_{1i}^2\left(\frac{1}{2m_1} + \frac{1}{2m_2}\right)$$

11-8

After the collision the energy is

$$E_{rf} = \frac{p_{1f}^2}{2m_1} + \frac{p_{2f}^2}{2m_2} = p_{1f}^2\left(\frac{1}{2m_1} + \frac{1}{2m_2}\right)$$

11-9

where p_{1f} and p_{2f} are the magnitudes of the final momenta of the bodies. We have used the fact that the total momentum after the collision is still zero, and hence the two masses still have momenta of equal magnitude though opposite direction. This is true to the extent that we can neglect any external force on the system during the collision. Setting the final energy equal to the initial energy for a perfectly elastic collision, we obtain

$$p_{1f}^2 = p_{1i}^2$$

11-10

or

$$\mathbf{p}_{1f} = \pm\mathbf{p}_{1i} \quad \text{and} \quad \mathbf{p}_{2f} = \pm\mathbf{p}_{2i}$$

11-11

The plus sign in Equation 11-11 corresponds to no collision at all, as would be the case if the masses were initially heading away from each other. Since only conservation of momentum and conservation of energy were used to derive Equation 11-11, it is not surprising that the result includes the case of no collision. If the bodies are originally heading toward each other and collide, Equation 11-11 gives for each body

$$\mathbf{p}_{1f} = -\mathbf{p}_{1i} \qquad \mathbf{p}_{2f} = -\mathbf{p}_{2i} \qquad\qquad 11\text{-}12$$

Since the velocity of each body is just its momentum divided by its mass, Equation 11-12 also implies that the final velocity of each body is related to its initial velocity by

$$\mathbf{u}_{1f} = -\mathbf{u}_{1i} \quad \text{and} \quad \mathbf{u}_{2f} = -\mathbf{u}_{2i} \qquad\qquad 11\text{-}13$$

The one-dimensional perfectly elastic collision is very simple in the zero-momentum reference frame. Each body is merely turned around and leaves with the speed and energy it had before the collision.

In other reference frames, the result does not look as simple. In general, even though the total kinetic energy is conserved, some or all of the kinetic energy of one body is transferred to the other body. In the familiar example of one body colliding with another of equal mass originally at rest, the first body comes to rest, transferring all its kinetic energy to the second. This result can easily be shown by first considering the collision of equal masses in the zero-momentum frame and then transforming to the laboratory frame, as illustrated in Figure 11-5.

We often want to calculate the energy transferred in an elastic collision from one body to the other in a reference frame different from the zero-momentum frame, e.g., the laboratory frame. It is always possible to do so by writing down the equations for conservation of energy and momentum and solving them for the two unknown final velocities in terms of the known masses and initial velocities. However, this procedure usually results in cumbersome algebra because the equation for conservation of kinetic energy is quadratic in the speeds. A much simpler procedure is to use the conservation-of-momentum equation and a result which we now state and prove:

The velocity of one body relative to the other is merely reversed in a one-dimensional elastic collision in all reference frames.

Elastic collisions

Another way of stating this theorem is that the relative speed of recession after the collision equals the relative speed of approach before the

CM frame

Before collision

After collision

(a)

Laboratory frame

Before collision

After collision

(b)

Figure 11-5
Perfectly elastic collision of equal masses in (a) the center-of-mass reference frame and (b) the laboratory reference frame. In the laboratory frame all the kinetic energy of the moving body is transferred to the initially stationary body. This occurs only when the masses are equal.

collision. This is easily proved by first considering the velocities in the zero-momentum frame. This result follows directly from Equation 11-13 in the center-of-mass frame. The velocity of one body *relative to the other* is $\mathbf{u}_2 - \mathbf{u}_1$ (or $\mathbf{u}_1 - \mathbf{u}_2$). According to Equation 11-13,

$$\mathbf{u}_{2f} - \mathbf{u}_{1f} = -\mathbf{u}_{2i} - (-\mathbf{u}_{1i}) = -(\mathbf{u}_{2i} - \mathbf{u}_{1i}) \qquad 11\text{-}14a$$

This is the theorem stated in the center-of-mass frame. We now consider another reference frame in which the center of mass moves with velocity $\mathbf{v}_{CM}$. According to the transformation Equations 10-14, a velocity $\mathbf{v}_{1i}$ in this frame is obtained by adding $\mathbf{v}_{CM}$ to the velocity $\mathbf{u}_{1i}$ in the center-of-mass frame. Thus the initial and final velocities in this frame are

$$\mathbf{v}_{1i} = \mathbf{u}_{1i} + \mathbf{v}_{CM} \qquad \mathbf{v}_{2i} = \mathbf{u}_{2i} + \mathbf{v}_{CM}$$

$$\mathbf{v}_{1f} = \mathbf{u}_{1f} + \mathbf{v}_{CM} \qquad \mathbf{v}_{2f} = \mathbf{u}_{2f} + \mathbf{v}_{CM}$$

When we add $\mathbf{v}_{CM}$ to each term in Equation 11-14a, the equation becomes

$$\mathbf{v}_{2f} - \mathbf{v}_{1f} = -(\mathbf{v}_{2i} - \mathbf{v}_{1i}) \qquad 11\text{-}14b$$

Our stated result holds for *any* reference frame moving with constant velocity $\mathbf{v}_{CM}$ relative to the center-of-mass frame.

Example 11-6 A 2-kg block slides with a speed of 10 m/sec along a smooth table and collides with an 8-kg block initially at rest. What are the final velocities of the blocks if the collision is elastic?

We shall illustrate two methods of solution. In the first, we use Equation 11-14 and work in the given frame, which is the laboratory frame. Let the moving block be body 1 and the stationary one block 2. Since we are working in one dimension, we can omit the vector notation and indicate the direction of the velocities with a positive or negative sign. The relative velocity before the collision is $v_{2i} - v_{1i} = 0 - 10 = -10$ m/sec. After the collision we have

$$v_{2f} - v_{1f} = -(-10) = +10 \text{ m/sec}$$

Conservation of momentum gives us a second relation between the final velocities. The total momentum before the collision is $(2 \text{ kg})(10 \text{ m/sec}) = 20$ kg-m/sec. Thus

$$m_1 v_{1f} + m_2 v_{2f} = 20 \text{ kg m/sec}$$

$$2v_{1f} + 8v_{2f} = 20 \text{ m/sec}$$

Solving these two equations for the two unknown final velocities gives

$$v_{2f} = 4 \text{ m/sec} \qquad \text{and} \qquad v_{1f} = -6 \text{ m/sec}$$

It is left as an exercise to check that this solution agrees with energy conservation.

We now work this problem by first transforming into the center-of-mass reference frame (Figure 11-6). The velocity of the center of mass in the original frame is

$$v_{CM} = \frac{m_1 v_1}{m_1 + m_2} = \frac{(2 \text{ kg})(10 \text{ m/sec})}{10 \text{ kg}} = 2 \text{ m/sec}$$

We transform to the center-of-mass frame by subtracting this velocity from that of each body, as illustrated in Figure 11-6b.

$$u_{1i} = 10 - 2 = 8 \text{ m/sec}$$

$$u_{2i} = 0 - 2 = -2 \text{ m/sec}$$

(a) Initial conditions:

$v_{CM} = 2$ m/sec

2 kg   10 m/sec   8 kg

Smooth surface

(b) Step 1: Convert to CM frame
CM at rest

2 kg   8 m/sec   2 m/sec   8 kg

(c) Step 2: Solve collision
CM at rest

8 m/sec   2 kg   8 kg   2 m/sec

(d) Step 3: Reconvert to laboratory frame

$v_{CM} = 2$ m/sec

6 m/sec   2 kg   8 kg   4 m/sec

Figure 11-6
Calculation of final velocities after an elastic collision (Example 11-6). (a) In the laboratory frame one body is initially at rest, and the center of mass moves to the right at 2 m/sec. (b) Transformation to the center-of-mass frame is accomplished by subtracting v_{CM} from each body. (c) In the center-of-mass frame the bodies are reversed by the elastic collision. (d) Transformation back to the laboratory frame is accomplished by adding v_{CM} to each body.

It is easily checked that the total momentum is zero in this frame. Since in this frame the velocity of each body is just turned around, we have

$$u_{1f} = -8 \text{ m/sec} \quad \text{and} \quad u_{2f} = 2 \text{ m/sec}$$

We now transform back into the original laboratory frame by adding the velocity $v_{CM} = 2$ m/sec to that of each body:

$$v_{1f} = -8 \text{ m/sec} + 2 \text{ m/sec} = -6 \text{ m/sec}$$

$$v_{2f} = 2 \text{ m/sec} + 2 \text{ m/sec} = 4 \text{ m/sec}$$

Example 11-7 A very large mass m_1 moving with speed v_{1i} collides elastically with a very small mass m_2 initially at rest (Figure 11-7). What is the speed of the small mass after the collision assuming that m_1 is much greater than m_2?

It should be intuitively clear that the large mass will not be affected very much by a collision with a very small mass. A cannonball will hardly be slowed down if it collides with a stationary piece of shot. Before the collision the relative velocity of approach is v_{1i}. Then after the collision the velocity of separation must be v_{1i}. For a first approximation we neglect any change in the velocity of m_1. Since it continues

m_1 m_2 m_1 m_2

$v_{2i} = 0$ $v_{2f} = 2v_{1i}$

v_{1i} $v_{1f} \approx v_{1i}$

Before collision   After collision

Figure 11-7
A very large mass m_1 moving with velocity v_{1i} collides elastically with a stationary small mass m_2. Since the velocity of recession after the collision equals the velocity of approach before the collision and the velocity of the large mass is approximately unchanged, the final velocity of the small mass must be approximately $2v_{1i}$.

Figure 11-8
Multiflash photograph of a golf club hitting a ball. Comparison of the distances traveled by the club and ball between successive flashes shows that the speed of the ball after the collision is approximately twice that of the club. (*Courtesy of Harold E. Edgerton.*)

to move with velocity v_{1i}, the velocity of the small mass m_2 must be $2v_{1i}$.

An example of such a collision is that of a golf club with the ball. The effective mass of the club is large because it is held by the player, who is in firm contact with the ground. Careful measurement of the distance between successive flashes in Figure 11-8 shows that the initial velocity of the ball is indeed twice that of the club.

The energy transferred is just the energy of the small mass after the collision, $\frac{1}{2}m_2(2v_{1i})^2 = 2m_2v_{1i}^2$. We can use the conservation of momentum to get a correction to our first approximation for the final velocity of the large mass. Since the small mass gains momentum $2m_2v_{1i}$ to the right, the large mass must lose this much momentum. If v_{1f} is the final velocity of the large mass, we have $m_1v_{1f} = m_1v_{1i} - 2m_2v_{1i}$, or $v_{1f} \approx v_{1i} - (2m_2/m_1)v_{1i}$.

We now calculate the energy transferred from the moving body to the stationary one for a general elastic collision in the laboratory frame. Let mass m_1 have initial velocity v_{1i} toward mass m_2, which is originally stationary. After the collision the bodies move with velocities v_{1f} and v_{2f}. The final energy of m_2 is the energy transferred since it is originally at rest. We thus wish to find v_{2f} in terms of v_{1i}. We can use either of the methods illustrated in Example 11-6. The second method, in which we transfer into and out of the center-of-mass frame, is probably the easier. The velocity of the center of mass in the laboratory frame is

$$v_{CM} = \frac{m_1 v_{1i}}{m_1 + m_2}$$

Again, we transform to the center-of-mass frame by subtracting v_{CM} from each velocity in the laboratory frame. In the center-of-mass frame the mass m_2 moves to the left with this velocity before the collision. After the collision in this frame m_2 moves to the right with velocity v_{CM}. Thus in the *laboratory frame*, m_2 moves with velocity $2v_{CM}$ after the collision,

$$v_{2f} = 2v_{CM} = \frac{2m_1 v_{1i}}{m_1 + m_2}$$

The kinetic energy of m_2 after the collision in this frame is thus

$$\tfrac{1}{2}m_2 v_{2f}^2 = \tfrac{1}{2}m_2 \frac{4m_1^2 v_{1i}^2}{(m_1 + m_2)^2} = \frac{4m_1 m_2}{(m_1 + m_2)^2}\,\tfrac{1}{2}m_1 v_{1i}^2 \qquad \text{11-15}$$

The energy transferred is proportional to the original energy of the incident body. The energy gained by particle 2 equals that lost by particle 1. If we call the energy transferred ΔE, the fractional energy loss of the incident particle is

$$\frac{\Delta E}{E} = \frac{4m_1 m_2}{(m_1 + m_2)^2} \qquad \text{11-16}$$

The fractional energy transferred has a maximum value of 1 if the masses are equal, as previously discussed. Then the incident particle is at rest after the collision. If the masses of the particles are very different, the fractional energy transfer is small. In the limit of one mass much larger than the other the fractional energy transfer approaches 4 times the ratio of the small mass to the large one, as can be seen from Equation 11-16. For example if m_1 is much larger than m_2, we neglect m_2 in the denominator and obtain $\Delta E/E \approx 4m_1 m_2/m_1^2 = 4m_2/m_1$.

The result that the energy transfer in an elastic collision is large only if the masses of the two bodies are about the same has an important application in slowing down neutrons in a nuclear reactor. The probability of inducing fission in ^{235}U is large only if the neutron is moving very slowly, whereas the neutrons emitted in the fission are fast-moving. In order to sustain a chain reaction, these fast neutrons must be slowed down before they have a chance to leak out of the reactor. The main process for slowing neutrons down is elastic collisions. From our calculations we have seen that efficient transfer of neutron energy by elastic collision can occur only in collisions with particles having masses near that of the neutron. Neither electrons in the reactor, with a mass about $\frac{1}{2000}$ times that of a neutron, nor the nuclei of nonfissionable ^{238}U (which makes up about 99 percent of natural uranium), with a mass about 238 times the mass of a neutron, can efficiently absorb energy from neutrons in collisions. Thus some material containing light nuclei is placed in a reactor to slow the neutrons down. This material, called a *moderator,* is usually water (containing hydrogen and oxygen nuclei) or carbon.

An elastic collision of two equal cannonballs from Johann Marcus Marci, *De Proportione Motus,* 1639. All of the kinetic energy of cannonball *a* is transferred to cannonball *b*. (*Courtesy of the Deutsches Museum, Munich.*)

11-7 Elastic Collisions in Three Dimensions

In the zero-momentum frame, Equations 11-8 to 11-10 also hold for three-dimensional collisions, but Equation 11-10 in terms of rectangular coordinates is now

$$p_{fx}^2 + p_{fy}^2 + p_{fz}^2 = p_{ix}^2 + p_{iy}^2 + p_{iz}^2$$

for each body. The *magnitude* of the momentum and the speed of each body are not changed by the collision, but the directions are not merely reversed, as in the one-dimensional case. Of course the final momenta of the bodies must be antiparallel to each other after the collision because the total momentum before and after the collision is zero in this frame. Figure 11-9 shows an elastic collision of spheres in the zero-momentum frame. The angle θ made by the final and initial velocity of each body depends on the perpendicular distance between

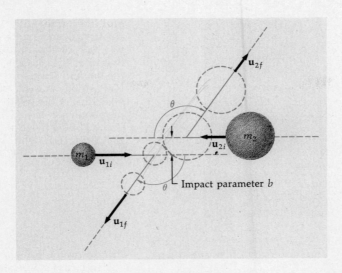

Figure 11-9
Off-center elastic collision of
two spheres in the zero-
momentum reference frame.
The perpendicular distance
between the original lines of
motion of the centers is called
the impact parameter b.
Energy and momentum con-
servation require that the
speed of each body be un-
changed by the collision.

the lines of the initial velocities (Figure 11-9). This distance is called
the *impact parameter b.* If b is zero, the collision is head on, the motion
of both bodies is always along a line, and the collision is one-dimensional. If b is greater than the sum of the two radii of the spheres, there
is no collision. If b is just smaller than this sum, a glancing collision
results and the deflection of each body is small.

Impact parameter

In order to transform into the laboratory frame (Figure 11-10), we
must add the velocity vector $\mathbf{v}_{CM} = -\mathbf{u}_{2i}$ to each body's velocity before
and after the collision. In this frame body 1 moves with velocity $\mathbf{v}_{1i}$ a
distance b from the parallel line through the center of body 2 while
body 2 is stationary. The angle of deflection of body 1 is not the same
in the laboratory frame as in the zero-momentum frame. (Since body 2
is stationary before the collision, we do not speak of its deflection in
the laboratory frame.)

Before collision   After collision

Figure 11-10
Collision of Figure 11-9
viewed in the laboratory reference frame. In this frame
one body is initially at rest,
and the center of mass moves
with velocity $\mathbf{v}_{CM} = -\mathbf{u}_{2i}$. The
velocity vectors in this frame
are obtained by adding $\mathbf{v}_{CM}$ to
the velocity vectors in the
zero-momentum frame.

We omit further complications of collisions in three dimensions except for the special case of equal masses, which we consider in the laboratory frame. Figure 11-11 shows the geometry of the collision. If $\mathbf{p}_{1i}$
and $\mathbf{p}_{1f}$ are the initial and final momentum vectors of body 1, the final

(a)   (b)

Before collision   After collision

Figure 11-11
Off-center elastic collision of
two equal spheres in the laboratory reference frame. (*a*)
After the collision, the
spheres move at right angles
to each other. (*b*) The momentum vectors for this collision form a right triangle.

Multiflash photograph of an elastic off-center collision of two balls of equal mass. The dotted ball is incident from the left and strikes the striped ball initially at rest. The final velocities of the two balls are perpendicular to each other. (*From* PSSC Physics, *2d ed., p. 384, D. C. Heath and Company, Lexington, Mass., 1965.*)

momentum of body 2 is given by the conservation of momentum,

$$\mathbf{p}_{2f} = \mathbf{p}_{1i} - \mathbf{p}_{1f} \qquad \text{or} \qquad \mathbf{p}_{1f} + \mathbf{p}_{2f} = \mathbf{p}_{1i} \qquad\qquad 11\text{-}17$$

Thus final momentum vectors add to form the triangle shown in the figure. Conservation of energy for this collision gives

$$\frac{p_{2f}{}^2}{2m} + \frac{p_{1f}{}^2}{2m} = \frac{p_{1i}{}^2}{2m} \qquad \text{or} \qquad p_{2f}{}^2 + p_{1f}{}^2 = p_{1i}{}^2 \qquad\qquad 11\text{-}18$$

where we have canceled out the masses because they are equal. Equation 11-18 is just the pythagorean theorem for a right triangle formed by the vectors $\mathbf{p}_{1f}$, $\mathbf{p}_{2f}$, and $\mathbf{p}_{1i}$ with $\mathbf{p}_{1i}$ as the hypotenuse of the triangle. Thus $\mathbf{p}_{1f}$ and $\mathbf{p}_{2f}$ are perpendicular, and so are the final velocities $\mathbf{v}_{1f}$ and $\mathbf{v}_{2f}$. We see that for the special case of an elastic collision of equal masses in the laboratory frame, the final velocities of the bodies are perpendicular to each other.

Proton-proton collision in a liquid-hydrogen bubble chamber. The incident proton enters from the left and interacts with a stationary proton in the chamber. The two particles move off at right angles after the collision. The slight curvature of the tracks is due to a magnetic field. (*Courtesy of Brookhaven National Laboratory.*)

11-8   Perfectly Inelastic Collisions

In a perfectly inelastic collision, all the energy of motion relative to the center of mass is lost. Thus in the zero-momentum frame, the bodies are at rest together with no kinetic energy. In the laboratory frame or any other reference frame, the bodies move together with the velocity of the center of mass in this frame. We have already considered a typical inelastic collision, a bullet embedding itself in a block. As we have seen, the *amount* of energy lost is the same in all reference frames. However, we are often interested in the *fraction* of the energy in the laboratory frame that is lost. We shall calculate this for the general case of a particle of mass m_1 with initial speed v_{1i} colliding inelastically with a particle of mass m_2 initially at rest.

The initial energy is

$$E_i = \tfrac{1}{2} m_1 v_{1i}{}^2 = \frac{p_{1i}{}^2}{2m_1} \qquad\qquad 11\text{-}19$$

where $p_{1i} = m_1 v_{1i}$ is the initial momentum of m_1. The latter form, $p_{1i}{}^2/2m_1$, is more convenient in this case because the final momentum is the same as the initial momentum. After the collision, both bodies move together with momentum $p_f = p_{1i}$. Thus the final energy is

$$E_f = \frac{p_f{}^2}{2(m_1 + m_2)} = \frac{p_{1i}{}^2}{2(m_1 + m_2)} \qquad\qquad 11\text{-}20$$

The ratio of the final energy to the initial energy is just $m_1/(m_1 + m_2)$. Thus

$$E_f = \frac{m_1}{m_1 + m_2} E_i \qquad \qquad 11\text{-}21$$

and

$$E_i - E_f = \left(1 - \frac{m_1}{m_1 + m_2}\right) E_i = \frac{m_2}{m_1 + m_2} E_i$$

If we call the energy loss $-\Delta E$, we have

$$-\frac{\Delta E}{E_i} = \frac{m_2}{m_1 + m_2} \qquad \qquad 11\text{-}22$$

Perfectly inelastic collisions are often used to measure the initial velocity v_{1i} when it is very large and difficult to measure directly, e.g., that of a rifle bullet. The bullet is fired into a large block which is suspended in an arrangement called a *ballistic pendulum* (Figure 11-12). In the impulse approximation, the block remains at rest during the collision and then moves with velocity v_f, which is related to v_{1i} by the conservation of momentum,

$$v_f = \frac{m_1}{m_1 + m_2} v_{1i}$$

After the collision energy is conserved, and the block plus bullet swing to a height h given by

$$(m_1 + m_2)gh = \tfrac{1}{2}(m_1 + m_2)v_f^2 = \frac{m_1{}^2 v_{1i}{}^2}{2(m_1 + m_2)}$$

or

$$v_{1i} = \frac{m_1 + m_2}{m_1} \sqrt{2gh} \qquad \qquad 11\text{-}23$$

By measuring h and the masses we can obtain v_{1i}.

11-9   Reaction Threshold

When two atoms or molecules collide and the objects emerging from the collision are different from the original ones, the collision is called a *reaction*. Atomic and molecular reactions are characterized by an exchange between kinetic energy and internal potential energy, and energy is sometimes radiated away from the system.

Culver Pictures

This collision, which will probably be inelastic, is observed by Laurel in the laboratory frame.

Figure 11-12
Ballistic pendulum. The bullet m_1 is stopped in the large block m_2, which swings up through a height h. The initial speed of the bullet is determined from measurement of h and the masses m_1 and m_2.

In this section we consider certain reactions as inelastic collisions. Consider the reaction in which a hydrogen atom is ionized by being struck by a proton, written

$$p + {}^1\text{H} \rightarrow p + p + e + Q \qquad\qquad 11\text{-}24$$

where Q is the excess kinetic energy in the zero-momentum reference frame of the final particles (those on the right) over the initial particles (those on the left). If Q is positive, the reaction is called *exothermic*; energy is given off, and the reaction may occur even if there is no initial kinetic energy (in the zero-momentum frame). If Q is negative, initial kinetic energy of the particles on the left side of the reaction is needed to make the reaction occur and the reaction is *endothermic*. For the reaction in Equation 11-24 $Q = -13.6$ eV: it takes 13.6 eV to remove the electron from the hydrogen atom.

In the zero-momentum frame the proton and ${}^1\text{H}$ atom approach each other with equal and opposite momentum. If the total kinetic energy is less than 13.6 eV, the ${}^1\text{H}$ atom cannot be ionized. If the total energy is greater than 13.6 eV, the atom can be ionized and the excess energy appears as kinetic energy of the final particles (two protons and one electron). If the energy is just 13.6 eV, the atom can be ionized with the particles relatively at rest after the reaction. Thus the minimum energy needed to produce this reaction in the zero-momentum reference frame is 13.6 eV. In the laboratory frame, where the hydrogen atom is initially at rest, the minimum kinetic energy of the incoming proton must be greater than 13.6 eV because not all of the original kinetic energy of the proton can be lost in ionizing the hydrogen atom. As we have seen, only the kinetic energy of motion relative to the center of mass can be lost. The minimum kinetic energy needed to produce the reaction in the laboratory frame is called the *reaction-threshold energy*. The reaction cannot take place in the laboratory frame at energies below the reaction threshold. We can use our results for perfectly inelastic collisions to calculate the reaction threshold, since at threshold the reaction products have no kinetic energy of relative motion but move together like the particles in a perfectly inelastic collision. Let the incoming object have mass m_1 and the stationary one have mass m_2. The energy loss in a perfectly inelastic collision is given by Equation 11-22,

$$-\Delta E = \frac{m_2}{m_1 + m_2} E_i$$

where E_i is the initial energy. In our case the initial energy E_i is the threshold energy E_{th}. The energy loss equals the magnitude of Q. Thus

$$\frac{m_2}{m_1 + m_2} E_{th} = |Q|$$

$$E_{th} = \frac{m_1 + m_2}{m_2} |Q| \qquad \text{for } Q \text{ negative} \qquad 11\text{-}25$$

Of course if Q is positive, there is no threshold energy.

Example 11-8 Reaction of Equation 11-24 Since the mass of the electron is $\frac{1}{1836}$ times that of the proton, the masses of a hydrogen atom and a proton are approximately equal: $m_1 \approx m_2$. Using $Q = -13.6$ eV gives

$$E_{th} = \frac{m + m}{m} \, 13.6 \text{ eV} = 2 \times 13.6 \text{ eV} = 27.2 \text{ eV}$$

In the laboratory frame, only half the initial kinetic energy can be used to ionize the hydrogen atom because half the energy is associated with center-of-mass motion, which cannot change. If the initial velocity of the proton is v_{1i} the velocity of the center of mass is $v_{CM} = \frac{1}{2}v_{1i}$ and the center-of-mass energy is

$$\tfrac{1}{2}(2m)v_{CM}{}^2 = \tfrac{1}{2}(2m)(\tfrac{1}{2}v_{1i})^2 = \tfrac{1}{2}(\tfrac{1}{2}mv_{1i}{}^2)$$

Thus in order for the proton to lose 13.6 eV to ionize the hydrogen atom, it must have an initial energy of 27.2 eV in the laboratory frame. The threshold energy is thus 27.2 eV.

Example 11-9 A hydrogen atom at rest in the laboratory is ionized by bombarding it with electrons. What is the threshold energy?

For this case, m_1 is very small compared with m_2. We have

$$E_{th} = \frac{m_1 + m_2}{m_2} |Q| = \left(1 + \frac{m_1}{m_2}\right)|Q| = (1 + \tfrac{1}{1836})|Q|$$

We can show in another way that the threshold energy is just slightly greater than 13.6 eV. Because the mass of the hydrogen atom is so much greater than that of the electron, the center of mass is practically at the hydrogen atom and moves with the very low velocity of

$$v_{CM} \approx \frac{m_e}{m_p}\, v_{1i}$$

where m_e is the electron mass, m_p the proton mass, and v_{1i} the initial velocity of the electron. Since v_{CM} is so small, the laboratory frame and the center-of-mass frame are almost the same; thus nearly all the initial kinetic energy is available for the reaction.

Example 11-10 What is the threshold in the laboratory for producing the nuclear reaction

$$n + {}^3\text{He} \rightarrow {}^2\text{H} + {}^2\text{H} + Q$$

by bombarding stationary ^{3}He atoms with neutrons?

The Q value of this reaction is $Q = -3.27$ MeV. (The inverse reaction, the combination of two deuterons to produce ^{3}He plus a neutron, ${}^2\text{H} + {}^2\text{H} \rightarrow {}^3\text{He} + n + 3.27$ MeV, is an important fusion reaction which produces energy.) Since the mass of ^{3}He is about 3 times that of the neutron, the quantity $(m_1 + m_2)/m_2$ in Equation 11-25 is $\frac{4}{3}$ and the threshold energy is

$$E_{th} = \frac{m_1 + m_2}{m_2} |Q| = \tfrac{4}{3}(3.27 \text{ MeV}) = 4.36 \text{ MeV}$$

In this case only one-fourth the energy of the neutron is wasted in center-of-mass motion. Again, if the particle initially at rest in the laboratory is much more massive than the bombarding particle, the laboratory frame is nearly the same as the center-of-mass frame and nearly all the initial energy is available for the reaction.

Question

7. What would be the threshold for the reaction in Example 11-10 if stationary neutrons could be bombarded by ^{3}He atoms?

11-10 Coefficient of Restitution

In general, collisions of macroscopic bodies are neither perfectly elastic nor perfectly inelastic. Some fraction of the initial energy of motion relative to the center of mass is lost. Consider a general collision in the zero-momentum frame. Figure 11-13 shows the force exerted by either body on the other. The total area under the curve is the impulse, which equals the total change in momentum of either particle. The time t_0 is the time at which the bodies are at rest. Before t_0, the bodies are moving toward each other and deforming each other. The maximum deformation of the bodies occurs at t_0. After t_0, the bodies move away from each other. It is convenient to break up the impulse into two parts, the impulse of deformation I_D, defined as the area under the curve before time t_0, and the impulse of restoration I_R, defined as the area after time t_0. Let p_i and p_f be the magnitudes of the initial and final momenta of either particle. (Since we are in the center-of-mass frame, the particles have equal and opposite momenta at all times.) The magnitude of the impulse of deformation equals p_i since each particle is brought to rest. Similarly the magnitude of the impulse of restoration equals p_f. Thus if t_i is any time before the force occurs and t_f is any time after the force has decreased to zero, the impulse of deformation is

$$I_D = \int_{t_i}^{t_0} F\, dt = p_i \qquad\qquad 11\text{-}26$$

and the impulse of restoration is

$$I_R = \int_{t_0}^{t_f} F\, dt = p_f \qquad\qquad 11\text{-}27$$

The ratio of the magnitudes of these impulses is called the *coefficient of restitution*:

$$\epsilon = \frac{I_R}{I_D} = \frac{p_f}{p_i} \qquad\qquad 11\text{-}28 \qquad \textit{Coefficient of restitution}$$

This coefficient is a measure of the degree to which the bodies return to their original shape after the collision. If the collision is perfectly elastic, $I_R = I_D$ and $\epsilon = 1$. The work done in deforming the bodies from $t = t_i$ to $t = t_0$ is momentarily stored as potential energy and returned to the kinetic energy of the bodies, almost as if a spring between the bodies were expanding to its original length after being compressed. If

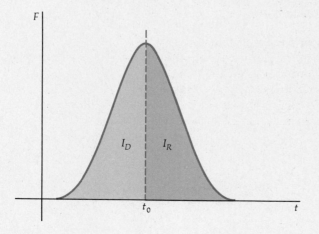

Figure 11-13
Force versus time for collision of two bodies showing impulse of deformation I_D and impulse of restoration I_R. The time t_0 is the instant at which there is no relative motion of the bodies. Before t_0 the bodies move toward each other, and deformation occurs. After t_0 they move away from each other. In a perfectly elastic collision $I_R = I_D$. In a perfectly inelastic collision $I_R = 0$.

the collision is perfectly inelastic, $I_R = 0$, $\epsilon = 0$, and the maximum deformation is permanent. The bodies remain at rest after the collision (in the zero-momentum frame). The original kinetic energy has been lost to deformation and radiated energy. The coefficient of restitution and the magnitudes of the initial and final moments of either particle are related by

$$p_f = \epsilon p_i \qquad\qquad 11\text{-}29$$

The final energy of the system is related to the initial energy by

$$E_{rf} = \frac{p_f^2}{2m_1} + \frac{p_f^2}{2m_2} = \epsilon^2 \left(\frac{p_i^2}{2m_1} + \frac{p_i^2}{2m_2}\right)$$

or

$$E_{rf} = \epsilon^2 E_{ri}$$

The fractional energy loss in the zero momentum frame is thus

$$\frac{-(E_{rf} - E_{ri})}{E_{ri}} = \frac{-\Delta E_{kr}}{E_{ri}} = 1 - \epsilon^2 \qquad\qquad 11\text{-}30$$

Equation 11-30 gives the fractional loss of the energy of motion relative to the center of mass E_{kr}, not the fractional loss in total kinetic energy in any other system. As with perfectly elastic collisions, it is convenient to work with the velocity of one body relative to the other in treating problems in other reference frames. From Equation 11-29 the speed of either particle after the collision is ϵ times its initial speed. Since the direction of each particle is reversed by the collision, the final velocities of the particles in the zero-momentum frame are related to their initial velocities by

$$u_{1f} = -\epsilon u_{1i} \qquad \text{and} \qquad u_{2f} = -\epsilon u_{2i}$$

Thus

$$u_{2f} - u_{1f} = -\epsilon(u_{2i} - u_{1i})$$

In another reference frame moving with velocity $-v_{CM}$ relative to the zero-momentum frame, we obtain the velocities of the particles by adding v_{CM}; thus

$$v_{2f} - v_{1f} = -\epsilon(v_{2i} - v_{1i}) \qquad\qquad 11\text{-}31$$

holds in all reference frames.

Example 11-11 The coefficient of restitution for steel on steel is measured by dropping a steel ball on a steel plate rigidly attached to the earth. If the ball is dropped from height h_i and rebounds to height h_f, what is the coefficient of restitution?

The speed of the ball just before it strikes the plate is

$$v_i = \sqrt{2gh_i}$$

For the ball to reach height h_f, the speed just after the collision must be $v_f = \sqrt{2gh_f}$. Since the plate is attached to the earth, we can neglect its rebound velocity. The relative speeds in this case are thus v_i and v_f

$$v_f = \epsilon v_i$$
$$\sqrt{2gh_f} = \epsilon \sqrt{2gh_i}$$
$$\epsilon = \sqrt{\frac{h_f}{h_i}}$$

Review

A. Define, explain, or otherwise identify:

Collision, 276 Q value of reaction, 292
Reaction, 276   Exothermic reaction, 292
Impulse, 276   Endothermic reaction, 292
Average force, 277   Reaction threshold, 292
Impulse approximation, 281   Impulse of deformation, 294
Perfectly inelastic collision, 282   Impulse of restoration, 294
Perfectly elastic collision, 282   Coefficient of restitution, 294
Laboratory reference frame, 283

B. True or false. If the statement is true only under certain conditions, write false and state the conditions under which it is true.

1. Only forces of very short duration exert impulses.

2. In a perfectly inelastic collision, all the kinetic energy of the particles is lost.

3. In a perfectly elastic collision, the energy of each particle is the same before and after the collision.

4. In a perfectly elastic collision, the relative velocity of recession after the collision equals the relative velocity of approach before the collision.

Exercises

Section 11-1, Impulse

1. Figure 11-14 shows the time variation of a force F_x acting on a 2-kg particle initially at rest. Find (a) the impulse of this force and (b) the final velocity of the mass.

Figure 11-14
Exercises 1 and 6.

2. Figure 11-15 shows the time variation of a force which acts on a 3-kg particle. (a) Find the impulse of the force. (b) If the particle is initially moving in the x direction with velocity $v_x = 2$ m/sec, what is its velocity after the impulse?

Figure 11-15
Exercises 2 and 7.

3. A 0.4-kg particle initially moving at 20 m/sec is stopped by a force which has the constant magnitude of 50 N for a short time Δt. (a) What is the impulse of the force? (b) Find the time interval Δt.

4. Find the impulse necessary to reduce the velocity of a 3000-lb car from 60 mi/h to zero.

5. A 10-lb object moving in a straight line is accelerated by a constant force of 50 lb. Its speed increases from 5 to 55 ft/sec. (a) What is the impulse delivered by the force in this time? (b) How long did it take for this increase in speed?

Section 11-2, Time Average of a Force

6. Find the average value of the force shown in Figure 11-14 for the time interval $t_i = 1$ sec to $t_f = 4$ sec.

7. Find the average value of the force shown in Figure 11-15 for the time interval $t_i = 1$ sec to $t_f = 5$ sec.

8. A particle of mass 2 kg is moving along the x axis at 4 m/sec, and 2 sec later it is moving along the y axis with the same speed. Find (a) the impulse that acted on the particle and (b) the average force acting on the particle for the 2-sec interval.

9. A 1-lb ball is dropped from a height of 10 ft above the floor. It rebounds to a height of 6 ft. (a) Find the impulse exerted by the floor on the ball. (b) If the ball was in contact with the floor for 10^{-3} sec, find the average force exerted by the floor on the ball during that time.

10. A man can exert an average force of 200 N on his machine gun. His gun fires 20-gm bullets at 1000 m/sec. How many bullets can he fire per minute?

Section 11-3, Pressure of a Gas

11. An object of mass m and energy E_k bounces perpendicularly off a wall without energy loss. Find an expression for the impulse I provided by the wall.

12. Within 60 sec, 50 golf balls are shot at a speed of 40 m/sec toward a net. The mass of each ball is 45 gm. They strike the net, loose all their energy, and fall to the ground. Find the average force exerted by the net.

13. During a 1-min interval one thousand 0.01-gm raindrops fall vertically on a car roof with an area of 3.2 m². The drops are falling at 5 m/sec when they strike the roof. Find the average force on the roof and the pressure.

14. In Exercise 13, replace the raindrops by hailstones of mass 2 gm, which bounce vertically off the roof without energy loss. Find the average force and the pressure.

15. Using the fact that 1 mole of gas occupies 22.4 ℓ at standard temperature and pressure of 1 atm $= 1.01 \times 10^5$ N/m² and contains Avogadro's number of molecules, find the average kinetic energy of a gas molecule under standard conditions.

16. Find the rms speed of an H_2 molecule if 1 mole of hydrogen gas is confined to a 10-ℓ container at a pressure of 3 atm.

Section 11-4, The Impulse Approximation

17. In Example 11-2, the weight of the golf ball was neglected. As a further check on the validity of the impulse approximation for this example, (a) find the distance the ball falls under the influence of gravity while it is in contact with the club during the collision, which lasts 0.001 sec, and (b) compare this distance with that traveled during the impulse due to the force of the club.

18. A 10-gm bullet traveling 1000 m/sec embeds itself in a 3-kg block. (*a*) Estimate the collision time assuming the bullet moves 10 cm before being brought to rest relative to the block. (*b*) How far does the block travel during this time? (*c*) Find the average force exerted by the bullet on the block during this time and compare it with the weight of the block. Is the impulse approximation a good approximation for this problem?

19. A 0.32-lb baseball travels 120 ft/sec toward home plate. It is hit by the bat, and its velocity is reversed, so that it travels at 120 ft/sec in the opposite direction. (*a*) Find the impulse exerted by the bat on the ball. (*b*) If the collision time is 0.001 sec, find the average force on the ball and compare it with the weight of the ball. Is the impulse approximation good for this problem?

Section 11-5, Energy Changes in Collisions; Reference Frames

20. A 10-gm particle collides with a 2-kg particle. The velocity of the 10-gm particle in the center-of-mass reference frame is 500 m/sec. (*a*) What is the velocity of the 2-kg particle in this frame? (*b*) Find the velocity and kinetic energy of the 10-gm particle in the laboratory frame, in which the 2-kg particle is at rest.

21. Draw a diagram indicating the initial and final velocities of each of the particles in the center-of-mass frame for each of the collisions shown in Figure 11-16.

Figure 11-16
Collisions in the laboratory frame (Exercises 21 and 22).

22. (*a*) For each of the collisions shown in Figure 11-16, find the total kinetic energy of the particles before and after the collision in the laboratory frame shown. (*b*) Find the total kinetic energy of the particles before and after the collision in the center-of-mass frame. (*c*) Show that your answer in part (*a*) is greater than in part (*b*) by the amount $\frac{1}{2}(m_1 + m_2)v_{CM}^2$, where v_{CM} is the velocity of the center of mass in the laboratory frame.

23. Draw a diagram indicating the initial and final velocities of each of the particles in the laboratory frame (in which the more massive particle is initially at rest) for the collisions in Figure 11-17.

Figure 11-17
Collisions in the zero-momentum frame (Exercises 23 and 24).

24. For the collisions in Figure 11-17 find the initial and final total kinetic energies of the particles (a) in the center-of-mass frame and (b) in the laboratory frame. (c) Show that the energy in the laboratory frame is greater than that in the center-of-mass frame by $\frac{1}{2}(m_1 + m_2)v_{CM}{}^2$, where v_{CM} is the center-of-mass velocity in the laboratory frame.

Section 11-6, Perfectly Elastic Collisions in One Dimension

25. Which of the collisions shown in Figure 11-18 are perfectly elastic? (All masses are in kg.)

Before   After

(a) 5 6 m/sec   7.5 m/sec 4   4 m/sec 5   4 5 m/sec

(b) 3 5 m/sec   3   3   3 5 m/sec

(c) 10 26 m/sec   3   10 14 m/sec   3 40 m/sec

(d) 6 13 m/sec   9 m/sec 5   6 m/sec 6   5 13.8 m/sec

Figure 11-18
Exercise 25.

26. A 4-lb object moving at 5 ft/sec makes a perfectly elastic head-on collision with a 1-lb object initially at rest. Find the final velocities of each of the objects.

27. A 15-gm mass is moving to the right with speed of 3 m/sec toward a 6-gm mass moving to the left with speed of 7.5 m/sec. Find the final velocities of each if they make a perfectly elastic head-on collision.

28. A 10-kg object traveling with a speed of 5 m/sec collides elastically with a 100-gm object initially at rest. (a) Find the velocities of each object after the collision. (b) Find the fraction of the initial kinetic energy lost by the 10-kg object.

29. Two blocks are sliding toward each other on a smooth surface. One block, of mass 10 kg, is coming from the left at 5 m/sec, and the other, of mass 6 kg, is coming from the right at 3 m/sec. The two blocks make a head-on elastic collision. Find (a) the velocity of the center of mass before the collision, (b) the initial velocities of the blocks in the center-of-mass frame, (c) the velocities of the blocks in the center-of-mass frame after the collision, and (d) the velocities of the blocks after the collision in the original frame.

30. Two particles $m_1 = 4$ kg and $m_2 = 6$ kg are moving to the right along the x axis, with m_1 chasing m_2. The velocity of m_1 is 10 m/sec, and that of m_2 is 5 m/sec. The particles make an elastic collision. Find the velocity of (a) the center of mass of the system, (b) each particle in the center-of-mass system before and after the collision, (c) each particle after the collision in the original frame. (d) Calculate the initial and final kinetic energies in the original frame and confirm that the total kinetic energy is conserved. (e) Calculate the total kinetic energy in the center-of-mass frame and verify that it is less than your answer to part (d) by $\frac{1}{2}(m_1 + m_2)v_{CM}{}^2$.

Section 11-7, Elastic Collisions in Three Dimensions

31. Figure 11-19 shows the results of an elastic collision between two equal masses as seen in the center-of-mass reference frame. (a) Find the velocity vectors before and after the collision as seen in the laboratory frame in which

Before   After

$$|\mathbf{u}_{1i}|=|\mathbf{u}_{2i}|=|\mathbf{u}_{1f}|=|\mathbf{u}_{2f}|$$

Figure 11-19
Elastic collision of equal
masses (Exercise 31).

one of the masses is initially at rest and show them in a drawing. (*b*) Express the final velocities $\mathbf{v}_1$ and $\mathbf{v}_2$ of the masses in the laboratory frame in terms of the unit vectors $\mathbf{i}$ and $\mathbf{j}$ and show explicitly that $\mathbf{v}_1 \cdot \mathbf{v}_2 = 0$.

32. Figure 11-20 shows the results of a collision of two unequal masses in the laboratory frame. (*a*) Show that momentum is conserved in this collision. (*b*) Show that this collision is elastic by computing the initial and final kinetic energies. (*c*) Find the velocity of the center of mass in this frame and make a drawing indicating the initial and final velocities of the masses in the center-of-mass reference frame.

Before   After

Figure 11-20
Exercise 32.

Section 11-8, Perfectly Inelastic Collisions

33. An 8-lb fish is swimming at 2 ft/sec to the right. It swallows a $\frac{1}{4}$-lb fish swimming toward him at 6 ft/sec to the left (Figure 11-21). What is the velocity of the larger fish immediately after his lunch?

2 ft/sec   6 ft/sec

8 lb $\frac{1}{4}$ lb

Figure 11-21
Inelastic collision of two fish
(Exercise 33).

34. A 150-lb baseball player jumps vertically into the air to catch a 0.32-lb baseball traveling horizontally at 140 ft/sec. If the velocity of the baseball player is 1 ft/sec upward just before he catches the ball, what is his velocity just after he catches the ball?

35. When a 10-gm bullet hits a small stationary target, 60 percent of the mechanical energy is lost. Find the mass of the target.

36. A 10-gm bullet is fired with velocity of 300 m/sec into a pendulum bob which has a mass of 990 gm. How high does the pendulum bob (plus bullet) swing after the collision?

37. A 15-gm bullet is fired into the bob of a ballistic pendulum which has a mass of 1.5 kg. With the bob at maximum height the strings make an angle of 60° with the vertical. The length of the pendulum is 2 m. Find the velocity of the bullet.

38. A 20-ton railway car stands on a hill with its brakes set. The brakes are released, and the car rolls down to the bottom of the hill 16 ft below its original position (Figure 11-22). It collides with a 10-ton car resting at the bottom of the track (with brakes off). The two cars couple together and roll up the track to a height H. Find H.

39. A 1-kg block of wood is attached to a spring of force constant 200 N/m and rests on a smooth surface, as shown in Figure 11-23. A 20-gm bullet is fired into the block, and the spring compresses 13.3 cm. (a) Find the original velocity of the bullet before the collision. (b) What fraction of the original mechanical energy is lost in this collision?

Figure 11-23
Exercise 39.

Section 11-9, Reaction Threshold, and Section 11-10, Coefficient of Restitution

40. The energy that must be supplied in the center-of-mass frame to separate a deuteron into its constituents, a neutron and a proton, is 2.2 MeV. What is the reaction threshold for the reaction $n + d \rightarrow n + n + p - 2.2$ MeV, where n stands for a neutron and d for the deuteron, at rest in the laboratory frame?

41. The Q value for the ionization of a lithium atom is $Q = -5.39$ eV. Find the threshold energy for the ionization of a lithium atom by bombardment with protons. (The mass of lithium is 7 times that of a proton.)

42. The energy needed to separate the two protons in an H_2 molecule is 4.48 eV. This process of separation is called *dissociation*. Suppose it is to be accomplished by a collision of H_2 with a proton. (a) Which takes more energy, bombarding stationary protons with H_2 molecules or bombarding stationary H_2 molecules with protons? (b) Calculate the threshold energy for each of these reactions.

43. A ball bounces to 80 percent of its original height. (a) What fraction of its mechanical energy is lost in each bounce? (b) Where does this energy go? (c) What is the coefficient of restitution of the ball-floor system?

44. A 2-kg object moving at 3 m/sec to the right collides with a 3-kg object moving at 2 m/sec to the left. The coefficient of restitution is 0.6. (a) Find the velocity of each object after the collision. (b) Transform this problem to the laboratory frame, in which the 3-kg object is originally at rest. Diagram the initial and final velocities in this frame.

Problems

1. A force varies with time according to $F = F_0 + Ct$, where F_0 and C are constants. Show both graphically and analytically that the average force during the time interval $t = 0$ to $t = t_1$ is $\frac{1}{2}(F_0 + F_1)$, where F_1 is the force at time t_1.

2. A 2-kg mass is accelerated from rest along a straight line. After 5 sec its speed is 20 m/sec. (a) What was the impulse of the force during the time $t = 0$ to $t = 5$ sec? (b) What was the average force for this interval? (c) If the force decreased linearly with time from some initial value to zero in 5 sec, what was the initial value?

3. Figure 11-24 shows the force acting on a 5-kg mass which moves along the x axis. At time $t = 0$, the mass is at rest at $x = 0$. (a) Make a graph of the impulse delivered by the force from $t = 0$ to time t as a function of t. (b) Make a graph of the speed of the mass as a function of time. (c) What is F_{av} for the period from $t = 0$ to $t = 12$ sec? (d) What is F_{av} for the period from $t = 0$ to $t = 6$ sec? From $t = 6$ sec to $t = 12$ sec?

Figure 11-24
Force acting on 5-kg mass
(Problem 3).

4. A 3000-lb car traveling 60 mi/h crashes into a concrete wall. Estimate the time of the collision by assuming that the center of the car travels halfway to the wall with uniform acceleration and therefore average speed of 30 mi/h. (Use any reasonable length for the car.) What is the impulse exerted by the wall on the car? Using your estimate of the time for the collision, find the average force exerted by the wall on the car.

5. You throw a 0.32-lb ball upward so that it reaches a height of 100 ft. Use a reasonable value for the distance the ball moves while it is in your hand to calculate the average acceleration of the ball in the hand, the impulse given the ball, the average force exerted while the ball is in your hand, and the time the ball is accelerating. Can you neglect the weight of the ball while it is being thrown?

6. A 6-ft 180-lb man steps off a ledge and falls 16 ft to the ground, making an inelastic collision with it. (a) How fast was he traveling just before he hit? (b) What was the impulse exerted on man by the ground? (c) Estimate the time of collision assuming that the force on the man is constant and that he travels 3 ft during the collision. (d) Using your result for part (c), find the average force exerted by the ground on the man. (e) Discuss the validity of the impulse approximation for this problem.

7. A handball of mass 300 gm is thrown straight against a wall with a speed of 8 m/sec. It rebounds with the same speed. (a) What impulse was delivered to the wall? (b) If the ball was in contact with the wall for 0.003 sec, what average force was exerted on the wall? (c) The ball is caught by a player who brings it to rest. In the process his hand moves back 0.5 m. What is the impulse received by the player? (d) What was the average force exerted on the player?

8. A stream of glass beads comes out of a horizontal tube at 100 per second and strikes a balance pan, as shown in Figure 11-25. They fall a distance of 0.5 m to the balance and bounce back to the same height. Each bead has mass

In this chapter we concentrate on the simplest kind of rotation, rotation of a rigid body about a fixed axis. In the next chapter we shall extend our discussion to systems in which the distance between any two particles can vary and consider the situation when the axis of rotation is not fixed in space.

12-1   Angular Velocity and Angular Acceleration

Consider one particle of a wheel rotating about its axis of symmetry, which is fixed in space. We can specify the position of the particle P_i by the distance r_i from the center of the wheel and the angle θ_i between a line from the center to the particle and a reference line fixed in space, as shown in Figure 12-2. In a small time dt, the particle moves along the arc of a circle a distance ds_i given by

$$ds_i = v_i \, dt \qquad\qquad 12\text{-}1$$

where v_i is the speed of the particle. The angle swept out by the line from the center to the particle, in radians, is this distance divided by the radius r_i:

$$d\theta = \frac{ds_i}{r_i} = \frac{v_i \, dt}{r_i} \qquad\qquad 12\text{-}2$$

Although the distance ds_i varies from particle to particle, the angle $d\theta$ swept out in a given time is the same for all the particles. For example, when one particle moves through a complete circle, so do all the other particles and $\Delta\theta = 2\pi$ rad for all the particles. The rate of change of angle with respect to time $d\theta/dt$ is the same for all the particles of the wheel. It is called the *angular velocity* ω of the wheel,

$$\omega = \frac{d\theta}{dt} \qquad\qquad 12\text{-}3 \qquad \textit{Angular velocity}$$

From Equation 12-2 the speed of the ith particle is related to its radius r_i and the angular velocity of the wheel by

$$v_i = r_i \frac{d\theta}{dt} = r_i\omega \qquad\qquad 12\text{-}4$$

Whether ω is positive or negative depends on whether θ is increasing or decreasing. The units of angular velocity are radians per second.

Figure 12-2
A wheel rotating about a fixed axis through its center. The distance ds_i moved by the ith particle in some time depends on r_i, but the angular displacement $d\theta$ is the same for all particles of the wheel.

Star tracks in a time exposure of the night sky. How can you decide whether these circular tracks are due to rotation of the earth or motion of the stars? (*Courtesy of Yerkes Observatory.*)

Since a radian is a dimensionless unit of angle, the dimensions of angular velocity are those of reciprocal seconds ($\sec^{-1}$). Although angular velocity is frequently expressed in other units than radians per second, it is important to remember that expressions like Equations 12-3 and 12-4 and the other results we obtain for rotational motion are valid only when angles are expressed in radians.

Since angles are often expressed in degrees, angular velocity is sometimes expressed in degrees per second or degrees per minute. In such cases, the angular velocity can be reexpressed in radians by using

$$2\pi \text{ rad} = 360° \qquad \text{or} \qquad \frac{\pi \text{ rad}}{180°} = 1$$

Angular velocity is also commonly expressed in revolutions per second and revolutions per minute. Conversion to radians is accomplished by using

$$2\pi \text{ rad} = 1 \text{ rev} \qquad \text{or} \qquad \frac{2\pi \text{ rad}}{1 \text{ rev}} = 1$$

The rate of change of angular velocity with respect to time is called the *angular acceleration* α. For rotation about a fixed axis,

$$\alpha = \frac{d\omega}{dt} = \frac{d^2\theta}{dt^2} \qquad\qquad\qquad 12\text{-}5 \qquad \textit{Angular acceleration}$$

The units of angular acceleration are radians per second per second. The relation between the *tangential* linear acceleration of the ith particle of the wheel and the angular acceleration is obtained by taking the derivative of the speed v_i in Equation 12-4 with respect to t:

$$a_{it} = \frac{dv_i}{dt} = r_i \frac{d\omega}{dt}$$

Thus

$$a_{it} = r_i \alpha \qquad\qquad\qquad\qquad 12\text{-}6$$

Each particle of the wheel also has a *radial* linear acceleration, the centripetal acceleration:

$$a_{ir} = -\frac{v_i^2}{r_i} = -r_i\omega^2 \qquad\qquad\text{12-7}$$

The three quantities angular displacement θ, angular velocity ω, and angular acceleration α are analogous to the linear displacement x, linear velocity v_x, and linear acceleration a_x, which we met in studying one-dimensional motion in Chapter 2. Because of the similarity of the definitions of the rotational and linear quantities, much of what we learned in Chapter 2 will be useful in treating problems of rotation about a fixed axis. For example, if the angular acceleration is constant, we can develop constant-angular-acceleration expressions which are exactly of the form of the constant-linear-acceleration expressions (Equations 2-11 to 2-13). If, for example, we have

$$\alpha = \frac{d\omega}{dt} = \alpha_0 = \text{constant}$$

then

$$\omega = \omega_0 + \alpha_0 t \qquad\qquad\text{12-8}$$

Expressions for constant angular acceleration

where ω_0 is the angular velocity at $t = 0$. Integrating again, we obtain

$$\theta = \theta_0 + \omega_0 t + \tfrac{1}{2}\alpha_0 t^2 \qquad\qquad\text{12-9}$$

As with the constant-linear-acceleration formulas, we can eliminate time from these equations to obtain an equation relating the angular displacement, angular velocity, and angular acceleration:

$$\omega^2 = \omega_0^2 + 2\alpha_0(\theta - \theta_0) \qquad\qquad\text{12-10}$$

Example 12-1 A wheel rotates with constant angular acceleration of $\alpha_0 = 2$ rad/sec^2. If the wheel starts from rest, how many revolutions does it make in 10 sec?

The number of revolutions is related to the angular displacement by the fact that each revolution is an angular displacement of 2π rad. Thus we need to find the angular displacement $\theta - \theta_0$ in radians for a time 10 sec and multiply by the conversion factor 1 rev/2π rad.

Equation 12-9 relates the angular displacement to the time. We are given $\omega_0 = 0$ (the wheel starts from rest). Let us choose $\theta_0 = 0$. We have

$$\theta = \tfrac{1}{2}\alpha_0 t^2 = \tfrac{1}{2}(2 \text{ rad/sec}^2)(10 \text{ sec})^2 = 100 \text{ rad}$$

The number of revolutions is thus

$$100 \text{ rad} \times \frac{1 \text{ rev}}{2\pi \text{ rad}} = \frac{50}{\pi} \text{ rev} = 15.9 \text{ rev}$$

It is convenient to assign directions to the rotational quantities θ, ω, and α. We cannot describe the rotation of a wheel by any direction in the plane of the wheel because, by symmetry, all directions in this plane are equivalent. The direction in space uniquely associated with the rotation is the direction of the axis of rotation. We therefore choose the direction for the angle of rotation along the axis of rotation. Since ω equals the rate of change of θ, it will also be along the axis of rotation. Similarly, since we are considering only rotation about axes which are fixed in space, the rate of change of ω, which is the angular acceleration α, must also be in this direction.

Direction of θ, ω, and α

The rotation of this nonrigid body, a galaxy in Ursa Major, is indicated by its spiral shape. (*Courtesy of Hale Observatories.*)

Consider a wheel rotating in the clockwise sense, as in Figure 12-3*a*. We have chosen the direction for ω along the axis of rotation, but we must still decide the sense of ω, that is, for this rotation, whether ω points into or out of the diagram. The choice is made by convention. If the rotation is clockwise, as in the figure, ω is inward. If it is counterclockwise, ω is outward. This arbitrary decision is called the *right-hand rule,* as illustrated in Figure 12-3*a*. When the axis of rotation is grasped by the right hand with the fingers following the rotation, the extended thumb points in the direction of ω. The direction of ω is also that of the advance of a rotating right-handed screw, as shown in Figure 12-3*b*. The sense of the angular acceleration (for rotation about a fixed axis) depends on whether ω is increasing or decreasing. If ω is increasing, α is parallel to ω. If ω is decreasing, α is antiparallel to ω.

(a)

(b)

Figure 12-3
(*a*) The right-hand rule for determining the direction of the angular velocity ω. (*b*) The direction of ω is also the direction of advance of a rotating right-handed screw.

Question

1. Two points are on a wheel turning at constant angular velocity, one point on the rim and the other halfway between the rim and the axis. Which moves the greatest distance in time Δt? Which turns through the greater angle? Which has the greatest speed? Angular velocity? Acceleration? Angular acceleration?

12-2   The Vector Nature of Rotation

Having assigned directions to the rotational quantities θ, ω, and α, we now ask whether these quantities are vectors. A quantity having magnitude and direction is a vector only if it also obeys the law of vector addition. The significant property of the law of vector addition for this discussion is that the sum of two vectors is independent of the order in which they are added:

$$\mathbf{A} + \mathbf{B} = \mathbf{B} + \mathbf{A}$$

Consider, for example, the two successive 90° rotations illustrated in Figure 12-4*a*. The axes of the two rotations are different. Figure 12-4*b* shows these same rotations with the order reversed, demonstrating that the final position of the object depends on the order in which the two rotations occur. Angular displacement is not a vector quantity because it does not obey the addition law for vectors. Figure 12-5 shows the same object undergoing much smaller successive rotations of about 20°. The difference in the final positions for the two sequences is much less than for 90°. As the magnitude of the successive changes in angle approaches zero, the difference in final positions also approaches zero. Thus in the limit as $\Delta\theta \to 0$ the angular displacement obeys the vector-addition law. For general rotations we define the angular velocity by

$$\boldsymbol{\omega} = \frac{d\boldsymbol{\theta}}{dt} = \lim_{\Delta t \to 0} \frac{\Delta\boldsymbol{\theta}}{\Delta t}$$

(Here we have written $\Delta\boldsymbol{\theta}$ in boldface to indicate that it has a direction even though it is not a vector.) Since $\Delta\boldsymbol{\theta} \to 0$ as $\Delta t \to 0$, angular velocity does obey the vector-addition law and is a vector quantity. Similarly, we define the angular acceleration for general rotations by

$$\boldsymbol{\alpha} = \frac{d\boldsymbol{\omega}}{dt}$$

Since the derivative of a vector is also a vector, $\boldsymbol{\alpha}$ is a vector.

Figure 12-4
(*a*) The book is rotated 90° about the *x* axis and then 90° about the *y* axis. (*b*) The body is rotated first about the *y* axis and then about the *x* axis. The result of the two rotations depends on the order.

Figure 12-5
The same as Figure 12-4 except for a small angle of rotation. (*a*) A rotation about the *x* axis followed by a rotation about the *y* axis. (*b*) A rotation about the *y* axis followed by a rotation about the *x* axis. The result is nearly the same for the two cases.

For rotations about a fixed axis, which we are considering in this chapter, the vector nature of the rotational quantities is not important. The angular velocity ω and the angular acceleration α have only one component, such as ω_z and α_z, for a wheel rotating about the z axis. Thus they can change only in magnitude. We are considering a simplification of general rotational motion, which resembles the simplification of linear motion in Chapter 2, where we restricted our discussion to one-dimensional motion. We consider some more complicated rotations in three dimensions in the next chapter.

Questions

2. A wheel is mounted on a vertical axis. A point on the east side is moving north, and a point on the west side is moving south. What is the direction of ω? What is the direction of α if the wheel is speeding up? If it is slowing down?

3. The axle of a wheel is mounted horizontally on a north-south line. The angular velocity points north. What is the direction of motion of a point on the rim at the top of the wheel? The angular acceleration α points south. Is the angular speed of the wheel increasing or decreasing?

12-3   Rotational Kinetic Energy and Moment of Inertia

The kinetic energy of a system of particles is just the sum of the kinetic energies of the individual particles. For a rotating wheel, we have

$$E_k = \Sigma \tfrac{1}{2} m_i v_i^2 = \Sigma \tfrac{1}{2} m_i (r_i \omega)^2 = \tfrac{1}{2} \omega^2 \Sigma m_i r_i^2 \qquad 12\text{-}11$$

We have taken the angular velocity out of the sum because it is the same for each particle. The sum $\Sigma m_i r_i^2$ is a property of the wheel called the *moment of inertia I*. The moment of inertia depends on the mass distribution relative to the axis of rotation of the wheel. In terms of I, the kinetic energy can be written

Moment of inertia

$$E_k = \tfrac{1}{2} I \omega^2 \qquad 12\text{-}12$$

If we compare this expression with that for the kinetic energy of translation of a single particle $\tfrac{1}{2} mv^2$, we see that in rotational motion, moment of inertia is analogous to mass in linear motion, just as angular velocity is analogous to linear velocity. Note that the distance r_i in Equation 12-11 is the perpendicular distance from the ith particle to the *axis* of rotation. In general, it is not the distance from the ith particle to the center of mass even though in a two-dimensional figure rotating about an axis perpendicular to the figure through the center of mass they are the same. An example should clarify this point.

Figure 12-6
Four equal masses connected by light rods rotating about an axis in the plane of the masses through the center of mass.

Example 12-2 Four equal masses are connected by light (massless) rods to form a rectangle of sides $2a$ and $2b$, as shown in Figure 12-6. The system rotates about an axis in the plane of the figure through the center. Find the moment of inertia about this axis and the kinetic energy if the angular velocity is ω.

Since each mass is moving in a circle of radius a, the linear velocity of each particle is $v = a\omega$. Thus its kinetic energy is

$$\tfrac{1}{2}mv^2 = \tfrac{1}{2}m(a\omega)^2 = \tfrac{1}{2}ma^2\omega^2$$

The total kinetic energy is the sum over the four particles:

$$E_k = \Sigma\tfrac{1}{2}m_iv_i^2 = 4(\tfrac{1}{2}ma^2\omega^2) = \tfrac{1}{2}(4ma^2)\omega^2$$

Therefore the moment of inertia is $4ma^2$.

To avoid confusing r_i with its usual meaning (the distance from the ith particle to the origin) we shall use ρ_i for the perpendicular distance from the ith particle to the axis of rotation. Then the moment of inertia is

$$I = \Sigma m_i\rho_i^2 \qquad\qquad 12\text{-}13$$

Example 12-3 Find the moment of inertia of the system of Example 12-2 for rotation about an axis parallel to the first axis but passing through two of the masses, as shown in Figure 12-7.

For this rotation, two of the masses are at a distance $2a$ from the axis of rotation and two are at zero distance. The moment of inertia is thus

$$I = \Sigma m_i\rho_i^2 = m(0)^2 + m(0)^2 + m(2a)^2 + m(2a)^2 = 8ma^2$$

The moment of inertia is larger about this axis than the one parallel to it through the center of mass.

Figure 12-7
Four equal masses connected by light rods rotating about an axis through two of the masses.

Questions

4. Can the moment of inertia of an object by specified without describing where the axis of rotation is? Can a body have more than one moment of inertia?

5. How does the kinetic energy of a rotating body change if its angular velocity is doubled?

6. A disk is made by surrounding a wooden core with an iron rim. Another disk, of the same diameter, thickness, and total mass, is made by surrounding an iron core with a wooden rim. Which has the greater kinetic energy when rotated with angular velocity ω about its axis of symmetry?

12-4 Calculating the Moment of Inertia

We can often simplify the calculation of the moments of inertia for various bodies by using general theorems relating the moment of inertia about one axis of the body to that about another axis. *Steiner's theorem*, or the *parallel-axis theorem*, relates the moment of inertia about an axis through the center of mass to that about a second, parallel axis. Let I_{CM} be the moment of inertia about an axis through the center of mass of a body and I be that about a parallel axis a distance h away. The parallel-axis theorem states that

$$I = I_{CM} + Mh^2 \qquad\qquad 12\text{-}14 \qquad\qquad \textit{Parallel-axis theorem}$$

where M is the total mass of the body. Examples 12-2 and 12-3 illustrate a special case of this theorem with $h = a$, $M = 4m$, and $I_{CM} = 4ma^2$.

We can prove the theorem using the result (developed in Chapter 10) that the kinetic energy of a system of particles is the sum of the kinetic energy of center-of-mass motion plus the energy of motion relative to the center of mass,

$$E_k = \tfrac{1}{2}Mv_{CM}^2 + E_{kr} \qquad\qquad 12\text{-}15$$

Consider a rigid body rotating with angular velocity about an axis a distance h from a parallel axis through the center of mass, as in Figure 12-8. When the system rotates through an angle $\Delta\theta$ measured about the axis of rotation, it rotates through the same angle $\Delta\theta$ measured about any other parallel axis. The motion of the body relative to the center of mass is thus a rotation about the center-of-mass axis with the same angular velocity. The kinetic energy of motion relative to the center of mass is thus

$$E_{kr} = \tfrac{1}{2}I_{CM}\omega^2$$

The velocity of the center of mass relative to any fixed point on the axis of rotation is

$$v_{CM} = h\omega$$

The kinetic energy of motion of the center of mass is thus

$$\tfrac{1}{2}Mv_{CM}^2 = \tfrac{1}{2}M(h\omega)^2 = \tfrac{1}{2}M\omega^2h^2$$

When the total kinetic energy of rotation is written $\tfrac{1}{2}I\omega^2$, Equation 12-15 becomes

$$E_k = \tfrac{1}{2}I\omega^2 = \tfrac{1}{2}M\omega^2h^2 + \tfrac{1}{2}I_{CM}\omega^2 = \tfrac{1}{2}(Mh^2 + I_{CM})\omega^2$$

Thus

$$I = Mh^2 + I_{CM}$$

The *plane-figure theorem* relates the moments of inertia about two perpendicular axes in a plane figure to the moment of inertia about a third axis perpendicular to the figure. If x, y, and z are perpendicular axes for a figure which lies in the xy plane, the moment of inertia about the z axis equals the sum of the moments of inertia about the x and y axes. This is not difficult to prove. Figure 12-9 shows a figure in the xy plane. The moment of inertia about the x axis is

$$I_x = \Sigma m_i y_i^2$$

where the sum is taken over all the elements of mass m_i. (In practice, as we shall see, the sum is often done by integration.) The moment of inertia about the y axis is

$$I_y = \Sigma m_i x_i^2$$

The moment of inertia about the z axis is

$$I_z = \Sigma m_i \rho_i^2$$

But for each element m_i, $\rho_i^2 = x_i^2 + y_i^2$. Thus

$$I_z = \Sigma m_i \rho_i^2 = \Sigma m_i(x_i^2 + y_i^2) = \Sigma m_i x_i^2 + \Sigma m_i y_i^2$$

or

$$I_z = I_y + I_x \qquad\qquad 12\text{-}16$$

Example 12-4 What is the moment of inertia about an axis through one of the masses and perpendicular to the plane of the masses shown in Figure 12-10?

Figure 12-8
Parallel-axis theorem. The moment of inertia about any axis equals the moment of inertia about a parallel axis through the center of mass plus Mh^2, where M is the total mass and h is the distance between the axes.

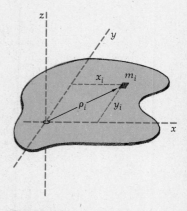

Figure 12-9
For a plane figure $I_z = \Sigma m_i \rho_i^2 = \Sigma m_i(x_i^2 + y_i^2) = \Sigma m_i x_i^2 + \Sigma m_i y_i^2 = I_y + I_x$.

Figure 12-10
Example 12-4.

The moment of inertia calculated about the y axis in this figure was found in Example 12-3 to be $8ma^2$. By similar reasoning, the moment of inertia about the x axis in this figure is $8mb^2$. Thus $I_z = I_x + I_y = 8ma^2 + 8mb^2$. This result is easily checked by direct calculation.

For continuous bodies the sum in Equation 12-13 defining the moment of inertia is replaced by an integral. Let dm be a mass element a distance x from the axis of rotation. The moment of inertia for this axis is then

$$I = \int x^2 \, dm \qquad\qquad 12\text{-}17 \qquad \textit{Moment of inertia}$$

Some examples will demonstrate how to calculate moments of inertia using Equation 12-17 and the two theorems discussed above (Equations 12-14 and 12-16). Moments of inertia of uniform bodies of varied shapes are given in Table 12-1.

Example 12-5 Find the moment of inertia of a uniform stick about an axis perpendicular to the stick through one end.

The mass element dm is shown in Figure 12-11. Since the total mass M is uniformly distributed along the length L, $dm = (M/L)\,dx$. The moment of inertia about the y axis is

$$I_y = \int_0^L x^2 \frac{M}{L} \, dx = \frac{M}{L} \int_0^L x^2 \, dx = \frac{M}{L} \left. \tfrac{1}{3} x^3 \right]_0^L$$

$$= \frac{M}{L} \frac{L^3}{3} = \tfrac{1}{3} ML^2 \qquad\qquad 12\text{-}18$$

The moment of inertia about the z axis is also $\tfrac{1}{3}ML^2$, and that about the x axis is zero, assuming that all the mass is right on the x axis.

Example 12-6 Find the moment of inertia of a uniform stick about the y' axis through the center of mass (Figure 12-12).

Since the axis is through the center of mass of the stick, the integration extends from $-L/2$ to $+L/2$. Thus

$$I_{CM} = \int_{-L/2}^{+L/2} x'^2 \frac{M}{L} \, dx' = 2 \int_0^{L/2} x'^2 \frac{M}{L} \, dx'$$

$$= \frac{2M}{L} \frac{(L/2)^3}{3} = \tfrac{1}{12} ML^2 \qquad\qquad 12\text{-}19$$

Figure 12-11
Calculation of I for a uniform stick with axis of rotation through one end.

Figure 12-12
Calculation of I for a uniform stick rotating about an axis through the center of mass.

Table 12-1
Moments of inertia of uniform bodies of various shapes

Cylindrical shell about axis		$I = MR^2$
Solid cylinder about axis		$I = \frac{1}{2}MR^2$
Hollow cylinder about axis		$I = \frac{1}{2}M(R_1{}^2 + R_2{}^2)$
Cylindrical shell about diameter through center		$I = \frac{1}{2}MR^2 + \frac{1}{12}ML^2$
Solid cylinder about diameter through center		$I = \frac{1}{4}MR^2 + \frac{1}{12}ML^2$
Thin rod about perpendicular line through center		$I = \frac{1}{12}ML^2$
Thin rod about perpendicular line through one end		$I = \frac{1}{3}ML^2$
Thin spherical shell about diameter		$I = \frac{2}{3}MR^2$
Solid sphere about diameter		$I = \frac{2}{5}MR^2$
Solid rectangular parallelepiped about axis through center perpendicular to face		$I = \frac{1}{12}M(a^2 + b^2)$

This is smaller than that about the axis through the end, as would be expected because, on the average, the mass is closer to this axis than to the end. This result can also be obtained from the result of Example 12-5 and the parallel-axis theorem. In this case $h = \frac{1}{2}L$, and

$$I = I_{CM} + M(\tfrac{1}{2}L)^2 = \tfrac{1}{3}ML^2$$

or

$$I_{CM} = \tfrac{1}{3}ML^2 - \tfrac{1}{4}ML^2 = \tfrac{1}{12}ML^2$$

Example 12-7 Find the moment of inertia of a hoop about an axis through the center and perpendicular to the plane of the hoop (Fig. 12-13a).

Since all the mass is at a distance R from this axis, the moment of inertia is simply $I = MR^2$.

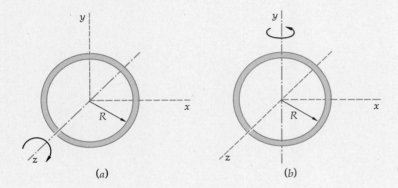

(a)   (b)

Figure 12-13
(a) Hoop rotating about an axis perpendicular to the plane of the hoop through its center. Since all the mass of the hoop is at distance R from this axis, the moment of inertia is just MR^2. (b) Hoop rotating about a diameter (Example 12-8). Since $I_y = I_x$ by symmetry and $I_y + I_x = I_z = MR^2$, it follows that $I_y = \frac{1}{2}MR^2$.

Example 12-8 Find the moment of inertia of a hoop about a diameter of the hoop (Fig. 12-13b).

Instead of solving this problem directly we use the plane-figure theorem. If we take the hoop to be in the xy plane with the center at the origin, by symmetry we have $I_x = I_y$. Since we have already found I_z to be MR^2, we have

$$I_z = I_x + I_y = 2I_x = MR^2$$

Therefore

$$I_x = I_y = \tfrac{1}{2}MR^2$$

Example 12-9 Find the moment of inertia of a uniform disk about the axis through its center and perpendicular to the plane of the disk.

We expect that I will be smaller than MR^2 since all the mass is less than the distance R from the axis. We can calculate I by taking mass elements as shown in Figure 12-14. Each mass element is a hoop with moment of inertia $r^2\,dm$. Since the area of each element is $2\pi r\,dr$, the mass of the element is $dm = (M/A)2\pi r\,dr$, where $A = \pi R^2$ is the area of the disk. Thus we have

$$I = \int r^2\,dm = \int_0^R r^2 \frac{M}{A}\,2\pi r\,dr = \frac{2\pi M}{\pi R^2}\int_0^R r^3\,dr$$

$$= \frac{2M}{R^2}\frac{R^4}{4} = \tfrac{1}{2}MR^2 \qquad\qquad 12\text{-}20$$

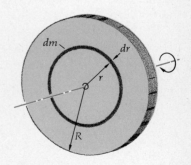

Figure 12-14
Calculation of I for a uniform disk about an axis through its center and perpendicular to the plane of the disk.

Example 12-10 Find the moment of inertia of a cylinder about its axis (Figure 12-15).

We can consider the cylinder to be a set of disks each with mass m_i and moment of inertia $\frac{1}{2}m_i R^2$. Then the moment of inertia of the complete cylinder is

$$I = \Sigma \tfrac{1}{2} m_i R^2 = \tfrac{1}{2} R^2 \Sigma m_i = \tfrac{1}{2} M R^2$$

where $M = \Sigma m_i$ is the total mass of the cylinder.

Example 12-11 Find the moment of inertia of a sphere about an axis through its center.

We can calculate this moment of inertia by treating the sphere as a set of disks. Consider the disk element in Figure 12-16 at height x above the center. The radius of the disk is

$$r = \sqrt{R^2 - x^2}$$

The mass of the disk is

$$dm = \frac{M}{V}\,\pi r^2\,dx = \frac{M}{V}\,\pi(R^2 - x^2)\,dx$$

where M is the total mass of the sphere and

$$V = \tfrac{4}{3}\pi R^3$$

is the volume of the sphere. The moment of inertia of the disk is

$$dI = \tfrac{1}{2} dm\, r^2 = \frac{1}{2}\frac{M}{V}\,\pi(R^2 - x^2)^2\,dx$$

The total moment of inertia of the sphere is

$$I = \int_{-R}^{+R} \frac{1}{2}\frac{M}{V}\,\pi(R^2 - x^2)^2\,dx = \frac{1}{2}\frac{M}{V}\,\pi 2 \int_0^R (R^2 - x^2)^2\,dx$$

$$= \frac{8\pi M R^5}{15 V} = \tfrac{2}{5} M R^2 \qquad\qquad 12\text{-}21$$

using $V = \tfrac{4}{3}\pi R^3$.

The moment of inertia is often given in handbooks in terms of the *radius of gyration k*, defined by

$$k^2 = \frac{I}{M} \qquad\qquad 12\text{-}22$$

where M is the total mass of the body. The radius of gyration is thus the distance from the axis at which a point mass M would have the same moment of inertia about the axis. For example, the moment of inertia about an axis through one end of a stick is

$$Mk^2 = \tfrac{1}{3}ML^2 \qquad \text{or} \qquad k = \frac{L}{\sqrt{3}}$$

The radius of gyration is a measure of the distribution of mass of a body relative to a given axis of rotation. A large radius of gyration means that, on the average, the mass is relatively far from the axis.

Questions

7. Through what point in a body must the axis of rotation pass if the moment of inertia is to be a minimum?

Figure 12-15
Cylinder rotating about its axis. The cylinder can be thought of as a stack of disks of mass m_i. The moment of inertia about this axis is $I = \Sigma \tfrac{1}{2} m_i R^2 = \tfrac{1}{2} M R^2$, where $M = \Sigma m_i$ is the total mass.

Figure 12-16
Calculation of the moment of inertia of a uniform sphere rotating about a diameter (Example 12-11). The sphere can be thought of as a set of disks of varying radius.

8. About what axis does a cube of a uniform substance have its smallest moment of inertia?

9. A disk, hoop, and sphere have the same radius and are uniform in density. Which has the greatest and which the least radius of gyration for an axis through the center of each and perpendicular to the plane of the disk and hoop? (Answer without looking up the moments of inertia.)

12-5 Torque

We now consider the dynamics of the rotation of a rigid body. In order to change the rotational kinetic energy of a rigid body, a force must do work on the body. Consider the forces F_1 and F_2 acting at the rim of a wheel, as in Figure 12-17. The force F_1 points along a radial line of the wheel; it is perpendicular to the motion of the point on the rim of the wheel at which the force acts. Thus it does no work on the wheel and cannot affect the wheel's kinetic energy. Since the kinetic energy is $\frac{1}{2}I\omega^2$, this force cannot affect the angular velocity of the wheel. For example, if the wheel is not rotating at all, a radial force F_1 will not produce rotation in either direction. However, the force F_2 has a component parallel or antiparallel to the motion of the rim of the wheel (depending upon how the wheel is rotating when the force is applied). This force does do work on the wheel which changes the wheel's kinetic energy. For example, if the wheel is rotating counterclockwise (ω out), the tangential component of F_2 will be in the direction of motion of the rim and the force will do positive work, increasing the kinetic energy and thus increasing the magnitude of the angular velocity. If the wheel is rotating in the opposite sense, F_2 will do negative work, decreasing ω and the kinetic energy.

Of course forces F_1 and F_2 shown in Figure 12-17 are not the only forces acting on the wheel. If the wheel is rotating about a fixed axis through the center of mass, the center of mass must be at rest. Then the resultant force acting on the wheel must be zero. The other forces not shown in this figure are exerted by the pivot at the axis of rotation and balance F_1 and F_2 so that the center of mass does not accelerate. If the pivot is frictionless, these forces are radial and do not affect the rotation. We shall ignore these forces for this discussion.

Let us now consider a single force F acting on a wheel which is already rotating in the counterclockwise sense (ω out), as in Figure 12-18. The force makes an angle ϕ with the radial line from the axis of rotation to the point of application of the force. The tangential component of the force is $F_t = F \sin \phi$. (We use ϕ here to avoid confusing this angle with the angle of rotation θ.) In a small time interval dt, the wheel rotates through an angle $d\theta = \omega\, dt$. The point of application of the force moves a distance $ds = r\, d\theta = r\omega\, dt$. The work done by the force is thus

$$dW = \mathbf{F} \cdot d\mathbf{s} = F_t\, ds = F \sin \phi\; r\, d\theta = Fr \sin \phi\; \omega\, dt \qquad 12\text{-}23$$

The rate at which the force does work is the power input, which equals the rate of change of kinetic energy:

$$P = \frac{dW}{dt} = F \sin \phi\; r\omega = \frac{d}{dt}(\tfrac{1}{2}I\omega^2) = I\omega\,\frac{d\omega}{dt} \qquad 12\text{-}24$$

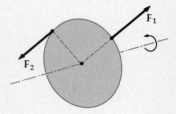

Figure 12-17
Two forces acting on a rotating wheel. F_1 is perpendicular to the motion and does no work on the wheel.

Figure 12-18
Only the tangential component F_t does work on the wheel.

Canceling ω in Eq. 12-24, we have

$$F \sin \phi \, r = I \frac{d\omega}{dt} = I\alpha \qquad \text{12-25}$$

The quantity $Fr \sin \phi$ is called the *torque* τ or moment of the force $\mathbf{F}$ about the point O. Note that the distance $D = r \sin \phi$ is the perpendicular distance between the line of action of the force $\mathbf{F}$ and the point O on the axis of rotation. If the line of action of the force goes through the axis of rotation, the torque is zero:

$$\tau = Fr \sin \phi = FD = F_t r \qquad \text{12-26}$$

Torque defined

The distance $D = r \sin \phi$ is called the *lever arm* of the force $\mathbf{F}$. In terms of the torque, Equations 12-23 and 12-25 are written

$$dW = \tau \, d\theta = \tau\omega \, dt \qquad \text{12-27}$$

and

$$\tau = I\alpha \qquad \text{12-28}$$

Again it is convenient to assign a direction to the torque. (In the next chapter we shall see that in general torque is a vector.) We have chosen a case where the torque increases the magnitude of ω, and we want the direction of torque for this case to be in the same direction as $\boldsymbol{\omega}$. We define the direction of torque to be the direction of rotation $\boldsymbol{\omega}$ which that torque acting alone will produce if the body starts from rest.

Equation 12-28 can then be written as a vector equation. If several forces exert torques on the wheel, it is the work done by the resultant torque that equals the change in kinetic energy. Thus we substitute $\Sigma\boldsymbol{\tau}$ for τ in the above equations and obtain

$$\Sigma\boldsymbol{\tau} = I\boldsymbol{\alpha} \qquad \text{12-29}$$

Equation 12-29 is the rotational analog of Newton's second law $\Sigma\mathbf{F} = m\mathbf{a}$ for linear motion. The resultant torque is analogous to the resultant force, the moment of inertia is analogous to the mass, and the angular acceleration is analogous to the linear acceleration.

Culver Pictures

Torque exerted by a wrench on a nut is proportional to the force and the lever arm. Charlie could exert a greater torque with the same force if he held the wrenches nearer their ends. What is the direction of the torque exerted by each wrench when he pulls on it?

$T = 10\,\text{N}$

Figure 12-19
String wrapped around a disk
(Example 12-12).

Example 12-12 A string is wound around the rim of a uniform disk pivoted to rotate about a fixed axis without friction. The mass of the disk is 3 kg, and its radius R is 25 cm. The string is pulled with a force of 10 N (Figure 12-19). If the disk is initially at rest, what is its angular velocity after 5 sec?

The moment of inertia about the axis of the disk is

$$I = \tfrac{1}{2}mR^2 = \tfrac{1}{2}(3 \text{ kg})(0.25 \text{ m})^2 = 0.0938 \text{ kg-m}^2$$

Since the direction of the string as it leaves the rim of the disk is always tangent to the disk, the lever arm of the force it exerts is just R. The applied torque is thus

$$\tau = FR = (10 \text{ N})(0.25 \text{ m}) = 2.5 \text{ N-m}$$

From Equation 12-29

$$\alpha = \frac{\Sigma \tau}{I} = \frac{2.5 \text{ N-m}}{0.0938 \text{ kg-m}^2} = 26.7 \text{ rad/sec}^2$$

Since α is constant, we find ω after 5 sec from Equation 12-8, setting $\omega_0 = 0$:

$$\omega = \omega_0 + \alpha t = 0 + (26.7 \text{ rad/sec}^2)(5 \text{ sec}) = 133 \text{ rad/sec}$$

This angular speed can be expressed in more familiar terms as

$$\omega = \frac{133 \text{ rad}}{1 \text{ sec}} \frac{60 \text{ sec}}{1 \text{ min}} \frac{1 \text{ rev}}{2\pi \text{ rad}} = 1270 \text{ rev/min}$$

Example 12-13 A mass m is tied to a light string wound around a wheel of moment of inertia I and radius R (Figure 12-20). The wheel bearing is frictionless. Find the tension in the string, the acceleration of m, and its speed after it has fallen a distance h from rest.

The only force which exerts a torque on the wheel is the tension T in the string. It has lever arm R. Hence

$$TR = I\alpha \qquad\qquad 12\text{-}30$$

Two forces act on the suspended mass, the upward tension **T** and the downward weight $m\mathbf{g}$. Hence $\Sigma \mathbf{F} = m\mathbf{a}$ for this body gives

$$mg - T = ma \qquad\qquad 12\text{-}31$$

(where we have taken down as the positive direction).

There are three unknowns, T, a, and α, in these two equations. However, the string provides a constraint by which a and α can be related. As the wheel turns through angle θ, an amount of string of length $s = R\theta$ unwraps and the mass m falls an equal distance $y = R\theta$. Thus we have

$$y = R\theta \qquad\qquad 12\text{-}32$$

$$\frac{dy}{dt} = R\frac{d\theta}{dt} \quad \text{or} \quad v = R\omega \qquad\qquad 12\text{-}33$$

Figure 12-20
Mass tied to string which is wrapped around a rotating wheel (Example 12-13). When the wheel turns through an angle θ, a length of string $R\theta$ unwraps and the mass drops a distance $y = R\theta$.

Differentiating again gives

$$a = R\alpha \qquad \qquad \text{12-34}$$

Thus, Equation 12-30 can be written

$$TR = I\frac{a}{R} \qquad \text{or} \qquad Ia = TR^2 \qquad \qquad \text{12-35}$$

Solving Equations 12-31 and 12-35 for a and T, we obtain

$$a = \frac{m}{m + I/R^2}\, g \qquad T = \frac{I/R^2}{m + I/R^2}\, mg \qquad \qquad \text{12-36}$$

Since the acceleration is constant, the speed after m has moved down a distance h from rest can be computed from the constant-acceleration relationship,

$$v^2 - v_0^2 = 2as$$

or

$$v^2 - 0 = 2\,\frac{m}{m + I/R^2}\, gh$$

$$v^2 = \frac{2m}{m + I/R^2}\, gh \qquad \qquad \text{12-37}$$

Energy is conserved for this system, since there is no friction. We can therefore obtain the same result using the conservation-of-energy principle. As m moves down the distance h, the potential energy of the system decreases by amount mgh. This must be balanced by the simultaneous increase in kinetic energy of the system. Since the system starts at rest, the increase in kinetic energy is the final kinetic energy:

$$E_k = \tfrac{1}{2}mv^2 + \tfrac{1}{2}I\omega^2 = \tfrac{1}{2}mv^2 + \tfrac{1}{2}I\frac{v^2}{R^2} = \tfrac{1}{2}\left(m + \frac{I}{R^2}\right)v^2$$

Equating this to mgh gives

$$\tfrac{1}{2}\left(m + \frac{I}{R^2}\right)v^2 = mgh$$

or

$$v^2 = \frac{2m}{m + I/R^2}\, gh$$

Questions

10. If force **F** produces no torque, does it have any effect on the motion of a body? Could it be removed without making any change in the motion?

11. What are two ways **F** can be applied to a body so that it produces no torque about the axis of rotation?

12. If the torque of **F** is zero about one point, will it necessarily be zero about another point? *Can* it be zero about any other point?

13. How can a small force produce a greater angular acceleration of a wheel than a large force?

14. If a body has no angular velocity at a given instant, can it have a torque acting on it? If a body has no angular acceleration at a given instant, can it have a torque acting on it?

12-6 Static Equilibrium of a Rigid Body

If an object remains stationary, it is said to be in *static equilibrium.* An important problem is to determine the forces acting on a body when it is in static equilibrium. In Chapter 5 we found that a necessary condition for a particle to be stationary is that the resultant force be zero. Then the particle does not accelerate, and if its velocity is initially zero, it remains zero. Since the acceleration of the center of mass of a body equals the resultant force divided by the total mass, this condition is also necessary for a rigid body to be in equilibrium. However, even if the center of mass of a body is at rest, the body may rotate. Thus it is also necessary that the resultant torque about the center of mass be zero. If the center of mass of a body is at rest and there is no rotation about it, there is no rotation about any point. The necessary conditions for static equilibrium of a rigid body are therefore:

Figure 12-21
The two parallel forces F_1 and F_2 can be replaced by a single resultant force ΣF which has the same effect. The point of application of ΣF is x_r, given by $|\Sigma F| x_r = F_1 x_1 + F_2 x_2$.

1. The resultant external force must be zero: $\Sigma F = 0$ 12-38*a*

2. The resultant external torque about any point must be zero: $\Sigma \tau = 0$ 12-38*b*

Conditions for static equilibrium

In giving examples of the application of these conditions we shall often wish to replace two or more forces acting on a body by a single equivalent force. When two parallel forces F_1 and F_2 act on a rod as in Figure 12-21, the single force having the same effect on the translation of the center of mass of the body is the sum $\Sigma F = F_1 + F_2$. If this single force is to have the same effect on rotation, we must choose the point of application so that the torque it exerts about any point equals the sum of the torques exerted by the original forces. Let x_1 and x_2 be the lever arms for the two original forces about the point O. The resultant force ΣF will produce the same torque about O if it is applied at distance x_r given by

$$x_r \Sigma F = F_1 x_1 + F_2 x_2 \qquad \text{12-39}$$

Figure 12-22
The weights of all the particles of a body can be replaced by the total weight acting at the center of gravity (which coincides with the center of mass if *g* does not vary over the body).

We can use this result to show that the force of gravity exerted on the various parts of a body can be replaced by a single force, the total weight, acting at the center of mass. Figure 12-22 shows an object made of several small particles, each of weight w_i. The total weight is $W = \Sigma w_i$. Generalizing Equation 12-39 to the case of several parallel forces and using $\Sigma F = W$, we have for the point of application of the resultant force x_g,

$$x_g W = \Sigma w_i x_i \qquad \text{12-40}$$

Equation 12-40 defines the coordinate of the *center of gravity.* If the acceleration of gravity does not vary over the body (nearly always the case), we write $w_i = m_i g$ and $W = Mg$ and cancel the common factor g. Then

$$x_g Mg = \Sigma m_i g x_i$$

or

$$M x_g = \Sigma m_i x_i$$

Usually the center of gravity is the same as the center of mass.

Figure 12-23
Ladder on rough floor leaning against a smooth wall (Example 12-14).

Example 12-14 A uniform 15-ft ladder weighs 48 lb and leans against a smooth vertical wall (Figure 12-23). The foot of the ladder is 9 ft from the wall. What is the minimum coefficient of friction necessary between the ladder and the floor if the ladder is not to slip?

The three forces acting on the ladder are (1) the weight **w** at the center of mass acting down, (2) the force F_1 exerted horizontally by the wall (since the wall is smooth it exerts only a normal force), and (3) the force exerted by the floor, which is the vector sum of the normal force **N** and the frictional force **f**. From our first condition we have

$$N = w = 48 \text{ lb} \qquad \text{and} \qquad F_1 = f$$

Since we know neither f nor F_1, we must use the second condition of equilibrium: the resultant torque about any point is zero. The most convenient point to choose for considering rotation is the point of contact between the ladder and the floor. Then since neither **N** nor **f** exerts any torque about this point, they will not appear in the equation. The torque exerted by the weight about this point is 48 lb times the lever arm, 4.5 ft. This torque tends to rotate the ladder clockwise and is thus directed inward. The torque exerted by F_1 is in the opposite direction and has the magnitude F_1 times its lever arm, 12 ft. Thus the second condition gives

$$w(4.5) - F_1(12) = 0$$

$$F_1 = \frac{4.5w}{12} = \frac{4.5(48)}{12} = 18.0 \text{ lb}$$

This equals the magnitude of the frictional force, but since f is related to the normal force by

$$f \leq \mu_s N$$

we have

$$\mu_s \geq \frac{f}{N} = \frac{18.0}{48} = 0.375$$

where μ_s is the coefficient of static friction.

Another way of solving this problem is perhaps easier. Let $F_2 = f + N$ be the force exerted by the floor. The ratio f/N is just the cotangent of the angle between the force F_2 and the horizontal. We can find this angle as follows. If we extend the lines of action of the forces **w** and F_1, we note that they meet at point P_1 in Figure 12-24. The torques exerted by these two forces about this point are zero. Since F_2 is the only other force acting, it must also exert zero torque about point P_1. Thus its line of action must also pass through this point. From the figure one sees that if this is so, the cotangent of the angle made by F_2 with the horizontal is $(4.5 \text{ ft})/(12 \text{ ft}) = 0.375 = f/N \leq \mu_s$. We note that if a body is in static equilibrium under the influence of three nonparallel coplanar forces, the lines of action of these forces must intersect at one point.

Figure 12-24
Forces acting on the ladder in Example 12-14. Point P_1 is the intersection of the lines of action of F_1 and **w**. The line of action of the force exerted by the floor $F_2 = N + f$ must also pass through P_1 so that there is no resultant torque about that point.

If two forces are antiparallel, we cannot replace them with a single force which has the same effect. Two equal but opposite forces acting as shown in Figure 12-25 are called a *couple*. The torque produced by these forces about point O is

$$\tau = Fx_2 - Fx_1 = F(x_2 - x_1) = FD$$

where F is the magnitude of either force and $D = x_2 - x_1$ is the distance between them. This result does not depend on the choice of the point O, and the torque produced by a couple is the same about all points in space.

$$F_1 = F_2 = F$$

Figure 12-25
Two forces equal in magnitude but opposite in direction constitute a couple. The couple exerts the same torque FD about any point in space. Since the resultant force of a couple is zero, it cannot be replaced by a single force.

Figure 12-26
Two antiparallel forces of
unequal magnitude can be replaced by force $\Sigma F = F_1 + F_2$
acting through the center of
mass plus a couple whose
torque equals that of the original forces about the center of
mass.

The two unequal antiparallel forces in Figure 12-26 can be replaced
by a single force equal to the resultant force plus a couple, as shown in
the figure. In general, any number of parallel and antiparallel forces
can be replaced by a single resultant force plus a couple. Since the
resultant force exerted by a couple is zero, the only way it can be balanced is by a second couple which exerts equal but opposite torque.
For example, the forces **N** and **w** in Figure 12-24 form a couple of
moment (48 lb) (4.5 ft) = 216 lb-ft. It is balanced by the forces **f** and $\mathbf{F}_1$,
which also form a couple. Since the separation of these forces is $D = 12$
ft, their magnitude must be (216 lb-ft)/(12 ft) = 18 lb as found in Example 12-14.

Review

A. Define, explain, or otherwise identify:

Rigid body, 304   Radius of gyration, 316
Angular velocity, 305   Torque, 318
Angular acceleration, 306   Center of gravity, 321
Moment of inertia, 310   Couple, 322
Parallel-axis theorem, 311

B. True or false:

1. Angular velocity and linear velocity have the same dimensions.

2. All parts of a rotating wheel have the same angular velocity.

3. All parts of a rotating wheel have the same angular acceleration.

4. Any quantity that has magnitude and direction is a vector.

5. The moment of inertia of a body depends on the location of the axis of rotation.

6. The moment of inertia of a body depends on the angular velocity of the
body.

7. Two forces can be equal in magnitude and direction but produce different
torques about some point.

8. Whenever the resultant force acting on a body is zero, the body is in static
equilibrium.

9. If a body is in static equilibrium, the resultant torque must be zero about
any point.

10. A couple can be replaced by a single force which has the same effect.

Exercises

Section 12-1, Angular Velocity and Angular Acceleration

1. Find a formula to convert radians per second to revolutions per minute.

2. A 12-in-diameter record rotates at $33\frac{1}{3}$ rev/min. (a) What is its angular velocity in radians per second? (b) Find the speed and (linear) acceleration of a point on the rim of the record.

3. A particle moves in a circle of radius 100 m with constant speed of 20 m/sec. (a) What is its angular velocity in radians per second about the center of the circle? (b) How many revolutions does it make in 30 sec?

4. A wheel starts from rest and has a constant angular acceleration of 2 rad/sec². (a) What is its angular velocity after 5 sec? (b) Through what angle has the wheel turned after 5 sec? (c) How many revolutions has it made in 5 sec? (d) After 5 sec, what is the speed and acceleration of a point 1.5 ft from the axis of rotation?

5. A turntable rotating at $33\frac{1}{3}$ rev/min is shut off. It brakes with constant angular acceleration and comes to rest in 2 min. (a) Find the angular acceleration. (b) What is the average angular velocity of the turntable? (c) How many revolutions does it make before stopping?

6. A disk of radius 10 cm rotates about its axis from rest with constant angular acceleration of 10 rad/sec². At $t = 5$ sec what is (a) the angular velocity of the disk and (b) the tangential and radial acceleration a_t and a_r of a point on the edge of the disk?

7. A spot on a record rests on the radial line $\theta = 0°$ (fixed in space). At $t = \frac{1}{4}$ sec after the turntable is turned on, the spot has advanced to $\theta = 10°$. Assuming constant angular acceleration, how long will it be before the record is rotating at 33.3 rev/min?

Section 12-2, The Vector Nature of Rotation, and Section 12-3, Rotational Kinetic Energy and Moment of Inertia

8. A coordinate system is fixed to a car. The rear axle coincides with the z axis, which is positive to the right when viewed from behind the car; the x axis is parallel to the ground pointing toward the front of the car; the y axis is vertically upward. (a) The car starts from rest and accelerates uniformly. What are the directions of $\boldsymbol{\omega}$ and $\boldsymbol{\alpha}$? (b) What are the directions of $\boldsymbol{\omega}$ and $\boldsymbol{\alpha}$ while the car slows down?

Figure 12-27
Exercise 9.

9. The masses in Figure 12-27 are connected by a very light rod whose moment of inertia may be neglected. They rotate about the y axis with angular velocity of 2 rad/sec. (a) Find the speed of each mass and use it to calculate the kinetic energy of this system directly from $\Sigma \frac{1}{2}m_i v_i^2$. (b) Find the moment of inertia about the y axis and calculate the kinetic energy from $E_k = \frac{1}{2}I\omega^2$.

10. Four point masses are at the corners of a square connected by massless rods, $m_1 = m_3 = 3$ kg and $m_2 = m_4 = 4$ kg. The length of the side of the square is $L = 2$ m (Figure 12-28). (*a*) Find the moment of inertia about an axis perpendicular to the plane of the masses and passing through m_4. (*b*) How much work is required to produce a rotation of 2 rad/sec about this axis?

11. Four 2-kg point masses are located at the corners of a rectangle of sides 3 and 2 m (Figure 12-29). (*a*) Find the moment of inertia of this system about an axis perpendicular to the plane of the masses and through one of the masses. (*b*) The system is set rotating about this axis with kinetic energy of 184 J. Find the number of revolutions the system makes per minute.

12. An irregularly shaped object rotates about an axis at 50 rev/min. The object does 300 J of work as it stops. What is the moment of inertia of the object?

Section 12-4, Calculating the Moment of Inertia

13. Use the parallel-axis theorem to find the moment of inertia of the four-mass system in Figure 12-28 about an axis perpendicular to the plane of the masses and through the center of mass. Check your result by direct computation.

14. (*a*) Find the moment of inertia I_x for the four-mass system of Figure 12-28 about the *x* axis which passes through m_3 and m_4. (*b*) Find I_y for that system about the *y* axis which passes through m_1 and m_4. (*c*) Use Equation 12-16 to calculate the moment of inertia I_z about the *z* axis through m_4 and perpendicular to the plane of the figure.

15. (*a*) Use the parallel-axis theorem to find the moment of inertia about an axis parallel to the *z* axis and through the center of mass of the system in Figure 12-29. (*b*) Let x' and y' be axes in the plane of the figure through the center of mass and parallel to the sides of the rectangle. Compute $I_{x'}$ and $I_{y'}$ and use your results and Equation 12-16 to check your result for part (*a*).

16. Find the moment of inertia of a disk of mass M and radius R about an axis through the edge of the disk parallel to the axis of the disk (see Figure 12-30).

17. Use Equation 12-16 to find the moment of inertia of a disk of radius R and mass M about an axis in the plane of the disk through its center (Figure 12-31).

18. Use the parallel-axis theorem and Equation 12-21 to find the moment of inertia of a solid sphere about an axis tangent to the sphere (Figure 12-32).

19. Find the moment of inertia about an axis tangent to a hoop of mass M and radius R.

20. Find the moment of inertia about an axis intersecting a hoop and parallel to the axis of the hoop.

Figure 12-28
Exercises 10, 13, and 14.

Figure 12-29
Exercises 11 and 15.

Figure 12-30
Exercise 16.

Figure 12-31
Exercise 17.

Figure 12-32
Exercise 18.

Section 12-5, Torque

21. A uniform disk of radius 0.12 m and mass 5 kg is pivoted so that it rotates freely about its axis. A string wrapped around the disk is pulled with a force of 20 N (Figure 12-33). (a) What is the torque exerted on the disk? (b) What is the angular acceleration of the disk? (c) If the disk starts from rest, what is its angular velocity after 3 sec? (d) What is its kinetic energy after 3 sec? (e) Find the total angle θ the disk turns through in 3 sec and (f) show that the work done by the torque $\tau\theta$ equals the kinetic energy.

22. A disk-shaped grindstone of mass 2 kg and radius 7 cm is spinning at 700 rev/min. When the power is shut off, a man continues to sharpen his ax by holding it against the grindstone for 10 sec until the grindstone stops rotating. (a) Find the angular acceleration of the grindstone assuming it to be constant. (b) What is the torque exerted by the ax on the grindstone? (Assume no other frictional torques.)

23. In order to start a playground merry-go-round rotating, a rope is wrapped around it and pulled. A force of 200 N is exerted on the rope for 10 sec. During this time the merry-go-round, which has a radius of 2 m, makes one complete rotation. (a) Find the angular acceleration of the merry-go-round assuming it to be constant. (b) What torque is exerted by the rope on the merry-go-round? (c) What is the moment of inertia of the merry-go-round?

24. A force F is exerted tangential to a wheel of radius R. When the wheel turns through an angle $d\theta$, the force acts through a distance $ds = R\,d\theta$. Show that the power input of the force is $\tau\omega$, where τ is the torque exerted by the force and ω is the angular velocity.

25. A rope is wrapped around a 3-kg cylinder of radius 10 cm which is free to turn about its axis. The rope is pulled with a force of 15 N. The cylinder is initially at rest at $t = 0$. (a) Find the torque exerted by the rope, the moment of inertia of the cylinder, and the angular acceleration of the cylinder. (b) Find the angular velocity of the cylinder at time $t = 4$ sec. What is the power input of the force at this time (see Exercise 24)?

26. A 1000-lb block is lifted by a steel cable which passes over a pulley to a motor-driven winch (see Figure 12-34). The diameter of the winch drum is 1 ft, and the moment of inertia of the pulley is negligible. (a) What force must be exerted by the cable to lift the block at a constant velocity of 3 in/sec? (b) What torque does the cable exert on the winch drum? (c) What is the angular velocity of the winch drum? (d) What power must be developed by the motor to drive the winch drum?

27. An engine develops 400 lb-ft of torque at 3500 rev/min. Find the horsepower developed by the engine.

28. Figure 12-35 shows a number of forces applied to an object pivoted on an axis through point O and perpendicular to the figure. Compute the torque of each force and the resultant torque. If the object is released from rest in the position shown, which way will it turn?

Figure 12-33
Exercise 21.

20 N

Figure 12-34
Exercise 26.

$r = 6$ in

T

T

Winch

1000 lb

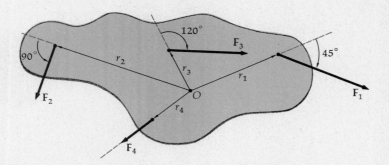

Figure 12-35
Exercise 28. The magnitudes of the vectors shown are

$F_1 = 10$ lb	$r_1 = 1.0$ ft
$F_2 = 6$ lb	$r_2 = 1.5$ ft
$F_3 = 8$ lb	$r_3 = 0.5$ ft
$F_4 = 4$ lb	$r_4 = 0.5$ ft

29. The system in Figure 12-36 is released from rest. The 30-kg mass is 1 m above the floor. The pulley is a uniform disk with a radius of 10 cm and mass 5 kg. Find the velocity of the 30-kg mass just before it hits the floor. *Hint:* Use conservation of energy; be sure to include the energy of rotation of the pulley.

Figure 12-36
Exercise 29.

$m = 5\,\text{kg}$
$r = 10\,\text{cm}$

30 kg

1 m

20 kg

Section 12-6, Static Equilibrium of a Rigid Body

30. An 80-lb child and a 60-lb child sit balanced on a seesaw. The total length of the board is 10 ft. Use the fact that the resultant torque about the fulcrum must be zero to find the position of the fulcrum.

31. A 20-lb board that is 12 ft long rests on two supports each 1 ft from the end of the board. An 80-lb block is placed on the board 3 ft from one end (and thus 2 ft from one support) (Figure 12-37). Find the force exerted by each support on the board.

Figure 12-37
Exercise 31.

1 ft — | — 10 ft — | — 1 ft
3 ft
20 lb
$w = 80$ lb

32. A 500-lb weight is supported by a cable attached to a strut hinged at point A (Figure 12-38). The strut is supported by a second cable under tension T_2, as shown. The mass of the strut is negligible. (*a*) What are the three forces acting on the strut? (*b*) Show that the vertical component of the tension T_2 must equal 500 lb. (*c*) Find the force exerted on the strut by the hinge.

33. Find the force exerted by the hinge A on the strut for the arrangement in Figure 12-39. (Neglect the mass of the strut.)

Figure 12-38
Exercise 32.

T_2
$90°$
$30°$
A
T_1
500 lb

Problems

1. A wheel mounted on a horizontal axle has a radial line painted on it which is used to determine its angular position relative to the vertical. The wheel has a constant angular acceleration. At time $t = 0$ the line points straight up. At $t = 1$ sec, the line is again vertical, having turned through one full revolution. At $t = 2$ sec, the line points straight down, the wheel having turned through $1\frac{1}{2}$ rev more since $t = 1$ sec. (*a*) What is the angular acceleration of the wheel? (*b*) What was its angular velocity at $t = 0$?

2. Calculate the kinetic energy of rotation of the earth and compare it with the kinetic energy of the earth's center-of-mass motion. Assume the earth to be a homogeneous sphere of mass 6.0×10^{24} kg and radius 6.4×10^6 m. The radius of the earth's orbit is 1.5×10^{11} m.

3. A flywheel has a mass of 100 kg and a radius of gyration of 0.5 m and rotates with angular velocity of 1200 rev/min. (*a*) A constant tangential force is applied at a radial distance of 0.5 m. What work must this force do to stop the wheel? (*b*) If the wheel is brought to rest in 2 min, what torque does the force produce? What is the magnitude of the force? (*c*) How many revolutions does the wheel make in these 2 min?

4. A wheel is mounted on an axis that is not frictionless. It is at rest initially. A constant external torque of 50 N-m is applied to the wheel for 20 sec. At the end of the 20 sec the wheel has an angular velocity of 600 rev/min. The external torque is then removed and the wheel comes to rest after 120 sec more. (*a*) What is the moment of inertia of the wheel? (*b*) What is the frictional torque (assumed to be constant)?

Figure 12-39
Exercise 33.

$45°$
$45°$
A
500 lb

5. A uniform cylinder of mass m_1 and radius R is pivoted on frictionless bearings. A string wrapped around the cylinder connects to a mass m_2, which is on a frictionless incline of angle θ, as shown in Figure 12-40. This system is released from rest with m_2 a height h above the bottom of the incline. (a) What is the acceleration of m_2? (b) What is the tension in the string? (c) What is the total energy of the system when m_2 is at height h? (d) What is the total energy when m_2 is at the bottom of the incline and has speed v? (e) What is the speed v? (f) Evaluate your answers for the extreme cases of $\theta = 0$, $\theta = 90°$, and $m_1 = 0$.

Figure 12-40
Problem 5.

6. An Atwood's machine has two masses, $m_1 = 500$ gm and $m_2 = 510$ gm, connected by a string of negligible mass which passes over a frictionless pulley (Figure 12-41). The pulley has mass 50 gm and radius of gyration $k = 3$ cm. The radius at which the string passes over the pulley is 4 cm. The string does not slip on the pulley. (a) Find the acceleration of the masses. (b) What is the tension in the string supporting m_1? In the string supporting m_2? By how much do they differ? (c) What would your answers have been if you had neglected the motion of the pulley?

7. A body of mass m is pivoted on a horizontal frictionless axle with its center of mass a distance h from the pivot, as shown in Figure 12-42. Its moment of inertia is $I = mk^2$ about this axis, where k is the radius of gyration. The line from the center of mass to the pivot makes an angle θ_0 with the vertical ($\theta_0 < 90°$). The body is released from rest. At some later time the angle is θ. (a) Show that the magnitude of the angular acceleration is

$$\alpha = \frac{gh \sin \theta}{k^2}$$

and that the tangential component of the acceleration of the center of mass is

$$a_t = \frac{gh^2 \sin \theta}{k^2}$$

Figure 12-41
Problem 6.

(b) Use conservation of energy to find the angular velocity and show that the magnitude of the radial acceleration of the center of mass is

$$a_r = 2\,\frac{gh^2}{k^2}\,(\cos \theta - \cos \theta_0)$$

(c) Show that the force exerted by the pivot has radial and tangential components given by

$$F_r = mg \cos \theta + 2\,\frac{mgh^2}{k^2}\,(\cos \theta - \cos \theta_0)$$

and

$$F_t = mg\,\frac{h^2}{k^2} \sin \theta - mg \sin \theta$$

(d) For the case of a simple pendulum show that part (c) gives the expected results for F_t at any θ and for F_r at $\theta = 0$. (e) Find F_r and F_t for a uniform stick pivoted at one end.

Figure 12-42
Problem 7.

8. A uniform rectangular plate has mass m and sides a and b. (a) Show by integration that its moment of inertia about an axis perpendicular to the plate and through one corner is $\frac{1}{3}m(a^2 + b^2)$. (b) What is the moment of inertia about an axis at the center of mass and perpendicular to the plate?

9. A cube of uniform material has mass m and side L. By integration, find its moment of inertia about an axis parallel to an edge and through the center of mass.

10. Find by integration the moment of inertia of a spherical shell of radius R and mass m about an axis through the center of the shell.

11. A hollow cylinder has mass m, outside radius R_2, and inside radius R_1.

Show that its moment of inertia about its symmetry axis is given by $I = \frac{1}{2}m(R_2^2 + R_1^2)$.

12. Figure 12-43 shows a pair of uniform spheres each of mass 500 gm and radius 5 cm. They are mounted on a uniform rod which has length $L = 30$ cm and mass 60 gm. (a) Calculate the moment of inertia of this system about an axis perpendicular to the rod through the center of the rod using the approximation that the two spheres can be treated as point masses a distance 20 cm from the axis of rotation and the mass of the rod is negligible. (b) Calculate the moment of inertia exactly and compare your result with your approximate value.

Figure 12-43
Problem 12.

13. A 6 by 3 by 3 ft box of uniform mass is placed on end on a rough, hinged plank, as shown in Figure 12-44. The plank is inclined at an angle θ, which is slowly increased. The coefficient of friction is great enough to prevent the box from sliding. Find the greatest angle that can be applied without tipping the box over. *Hint:* First show that if the center of gravity of the box does not lie above any portion of the base, the conditions for static equilibrium cannot be satisfied.

Figure 12-44
Problem 13.

14. A 200-lb boy sits on top of a ladder of negligible weight which rests on a frictionless floor. There is a cross brace halfway up the ladder (Figure 12-45). The angle at the apex is $\theta = 30°$. (a) What is the force exerted by the floor on each leg of the ladder? (b) Find the tension in the cross brace. (c) If the cross brace is moved down toward the bottom of the ladder (with the same angle θ), will its tension be greater or less?

Figure 12-45
Problem 14.

15. A wheel of mass M and radius R rests on a horizontal surface against a step of height h ($h < R$). The wheel is to be raised over the step by a horizontal force F applied to the axle of the wheel. Find the force F necessary to raise the wheel over the step.

CHAPTER 13   Rotation in Space and Angular Momentum

In a general motion, the axis of rotation of a body is not fixed in space. The motion is complex because the directions as well as the magnitudes of the angular velocity and acceleration change. Another complication arises for systems which are not rigid. The moment of inertia may change in time. In describing these complex motions of a system of particles we shall find it useful to introduce the concept of angular momentum. As you might expect, angular momentum plays a role in rotational motion analogous to that of (linear) momentum in linear motion. In particular, we shall see that the time rate of change of the angular momentum of a system equals the resultant torque acting on the system.

13-1   Torque as a Vector Product

We begin by considering a single particle of mass m moving with velocity $\mathbf{v} = d\mathbf{r}/dt$ and momentum $\mathbf{p} = m\mathbf{v}$, where $\mathbf{r}$ is the radius vector of the particle from the origin O. We assume that the point O is in an inertial reference frame so that Newton's law $\Sigma\mathbf{F} = d\mathbf{p}/dt$ holds, where $\Sigma\mathbf{F}$ is the resultant force. For the moment let us consider a single force $\mathbf{F}$ acting on the particle (Figure 13-1). The torque exerted by $\mathbf{F}$ relative to the point O is defined to be a vector of magnitude $Fr \sin \phi$, where ϕ is the angle between $\mathbf{F}$ and $\mathbf{r}$, and direction perpendicular to the plane formed by $\mathbf{F}$ and $\mathbf{r}$ shown in Figure 13-1. This is the same definition we gave in the last chapter for torque. Here we want to emphasize that torque is defined *relative to a point in space* (and not relative to an axis, like the moment of inertia of a body). The torque is conveniently written as the *vector product*, or *cross product*, of $\mathbf{r}$ and $\mathbf{F}$:

$$\tau = \mathbf{r} \times \mathbf{F} \qquad\qquad 13\text{-}1$$

In general, the cross product of two vectors $\mathbf{A}$ and $\mathbf{B}$ is defined to be:

Figure 13-1
Force $\mathbf{F}$ acting on a particle at position $\mathbf{r}$. The torque τ is perpendicular to both $\mathbf{F}$ and $\mathbf{r}$ and has the magnitude $Fr \sin \phi$.

a vector whose magnitude equals the area of the parallelogram formed by the two vectors (Figure 13-2a) and whose direction is perpendicular to the plane containing **A** *and* **B** *and in the sense given by the right-hand rule as* **A** *is rotated into* **B** *through the smallest angle between the vectors.*

If ϕ is the angle between the two vectors and $\hat{n}$ is a unit vector perpendicular to each and in the sense described, the cross product of **A** and **B** is

$$\mathbf{A} \times \mathbf{B} = AB \sin \phi \, \hat{n} \qquad \text{13-2}$$

The relation between the vectors **A**, **B**, and **A** × **B** is shown in Figure 13-2b.

If **A** and **B** are parallel, **A** × **B** is zero. From the definition, Equation 13-2, it follows that

$$\mathbf{A} \times \mathbf{A} = 0 \qquad \text{13-3}$$

and

$$\mathbf{A} \times \mathbf{B} = -\mathbf{B} \times \mathbf{A} \qquad \text{13-4}$$

It should be especially noted that the order in which the two vectors are multiplied is significant. Unlike the multiplication of ordinary numbers, changing the order of two vectors in a cross product changes the result. In fact, as indicated in Equation 13-3, changing the order of the factors in a cross product changes the sign of the result. The cross products of rectangular unit vectors are easily found. For example, $\mathbf{i} \times \mathbf{j} = |\mathbf{i}||\mathbf{j}| \sin 90° \, \mathbf{k} = \mathbf{k}$; $\mathbf{k} \times \mathbf{k} = 0$. Similarly,

$$\mathbf{i} \times \mathbf{i} = 0 \qquad \mathbf{i} \times \mathbf{j} = \mathbf{k} \qquad \mathbf{i} \times \mathbf{k} = -\mathbf{j}$$

$$\mathbf{j} \times \mathbf{i} = -\mathbf{k} \qquad \mathbf{j} \times \mathbf{j} = 0 \qquad \mathbf{j} \times \mathbf{k} = \mathbf{i}$$

$$\mathbf{k} \times \mathbf{i} = \mathbf{j} \qquad \mathbf{k} \times \mathbf{j} = -\mathbf{i} \qquad \mathbf{k} \times \mathbf{k} = 0$$

Some properties of the cross product of two vectors follow:

1. Associative law

$$\mathbf{A} \times (\mathbf{B} + \mathbf{C}) = \mathbf{A} \times \mathbf{B} + \mathbf{A} \times \mathbf{C} \qquad \text{13-5}$$

2. Derivative: if **A** and **B** are functions of some variable such as t, the derivative of **A** × **B** follows the usual product rule for derivatives:

$$\frac{d}{dt}(\mathbf{A} \times \mathbf{B}) = \mathbf{A} \times \frac{d\mathbf{B}}{dt} + \frac{d\mathbf{A}}{dt} \times \mathbf{B} \qquad \text{13-6}$$

We must keep the order straight here since, for example, $\mathbf{B} \times d\mathbf{A}/dt = -(d\mathbf{A}/dt) \times \mathbf{B}$.

From Equation 13-1 we see that the magnitude of the torque $Fr \sin \phi$ can be thought of as the product of F with the distance $r \sin \phi$, which is the perpendicular distance from the line of the force to the origin, called the lever arm. Alternatively, we can think of it as the product of r and $F \sin \phi$, which is the component of the force perpendicular to **r**.

Figure 13-2
(a) The vector product **A** × **B** is a vector **C** perpendicular to both **A** and **B** and of magnitude $AB \sin \phi$, which is the area of the parallelogram shown. (b) The direction of **A** × **B** is the direction of rotation when **A** is rotated into **B** through the angle ϕ.

(a)

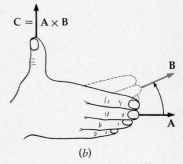

(b)

Questions

1. Will a force acting on a body produce a torque if the body is not mounted on an axle?

2. A body is mounted on pivots so that it is free to turn about the z axis. A force $\mathbf{F}$ is applied at point (x,y,z). Does the z component of the torque depend on what value z has? On what value F_z has?

13-2 Angular Momentum of a Particle

We define the angular momentum $\mathbf{L}$ of a particle relative to the origin O to be the cross product of the position vector $\mathbf{r}$ and the linear momentum $\mathbf{p}$ (see Figure 13-3):

$$\mathbf{L} = \mathbf{r} \times \mathbf{p} \qquad \text{13-7}$$

Angular momentum defined

Like torque, angular momentum is defined relative to a point in space. The magnitude is the magnitude of the momentum p times $r \sin \phi$, which is the perpendicular distance from the line of motion to the origin. Alternatively, L is the distance r times $p \sin \phi$, which is the component of the momentum perpendicular to $\mathbf{r}$. We shall now show that Newton's second law implies that the rate of change of angular momentum equals the resultant torque acting on the particle. If we have a number of forces acting on a particle, the resultant torque relative to the point O is the sum of the torques due to each force:

$$\Sigma\boldsymbol{\tau} = \mathbf{r} \times \mathbf{F}_1 + \mathbf{r} \times \mathbf{F}_2 + \cdots = \mathbf{r} \times \Sigma\mathbf{F}$$

According to Newton's law, the resultant force equals the rate of change of linear momentum $d\mathbf{p}/dt$. Thus

$$\Sigma\boldsymbol{\tau} = \mathbf{r} \times \Sigma\mathbf{F} = \mathbf{r} \times \frac{d\mathbf{p}}{dt} \qquad \text{13-8}$$

Figure 13-3
A particle with momentum $\mathbf{p}$ at position $\mathbf{r}$ has angular momentum relative to the origin $\mathbf{L} = \mathbf{r} \times \mathbf{p}$, which is perpendicular to both $\mathbf{r}$ and $\mathbf{p}$.

We can compute the rate of change of the angular momentum using the product rule for derivatives:

$$\frac{d\mathbf{L}}{dt} = \frac{d}{dt}(\mathbf{r} \times \mathbf{p}) = \frac{d\mathbf{r}}{dt} \times \mathbf{p} + \mathbf{r} \times \frac{d\mathbf{p}}{dt}$$

The first term on the right of this equation is zero because

$$\frac{d\mathbf{r}}{dt} \times \mathbf{p} = \mathbf{v} \times m\mathbf{v} = 0$$

Thus

$$\frac{d\mathbf{L}}{dt} = \mathbf{r} \times \frac{d\mathbf{p}}{dt} \qquad \text{13-9}$$

Comparing Equations 13-8 and 13-9, we have

$$\Sigma\boldsymbol{\tau} = \frac{d\mathbf{L}}{dt} \qquad \text{13-10}$$

Resultant torque on a particle

Equation 13-10 is the rotational analog of Newton's second law $\Sigma\mathbf{F} = d\mathbf{p}/dt$. It follows directly from that law and from the definitions of torque and angular momentum. We shall give two examples of the calculation of the angular momentum for a single particle.

Example 13-1 Find the angular momentum for a point mass moving in a circle of radius r. The speed of the particle v and the magnitude of its angular velocity are related by $v = r\omega$ (see Equation 12-4). Choosing the xy plane to be the plane of the circle (Figure 13-4), we have for the

Figure 13-4
Particle moving in a circle
(Example 13-1). The angular
momentum is along the z axis
parallel to the angular velocity
ω and has magnitude $mvr = mr^2(v/r) = I\omega$.

angular momentum relative to the center of the circle,

$$\mathbf{L} = \mathbf{r} \times \mathbf{p} = \mathbf{r} \times m\mathbf{v} = rmv \sin 90° \, \mathbf{k} = rmv\mathbf{k} = mr^2\omega\mathbf{k}$$

Note that in this case the angular momentum is in the same direction
as the angular velocity. Since the quantity mr^2 is the moment of inertia
I for a single particle about the z axis, we have

$$\mathbf{L} = mr^2\boldsymbol{\omega} = I\boldsymbol{\omega}$$

If the only force acting on the particle is the centripetal force directed
toward the origin, there will be no torque about the origin. Then, according to Equation 13-10, the angular momentum will be constant.
This implies that ω and hence the speed will be constant.

Example 13-2 Find the angular momentum relative to the origin of a particle moving in a straight line a perpendicular distance b from the origin with constant speed.

This situation is shown in Figure 13-5. The angular momentum is

$$\mathbf{L} = \mathbf{r} \times \mathbf{p} = -rmv \sin \phi \, \mathbf{k}$$

The distance $r \sin \phi$ is just the perpendicular distance b from the line
of motion to the origin, as can be seen from the figure. Thus

$$\mathbf{L} = -mvb\mathbf{k} \qquad\qquad 13\text{-}11$$

Figure 13-5
Particle moving in a straight
line parallel to the x axis and
a distance b from it with constant speed v. The angular
momentum relative to the ori-
gin is $\mathbf{L} = \mathbf{r} \times m\mathbf{v} = -rmv \sin \phi \, \mathbf{k} = -mvb\mathbf{k}$.

Although we usually associate angular momentum with rotational
motion, Example 13-2 illustrates that even a particle moving in a
straight line has angular momentum about a point not on the line. We
shall use this result in Examples 13-6 and 13-8.

Questions

3. What is the angle between a particle's linear momentum $\mathbf{p}$ and its
angular momentum $\mathbf{L}$?

4. Two particles have the same momentum $\mathbf{p}$. Are their angular momenta also equal? Is it possible for two particles with the same momentum $\mathbf{p}$ also to have the same angular momentum if they are not at
the same place?

5. A particle moves along a straight line at constant speed. How does
its angular momentum about any point vary in time?

6. Two particles, A and B, move along parallel lines a distance D apart. They have the same speed v but travel in opposite directions. What is magnitude of A's angular momentum about a point on its own path? About a point on B's path? About particle B?

7. A particle moving at constant velocity has zero angular momentum about a particular point. Show that the particle either has passed through that point or will pass through it.

13-3 Torque and Angular Momentum for a System of Particles

The total angular momentum of a system of particles is the sum of the angular momenta of the individual particles.

$$L = \Sigma L_i$$

Let τ_i be the resultant torque acting on the ith particle. The resultant torque acting on the system is then

$$\Sigma \tau_i = \Sigma \frac{dL_i}{dt} = \frac{d}{dt}(\Sigma L_i) = \frac{dL}{dt} \qquad 13\text{-}12$$

In Equation 13-12 the sum of the torques may include internal torques as well as those due to forces external to the system. We shall now show that if the internal forces between any two particles act parallel to the line joining the particles, the sum of the internal torques is zero. Then

$$\Sigma \tau_{\text{ext}} = \frac{dL}{dt} \qquad 13\text{-}13$$

Consider two particles as shown in Figure 13-6. Although $F_1 = -F_2$ by Newton's third law, it is not immediately obvious that the internal torques cancel. The sum of the two torques in this figure is

$$\tau_1 + \tau_2 = r_1 \times F_1 + r_2 \times F_2 = r_1 \times F_1 + r_2 \times (-F_1)$$
$$= (r_1 - r_2) \times F_1$$

The vector $r_1 - r_2$ is along the line joining the two particles. Thus, if the force F_1 acts parallel to the line joining m_1 and m_2, F_1 and $r_1 - r_2$ are either parallel or antiparallel and

$$(r_1 - r_2) \times F_1 = 0$$

If this is true for all the internal forces, the internal torques cancel in pairs.

Equation 13-13 is the rotational analog of the result for linear motion (obtained in Chapter 10) that the resultant external force equals the rate of change of the total linear momentum of a system. Before we give examples of its use we discuss the problem of finding the total angular momentum for some typical systems. In many cases of a body rotating with angular velocity $\boldsymbol{\omega}$ the angular momentum is parallel to $\boldsymbol{\omega}$ and has the magnitude $I\omega$, where I is the moment of inertia about the axis of rotation. This is true whenever the body is rotating about a symmetry axis through the center of mass and the angular momentum is taken relative to the center of mass. Thus in these cases,

$$L = I\boldsymbol{\omega} \qquad 13\text{-}14$$

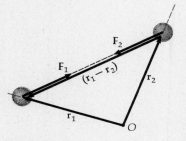

Figure 13-6
The internal forces F_1 and F_2 produce no net torque about O if they act along the line joining the particles.

Multiflash photograph of a diver. The center of mass moves in a parabolic path after the diver leaves the board. The angular momentum is provided by the initial torque due to the force of the board. This force does not pass through the center of mass if the diver leans forward as he jumps. If the diver wanted to undergo $1\frac{1}{2}$ rev in the air, he would draw in his arms and legs, decreasing his moment of inertia to increase his angular velocity. (*Courtesy of Harold E. Edgerton.*)

Equation 13-13 is then

$$\Sigma \tau_{\text{ext}} = \frac{d}{dt}(I\boldsymbol{\omega}) \qquad\qquad 13\text{-}15$$

In the case of a rigid body the moment of inertia is constant. Then Equation 13-15 reduces to Equation 12-29:

$$\Sigma \tau_{\text{ext}} = \frac{d}{dt}(I\boldsymbol{\omega}) = I\frac{d\boldsymbol{\omega}}{dt} = I\boldsymbol{\alpha} \qquad\qquad 13\text{-}16$$

Figure 13-7
Particles m_1 and m_2 rotating about their center of mass with angular velocity $\boldsymbol{\omega}$. Their total angular momentum about O is $\mathbf{L} = I\boldsymbol{\omega}$.

Example 13-3 Find the angular momentum of a dumbbell rotating about an axis through the center of mass and perpendicular to the line joining the masses.

Let the angular velocity be $\boldsymbol{\omega}$ along the axis of rotation, which we call the z axis, as shown in Figure 13-7. The total angular momentum about the center of mass at the origin O is

$$\mathbf{L} = \mathbf{L}_1 + \mathbf{L}_2 = \mathbf{r}_1 \times m_1\mathbf{v}_1 + \mathbf{r}_2 \times m_2\mathbf{v}_2 = (r_1 m_1 v_1 + r_2 m_2 v_2)\mathbf{k}$$

The speeds of the particles are related to the angular velocity by $v = r\omega$. Thus

$$\mathbf{L} = (m_1 r_1{}^2 \omega + m_2 r_2{}^2 \omega)\mathbf{k} = (m_1 r_1{}^2 + m_2 r_2{}^2)\omega\mathbf{k} = I\boldsymbol{\omega}$$

where $I = m_1 r_1{}^2 + m_2 r_2{}^2$ is the moment of inertia.

Example 13-4 Find the angular momentum of a disk rotating about an axis through the center of mass and perpendicular to the plane of the disk.

The calculation of the angular momentum of the disk about the center of mass is the same as that for the dumbbell in Example 13-3 except that there are more particles (Figure 13-8). The angular momentum of each particle is along the axis of rotation parallel to the angular velocity $\boldsymbol{\omega}$. Also, the speed of each particle is related to the angular velocity by $v_i = r_i\omega$. Thus we again obtain for the total angular momentum

Figure 13-8
Disk rotating about its axis (Example 13-4). The angular momentum is $\mathbf{L} = I\boldsymbol{\omega}$.

$$\mathbf{L} = \Sigma m_i r_i v_i \mathbf{k} = \Sigma m_i r_i (r_i \omega)\mathbf{k} = (\Sigma m_i r_i{}^2)\omega\mathbf{k} = I\boldsymbol{\omega}$$

(where $\mathbf{k}$ is the unit vector in the direction of $\boldsymbol{\omega}$).

Example 13-5 A disk rotates about an axis perpendicular to the plane of the disk but a distance h from the symmetry axis, as shown in Figure 13-9. Calculate the angular momentum about the origin O' on the disk at the axis of rotation.

Again the angular momentum of each particle is parallel to ω. The calculation is the same as in the previous example except that the momentum of inertia I' is now about the new axis of rotation.

$$\mathbf{L} = I'\boldsymbol{\omega}$$

We can use the parallel-axis theorem to relate the angular momentum relative to O' in Example 13-5 to that about the center of mass found in Example 13-4. According to this theorem, the moment of inertia I' about axis z' is related to that about the z axis through the center of mass a distance h away by

$$I' = I_{CM} + Mh^2$$

If we multiply each term by ω, we obtain

$$I'\omega = I_{CM}\omega + Mh^2\omega \qquad\qquad 13\text{-}17$$

Figure 13-9
Disk rotating about an axis perpendicular to the disk but at a distance h from the symmetry axis. Again, the angular momentum is $\mathbf{L} = I'\boldsymbol{\omega}$, where I' is the moment of inertia of the disk about the axis of rotation.

The quantity $I'\omega$ is the magnitude of the angular momentum about the point O'. The quantity $I_{CM}\omega$ is the magnitude of the angular momentum about the center of mass O. The speed of the center of mass relative to O' is $v_{CM} = h\omega$. Let $\mathbf{r}_{CM}$ be the vector from O' to the center of mass O. This vector is perpendicular to $\mathbf{v}_{CM}$ and has the magnitude h. Then the term $Mh^2\omega$ is the magnitude of the vector $\mathbf{r}_{CM} \times M\mathbf{v}_{CM}$. This vector is the angular momentum of a particle of mass M (the total mass of the disk) moving with velocity $\mathbf{v}_{CM}$. Equation 13-17 is thus

$$\mathbf{L} = \mathbf{L}_{CM} + \mathbf{r}_{CM} \times M\mathbf{v}_{CM} \qquad 13\text{-}18$$

This result, obtained by considering rotation of a disk about two parallel axes, holds in general.

The angular momentum about any point in space O' is the sum of the angular momentum about the center of mass of the system plus the angular momentum associated with center-of-mass motion about the point O'.

This theorem follows directly from the definition of angular momentum and the properties of the center of mass. Its general derivation will be outlined in Section 13-8.

One result of Equation 13-18 is that if the only motion of a body is rotation about an axis through its center of mass, the angular momemtum of the body about any point in space is $\mathbf{L}_{CM}$. This follows from the fact that in this case $\mathbf{v}_{CM} = 0$. The angular momentum of a body about its center of mass is often called the *spin* of the body. For example, in the motion of a gyroscope (Section 13-6) the angular momentum consists of two parts, $\mathbf{L}_{CM}$, due to the spinning of the wheel, and $\mathbf{r}_{CM} \times m\mathbf{v}_{CM}$, due to the precession of the gyroscope. Equation 13-18 is also used to find the angular momentum of an electron in an atom. The electron has an intrinsic angular momentum, called *spin*, just as if it were a tiny spinning ball. The total angular momentum of the electron is the sum of this spin angular momentum and the angular momentum associated with the orbital motion of the electron around the nucleus.

We conclude this section with an example of the use of Equation 13-13.

Spin defined

Example 13-6 Two masses m_1 and m_2 in an Atwood's machine are connected by a string passing over a pulley, as shown in Figure 13-10. The pulley has radius R and moment of inertia I about its axis of rotation. Find the acceleration of the masses and the angular acceleration of the pulley.

Let us compute the angular momentum about the center of the pulley. We note that although the masses are not rotating, they do have angular momentum. In Example 13-2 we saw that relative to some point O the angular momentum of a particle moving with velocity v along a line is mvb, where b is the distance from the line to the point. In this case $b = R$, the radius of the pulley. The angular momentum of each mass is in the same direction, the direction of the angular velocity of the pulley, which is into the page. The magnitude of the total angular momentum of the two masses plus pulley is

$$L = m_1 vR + m_2 vR + I\omega$$

where v is the speed of the masses. If we assume that the string does not slip on the pulley, the speed of the string v must equal the speed

Figure 13-10
Atwood's machine. The angular momentum of each mass and that of the pulley about the center of the pulley is into the page. The rate of change of the total angular momentum equals the resultant torque about this point, which is just $m_2gR - m_1gR$.

of the rim of the pulley $R\omega$. We eliminate ω from the equation:

$$L = (m_1 + m_2)vR + I\frac{v}{R}$$

The only external forces acting on this system are the weights of the masses and pulley and the supporting force at the axis of the pulley. This force and the weight of the pulley do not exert any torque about the center of the pulley. The resulting external torque on this system is thus $m_2 gR - m_1 gR$. The direction of the torque is into the page, parallel to the angular momentum. Therefore Equation 13-13 is

$$\Sigma\tau_{\text{ext}} = (m_2 - m_1)gR = \frac{dL}{dt} = \left[(m_2 + m_2)R + \frac{I}{R}\right]\frac{dv}{dt}$$

and the acceleration is

$$a = \frac{dv}{dt} = \frac{m_2 - m_1}{m_1 + m_2 + I/R^2}g$$

The effect of taking into account the rotation of the pulley is to reduce the acceleration of the masses. The angular acceleration of the pulley is

$$\alpha = \frac{d\omega}{dt} = \frac{1}{R}\frac{dv}{dt} = \frac{a}{R}$$

Questions

8. If the total angular momentum of a system of particles is zero, are all the particles at rest?

9. If the total angular momentum of a system is constant, can we conclude that no net force acts on the system?

10. If no net force acts on a system, will there be no torque on the system?

11. Two external forces act on an extended body and, in general, will produce a net torque on the body. Are there any points about which the total torque of these forces is zero?

13-4 Conservation of Angular Momentum

If the resultant external torque acting on a system is zero, the total angular momentum is constant. We thus have a third conservation law for isolated systems. Energy, linear momentum, and angular momentum are conserved. The law of conservation of angular momentum is a fundamental law of nature. Even on a microscopic scale in atomic and nuclear physics, in which newtonian mechanics does not hold, the angular momentum of an isolated system is constant in time.

This section gives several examples of how the law of conservation of angular momentum is used.

Bradley Smith/Photo Researchers, Inc.

Because the torque exerted by the ice is small, the angular momentum of the skater is approximately constant. When he reduces his moment of inertia by drawing in his arms, his angular velocity increases.

Example 13-7 A disk with moment of inertia I_1 is rotating with angular velocity $\boldsymbol{\omega}_i$ about a frictionless shaft. It drops onto another disk with moment of inertia I_2 initially at rest (see Figure 13-11). Because of surface friction, the two disks eventually attain a common angular velocity. What is it?

Each disk exerts a torque on the other, but there is no torque external to the two-disk system. The angular momentum of the first disk about its center of mass is $I_1\boldsymbol{\omega}_i$. Since the center of mass is at rest, this is also the angular momentum about any point. When both disks are rotating together, the total angular momentum is

$$I_1\boldsymbol{\omega}_f + I_2\boldsymbol{\omega}_f = (I_1 + I_2)\boldsymbol{\omega}_f = I_1\boldsymbol{\omega}_i$$

Thus the final angular velocity is

$$\boldsymbol{\omega}_f = \frac{I_1}{I_1 + I_2}\,\boldsymbol{\omega}_i$$

This interaction of the disks is analogous to an inelastic collision of two masses in one dimension. Energy is not conserved in this collision. We can see this best by writing the energy in terms of the angular momentum. The initial kinetic energy is

$$E_{ki} = \tfrac{1}{2}I_1\omega_i{}^2 = \frac{(I_1\omega_i)^2}{2I_1} = \frac{L_i{}^2}{2I_1}$$

The final energy is

$$\tfrac{1}{2}(I_1 + I_2)\omega_f{}^2 = \frac{[(I_1 + I_2)\omega_f]^2}{2(I_1 + I_2)} = \frac{L_f{}^2}{2(I_1 + I_2)}$$

Since $L_f = L_i$, the final kinetic energy is less than the initial energy by the factor $I_1/(I_1 + I_2)$.

Example 13-8 A playground merry-go-round is at rest, pivoted about a frictionless axis. A child runs along a path tangential to the rim with initial speed v_i and jumps onto the merry-go-round (Figure 13-12). What is the angular velocity of the merry-go-round and child?

We cannot expect that energy will be conserved because the child makes an inelastic collision with the rim of the merry-go-round. Linear momentum is not conserved either. The pivot of the merry-go-round exerts an impulse during the collision, but because it is frictionless, it cannot exert any torque. Thus, angular momentum about the pivot is conserved. This problem again demonstrates that we need not have circular motion to have angular momentum. Figure 13-12 shows that the initial angular momentum of the child about the pivot point is

$$\mathbf{L}_i = \mathbf{r} \times m\mathbf{v}_i = mv_iR\mathbf{k}$$

where R is the perpendicular distance between the pivot and the line of motion of the child, which is also the radius of the merry-go-round, and m is the mass of the child. The direction of the angular momentum is shown in Figure 13-12. After the child is on the merry-go-round, the angular momentum is

$$mv_fR\mathbf{k} + I\omega\mathbf{k} = (mR\omega R + I\omega)\mathbf{k} = (mR^2 + I)\omega\mathbf{k}$$

where we have used $v_f = R\omega$ because the child is at rest relative to the rim of the merry-go-round after having jumped on. Since $\mathbf{L}_f = \mathbf{L}_i$, we have

$$(mR^2 + I)\omega\mathbf{k} = mv_iR\mathbf{k} \qquad \text{or} \qquad \omega = \frac{mv_iR}{mR^2 + I}$$

Example 13-9 Show that a planet moving around the sun sweeps out equal areas in equal times.

Figure 13-13 shows a planet moving in an orbit about the sun (here

Figure 13-11
Inelastic rotational collision (Example 13-7). The disk I_1, initially rotating with angular velocity $\boldsymbol{\omega}_i$, drops onto disk I_2, which is initially at rest. Because of the internal frictional forces between the disks, the two disks eventually turn together with a common angular velocity $\boldsymbol{\omega}_f$. If the shaft is frictionless, angular momentum is conserved, and $I_1\boldsymbol{\omega}_i = (I_1 + I_2)\boldsymbol{\omega}_f$.

Figure 13-12
Example 13-8. A child runs tangentially to the rim of a merry-go-round and jumps on. If the pivot is frictionless, angular momentum is conserved.

Figure 13-13
Planet orbiting sun (Example
13-9). The area swept out in
time dt is half the area of the
parallelogram indicated,
which is the magnitude of the
cross product of **r** and **v** dt.
Thus $dA = \frac{1}{2}|\mathbf{r} \times \mathbf{v}\, dt| =$
$(1/2m)|\mathbf{r} \times m\mathbf{v}|\, dt = (1/2m)L\, dt$.

we are not using the approximation of a circular orbit). Since the force
on the planet is directed toward the sun, there is no torque about the
sun and the angular momentum about the sun is conserved. (We shall
assume the sun to be at rest.) In time dt the planet moves a distance
$v\, dt$ and sweeps out the area indicated in Figure 13-13. This is half the
area of the parallelogram formed by the vectors **r** and **v** dt, which is
r $\times$ **v** dt. Thus the area dA swept out in dt by the radius vector **r** is

$$dA = \tfrac{1}{2}\,|\mathbf{r} \times \mathbf{v}\, dt| = \frac{1}{2m}\,|\mathbf{r} \times m\mathbf{v}|\, dt = \frac{1}{2m}\,L\, dt$$

or

$$\frac{dA}{dt} = \frac{L}{2m}$$

where **L** is the angular momentum of the planet. Since **L** is a constant,
the rate at which the radius vector of the planet sweeps out area is also
constant. Expressed differently, the radius vector sweeps out equal
areas in equal times. This fact, deduced from astronomical observation
early in the seventeenth century by Johannes Kepler, is one of three
empirical laws known as *Kepler's laws of planetary motion*. It is a
consequence of the fact that the force of gravity is a central force. We
see also that since **L** is constant in direction as well as magnitude, the
motion of a planet must remain in the plane formed by **r** and **v**.

Questions

12. A man sits on a spinning piano stool with his arms folded. If he
extends his arms, what happens to his angular velocity?

13. Does a particle moving at constant speed along a straight line
sweep out equal areas in equal times with respect to any arbitrary
point?

14. A particle moves under the influence of a central force $\mathbf{F} = f(r)\hat{\mathbf{r}}$.
Will its angular momentum about the center of force be constant?
Would Kepler's law of equal areas apply to this motion?

15. It is said that a cat always lands on its feet. If a cat starts falling feet
up, how can it land on its feet without violating the law of conservation of angular momentum?

13-5 Translation and Rotation

In general, the motion of a system of particles is very complicated
when the axis of rotation is not fixed. As we have mentioned, we can
consider any such motion as a combination of a translation of the

center of mass plus a rotation about the center of mass. The description of the translation is not difficult. The center of mass moves as a point particle under the influence of the net external force. The analysis of the rotational motion is simplified by an important theorem concerning the angular momentum relative to the center of mass:

The resultant torque about the center of mass equals the rate of change of angular momentum relative to the center of mass no matter how the center of mass is moving:

$$\Sigma\boldsymbol{\tau}_{CM} = \frac{d\mathbf{L}_{CM}}{dt} \qquad\qquad 13\text{-}19$$

Torque relative to the center of mass

Equation 13-19, stating that the resultant torque equals the rate of change of the angular momentum, is the same as Equation 13-13 except that now the torques and angular momentum are taken relative to the center of mass. Since we used Newton's second law to derive Equation 13-13, our derivation is valid only if the torques and angular momentum are taken relative to a point fixed in an inertial reference frame. This theorem states that the result is also valid if the torques and angular momentum are taken relative to the center of mass even if the center of mass is accelerating. The proof is given in Section 13-8.

In this section we apply this theorem to a special class of translational and rotational motion which can be easily treated: motion of a rigid body rotating about an axis of symmetry which moves so that it remains parallel to a line fixed in space, e.g., a rolling ball or cylinder.

Consider a cylinder rolling down an inclined plane, as in Figure 13-14. The forces on the cylinder are its weight, the normal force of the incline, and friction exerted by the incline. (If there were no friction, a cylinder released from rest at the top with no rotation would slide down the plane without rotating.) As for the general motion of a system of particles, the resultant force equals the total mass times the acceleration of the center of mass of the cylinder. If the cylinder rolls without slipping, the linear distance s moved by the center of mass is related to the angle of rotation of the cylinder ϕ by

$$s = R\phi \qquad\qquad 13\text{-}20$$

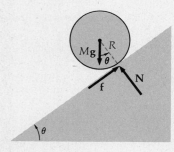

Figure 13-14
Forces on a cylinder rolling down an incline.

(see Figure 13-15). Thus the linear velocity of the center of mass is related to the angular velocity of rotation by

$$v_{CM} = \frac{ds}{dt} = R\frac{d\phi}{dt} = R\omega \qquad\qquad 13\text{-}21$$

and the acceleration of the center of mass is

$$a_{CM} = \frac{dv_{CM}}{dt} = R\frac{d\omega}{dt} = R\alpha \qquad\qquad 13\text{-}22$$

Condition for rolling without slipping

where α is the angular acceleration. As the cylinder accelerates down the incline, the angular velocity of rotation must increase if it is to roll without slipping. Thus the angular momentum of the cylinder about the center of mass increases. This increase is due to the torque exerted by the frictional force on the cylinder. (The weight Mg and the normal force $\mathbf{N}$ act through the center of mass and therefore exert no torque about this point.) The magnitude of the torque exerted by friction is fR. According to Equation 13-19, we can set this torque equal to the rate of change of angular momentum about the center of mass even though the center of mass is accelerating. The magnitude of the angu-

Figure 13-15
When the cylinder rolls without slipping, the point of contact moves the same distance $s = R\phi$ whether measured from A to B along the cylinder or from A' to B' along the plane. This distance is also the distance moved by the center of mass.

Fundamental Photographs

Path of a point on the rim of a rolling checker. The motion is simpler when viewed in the center-of-mass reference frame, which moves with the center of the checker. In this frame the point on the rim moves in a circle.

lar momentum about the center of mass is

$$L_{CM} = I_{CM}\omega \qquad \qquad 13\text{-}23$$

where I_{CM} is the moment of inertia about the axis of rotation, which is constant. Since the direction of the axis of rotation does not change (the axis remains parallel to its original direction), only the magnitude of the angular momentum changes. Thus

$$\frac{dL_{CM}}{dt} = I_{CM}\frac{d\omega}{dt} = I_{CM}\alpha \qquad \qquad 13\text{-}24$$

Setting the torque equal to the rate of change of the angular momentum, we obtain

$$fR = I_{CM}\alpha \qquad \qquad 13\text{-}25$$

The linear acceleration of the center of mass of the cylinder is parallel to the incline. The resultant force in this direction is $Mg\sin\theta - f$. Thus $\Sigma F = Ma_{CM}$ gives

$$Mg\sin\theta - f = Ma_{CM} \qquad \qquad 13\text{-}26$$

We can solve Equations 13-25 and 13-26 for any of the unknowns α, a_{CM}, and f using the condition for rolling without slipping (Equation 13-22). We first eliminate $\alpha = a_{CM}/R$.

$$fR = I_{CM}\frac{a_{CM}}{R}$$

$$f = \frac{I_{CM}}{R^2}\,a_{CM} \qquad \qquad 13\text{-}27$$

Putting this into Equation 13-26 gives

$$Mg\sin\theta - \frac{I_{CM}}{R^2}\,a_{CM} = Ma_{CM}$$

$$a_{CM} = \frac{Mg\sin\theta}{M + I_{CM}/R^2} \qquad \qquad 13\text{-}28$$

For a cylinder, $I_{CM} = \tfrac{1}{2}MR^2$. Then

$$a_{CM} = \frac{Mg\sin\theta}{M + \tfrac{1}{2}M} = \tfrac{2}{3}g\sin\theta \qquad \qquad 13\text{-}29$$

We can use this to find the force of friction and the angular acceleration

$$f = \frac{\tfrac{1}{2}MR^2}{R^2}\,a_{CM} = \tfrac{1}{3}Mg\sin\theta \qquad \qquad 13\text{-}30$$

$$\alpha = \frac{a_{CM}}{R} = \frac{2}{3}\frac{g}{R}\sin\theta \qquad \qquad 13\text{-}31$$

The frictional force in Equation 13-30 was found from the total mass, the moment of inertia, and the angle of inclination without any mention of the coefficient of friction. Since the cylinder is rolling without slipping, the surfaces of the cylinder and plane in contact are always instantaneously at rest relative to each other. Thus the friction is static friction, which in general is *not* equal to its maximum, limiting value $\mu_s N$. If μ_s is the coefficient of static friction, we have

$$f \leq \mu_s N = \mu_s Mg \cos \theta$$

Using $f = \frac{1}{2} Mg \sin \theta$ from Equation 13-30 for rolling without slipping, we have

$$\tfrac{1}{3} Mg \sin \theta \leq \mu_s Mg \cos \theta \qquad \text{or} \qquad \tan \theta \leq 3\mu_s$$

If the incline is too steep, or if the coefficient of static friction between it and the cylinder is too small, the cylinder will slip as it moves down the incline.

The linear acceleration is less than $g \sin \theta$, of course, because of the frictional force directed up the incline. Since the acceleration is constant, we can find the velocity of the cylinder at the bottom using the constant-acceleration formulas. If the original height of the center of mass of the cylinder is h, the total distance traveled is $s = h/(\sin \theta)$. The velocity at the bottom is then given by

$$v_{CM}^2 = 2a_{CM}s = 2(\tfrac{2}{3} g \sin \theta)\, \frac{h}{\sin \theta} = \tfrac{4}{3} gh$$

$$v_{CM} = \sqrt{\tfrac{4}{3} gh} \qquad\qquad\qquad 13\text{-}32$$

We can also obtain this result from energy considerations. We note that since the friction is static, there is no mechanical-energy dissipation. Thus the total mechanical energy, the kinetic energy plus the potential energy, is conserved. At the top of the incline the total energy is the potential energy Mgh. At the bottom the total energy is kinetic energy, which in general can be written $\frac{1}{2} Mv_{CM}^2 + E_{kr}$. Here, the energy relative to the center of mass is just the rotational energy $\frac{1}{2} I_{CM} \omega^2$. Conservation of energy gives

$$\tfrac{1}{2} Mv_{CM}^2 + \tfrac{1}{2} I_{CM} \omega^2 = Mgh \qquad\qquad 13\text{-}33$$

Using the rolling condition $v_{CM} = R\omega$, we can eliminate either v_{CM} or ω. Eliminating ω gives

$$\tfrac{1}{2} Mv_{CM}^2 + \tfrac{1}{2} I_{CM} \left(\frac{v_{CM}}{R}\right)^2 = Mgh$$

or

$$v_{CM}^2 = \frac{2Mgh}{M + I_{CM}/R^2}$$

For $I_{CM} = \frac{1}{2} MR^2$ for a cylinder, we obtain

$$v_{CM}^2 = \frac{2Mgh}{M + \frac{1}{2}M} = \tfrac{4}{3} gh$$

in agreement with the result found from the acceleration.

Question

16. A wheel rolls along a level surface at speed v_0 without slipping. Relative to the surface, what is the speed of the bottom of the wheel? Of the center of the wheel? Of the top of the wheel? Is there any frictional force acting on the wheel?

13-6   Motion of a Gyroscope

We now consider an example of a gyroscope or symmetric top, in which the axis of rotation changes direction. In general such motions are very complicated. Figure 13-16 shows such a system consisting of a bicycle wheel free to turn on an axle which is pivoted at a point a distance D from the center of the wheel but free to turn in any direction.

When the axle is held horizontal and released, if the wheel is not spinning it simply falls. The torque about the point O is MgD in the direction into the diagram in Figure 13-16. As the wheel falls, its angular momentum due to center-of-mass motion is also into the page. Since the center of mass accelerates downward, the upward force $\mathbf{F}$ exerted by the support at O is evidently less than Mg.

Now assume that the wheel is spinning. The angular momentum relative to point O is the angular momentum relative to the center of mass, in this case the spin, plus the angular momentum due to motion of the center of mass. It is quite easy in practice to make the spin angular momentum very large so that to a first approximation we can neglect the contribution due to motion of the center of mass. From Figure 13-16 we see that the torque is perpendicular to the angular momentum. In order for the angular momentum to change in the direction of the torque, the axle must move in the horizontal plane, as shown. In time dt the angular-momentum change has the magnitude

$$dL = \tau\, dt = MgD\, dt$$

The angle $d\phi$ through which the axle moves is

$$d\phi = \frac{dL}{L} = \frac{MgD\, dt}{L}$$

The movement of the axle is called *precession*. The angular velocity of precession is

$$\omega_p = \frac{d\phi}{dt} = \frac{MgD}{L} \qquad\qquad 13\text{-}34$$

Since the center of mass does not drop, the support point evidently exerts an upward force equal to Mg.

The observation that the wheel moves in a horizontal plane instead of falling is at first surprising. We are more familiar with situations like a falling stick, where there is no initial angular momentum, so that the direction of the change in angular momentum is also the direction of the angular momentum. There is an analogous situation in circular motion, e.g., that of the moon about the earth. The earth exerts a force on the moon toward the earth. Why doesn't the moon move toward the earth and hit it? If the moon were held with no initial momentum and released, a change in momentum (from zero) toward the earth

Figure 13-16
Gyroscope. The weight $M\mathbf{g}$ produces a torque about the pivot into the paper which causes a *change* in the angular momentum in that direction. If the wheel is initially spinning so there is initial angular momentum $\mathbf{L}$ along the axle, the change is perpendicular to $\mathbf{L}$ and the axle moves in the direction of the torque. This motion is called precession.

would result in the moon's moving toward the earth. However, since the moon has an initial momentum perpendicular to the line joining the earth, a change in momentum toward the earth merely results in the moon's being deviated from straight-line motion into a circular arc. Thus though $d\mathbf{p}$ is always toward the earth, $\mathbf{p}$ is tangential to the circle. For the gyroscope, if there is no initial angular momentum, the torque (into the page) causes an angular momentum (into the page) associated with center-of-mass motion as it falls; but if there is a large initial angular momentum along the axis of the wheel, this same torque merely deflects the angular momentum into the page. In this case the pivot exerts an upward force sufficient to prevent the center of mass from falling.

If the axle is not horizontal but makes an angle θ with the vertical, as in Figure 13-17, the torque about point O is $MgD \sin \theta$. The angle of precession in time dt is now

$$d\phi = \frac{dL}{L \sin \theta} = \frac{MgD \sin \theta \, dt}{L \sin \theta} = MgD \, dt \qquad \text{13-35}$$

The angular velocity of precession ω_p is thus independent of angle θ.

A careful observation of the motion of a gyroscope reveals that if the axle is held horizontally and released from rest, the motion of the axle is not confined to the horizontal plane. It dips down at first, and as the gyroscope precesses, there is a small vertical oscillation called *nutation*. This effect was neglected in our previous discussion because we neglected the contribution of the center-of-mass motion to the total angular momentum about the pivot. If the spin angular momentum is much greater than that due to the motion of the center of mass during precession, the nutation is very small. The precessional motion of the center of mass results in a small component of angular momentum $MD^2\omega_p$ in the vertical direction. However, there is no torque in this direction. In order for the axle to precess in the horizontal plane without nutation, it must be given an angular impulse $MD^2\omega_p$ as it is released. If this is not done, the vertical component of the total angular momentum must remain zero. Then as the axle begins to precess, it must dip down so that there is a downward component of *spin* angular momentum to cancel the vertical angular momentum due to center-of-mass motion. We can analyze the motion qualitatively from the moment of release.

Figure 13-17
The rate of precession of a gyroscope is independent of the angle its axis makes with the vertical.

Figure 13-21
This arrangement of four rotating masses is dynamically balanced. The total angular-momentum vector L is now parallel to the angular-velocity vector $\boldsymbol{\omega}$, and so L does not change during the rotation.

angular momentum is exerted by the bearings. Its direction is perpendicular to the axis of rotation, and its effect is to maintain a constant direction for the angular velocity $\boldsymbol{\omega}$ as the direction of the angular-momentum vector changes. The rotating system exerts an equal and opposite torque on the support bearings, causing wear. Such a system is said to be *dynamically imbalanced*. The greater the angular velocity the greater the wear on the bearings. Note that there is no static imbalance. If we pivot the dumbbell at the center of mass, it will be in static equilibrium at any orientation. If we have a system of unknown mass distribution, e.g., an automobile wheel, we cannot detect or correct dynamic imbalance by static balance methods.

We can correct the dynamic imbalance of our two-mass system by making the angle θ equal to 90°, as in Figure 13-20, or by adding masses, as in Figure 13-21. Then L and $\boldsymbol{\omega}$ will be parallel, and no torque will be required to maintain a constant angular velocity.

Figure 13-22 shows a wheel rotating about an axis which is off center but parallel to the symmetry axis through the center of mass and a distance h from it. The angular momentum about a point on the axis of rotation in the plane of the wheel is the sum of the angular momentum about the center of mass I_{CM} and the angular momentum associated with motion of the center of mass, both parallel to the axis of rotation. The angular momentum is just $I\boldsymbol{\omega}$, where I is the moment of inertia about the axis of rotation. If the wheel rotates with constant angular velocity, the angular momentum is constant and no torque is required. However, since the center of mass moves in a circle of radius h, there must be a net *force* on the wheel of magnitude $Mv_{CM}^2/h = M(h\omega)^2/h = Mh\omega^2$ and directed toward the axis of rotation from the center of mass. This force is exerted by the bearings. Again, the equal but opposite force exerted on the bearings causes wear on the bearings, particularly if ω is large. This *static imbalance* can be detected and corrected by pivoting the wheel on a horizontal axle and balancing so that the axis of rotation passes through the center of mass.

Figure 13-22
Static imbalance. When the wheel rotates about this axis, the angular momentum L is parallel to the angular velocity $\boldsymbol{\omega}$. The bearings do not need to exert a torque to maintain rotation, but they must exert a force on the wheel because the center of mass of the wheel moves in a circle and therefore accelerates.

13-8   Derivation of Relations for Torque and Angular Momentum about the Center of Mass

In this section we give general derivations of the important theorems about the angular momentum relative to the center of mass expressed in Equations 13-18 and 13-19. Figure 13-23 shows a general system of particles. We write the position vector of the ith particle relative to origin O as the sum of the position vector of the center of mass $\mathbf{r}_{CM}$ and the vector from the center of mass to the particle $\mathbf{r}_{ir}$,

$$\mathbf{r}_i = \mathbf{r}_{CM} + \mathbf{r}_{ir} \qquad \text{13-37}$$

The vector $\mathbf{r}_{CM}$ is defined by

$$M\mathbf{r}_{CM} = \Sigma m_i \mathbf{r}_i$$

Substituting $\mathbf{r}_{CM} + \mathbf{r}_{ir}$ for $\mathbf{r}_i$ in this equation, we have

$$M\mathbf{r}_{CM} = \Sigma m_i(\mathbf{r}_{CM} + \mathbf{r}_{ir}) = \mathbf{r}_{CM}\Sigma m_i + \Sigma m_i \mathbf{r}_{ir} = M\mathbf{r}_{CM} + \Sigma m_i \mathbf{r}_{ir}$$

Thus

$$\Sigma m_i \mathbf{r}_{ir} = 0 \qquad \text{13-38}$$

Figure 13-23
Relationship among r_i, r_{CM}, and r_{ir}.

The velocity of the ith particle is

$$\mathbf{v}_i = \frac{d\mathbf{r}_i}{dt} = \frac{d\mathbf{r}_{CM}}{dt} + \frac{d\mathbf{r}_{ir}}{dt} = \mathbf{v}_{CM} + \mathbf{u}_i$$

where $\mathbf{u}_i$ is the velocity relative to the center of mass. We note from differentiating Equation 13-38 that

$$\Sigma m_i \mathbf{u}_i = 0 \qquad\qquad\qquad \text{13-39}$$

The angular momentum of the ith particle about O is

$$\begin{aligned}\mathbf{L}_i &= \mathbf{r}_i \times m_i \mathbf{v}_i = (\mathbf{r}_{CM} + \mathbf{r}_{ir}) \times m_i (\mathbf{v}_{CM} + \mathbf{u}_i) \\ &= \mathbf{r}_{CM} \times m_i \mathbf{v}_{CM} + \mathbf{r}_{ir} \times m_i \mathbf{u}_i + \mathbf{r}_{CM} \times m_i \mathbf{u}_i + \mathbf{r}_{ir} \times m_i \mathbf{v}_{CM}\end{aligned}$$

The total angular momentum is the sum of $\mathbf{L}_i$ over all the particles

$$\begin{aligned}\mathbf{L} = \Sigma \mathbf{L}_i &= (\mathbf{r}_{CM} \times M\mathbf{v}_{CM}) + (\Sigma \mathbf{r}_{ir} \times m_i \mathbf{u}_i) + (\mathbf{r}_{CM} \times \Sigma m_i \mathbf{u}_i) \\ &\quad + (\Sigma m_i \mathbf{r}_{ir}) \times \mathbf{v}_{CM}\end{aligned}$$

The last two terms in this expression are zero by Equations 13-38 and 13-39. The first term is the angular momentum associated with center-of-mass motion, and the second term is the angular momentum relative to the center of mass $\mathbf{L}_{CM}$. We thus have

$$\mathbf{L} = \mathbf{L}_{CM} + \mathbf{r}_{CM} \times M\mathbf{v}_{CM} \qquad\qquad \text{13-18}$$

We derive Equation 13-19 relating the torque about the center of mass to the rate of change of $\mathbf{L}_{CM}$ by first considering the torque about point O, which we assume to be in an inertial reference frame. If $\mathbf{F}_i$ is the external force acting on the ith particle, the net external torque about O is

$$\begin{aligned}\Sigma \boldsymbol{\tau}_{\text{ext}} &= \Sigma \mathbf{r}_i \times \mathbf{F}_i = \Sigma (\mathbf{r}_{CM} + \mathbf{r}_{ir}) \times \mathbf{F}_i \\ &= \mathbf{r}_{CM} \times \Sigma \mathbf{F}_i + \Sigma \mathbf{r}_{ir} \times \mathbf{F}_i\end{aligned}$$

The second term in this equation is the resultant torque about the center of mass, which we shall call $\Sigma \boldsymbol{\tau}_{CM}$. Thus

$$\Sigma \boldsymbol{\tau}_{\text{ext}} = \Sigma \boldsymbol{\tau}_{CM} + \mathbf{r}_{CM} \times \Sigma \mathbf{F}_i \qquad\qquad \text{13-40}$$

Computing the rate of change of the angular momentum about the origin O using Equation 13-18 gives

$$\frac{d\mathbf{L}}{dt} = \frac{d\mathbf{L}_{CM}}{dt} + \frac{d\mathbf{r}_{CM}}{dt} \times M\mathbf{v}_{CM} + \mathbf{r}_{CM} \times M \frac{d\mathbf{v}_{CM}}{dt}$$

The second term in this equation is zero because $d\mathbf{r}_{CM}/dt = \mathbf{v}_{CM}$ and $\mathbf{v}_{CM} \times M\mathbf{v}_{CM} = 0$. Writing $\mathbf{a}_{CM}$ for $d\mathbf{v}_{CM}/dt$, we have

$$\frac{d\mathbf{L}}{dt} = \frac{d\mathbf{L}_{CM}}{dt} + \mathbf{r}_{CM} \times M\mathbf{a}_{CM} \qquad\qquad \text{13-41}$$

When we set the resultant torque about O (Equation 13-40) equal to the rate of change of angular momentum about O (Equation 13-41), we get

$$\Sigma \boldsymbol{\tau}_{\text{ext}} = \Sigma \boldsymbol{\tau}_{CM} + \mathbf{r}_{CM} \times \Sigma \mathbf{F}_i = \frac{d\mathbf{L}}{dt} = \frac{d\mathbf{L}_{CM}}{dt} + \mathbf{r}_{CM} \times M\mathbf{a}_{CM}$$

But since $\Sigma \mathbf{F}_i = M\mathbf{a}_{CM}$,

$$\Sigma \boldsymbol{\tau}_{CM} = \frac{d\mathbf{L}_{CM}}{dt} \qquad\qquad \text{13-19}$$

which is the theorem to be proved.

Review

A. Define, explain, or otherwise identify:

Cross product, 330   Precession, 343
Vector product, 330   Nutation, 344
Angular momentum, 332   Dynamic imbalance, 347
Spin, 336   Static imbalance, 347

B. True or false:

1. $\mathbf{A} \times \mathbf{B}$ is the same as $\mathbf{B} \times \mathbf{A}$.

2. Angular momentum and torque are defined relative to a point in space.

3. A particle must move in a circle to have angular momentum.

4. If the resultant torque on a body is zero, its angular momentum must be zero.

5. The angular momentum of a particle is always perpendicular to its velocity.

6. If the angular momentum of a body does not change, the resultant torque on the body must be zero.

7. In general, when a body rolls down an incline without slipping, the frictional force has the magnitude $\mu_s N$.

Exercises

Section 13-1, Torque as a Vector Product

1. A force of magnitude F is applied horizontally in the negative x direction to the rim of a disk of radius R, as shown in Figure 13-24. Write $\mathbf{F}$ and $\mathbf{r}$ in terms of the unit vectors $\mathbf{i}$, $\mathbf{j}$, and $\mathbf{k}$ and compute the torque produced by the force about the origin at the center of the disk.

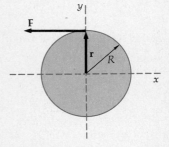

Figure 13-24
Exercise 1.

2. A 0.5-kg particle falls under the influence of gravity. (a) It is at $y = 10$ m and $x = 2$ m at time t_1. What is the torque about the origin exerted by gravity on the particle at this time? (b) At some later time the particle is at $y = 0$, $x = 2$ m. What is the torque about the origin at this time?

3. Compute the torque about the origin for the force $\mathbf{F} = -mg\mathbf{j}$ and $\mathbf{r} = x\mathbf{i} + y\mathbf{j}$ and show that this torque is independent of the coordinate y.

4. If $\mathbf{A} \times \mathbf{B} = 0$, what can be said about the vectors $\mathbf{A}$ and $\mathbf{B}$?

5. Find $\mathbf{A} \times \mathbf{B}$ for (a) $\mathbf{A} = 5\mathbf{i}$ and $\mathbf{B} = 5\mathbf{i} + 5\mathbf{j}$, (b) $\mathbf{A} = 5\mathbf{i}$ and $\mathbf{B} = 5\mathbf{i} + 5\mathbf{k}$, (c) $\mathbf{A} = 2\mathbf{i} + 2\mathbf{j}$ and $\mathbf{B} = -2\mathbf{i} + 2\mathbf{j}$.

6. Under what conditions is the magnitude of $\mathbf{A} \times \mathbf{B}$ equal to $\mathbf{A} \cdot \mathbf{B}$?

7. Show that for general vectors $\mathbf{A} = A_x\mathbf{i} + A_y\mathbf{j} + A_z\mathbf{k}$ and $\mathbf{B} = B_x\mathbf{i} + B_y\mathbf{j} + B_z\mathbf{k}$,

$$\mathbf{A} \times \mathbf{B} = \begin{vmatrix} \mathbf{i} & \mathbf{j} & \mathbf{k} \\ A_x & A_y & A_z \\ B_x & B_y & B_z \end{vmatrix}$$
$$= (A_yB_z - A_zB_y)\mathbf{i} + (A_zB_x - A_xB_z)\mathbf{j} + (A_xB_y - A_yB_x)\mathbf{k}$$

Section 13-2, Angular Momentum of a Particle

8. A 2-kg particle moves with constant speed of 3 m/sec in the xy plane in the y direction along the line $x = 5$ m. (a) Find the angular momentum $\mathbf{L}$ relative to the origin. (b) What torque about the origin is needed to maintain this motion?

9. A body of mass 3 kg moves at constant speed of 4 m/sec around a circle of radius 5 m. (a) What is its angular momentum about the center of the circle?

(b) What is its moment of inertia about an axis through the center of the circle and perpendicular to the plane of the motion? (c) What is the angular velocity of the particle?

10. A 3-kg body moves at constant speed of 4 m/sec along a straight line. (a) What is its angular momentum about a point 5 m from the line? (b) Describe qualitatively how its angular velocity about that point varies with time.

11. A particle travels in a circular path. (a) If its linear momentum p is doubled, how is its angular momentum affected? (b) If the radius of the circle is doubled but the speed is unchanged, how is the angular momentum of the particle affected?

12. A particle of mass m moves with speed v in a circle of radius r. Show that the kinetic energy of the particle can be written $E_k = L^2/2mr^2 = L^2/2I$, where L is the angular momentum of the particle and $I = mr^2$ is its moment of inertia.

13. A 2-kg mass moves in a circle of radius 3 m. Its angular momentum relative to the center of the circle depends on time according to $L = 4t$, where t is in seconds and L in kg-m²/sec. (a) Find the torque acting on the particle. (b) Find the angular velocity as a function of time.

14. A planet moves in an ellipitical orbit about the sun with the sun at one focus of the ellipse. (a) What is the torque produced by the gravitational force of attraction of the sun for the planet? (b) At position A in Figure 13-25 the planet is a distance r_1 from the sun and is moving with speed v_1 perpendicular to the line from the sun to the planet. At position B it is at distance r_2 moving with speed v_2, again perpendicular to the line from the sun to the planet. What is the ratio of v_1 and v_2 in terms of r_1 and r_2?

Figure 13-25
Planet moving in elliptical path about the sun (Exercise 14).

Section 13-3, Torque and Angular Momentum for a System of Particles

15. Calculate the angular momentum of the earth spinning about its axis and compare it with the angular momentum the earth has about the sun. (Assume the earth to be a homogeneous sphere of mass 6.0×10^{24} kg and radius 6.4×10^6 m.) The radius of the earth's orbit is 1.5×10^{11} m.

16. A homogeneous cylinder of mass 100 kg and radius 0.3 m is mounted so that it turns without friction on its fixed axis of symmetry. It is rotated by a drive belt that wraps around its perimeter and exerts a constant torque. At time $t = 0$, its angular velocity is zero. At time $t = 30$ sec, the angular velocity is 600 rev/min. (a) What is its angular momentum at that time? (b) At what rate is the angular momentum increasing? What is the torque acting on the cylinder? (c) What is the magnitude of the force acting on the rim of the cylinder?

17. A 15-gm coin of diameter 1.5 cm is spinning about a vertical diameter at a fixed point on a tabletop at 10 rev/sec. (a) What is the angular momentum of the coin about its center of mass? (b) What is its angular momentum about a point on the table 10 cm from the coin?

18. The coin in Exercise 17 spins about a vertical diameter at 10 rev/sec but also travels in a straight line across the tabletop at 5 cm/sec. (a) What is the angular momentum of the coin about a point on the line of motion? (b) What is the angular momentum of the coin about a point 10 cm from the line of motion? (There are two answers to this question. Explain why and give both.)

19. A 4-kg mass rests on a frictionless horizontal table. It is connected to a second mass of 2 kg by a string which passes over a frictionless pulley, as shown in Figure 13-26. The pulley is a uniform cylinder of radius 4 cm and mass 1 kg. (a) What is the net external torque on the system (two masses plus pulley) about the center of the pulley? (b) If the masses are moving with speed v with the pulley turning at angular velocity $\omega = v/r$, what is the total angular momentum of the system about the center of the pulley? (Assume that the center of mass of the 4-kg-mass is at the height of the string.) (c) Find the acceleration

Figure 13-26
Exercise 19.

of the masses by differentiating your result for L in part (b) and setting dL/dt equal to the resultant torque.

20. (a) Assuming that the incline is smooth in Figure 13-27 and that the string passes through the center of mass of m_2, find the resultant torque acting on the system about the center of the pulley. (b) Write an expression for the total angular momentum of the system about the center of the pulley when the masses are moving with speed v. Assume the pulley has a moment of inertia I and radius r. (c) Find the acceleration of the masses from your results of parts (a) and (b) by setting the resultant torque equal to the rate of change of the angular momentum of the system.

21. A uniform stick of length l and mass M lies on a smooth table. It rotates with angular velocity about an axis perpendicular to the table and through one end of the stick. (a) What is the angular momentum of the stick about the end? (b) What is the speed of the center of mass of the stick? (c) What is the angular momentum of the stick about the center of mass? (d) Show that Equation 13-18 is satisfied for this situation, where L is the angular momentum about the end of the stick.

Figure 13-27
Exercise 20.

Section 13-4, Conservation of Angular Momentum

22. A merry-go-round of radius 2 m and moment of inertia 500 kg-m² is rotating at 0.25 rev/sec. A child of mass 25 kg sitting at the center crawls out to the rim. Find (a) the new angular velocity of the merry-go-round and (b) the initial and final kinetic energy.

23. A disk is rotating freely at 1800 rev/min about a vertical axis through its center. A second disk mounted on the same shaft above the first is initially at rest. The moment of inertia of the second disk is twice that of the first. The second disk is dropped onto the first one, and the two eventually rotate together with a common angular velocity. (a) Find the new angular velocity. (b) Show that kinetic energy is lost during the "collision" of the two disks.

24. A circular platform is mounted on a vertical frictionless axle. Its radius is $r = 5$ ft, and its moment of inertia is $I = 200$ slug-ft². It is at rest initially. A 150-lb man stands on the edge of the platform and begins to walk along the edge at a speed $v_0 = 3$ ft/sec *relative to the ground.* (a) What is the angular velocity of the platform? (b) When the man has walked once around the platform so that he is at his original position on it, what is his angular displacement relative to the ground?

25. A man stands at the center of a circular platform holding his arms extended horizontally with an 8-lb weight in each hand. He is set rotating about a vertical axis with angular velocity of 0.5 rev/sec. The moment of inertia of the man plus platform is 4 slug-ft², assumed constant. The weights are 3 ft from the axis of rotation. He now pulls the weights in toward his body until they are 6 in from the axis of rotation. Find (a) his new angular velocity and (b) the initial and final kinetic energy of the man and platform. (c) How much work must the man do to pull in the weights?

26. A particle is traveling with a constant velocity $\mathbf{v}$ along a line which is a distance b from the origin O. Let dA be the area swept out by the position vector from O to the particle in time dt (Figure 13-28). Show that dA/dt is constant in time and equal to $\frac{1}{2}L/m$, where L is the angular momentum of the particle about the origin.

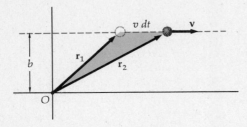

Figure 13-28
Area swept out in time dt by a particle moving in a straight line (Exercise 26).

Helicopter with two rotors
(Exercise 27).

Russ Kinne/Photo Researchers

27. Explain why a helicopter with just one main rotor has a second smaller rotor mounted on a horizontal axis at the rear. Describe the resultant motion of the helicopter if this rotor fails during a flight.

Section 13-5, Translation and Rotation

28. A sphere, disk, and hoop made of homogeneous materials have the same radius (10 cm) and mass (3 kg). They are released from rest at the top of a 30° incline and roll down without slipping through a vertical distance of 2 m. (a) What are their speeds at the bottom? (b) Find the frictional force f in each case. (c) If they start together at $t = 0$, at what time does each reach the bottom?

29. A ball rolls without slipping along a horizontal plane. (a) Show that the frictional force on the ball must be zero. *Hint:* Consider a possible direction for a frictional force and what effect such a force would have on the velocity of the center of mass and on the angular velocity (b) If the plane is not horizontal, is the frictional force zero?

30. A 100-kg uniform disk of radius 0.60 m is placed flat on some smooth ice. Two skaters wind ropes around the disk in the same sense. Each skater thus pulls on his rope and skates away, exerting constant forces for 5 sec (Figure 13-29). Describe the motion of the disk; i.e., what is the acceleration, velocity, and the position of the center of mass as a function of time, and what are the angular acceleration and angular velocity as a function of time?

Figure 13-29
Exercise 30.

31. A homogeneous cylinder of radius 6 in weighs 100 lb. It is rolling along the floor without slipping at a speed of 15 ft/sec. How much work is needed to stop the disk?

Section 13-6, Motion of a Gyroscope

32. A bicycle wheel is mounted in the middle of a 2-ft-long axle. The tire and rim weigh 8 lb and have a radius of 12 in. The wheel is spun at 10 rev/sec, and the axle is then placed in a horizontal position with one end resting on a pivot. (a) What is the angular momentum due to the spinning of the wheel? (Treat the wheel as a hoop.) (b) What is the angular velocity of precession? How long does it take for the axle to swing through 360° around the pivot? (c) What is the angular momentum associated with the motion of the center of mass, i.e., due to the precession? In what direction is this angular momentum?

33. A uniform disk of mass 2 kg and radius 6 cm is mounted in the center of a 10-cm axle and spun at 900 rev/min. The axle is then placed in a horizontal position with one end resting on a pivot. The other end is given an initial horizontal velocity so that the precession is smooth with no nutation. (a) Find the angular velocity of precession. (b) What is the speed of the center of mass during the precession? (c) What are the magnitude and direction of the acceleration of the center of mass? (d) What are the vertical and horizontal components of the force exerted by the pivot?

Section 13-7, Static and Dynamic Imbalance

34. A uniform disk of radius 30 cm, thickness 3 cm, and mass 5 kg rotates at $\omega = 10$ rad/sec about an axis parallel to the symmetry axis but 0.5 cm from that axis. (a) Find the net force on the bearings due to this imbalance. (b) Where should a 100-gm mass be placed on the disk to correct this problem?

35. A 2-kg mass attached to a string of length 1 m moves in a horizontal circle as a conical pendulum (Figure 13-30). The string makes an angle $\theta = 30°$ with the vertical. (a) Show that the angular momentum of the mass about the point of support P has a horizontal component toward the center of the circle as well as a vertical component and find these components. (b) Find the magnitude of dL/dt and show that it equals the magnitude of the torque exerted by gravity about the point of support.

Figure 13-30
Conical pendulum (Exercise 35).

Problems

1. A particle moves in a circle of radius r with angular velocity $\boldsymbol{\omega}$. (a) Show that its velocity is $\mathbf{v} = \boldsymbol{\omega} \times \mathbf{r}$. (b) Show that its centripetal acceleration is $\mathbf{a}_r = \boldsymbol{\omega} \times \mathbf{v} = \boldsymbol{\omega} \times (\boldsymbol{\omega} \times \mathbf{r})$.

2. A particle located at $\mathbf{r} = x\mathbf{i} + y\mathbf{j} + z\mathbf{k}$ has momentum $\mathbf{p} = p_x\mathbf{i} + p_y\mathbf{j} + p_z\mathbf{k}$. A force $\mathbf{F} = F_x\mathbf{i} + F_y\mathbf{j} + F_z\mathbf{k}$ acts on it. (a) Calculate the components of the angular momentum of the particle and of the torque about the origin in terms of the components of these three vectors. (b) Compute the time derivative of the z component of angular momentum and show that $dL_z/dt = v_x p_y - v_y p_x + xF_y - yF_x$, where v_x and v_y are the x and y components of the velocity of the particle. Is this expression the same as that for the z component of the torque? Explain.

3. A wheel of radius R rolls without slipping at speed V. (a) Show that the x and y coordinates of point P in Figure 13-31 are $r_0 \cos \theta$ and $R + r_0 \sin \theta$. (b) Show that the total velocity $\mathbf{v}$ of point P has components $v_x = V + (r_0 V \sin \theta)/R$ and $v_y = -(r_0 V \cos \theta)/R$. (c) Show that $\mathbf{v}$ and $\mathbf{r}$ are perpendicular to each other by calculating their scalar product. (d) Show that $v = r\omega$, where $\omega = V/R$ is the angular velocity of the wheel. (e) These results demonstrate that in the case of rolling without slipping, the motion is the same as if the rolling object were instantaneously rotating about the point of contact with angular speed $\omega = V/R$. Calculate the kinetic energy of the wheel assuming that it is in pure rotation about point O and show that the result is the same as calculated from the sum of the translational kinetic energy of the center of mass and the rotational kinetic energy of rotation about the center of mass.

Figure 13-31
Problem 3.

4. A mass m is attached to a light string which passes through a small hole in a frictionless tabletop. Initially the mass is sliding with speed v_0 in a circle of radius r_0 about the hole. A man under the table now begins to pull the string in slowly. (a) Show that when the mass is moving in a circle of radius r, the tension in the string is

$$T = L_0^2/mr^3$$

where $L_0 = mv_0 r_0$ is the initial angular momentum. (b) The string is pulled in until the radius of the circular orbit is r_f. Using the result of part (a), calculate the work done by integrating $T\, dr$ and show that the work done is

$(L_0^2/2m)(r_f^{-2} - r_0^{-2})$. (c) What is the velocity v_f when the radius of the circle is r_f? Show that the work done as calculated in part (b) equals the change in kinetic energy $\frac{1}{2}mv_f^2 - \frac{1}{2}mv_0^2$. (d) If $m = 0.5$ kg, $r_0 = 1$ m, and $v_0 = 3$ m/sec and the maximum tension the string can withstand without breaking is 200 N, find the minimum value of r_f before the string breaks.

5. A uniform ball of radius r rolls without slipping along the loop-the-loop track in Figure 13-32. It starts at rest at height h above the bottom of the loop. If the ball is not to leave the track at the top of the loop, what is the least value h can have (in terms of the radius R of the loop)? What would h have been if the ball were to slide along a frictionless track instead of rolling?

Figure 13-32
Problem 5.

6. A heavy homogeneous cylinder has mass m and radius R. It is accelerated by a force T, which is applied through a rope wound around a light drum of radius r attached to the cylinder (Figure 13-33). The coefficient of static friction is sufficient for the cylinder to roll without slipping. (a) Find the friction force. (b) Find the acceleration a of the center of the cylinder. (c) Is it possible to choose r so that a is greater than T/m? How? (d) What is the direction of the friction force in the circumstances of part (c)?

Figure 13-33
Problem 6.

7. Assuming the earth to be a homogeneous sphere of radius r and mass m, show that the period T of rotation about its axis is related to its radius by $T = (4\pi m/5L)r^2$, where L is the angular momentum of the earth due to its rotation. Suppose that the radius r changes by a very small amount Δr due to some internal effect, e.g., thermal expansion. (a) Show that the fractional change in the period T is given approximately by $\Delta T/T = 2\Delta r/r$. Hint: Use differentials dr and dT to approximate the changes in these quantities. (b) By how many miles would the earth need to expand for the period to change by $\frac{1}{4}$ d/y, so that leap year would not be needed?

8. A particle moves with constant speed v in the xy plane along a line parallel to the x axis a distance b from this axis. Let $\mathbf{r}$ be the radius vector from the origin to the particle at some instant, and let θ be the angle between $\mathbf{r}$ and the x axis. (a) Let v_r be the component of the velocity along the radius vector and v_t be the component perpendicular to the radius vector. Show that $v_r = v \cos \theta$ and $v_t = v \sin \theta$. (b) Show that the angular velocity of the particle about the origin is $\omega = v_t/r = (v/b) \sin^2 \theta$. Using this result and the moment of inertia of the particle about the z axis $I = mr^2$, show that mbv and $I\omega$ are equivalent expressions for the angular momentum of the particle about the origin.

9. Prove that $\mathbf{A} \times (\mathbf{B} + \mathbf{C}) = \mathbf{A} \times \mathbf{B} + \mathbf{A} \times \mathbf{C}$ by writing out both sides in terms of their rectangular components and the unit vectors $\mathbf{i}$, $\mathbf{j}$, and $\mathbf{k}$.

10. Prove that $d(\mathbf{A} \times \mathbf{B})/dt = \mathbf{A} \times d\mathbf{B}/dt + (d\mathbf{A}/dt) \times \mathbf{B}$ by writing out $\mathbf{A} \times \mathbf{B}$ in terms of the components of the vectors and the unit vectors $\mathbf{i}$, $\mathbf{j}$, and $\mathbf{k}$ and differentiating directly.

CHAPTER 14   Oscillations

Motion which repeats itself is called *periodic*, the time required for each repetition being the *period*. Systems which display periodic motion occur frequently, e.g., the motion of a mass on a spring, the motion of the moon about the earth, the oscillation of a pendulum, the oscillations of atoms in a molecule, the vibration of a string of a violin. The study of periodic motion has many applications. In addition to the examples listed above, periodic motion occurs in many types of wave motion. For example, in a sound wave, air molecules oscillate along the line of propagation of the wave. Light and other electromagnetic waves are characterized by the oscillation of electric and magnetic field vectors perpendicular to the line of propagation of the wave.

14-1 Simple Harmonic Motion

We shall concentrate on the simplest form of oscillation, called *simple harmonic motion*. In simple harmonic motion in one dimension, the displacement x of the particle from equilibrium as a function of time is given by an equation such as

$$x = A \cos (\omega t + \delta) \tag{14-1}$$

Position function for simple harmonic motion

where A, ω, and δ are constants. This function is plotted in Figure 14-1. The maximum displacement A is called the *amplitude*. The quantity $\omega t + \delta$ is called the *phase* of the motion, and the constant δ is called the *phase constant*. When the phase increases by 2π from its value at time t, the particle again has the same position and velocity as at time t, since $\cos (\omega t + \delta + 2\pi) = \cos (\omega t + \delta)$. During the time that the phase increases by 2π, the particle performs a full cycle of the motion. We can determine the *period T* of the motion by noting that the phase at time $t + T$ is just 2π plus the phase at time t:

$$\omega(t + T) + \delta = 2\pi + \omega t + \delta \qquad \text{or} \qquad \omega T = 2\pi$$

or

$$T = \frac{2\pi}{\omega} \tag{14-2}$$

Amplitude, phase, and phase constant defined

Period defined

Figure 14-1
Plot of x versus t for simple harmonic motion.

The number of vibrations per unit time $1/T$ is called the *frequency f:*

Frequency and angular frequency defined

$$f = \frac{1}{T} = \frac{\omega}{2\pi} \qquad\qquad 14\text{-}3$$

The constant $\omega = 2\pi f$ is the *angular frequency*. It has the units radians per second, the same units as angular velocity, also designated ω. In Section 14-2 we shall see that angular frequency is very closely related to the angular velocity of a circular motion which is associated with simple harmonic motion.

In terms of the frequency or period, Equation 14-1 is

$$x = A \cos (2\pi f\, t + \delta) = A \cos \left(\frac{2\pi t}{T} + \delta\right) \qquad 14\text{-}4$$

The phase constant δ depends on our choice of zero time. If we choose $t = 0$ when $x = A$, the phase constant is zero. On the other hand, if we choose $t = 0$ when $x = 0$, δ is either $\pi/2$ or $3\pi/2$, depending on whether x is increasing or decreasing at $t = 0$. For example, if $\delta = 3\pi/2$,

$$x = A \cos \left(\omega t + \frac{3\pi}{2}\right) = A \sin \omega t$$

Then x is increasing at $t = 0$, as can be seen from a graph of $x = A \sin \omega t$ versus t.

We can find the general relation between the initial position x_0 and the constants A and δ by setting $t = 0$ in Equation 14-1:

$$x_0 = A \cos \delta \qquad\qquad 14\text{-}5$$

The phase constant is not very important for the description of one-dimensional simple harmonic motion of a single particle since we can always choose our zero time to make $\delta = 0$. If we have two particles undergoing simple harmonic motion, or if we consider the combination of simple harmonic motion of a particle in two dimensions, we have two phase constants. If they are not equal, we can make only one of them equal to zero by our choice of zero time. Then the other one, the relative phase constant of the two motions, is important in the description of the motion.

The velocity of a particle undergoing simple harmonic motion is

$$v_x = \frac{dx}{dt} = -A\omega \sin (\omega t + \delta)$$

$$= A\omega \cos \left(\omega t + \delta + \frac{\pi}{2}\right) \qquad 14\text{-}6$$

The phase of the velocity differs from that of the position by $\pi/2$ rad, or $90°$. When $\cos(\omega t + \delta) = 1$, $\sin(\omega t + \delta) = 0$, and so when x is its maximum or minimum value, the velocity is zero. Similarly when $\sin(\omega t + \delta) = 1$, $\cos(\omega t + \delta) = 0$. The speed is maximum when the particle is at its equilibrium position $x = 0$. According to Equation 14-6, the initial velocity is related to A and ω by

$$v_0 = -A\omega \sin \delta \qquad\qquad 14\text{-}7$$

Since Equations 14-5 and 14-7 can be solved for A and δ in terms of the initial position x_0 and initial velocity v_0, the amplitude A and the phase constant δ are completely determined by the initial conditions.

The acceleration of the particle is

$$a_x = \frac{d^2x}{dt^2} = \frac{dv_x}{dt} = -\omega^2 A \cos(\omega t + \delta)$$

or

$$a_x = -\omega^2 x \qquad\qquad 14\text{-}8$$

In simple harmonic motion, *the acceleration is proportional to the displacement and in the opposite direction.*

Acceleration is proportional to displacement in simple harmonic motion

According to our discussion of one-dimensional motion in Chapter 2, if the acceleration of a particle is known, the position $x(t)$ is completely determined by the initial conditions, e.g., the initial position and velocity. As we have seen, these are related to the constants A and δ in Equation 14-1. Thus we could begin with Equation 14-8, relating the acceleration to the position, and work backward to obtain Equation 14-1 (see Problem 13). That is, the general solution of the differential equation 14-8 is of the form of Equation 14-1; the two equations are equivalent. We can therefore take either Equation 14-1 or 14-8 as our definition of simple harmonic motion.

Equation 14-8 is important because the acceleration of a particle is just the resultant force divided by the mass. *Whenever a force is proportional to the displacement (and in the opposite direction), we can conclude that the motion is simple harmonic.* For example, if a mass m is acted upon by a spring of force constant k, the force is $-kx$ and the acceleration is

Conditions for simple harmonic motion

$$a_x = \frac{F_x}{m} = -\frac{k}{m}x \qquad\qquad 14\text{-}9$$

This equation is the same as Equation 14-8 with k/m replacing ω^2. The solution of this equation is Equation 14-1 with $\omega = \sqrt{k/m}$ and the constants A and δ determined by the initial position and velocity of the mass. Note that the angular frequency ω and thus the period $T = 2\pi/\omega$ are determined only by the force constant and the mass. They do not depend on the amplitude A. This is an important property of simple harmonic motion.

In simple harmonic motion, the frequency and period are independent of the amplitude.

Frequency and period are independent of the amplitude

We can write the general position function $x(t)$ for simple harmonic motion in terms of the initial position and velocity, rather than the amplitude and phase constant as in Equation 14-1. We use the trigonometric identity for the cosine of the sum of two angles,

$$\cos(\theta + \phi) = \cos\theta \cos\phi - \sin\theta \sin\phi$$

Then Equation 14-1 can be written

$$A \cos (\omega t + \delta) = A \cos \delta \cos \omega t - A \sin \delta \sin \omega t$$

But according to Equations 14-4 and 14-7, $A \cos \delta = x_0$ and $-A \sin \delta = v_0/\omega$. Then

$$x(t) = A \cos (\omega t + \delta) = x_0 \cos \omega t + \frac{v_0}{\omega} \sin \omega t \qquad 14\text{-}10$$

Position function in terms of the initial conditions

Questions

1. What is the phase constant δ in Equation 14-1 if the position of the oscillating particle at time $t = 0$ is (a) 0, (b) $-A$, (c) A, (d) $A/2$?

2. How far does a particle oscillating with amplitude A move in one full period?

3. How far apart are the extreme positions of a particle oscillating with amplitude A?

4. If you know that the speed of an oscillator of amplitude A is zero at certain times, can you say exactly what its displacement is at those times? Can you say what direction it will be moving in a moment? If not, how close can you come?

5. If you are told that the speed of an oscillator of amplitude A has its maximum value at a certain time, can you say exactly what its displacement is? Can you say in what direction it is moving?

6. Can the acceleration and displacement of a simple harmonic oscillator ever be in the same directions? The acceleration and the velocity? The velocity and the displacement? Explain.

7. What is the magnitude of the acceleration of an oscillator of amplitude A and angular frequency ω when its speed is a maximum? When its displacement is a maximum?

14-2 Circular Motion and Simple Harmonic Motion

There is a simple relation between circular motion with constant angular velocity and simple harmonic motion. Consider a particle moving in a circle of radius A with constant angular velocity ω, as shown in Figure 14-2. The angular displacement of the particle relative to the x axis is given by

$$\theta = \omega t + \delta \qquad 14\text{-}11$$

where δ is the angular displacement at $t = 0$. From Figure 14-2 we see that the x component of the position of the particle is given by

$$x = A \cos \theta = A \cos (\omega t + \delta) \qquad 14\text{-}12$$

Thus the projection on a straight line of uniform circular motion at angular velocity ω is simple harmonic motion with angular frequency ω. The frequency and period of the circular motion are the same as the corresponding frequency and period of the projected simple harmonic motion. The relation between circular motion and simple harmonic motion can be demonstrated with a turntable and a mass on a spring (Figure 14-3).

Projection of circular motion on a straight line is simple harmonic motion

The projection of the circular motion on the y axis is $y = A \cdot \sin \theta = A \sin (\omega t + \delta) = A \cos (\omega t + \delta - \pi/2)$ (Figure 14-2). We can therefore consider the circular motion of a particle to be the combination of perpendicular simple harmonic motions having the same amplitude and frequency but having a relative phase difference of $\pi/2$. We shall consider combinations of perpendicular simple harmonic motions with other phase differences or with different amplitudes in a later section.

Figure 14-2
Particle moving with constant angular velocity ω in a circle of radius A. Its angular displacement is $\theta = \omega t + \delta$. Point P on the x axis moves with simple harmonic motion $x = A \cos (\omega t + \delta)$. The projection on the y axis, $y = A \sin (\omega t + \delta)$, is also simple harmonic motion but differs in phase by 90° from x.

Question

8. At what points does the mass traveling on the circle in Figure 14-2 have the same displacement as the oscillating particle? The same speed? The same acceleration?

14-3 A Mass on a Spring

If a mass is attached to a spring stretched a distance x from its equilibrium length, the force on the mass is $F_x = -kx$, where k is called the *force constant* of the spring. Newton's second law for the motion of the mass is

$$F_x = m \frac{d^2x}{dt^2} = -kx$$

or

$$\frac{d^2x}{dt^2} = a_x = -\frac{k}{m} x \qquad\qquad 14\text{-}13$$

This is the same as Equation 14-8 with

$$\omega^2 = \frac{k}{m} \qquad\qquad 14\text{-}14$$

The mass oscillates with simple harmonic motion. The position of the mass is given by either Equation 14-1 or 14-10:

$$x = A \cos (\omega t + \delta) = x_0 \cos \omega t + \frac{v_0}{\omega} \sin \omega t$$

The velocity of the mass is

$$v_x = \frac{dx}{dt} = -\omega A \sin (\omega t + \delta) = -\omega x_0 \sin \omega t + v_0 \cos \omega t$$

Figure 14-3
The shadow of a peg on a turntable is projected on the screen along with the shadow of a mass on a spring. When the period of rotation of the turntable equals the period of oscillation of the mass, the shadows move together.

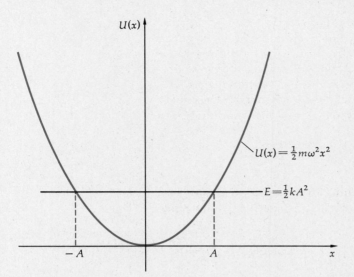

Figure 14-4
The potential-energy function
$U(x) = \frac{1}{2}kx^2 = \frac{1}{2}m\omega^2 x^2$ for a
mass on a spring. The hori-
zontal line represents the total
energy $\frac{1}{2}kA^2$ for amplitude A.

The potential energy of the mass on the spring is

$$U(x) = \tfrac{1}{2}kx^2 = \tfrac{1}{2}m\omega^2 x^2 \qquad\qquad 14\text{-}15$$

where we use $\omega^2 = k/m$. This is the parabolic potential-energy function discussed in Example 9-5. It is sketched again in Figure 14-4.

The total energy is

$$E = U(x) + \tfrac{1}{2}mv_x{}^2 = \tfrac{1}{2}m\omega^2 x^2 + \tfrac{1}{2}m\left(\frac{dx}{dt}\right)^2$$

Using Equations 14-1 and 14-6 for x and dx/dt, we obtain

$$\begin{aligned}
E &= \tfrac{1}{2}m\omega^2 A^2 \cos^2(\omega t + \delta) + \tfrac{1}{2}m\omega^2 A^2 \sin^2(\omega t + \delta) \\
&= \tfrac{1}{2}m\omega^2 A^2 \left[\cos^2(\omega t + \delta) + \sin^2(\omega t + \delta)\right] \\
&= \tfrac{1}{2}m\omega^2 A^2 = \tfrac{1}{2}kA^2 \qquad\qquad 14\text{-}16
\end{aligned}$$

The total energy is thus constant and equal to the maximum potential energy or the maximum kinetic energy. The total energy is shown by the horizontal line in Figure 14-4. As discussed in Chapter 9, the kinetic energy is represented on this graph by the vertical distance between the total energy and the potential energy. It is easily seen from the figure that the two turning points are at equal distances from the equilibrium point $x = 0$ and that the maximum velocity occurs at $x = 0$.

Example 14-1 A 2-kg mass stretches a spring 10 cm when it hangs vertically in equilibrium. The mass is then attached to the spring resting on a smooth table and fixed at one end, as shown in Figure 14-5. The mass is held a distance 5 cm from the equilibrium position and released. Find the frequency f, angular frequency ω, period T, amplitude A, and phase constant δ for the resulting simple harmonic motion. What is the maximum speed of the mass, and when does it occur?

The force constant of the spring is determined from the first measurement. We have for the vertical-equilibrium case $ky = mg$, where y is the amount the spring is stretched. Using $g \approx 10$ m/sec², $m = 2$ kg, and $y = 10$ cm $= 0.1$ m, we have

$$k = \frac{mg}{y} = \frac{(2 \text{ kg})(10 \text{ m/sec}^2)}{0.1 \text{ m}} = 200 \text{ N/m}$$

Figure 14-5
Mass m is attached to a spring and slides without friction on a horizontal surface.

We are given that the initial position of the mass is $x_0 = 5$ cm $= 0.05$ m and that the initial velocity is zero. Then from Equations 14-5 and 14-7 we have $\delta = 0$ and $A = 0.05$ m. The equation of motion of the mass is

$$x = (0.05 \text{ m}) \cos \omega t$$

where $\omega = \sqrt{k/m} = \sqrt{200/2} = 10$ rad/sec. The period, found from $\omega T = 2\pi$, is

$$T = \frac{2\pi}{10} = 0.63 \text{ sec}$$

The reciprocal of the period is the frequency. The units of frequency are reciprocal seconds, often written cycles per second or vibrations per second for easier reading. The unit cycles per second is now called the hertz (Hz). Thus

$$f = \frac{1}{T} = 1.59 \text{ cycles/sec} = 1.59 \text{ Hz}$$

The velocity of the mass is

$$v_x = \frac{dx}{dt} = -\omega A \sin \omega t = -(10 \text{ rad/sec})(0.05 \text{ m}) \sin \omega t$$

$$= -(0.5 \text{ m/sec}) \sin \omega t$$

The maximum speed is 0.5 m/sec. This occurs first when $\omega t_1 = \pi/2$ or $t_1 = \frac{1}{4}T = 0.16$ sec. At this time, $x = 0$ and v_x is negative, indicating that the motion is to the left. The speed is maximum again one-half cycle later, when $x = 0$ but the mass is moving to the right. The functions $x(t)$ and $v_x(t)$ are sketched in Figure 14-6.

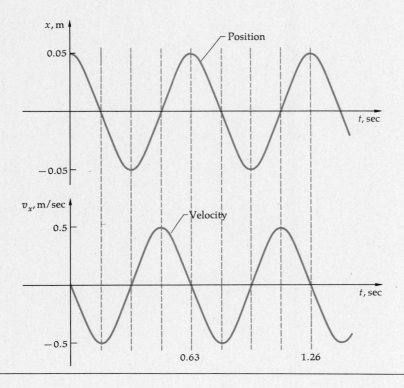

Figure 14-6
Position and velocity of mass versus time for Example 14-1.

Figure 14-7
Example 14-2. Two identical
mass-spring systems starting
at rest with different displacements. Since the period does
not depend on the amplitude,
both masses reach their equilibrium positions at the same
time.

Example 14-2 A second spring identical to that in Example 14-1 is attached to a second particle, also of mass 2 kg. This spring is stretched a
distance of 10 cm from equilibrium and released at the same time as
the first, which is stretched to 5 cm. Which mass reaches the equilibrium position first?

Figure 14-7 shows the initial positions of the masses, and Figure
14-8 is a sketch of the two position functions $x_1(t)$ and $x_2(t)$. Since both
the springs have the same force constant and the masses are equal, the
angular frequencies and periods of the two motions are the same.
Only the amplitudes differ. *Thus they both reach the equilibrium position
at the same time.* Particle 2 has twice as far to go to reach equilibrium as
particle 1, but it begins with twice the initial acceleration. The equations of motion of the two particles are

$$x_1 = (0.05 \text{ m}) \cos 10t \qquad x_2 = (0.10 \text{ m}) \cos 10t$$

where t must be in seconds because we put in the value $\omega = 10$
rad/sec.

This example illustrates that the angular frequency and period in
simple harmonic motion are independent of the amplitude. Thus the
time $\frac{1}{4}T$ to reach the equilibrium position is the same for each particle.
Of course the energies of the two particles are different: more work is
required to stretch the second spring 10 cm than to stretch the first one
5 cm. The energies are

$$E_1 = \tfrac{1}{2}kA_1{}^2 = \tfrac{1}{2}(200)(0.05^2) = 0.25 \text{ J}$$

$$E_2 = \tfrac{1}{2}kA_2{}^2 = \tfrac{1}{2}(200)(0.1^2) = 1.0 \text{ J}$$

You should show that at the equilibrium position the velocity of the
second mass is twice that of the first.

Figure 14-8
Plot of position versus time
for the masses in Figure 14-7.

Example 14-3 A mass on a spring at rest at $x = 0$ is struck a blow with a hammer, which delivers an impulse I. What is the subsequent motion?

We choose $t = 0$ just after the impulse. The mass is thus at $x = 0$ with an initial velocity $v_0 = p_0/m = I/m$, where p_0, the initial momentum, is equal to the impulse. The form of Equation 14-10 is useful here since x_0 is zero. Thus

$$x = \frac{v_0}{\omega} \sin \omega t = \frac{I}{m\omega} \sin \omega t$$

Questions

9. A mass m oscillates at frequency f when it is attached to a horizontal spring as in Figure 14-5. It is released from rest when its displacement is A. If a second mass m is attached to the first and the two are released at the same displacement, how will the frequency be changed? The angular frequency? The period? The amplitude? The maximum speed? The maximum acceleration? The maximum force exerted by the spring?

10. Explain how each of the following quantities will change if the impulse I in Example 14-3 is doubled: the amplitude, the frequency, the period, the maximum speed, the total energy, the phase constant.

11. The effect of the mass of a spring on the motion of an object attached to it is usually neglected; describe qualitatively its effect when it is not neglected.

14-4 The Simple Pendulum

Another important example of periodic motion is that of a simple pendulum. If the angle made by the string with the vertical is not too great, the motion of the bob of the pendulum is simple harmonic.

Consider a mass on a string of length L, as shown in Figure 14-9. The forces on the mass are the weight mg and the tension T in the string. The tangential force has magnitude $mg \sin \theta$ and is in the direction of decreasing θ. Let s be the arc length measured from the bottom

Figure 14-9
Forces on a simple pendulum.

of the circle. The arc length is related to the angle measured from the vertical by

$$s = L\theta \qquad\qquad 14\text{-}17$$

The tangential acceleration is d^2s/dt^2. The tangential component of $\Sigma\mathbf{F} = m\mathbf{a}$ is

$$\Sigma F_t = -mg \sin\theta = m\frac{d^2s}{dt^2}$$

or

$$\frac{d^2s}{dt^2} = -g \sin\theta = -g \sin\frac{s}{L} \qquad\qquad 14\text{-}18$$

If s is much less than L, the angle $\theta = s/L$ is small and we can approximate $\sin\theta$ by the angle θ. Using $\sin(s/L) \approx s/L$ in Equation 14-18, we have

$$\frac{d^2s}{dt^2} = -\frac{g}{L} s \qquad\qquad 14\text{-}19$$

Motion of a pendulum is simple harmonic for small amplitudes

We see that for small angles for which the approximation $\sin\theta \approx \theta$ is valid, the acceleration is proportional to the displacement. The motion of the pendulum is simple harmonic for small displacement. If we write ω^2 for g/L, Equation 14-19 becomes

$$\frac{d^2s}{dt^2} = -\omega^2 s$$

$$\omega^2 = \frac{g}{L} \qquad\qquad 14\text{-}20$$

The solution of this equation is

$$s = s_0 \cos(\omega t + \delta) \qquad\qquad 14\text{-}21$$

where s_0 is the maximum displacement measured along the arc of the circle. The period of the motion is

$$T = \frac{2\pi}{\omega} = 2\pi\sqrt{\frac{L}{g}} \qquad\qquad 14\text{-}22$$

It is often more convenient to measure the displacement of the pendulum in terms of the angle made with the vertical $\theta = s/L$. Equations 14-18, 14-19, and 14-21 can be written in terms of the angular displacement and the angular acceleration $d^2\theta/dt^2$ by dividing each side by L, giving

$$\frac{d^2\theta}{dt^2} = -\frac{g}{L} \sin\theta \qquad\qquad 14\text{-}18a$$

which for small θ becomes

$$\frac{d^2\theta}{dt^2} = -\frac{g}{L} \theta \qquad\qquad 14\text{-}19a$$

The solution of this equation is

$$\theta = \theta_0 \cos(\omega t + \delta) \qquad\qquad 14\text{-}21a$$

where $\theta_0 = s_0/L$ is the maximum angular displacement. The criterion for simple harmonic motion stated in terms of these angular quantities is that the angular acceleration be proportional to the angular displacement, as in Equation 14-19a.

Example 14-4 What is the period of a pendulum 1 m long when $g = 9.8$ m/sec²?

The angular frequency is given by Equation 14-20,

$$\omega = \sqrt{\frac{g}{L}} = \sqrt{\frac{9.8 \text{ m/sec}^2}{1 \text{ m}}} = 3.13 \text{ rad/sec}$$

The period is

$$T = \frac{2\pi}{\omega} = \frac{2\pi}{3.13} = 2.01 \text{ sec}$$

A time of this magnitude is easily measured accurately. For example, with a watch which can measure time intervals to ±1 sec, we can measure such a period to ±1 part in 200 by measuring the time for 100 vibrations.

The potential energy of the simple pendulum is the gravitational potential energy mgy of the mass, where y is the height measured from some reference level. It is convenient to choose $y = 0$ at the lowest point of the mass at $\theta = 0$. Then y is related to θ by

$$y = L - L \cos \theta = L(1 - \cos \theta)$$

as can be seen from Figure 14-10. The potential energy is then

$$U = mgL(1 - \cos \theta) \qquad \qquad 14\text{-}23$$

and the total energy is

$$E = \tfrac{1}{2}mv^2 + U = \tfrac{1}{2}mv^2 + mgL(1 - \cos \theta) \qquad \qquad 14\text{-}24$$

For small angles, we can approximate $\cos \theta$ by

$$\cos \theta = 1 - \frac{\theta^2}{2} + \cdots \approx 1 - \frac{\theta^2}{2} \qquad \qquad 14\text{-}25$$

Then $1 - \cos \theta \approx \tfrac{1}{2}\theta^2$, and the potential energy is

$$U(\theta) \approx \tfrac{1}{2}mgL\theta^2 \qquad \qquad 14\text{-}26a$$

According to Equation 14-15, the potential energy for a mass on a spring can be written $U = \tfrac{1}{2}m\omega^2 x^2$. If we use $\theta = s/L$ and $\omega^2 = g/L$, we have for the potential energy of a simple pendulum,

$$U = \tfrac{1}{2}mgL \left(\frac{s}{L}\right)^2 = \tfrac{1}{2}m \frac{g}{L} s^2 = \tfrac{1}{2}m\omega^2 s^2 \qquad \qquad 14\text{-}26b$$

The simple pendulum was used for early determinations of the acceleration of gravity because both the period and the length are easily measured. Direct measurement by observation of free fall, in con-

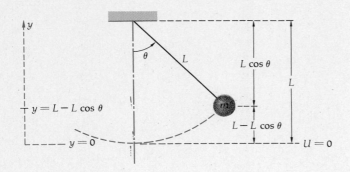

Figure 14-10
The height of the mass above its equilibrium position is $y = L - L \cos \theta$. Its potential energy is $U = mgy = mgL(1 - \cos \theta)$ relative to $U = 0$ at $\theta = 0$.

trast, is difficult because the time of fall over reasonable distances is too short for easy measurement. From Equation 14-22 we have, in terms of L and T,

$$g = \frac{4\pi^2 L}{T^2} \qquad\qquad 14\text{-}27$$

The pendulum mass is not involved in the determination of g because, according to Newton's law of gravitation, the force of gravity on an object is proportional to its mass or inertia m. This characteristic is unique to gravity among all the forces we know and is a matter of considerable interest. One consequence is that all objects near the earth fall with the same acceleration if air resistance is negligible, a fact that has seemed surprising to men since ancient times. (The well-known story of how Galileo demonstrated this by dropping weights from the Leaning Tower of Pisa is one example of the excitement this discovery aroused in the sixteenth century.)

Another consequence is that the period of a simple pendulum depends only on its length and not on the mass of the pendulum bob. Newton noted this and used the simple pendulum as an experimental test of his conclusion that the force of gravity is proportional to the mass of the object upon which it acts. He reasoned as follows: suppose the weight of an object were proportional not to m but to some other property of the body. That is, suppose

$$w = gm_G$$

where g is a constant and m_G stands for a measure of this property. (It has been customary in recent years to call m_G the gravitational mass to distinguish it from the inertial mass m.) The acceleration of this body in free fall would then be

$$a = \frac{w}{m} = \frac{m_G}{m} g$$

Thus one would expect different objects to have different free-fall accelerations depending on the ratio m_G/m. It would be reasonable to suppose that m_G/m would depend on such things as the chemical composition of the body, or its temperature, or other physical characteristics.

The experimental fact, however, is that a is the same for all bodies. This means that for every body m_G/m has the same value. That is, m_G must be proportional to m in all circumstances. Since this is the case, we need not maintain the distinction between m_G and m, and indeed this is our custom. We must keep in mind, however, that this is an experimental conclusion limited by the accuracy of experiment. As an experimental law, the statement that m_G is proportional to m is known as the *principle of equivalence*. Experiments testing it were carried out by Simon Stevin in the 1580s (he also discovered the law of vector addition for forces). Galileo publicized this law widely, and his contemporaries made considerable improvements on the experimental accuracy with which the law was established.   *Principle of equivalence*

The most precise early experiments made to back up the principle of equivalence were those of Newton, using simple pendulums. He noted that if m_G were different from the inertial mass m, derivation of the formula for the period of the pendulum would lead not to Equation 14-18 but to

$$T = 2\pi \sqrt{\frac{mL}{m_G g}}$$

Thus, one would expect the periods of pendulums with the same length but different masses and made of different materials to differ. This would be the case unless m_G is exactly proportional to m for every body. Newton conducted careful measurements with different types of pendulum bobs and found to high accuracy that the pendulum period is independent of the mass or composition of the bob. His measurements with the pendulum were much more precise than earlier experiments with falling bodies. Newton was able to establish the proportionality of m_G and m to an accuracy of about 1 part in 1000. Experiments comparing gravitational mass with inertial mass have been improved steadily over the years, until recently the proportionality of m_G and m has been demonstrated to an accuracy of about 1 part in 10^{12}. This accuracy means that the principle of equivalence is one of the best established of all physical laws.

Since the proportionality of m_G and m is so well established, we never distinguish between them, and put $m_G = m$. (This amounts to choosing the constant of proportionality equal to 1, which in turn determines the units of G in the law of gravity.)

The motion of a simple pendulum is simple harmonic only if the angular displacement is small so that $\sin \theta \approx \theta$ is valid. Figure 14-11 shows a plot of θ and $\sin \theta$. Even for the rather large angle $\theta = \pi/6 = 0.523$ (which is 30°), the difference between θ and $\sin \theta = \sin 30° = 0.500$ is only 4.6 percent. If the angular displacement is large, the angular acceleration given by Equation 14-18a is not proportional to the angular displacement. The motion of the pendulum for large angles is not simple harmonic. However, the motion is periodic, though the period is not independent of the amplitude, as in simple harmonic motion. From Figure 14-11 we see that at large angles $\sin \theta$ is less than θ. The force which accelerates the mass back toward equilibrium has the magnitude $mg \sin \theta$; this is less than $mg\theta$, which would produce simple harmonic motion. Thus the acceleration at large angles is less than it must be for simple harmonic motion, and the period is slightly longer. We can see this also from Figure 14-12; it compares the actual potential energy, which is proportional to $1 - \cos \theta$, with the approximation, proportional to $\frac{1}{2}\theta^2$. For a given total energy E, the pendulum travels farther between a turning point and equilibrium in the actual potential energy than it would in the parabolic potential-energy function for simple harmonic motion. The period is therefore

Figure 14-11
Comparison of θ and $\sin \theta$. For sufficiently small angles the curves are approximately the same.

Distances to
turning point
—Actual—
—SHM—

Figure 14-12
Comparison of the potential-
energy function $U = mgL(1 - \cos\theta)$ with the approximation
$U = \frac{1}{2}mgL\theta^2$. SHM stands for
simple harmonic motion.

slightly longer. We omit the details of the difficult solution of Equation 14-18a for large angles. The period can be expressed in the power series

$$T = T_0 \left(1 + \frac{1}{2^2} \sin^2 \tfrac{1}{2}\theta_0 + \frac{1}{2^2}\frac{3^2}{4^2} \sin^4 \tfrac{1}{2}\theta_0 + \cdots \right) \qquad \text{14-28}$$

Large-amplitude motion of a pendulum

where θ_0 is the maximum angular displacement and $T_0 = 2\pi \sqrt{L/g}$ is the period in the limit of small angles.

Because the actual period of a simple pendulum does vary with amplitude θ_0, the simple pendulum makes a poor clock unless it is modified to compensate for energy loss due to friction and air resistance.

Example 14-5 A simple pendulum clock is calibrated to keep accurate time at an amplitude of $\theta_0 = 10°$. When the amplitude has decreased so that it is very small, $\theta_0 \ll 10°$, how much time does the clock gain in 1 d?

The original period is approximately

$$T \approx T_0(1 + \tfrac{1}{4} \sin^2 5°)$$

since $\sin^4 \tfrac{1}{2}\theta_0 \ll \sin^2 \tfrac{1}{2}\theta_0$ in Equation 14-28. After the amplitude has decreased, the period is just T_0. Since this is less, the frequency is greater and the clock gains time. The fractional change in the period is

$$-\frac{\Delta T}{T} = \frac{T - T_0}{T_0} = \tfrac{1}{4} \sin^2 5° = \tfrac{1}{4}(0.0872)^2 \approx 2 \times 10^{-3}$$

The number of minutes in 1 d is

$$\frac{24 \text{ h}}{1 \text{ d}} \frac{60 \text{ min}}{1 \text{ h}} = 1440 \text{ min/d}$$

Thus a fractional change of 2×10^{-3} corresponds to an accumulated error in 1 d of $2 \times 10^{-3} \times 1440$ min $= 2.88$ min ≈ 3 min. Though the fractional change in period is only 2×10^{-3}, corresponding to a percentage change of 0.2 percent, this results in an intolerable error in timekeeping by today's standards for clocks. For this reason pendulum clocks are designed to maintain constant amplitude.

Question

12. The string or wire supporting a pendulum increases slightly in length when its temperature is raised. How would this affect a clock operated by the pendulum?

14-5 The Physical Pendulum

Any rigid body suspended from some point other than the center of mass will oscillate when displaced from its equilibrium position. Consider a plane figure suspended from a point a distance D from the center of mass, as shown in Figure 14-13. The torque about the suspension point is $MgD \sin \theta$ in a direction tending to decrease θ. The angular acceleration of the body is related to the torque by

$$\Sigma \tau = I\alpha = I \frac{d^2\theta}{dt^2}$$

where I is the amount of inertia about the point of suspension. Therefore

$$-MgD \sin \theta = I \frac{d^2\theta}{dt^2} \qquad \text{14-29}$$

For a simple pendulum this is the same as Equation 14-18a since $I = ML^2$ and $D = L$. Once again, the motion is simple harmonic only if the angular displacements are small, so that the approximation $\sin \theta \approx \theta$ holds. For this case, we have

$$\frac{d^2\theta}{dt^2} = -\frac{MgD}{I}\theta = -\omega^2\theta \qquad \text{14-30}$$

where $\omega^2 = MgD/I$. The period is

$$T = \frac{2\pi}{\omega} = 2\pi \sqrt{\frac{I}{MgD}} \qquad \text{14-31}$$

For large angles, the period is given by Equation 14-28, where T_0 is now given by Equation 14-31. The result we have just obtained can be used to measure the moment of inertia of a plane figure. The center of mass can be located by suspending the body from two different points, as discussed previously. To find the moment of inertia about some point P we suspend the body from point P and measure the period of oscillation. The moment of inertia is then obtained from

$$I = \frac{MgDT^2}{4\pi^2} \qquad \text{14-32}$$

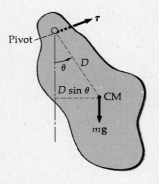

Figure 14-13
Physical pendulum. The weight produces a torque of magnitude $MgD \sin \theta$ about the pivot, tending to decrease the angle θ.

Example 14-6 What is the period of oscillation of a stick pivoted at one end if the amplitude of oscillation is small?

The moment of inertia of a uniform stick of length L about an axis at one end was shown in Chapter 12 to be $I = \frac{1}{3}ML^2$. The distance from the pivot to the center of mass is $\frac{1}{2}L$. Substituting these values in Equation 14-31 gives

$$T = 2\pi \sqrt{\frac{\frac{1}{3}ML^2}{Mg(\frac{1}{2}L)}} = 2\pi \sqrt{\frac{2L}{3g}}$$

If $L = 1$ m, the value of T obtained from this result is 1.64 sec.

14-6 A Mass on a Vertical Spring

When a mass hangs from a vertical spring, as in Figure 14-14, there is a force mg downward in addition to the force of the spring $-ky$ (y is measured downward from the unstretched position of the spring). The

motion of the mass is given by

$$m \frac{d^2y}{dt^2} = -ky + mg \qquad 14\text{-}33$$

which differs from Equation 14-13 in containing the constant-force term mg. We handle this extra term in a simple way. When the mass hangs in equilibrium from the spring, the spring is stretched by y_0, where $ky_0 = mg$. Let us measure the extension of the spring from this equilibrium point; i.e., let $y' = y - y_0$. Then $dy'/dt = dy/dt$ and $d^2y'/dt^2 = d^2y/dt^2$. Multiplying y' by k, we obtain

$$ky' = k(y - y_0) = ky - ky_0 = ky - mg$$

Thus $ky = ky' + mg$, and Equation 14-33 becomes

$$m \frac{d^2y'}{dt^2} = -ky' \qquad 14\text{-}34$$

which has the familiar solution $y' = A \cos(\omega t + \delta)$ with $\omega^2 = k/m$. The mass oscillates about the equilibrium point where the total force on the mass is zero.

The potential energy of the spring is not $\frac{1}{2}ky'^2$ but $\frac{1}{2}ky^2 = \frac{1}{2}k(y' + y_0)^2$. When the spring is stretched from $y = y_0$ to some value y, the potential energy of the *spring* is increased by

$$\Delta U_{sp} = \frac{1}{2}ky^2 - \frac{1}{2}ky_0^2 = \frac{1}{2}ky'^2 + ky_0y' + \frac{1}{2}ky_0^2 - \frac{1}{2}ky_0^2$$
$$= \frac{1}{2}ky'^2 + mgy' \qquad 14\text{-}35$$

but the potential energy due to the earth's gravity is decreased by mgy'. When the spring is stretched from y_0 to y, the total potential-energy change is

$$\Delta U = \frac{1}{2}ky^2 - \frac{1}{2}ky_0^2 - mgy' = \frac{1}{2}ky'^2 \qquad 14\text{-}36$$

That is, when the spring is stretched by amount y' from equilibrium, the total change in potential energy, *including gravitational potential energy*, is $\frac{1}{2}ky'^2$. Thus if we measure from the equilibrium position, we can forget about the effect of the earth. The potential-energy functions $\frac{1}{2}ky^2$ and $-mgy$ are shown as dashed curves in Figure 14-15. Their sum is the solid curve.

Figure 14-14
Mass on a vertical spring. In equilibrium the spring is stretched by the amount $y_0 = mg/k$. The effect of gravity can be neglected if the position of the mass is measured from its equilibrium position.

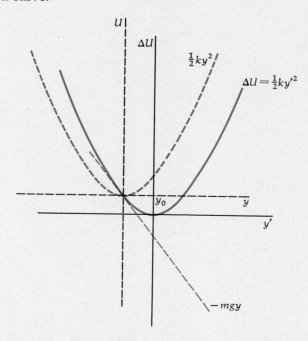

Figure 14-15
Shown as dashed lines are the spring potential energy $\frac{1}{2}ky^2$ and the gravitational potential energy $-mgy$ for a mass on a vertical spring with y taken to be positive downward. The total potential energy, the sum of these, is $\frac{1}{2}ky'^2 - \frac{1}{2}mgy_0$, where y' is measured from the equilibrium position of the mass. If ΔU is measured from the constant value $-\frac{1}{2}mgy_0$, then $\Delta U = \frac{1}{2}ky'^2$.

14-7 General Motion near Equilibrium

Whenever a particle is displaced from a position of stable equilibrium, the motion of the particle is simple harmonic if the displacements are small enough. Figure 14-16 shows some arbitrary resultant force as a function of position. At positions x_1 and x_2 the force is zero; these are positions of equilibrium. However, the equilibrium at x_2 is unstable, for if the particle is displaced slightly in the positive x direction, the force is positive, while if it is displaced slightly in the negative x direction, the force is negative. In both cases, the force accelerates the particle away from equilibrium. The position x_1 is one of stable equilibrium. If the particle is displaced slightly in either direction from equilibrium, the force accelerates it back toward equilibrium. The particle thus oscillates about this equilibrium point. As we can see from Figure 14-16b, the plot of force versus displacement is approximately

Figure 14-16
(a) An arbitrary force F_x versus x. Points x_1 and x_2 are equilibrium points where the force is zero. At x_1 the equilibrium is stable because for small displacements from equilibrium the force is toward x_1. For small displacements from x_2 the force is away from x_2 so the equilibrium is unstable at that point. (b) Near x_1 the force F_x can be approximated by a straight line, $F_x = -k(x - x_1)$. For small displacements $\epsilon = x - x_1$ the motion is approximately simple harmonic.

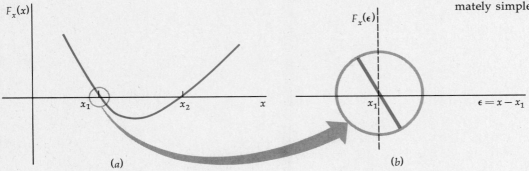

(a)   (b)

a straight line if we consider only small displacements from the equilibrium point x_1. Let ϵ measure the displacement from equilibrium:

$$\epsilon = x - x_1$$

The equation for the force for small ϵ is

$$F_x = -k\epsilon$$

where k is the magnitude of the slope of F_x versus x near x_1. Since the force is proportional to the displacement, the motion will be simple harmonic.

We can also examine the motion from the point of view of the potential-energy function $U(x)$ associated with the force. Figure 14-17 shows $U(x)$ versus x. As discussed in Chapter 8, the maximum at x_2 corresponds to unstable equilibrium, whereas the minimum at x_1 cor-

Figure 14-17
Potential-energy function $U(x)$ corresponding to the force in Figure 14-16. The minimum at x_1 indicates stable equilibrium whereas the maximum at x_2 indicates unstable equilibrium. Near x_1 the curve is approximately parabolic in shape, as in simple harmonic motion.

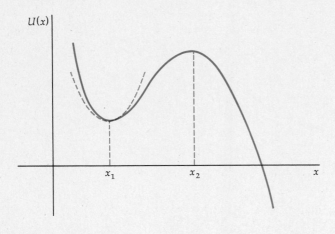

responds to stable equilibrium. The dashed curve in this figure is a parabolic curve which approximately fits $U(x)$ near the stable equilibrium point x_1. As long as the displacements from point x_1 are not too great, $U(x)$ is approximately parabolic and the motion is simple harmonic.

Questions

13. Give several examples of familiar motions which are either exactly or approximately simple harmonic motions.

14. The force on a particle is represented by the potential-energy function $U(x)$. The particle may execute approximate simple harmonic motion about a point x_1 only if $dU/dx = 0$ at that point. Explain why. The motion will be approximately simple harmonic for small displacements from x_1 *only* if d^2U/dx^2 is positive at x_1. Explain.

15. A ball bounces up and down on a table, reaching a maximum height h above the table and making perfectly elastic collisions with the table. Is this motion periodic? If so, what are the period and frequency? How does the motion differ from simple harmonic motion?

14-8 Combinations of Two Simple Harmonic Motions

The phase constant δ is important only if there are two or more simple harmonic motions. The simple example of two particles oscillating along the same direction with the same frequency and amplitude illustrates the role played by the phase constant in such cases. The equations of motion of the two particles are

$$x_1 = A \cos (\omega t + \delta_1) \qquad x_2 = A \cos (\omega t + \delta_2)$$

The difference in phase of the two motions at any time is

$$(\omega t + \delta_2) - (\omega t + \delta_1) = \delta_2 - \delta_1 = \delta_r$$

where δ_r is called the *relative phase* of the motion. Let us choose our zero time so that δ_1 is zero. Since the relative phase is independent of time, the phase constant δ_2 must then be δ_r. The equations of motion are then

$$x_1 = A \cos \omega t \qquad \text{and} \qquad x_2 = A \cos (\omega t + \delta_r)$$

It is interesting to look at the motion of one particle relative to the other. Let us imagine that we are sitting on particle 1 and observing particle 2. The position of particle 2 relative to particle 1 is

$$x_r = x_2 - x_1 = A \cos (\omega t + \delta_r) - A \cos \omega t$$

We can simplify this by using the trigonometric identity

$$\cos A - \cos B = -2 \sin \tfrac{1}{2}(A - B) \sin \tfrac{1}{2}(A + B)$$

Then

$$x_r = -A (2 \sin \tfrac{1}{2}\delta_r) \sin (\omega t + \tfrac{1}{2}\delta_r)$$
$$= 2A \sin \tfrac{1}{2}\delta_r \cos (\omega t + \tfrac{1}{2}\delta_r + \tfrac{1}{2}\pi) \qquad\qquad 14\text{-}37$$

where we have also used the identity $\cos (\theta + \tfrac{1}{2}\pi) = -\sin \theta$. Equation 14-37 gives simple harmonic motion with amplitude $2A \sin \tfrac{1}{2}\delta_r$. For example, if δ_r is zero, $x_r = 0$. There is no motion of one particle relative to the other; they move back and forth in phase. On the other hand, if the relative phase is 180°, the relative position is given by

$$x_r = 2A \sin 90° \cos (\omega t + \tfrac{1}{2}\pi + \tfrac{1}{2}\pi) = -2A \cos \omega t$$

Since we have chosen our zero time so that particle 1 is at its maximum displacement, particle 2 will be at its maximum negative displacement at zero time for $\delta_r = 180°$. Thus the relative motion is simple harmonic motion with amplitude $2A$.

Another interesting combination of two simple harmonic motions is the motion of a particle in a plane such that both its x and y coordinates vary as in simple harmonic motion. If we consider only cases in which the frequencies and amplitudes are equal,

$$x = A \cos (\omega t + \delta_1) \qquad y = A \cos (\omega t + \delta_2)$$

Again we can choose one of the phase constants to be zero by our choice of zero time. If we choose δ_1 to be zero and call $\delta_2 - \delta_1 = \delta_r$ the relative phase, as before, we have

$$x = A \cos \omega t \qquad\qquad\qquad\qquad 14\text{-}38$$

$$y = A \cos (\omega t + \delta_r) \qquad\qquad\qquad 14\text{-}39$$

We have already noted (Section 14-2) that when δ_r is $\pm 90°$, these equations are those for motion of a particle in a circle of radius A. Then

$$y = A \cos (\omega t \pm 90°) = \mp A \sin \omega t$$

and

$$x^2 + y^2 = A^2 \cos^2 \omega t + A^2 \sin^2 \omega t = A^2$$

which is the equation for a circle in the xy plane.

If the relative phase is zero, we have

$$y = A \cos \omega t = x$$

The motion is thus along the straight line $y = x$. Figure 14-18 shows the path of the particle described by Equations 14-38 and 14-39 for $\delta_r = 30°$. For relative phase angles between 0 and 90° the motion is an ellipse, of which the major axis is the line $y = x$. (The case $\delta_r = 0$ is a special case of an ellipse with zero minor axis; similarly, $\delta_r = 90°$ is the special case of equal major and minor axes, the circle.) This is also the case for relative phases between 270 and 360°. For δ_r between 90 and 270° the motion is an ellipse with major axis along the line $x = -y$. The special case of $\delta_r = 180°$ describes linear motion along this line, as can be seen from

$$y = A \cos (\omega t + 180°) = - A \cos \omega t = - x$$

If amplitudes are not equal, the combination of two simple harmonic motions of equal frequency describes the x and y coordinates for elliptical motion, the orientation and eccentricity depending on the difference in amplitudes and on δ_r. For example, if $\delta_r = 90°$ and the amplitudes are different, we have

$$x = A \cos \omega t \qquad y = B \cos (\omega t + 90°) = -B \sin \omega t$$

$$\frac{x^2}{A^2} + \frac{y^2}{B^2} = \cos^2 \omega t + \sin^2 \omega t = 1$$

which is the equation for an ellipse with major axis along the x or y axis, depending on whether A is greater or less than B.

Figure 14-18
Plot of $x = A \cos \omega t$, $y = A \cos (\omega t + \delta_r)$ for $\delta_r = 30°$.

Review

A. Define, explain, or otherwise identify:

Periodic motion, 355   Phase constant, 355
Simple harmonic motion, 355   Period, 355
Phase, 355   Angular frequency, 356
Amplitude, 355   Principle of equivalence, 366

B. True or false:

1. All periodic motion is simple harmonic motion.

2. All simple harmonic motion is periodic motion.

3. In simple harmonic motion, the period is proportional to the amplitude.

4. In simple harmonic motion, the total energy is proportional to the square of the amplitude.

5. In simple harmonic motion, the phase constant depends on the initial conditions.

6. The motion of a simple pendulum is simple harmonic for any initial angular displacement.

7. The motion of a simple pendulum is periodic for any initial angular displacement.

8. In simple harmonic motion the acceleration is proportional to the displacement and in the opposite direction.

9. Any motion in which the acceleration is proportional to the displacement and in the opposite direction is simple harmonic motion.

10. Motion near a position of stable equilibrium is generally simple harmonic if the displacements are small.

Exercises

Section 14-1, Simple Harmonic Motion

1. A particle has displacement x given by $x = 3 \cos (5\pi t + \pi)$, where x is in meters and t in seconds. (a) What are the frequency f and period T of the motion? (b) What is the greatest distance the particle travels from equilibrium? (c) Where is the particle at time $t = 0$? At time $t = \frac{1}{2}$ sec?

2. (a) Find an expression for the velocity of the particle whose position is given in Exercise 1. (b) What is the maximum velocity? (c) When does this maximum velocity occur?

3. A particle in simple harmonic motion is at rest a distance of 6 in from its equilibrium position at time $t = 0$. Its period is 2 sec. Write expressions for its position x, its velocity v, and its acceleration a as functions of time.

4. The position of a particle traveling in one dimension is given by $x = 5 \cos 4\pi t$, where x is in meters and t in seconds. (a) Find the amplitude, angular frequency, frequency, and period of the motion. (b) Find an expression for the velocity of the particle at any time t. (c) What is the velocity at time $t = 0$?

5. The position of a particle is given by $x = 4 \sin 2t$, where x is in feet and t is in seconds. (a) What is the maximum value of x? What is the first time after $t = 0$ at which this maximum value occurs? (b) Find an expression for the velocity of the particle as a function of time. What is the velocity at time $t = 0$? (c) Find an expression for the acceleration of the particle as a function of time. What is the acceleration at time $t = 0$? What is the maximum value of the acceleration?

6. A particle oscillates with simple harmonic motion with period $T = 2$ sec. It

is initially at its equilibrium position and moving with speed 4 m/sec in the direction of increasing x. Write expressions for its position x, its velocity v, and its acceleration a as functions of time.

Section 14-2, Circular Motion and Simple Harmonic Motion, and Section 14-3, A Mass on a Spring

7. A particle travels in a circle in the xy plane with center at the origin. The radius of the circle is 40 cm, and the speed of the particle is 80 cm/sec. (a) What is the angular velocity of the particle? (b) What are the frequency f and period T of the circular motion? (c) Write the x and y components of the position vector $\mathbf{r}$ as functions of time.

8. A 2-kg mass is attached to a spring of force constant $k = 5 \times 10^3$ N/m. The spring is stretched 10 cm from equilibrium and released. (a) Find the angular frequency, the frequency f, and the amplitude of oscillation. (b) Find $x(t)$, $v(t)$, and $a(t)$. (c) Write expressions for the kinetic and potential energies as functions of time. What is the total energy?

9. A 3-kg mass is attached to a spring and oscillates with amplitude of 10 cm and frequency $f = 2$ Hz. (a) What is the force constant of the spring? (b) What is the total energy of the motion? (c) Write an equation $x(t)$ describing the position of the mass relative to its equilibrium position. Can the phase constant be determined from the information given?

10. A particle is attached to a spring. At $t = 0$ it is in its equilibrium position and has speed 5 cm/sec toward the negative side of the x axis. Its frequency is $f = 3$ Hz. (a) At what value of t does it next come to rest? (b) Where is it at that time? (c) What is its acceleration at that time? (d) Write an expression for its position $x(t)$ at any time t.

11. A 100-gm mass executes simple harmonic motion with a frequency of 20 Hz and amplitude 0.5 cm. (a) What is the constant k for the force acting on it? (b) What is the maximum acceleration? (c) What is the total energy of the motion?

12. A mass $m = 500$ gm executes simple harmonic motion with a period of 0.5 sec. Its total energy is 5 J. (a) What is the amplitude of the oscillation? (b) What is the maximum speed? (c) What is the maximum acceleration?

13. When the displacement of a mass oscillating on a spring is half its amplitude, what fraction of its total energy is its kinetic energy? At what displacement are its kinetic and potential energies equal?

14. A 100-gm particle is attached to a spring and oscillates with a frequency of 10 Hz and total energy of 1.25 J. (a) What is the force constant of the spring? (b) What is the amplitude of the oscillation?

Section 14-4, The Simple Pendulum

15. Find the length of a simple pendulum if the period of the pendulum is 1 sec at a point where $g = 9.8$ m/sec^2.

16. What would be the period of the pendulum in Exercise 15 on the moon, where the acceleration of gravity is one-sixth that on earth?

17. If the period of a pendulum 70 cm long is 1.68 sec, what is the value of g at the location of the pendulum?

18. A pendulum set up in the stairwell of a 10-story building consists of a heavy weight suspended on a 110-ft wire. What is its period of oscillation ($g = 32$ ft/sec^2)?

19. Derive Equation 14-18a by setting the torque on the mass about the support point equal to $I\alpha$.

Section 14-5, The Physical Pendulum

20. A thin disk of mass 5 kg and radius 20 cm is suspended by an axis perpendicular to the disk through its rim. It is displaced slightly from equilibrium and released. Find the period of the subsequent simple harmonic motion.

21. A circular hoop of radius 50 cm is hung on a narrow horizontal rod and allowed to swing in the plane of the hoop. What is the period of its oscillation assuming that the amplitude is small?

22. A 3-kg plane figure is suspended at a point 10 cm from its center of mass. When it is set oscillating with small amplitude, the period of oscillation is 2.6 sec. Find the moment of inertia I about an axis perpendicular to the plane of the figure and through the pivot point.

Section 14-6, A Mass on a Vertical Spring

23. A 4-lb weight is suspended from a vertically hanging spring of force constant $k = 24$ lb/ft. (a) Find the distance y_0 the spring is stretched when the weight hangs in equilibrium and the potential energy of the spring relative to the unstretched length. (b) The weight is then pulled downward a distance $y' = 3$ in below its equilibrium point. Find the change in the potential energy of the spring, the change in the gravitational potential energy, and the total change in potential energy. Show that the total change in potential energy equals $\frac{1}{2}ky'^2$. (c) The weight is then released. Find the period, frequency, and amplitude of the subsequent oscillation.

24. A 3-kg mass oscillates on a vertical spring of force constant $k = 500$ N/m. Its maximum kinetic energy is 5 J. (a) If the total potential energy is chosen to be zero at equilibrium, what is the maximum potential energy of oscillation? (b) What are the amplitude and period of oscillation? (c) What is the maximum stretching of the spring from its natural length?

Section 14-7, General Motion near Equilibrium

There are no exercises for this section.

Section 14-8, Combinations of Two Simple Harmonic Motions

25. Two identical mass-spring systems are situated as in Figure 14-19. Each mass is 4 kg, and the spring constants are $k_1 = k_2 = 100$ N/m. Each spring is initially stretched 4 cm, but the masses are released separately. (a) What must the relative phase be for the relative motion to be simple harmonic with maximum amplitude? What is the maximum amplitude? (b) If the first mass is released at time $t = 0$, at what time t should the second be released if the relative amplitude is to be a maximum?

Equilibrium

$k = 100$ N/m 4 kg Released at $t = 0$

|←4 cm→| 4 kg

$k = 100$ N/m Released at $t = ?$

Figure 14-19
Exercise 25.

26. (a) For the situation of Exercise 25, what should the time of release of the second mass be for the amplitude of the relative motion to be 4 cm? (b) If the second mass is released just as the first passes through equilibrium for the first time, what is the amplitude of the relative motion?

27. A particle moves so that its x and y coordinates are given by $x = 10 \cos \pi t$ and $y = 5 \cos (\pi t + \pi/2)$. Sketch the path of the particle in the xy plane.

Problems

1. The period of an oscillating particle is 8 sec. At $t = 0$ it is at its equilibrium position. (*a*) How does the distance it travels in the first 4 sec compare with that it travels in the second 4 sec? (*b*) The distance traveled in the first 2 sec and the second 2 sec? (*c*) The first second and the second second?

2. A block of wood slides on a smooth horizontal surface. It is attached to a spring and oscillates with a period of 0.3 sec. A second block rests on top of it. The coefficient of static friction between the blocks is $\mu_s = 0.25$. (*a*) If the amplitude of oscillation is 1 cm, will the block on top slip? (*b*) What is the greatest amplitude of oscillation for which the blocks will not slip?

3. A mass suspended on a vertical spring oscillates with a period of 0.5 sec. When the mass is attached to the spring and allowed to hang at rest, by how much is the spring stretched?

4. The equation of motion of a certain oscillating particle is $x = 6.0 \cos (9.5t + 1.0)$, where x is in centimeters and t is in seconds. (*a*) Find the speed v as a function of time. What is the maximum speed of the particle? When does it occur? (*b*) Find the acceleration a as a function of time. What is a_{max}? When does it occur? (*c*) Sketch the acceleration a versus position x.

Figure 14-20
Problem 5.

5. (*a*) A small particle of mass m slides without friction in a spherical bowl of radius r. Show that the motion of the mass is the same as if it were attached to a string of length r. (*b*) A mass m_1 is displaced a small distance s_1 from the bottom of the bowl, where s_1 is much smaller than r. A second mass m_2 is displaced in the opposite direction a distance $s_2 = 3s_1$ (s_2 is also much smaller than r) (Figure 14-20). If the masses are released at the same time, where do they meet? Explain.

6. Show that for the situations shown in Figures 14-21*a* and *b* the mass oscillates with angular frequency $\omega = \sqrt{k_{eff}/m}$, where k_{eff} is given by (*a*) $k_{eff} = k_1 + k_2$ and (*b*) $1/k_{eff} = 1/k_1 + 1/k_2$.

Figure 14-21
Problem 6.

7. A mass m_1 slides on a smooth horizontal surface and is attached to a spring of force constant k. It oscillates with amplitude A. When the spring is at its greatest extension and the mass is instantaneously at rest, a second mass m_2 is placed on top of m_1. (*a*) What is the smallest value the coefficient of static friction μ_s can have without permitting m_2 to slip on m_1? (*b*) Explain how the total energy E, the amplitude A, the angular frequency ω, and the period T are changed by placing m_2 on m_1 in this way, assuming no slipping. Check your results with the expression for the total energy $E = \frac{1}{2}m\omega^2A^2$.

8. A weight is suspended from a spring and set into a vertical oscillation with a frequency of 4 Hz and an amplitude of 7 cm. A very small bit of rock is placed on top of the oscillating weight just as it reaches its lowest point. (*a*) At what distance above the equilibrium position does the rock lose contact with the weight? (*b*) What is the velocity of the rock when it leaves the weight? (*c*) What is the greatest distance above the equilibrium position reached by the rock? (Assume that the rock has no effect on the oscillation and use the fact that the maximum downward acceleration of the rock is g.)

9. A spring has force constant $k = 150$ N/m. It is suspended from a rigid support. A 1-kg mass is attached at the bottom end and released from rest when the spring is unstretched. (a) How far down does the mass move before it starts upward again? (b) How far below the starting point is the equilibrium position for the 1-kg mass? (c) What is the period of the oscillation? (d) Relative to this equilibrium position, what is the total energy of the mass-spring system? (e) What is the speed of the mass when it first reaches the equilibrium position? How long after it started does the mass have this speed? (f) If instead of being attached to the spring the mass had been dropped, when would it have reached the (previous) equilibrium level, and what would be its speed?

10. The acceleration of gravity g varies with location on the earth because of the earth's rotation and because the earth is not exactly spherical. This was first discovered in the seventeenth century, when it was noted that a pendulum clock carefully adjusted to keep correct time in Paris lost about 90 sec/d near the equator. (a) Show that a small change in g produces a small change in the period of a pendulum T given by

$$\frac{\Delta T}{T} \approx -\frac{1}{2}\frac{\Delta g}{g}$$

(Use differentials to approximate ΔT and Δg.) (b) How great a change in g is needed to account for a change in period of 90 sec/d?

11. A physical pendulum consists of a spherical bob of radius r and mass m suspended from a string of length $L - r$ (Figure 14-22). (The distance from the center of the sphere to the point of support is L.) Often when r is much less than L, this situation is treated as a simple pendulum of length L. (a) Using the parallel-axis theorem, find the moment of inertia of this pendulum about the point of support. Show that the period can be written

$$T = 2\pi \sqrt{\frac{L}{g}} \sqrt{1 + \frac{2r^2}{5L^2}} = T_0 \sqrt{1 + \frac{2r^2}{5L^2}}$$

Figure 14-22
Problem 11.

where $T_0 = \sqrt{L/g}$ is the period of a simple pendulum of length L. (b) Using the binomial approximation $(1 + x)^n \approx 1 + nx$ for $x \ll 1$, show that for r much smaller than L, the period is $T \approx T_0(1 + r^2/5L^2)$. (c) If L is 1 m and $r = 2$ cm, find the error made in using the approximation $T = T_0$ for this pendulum. How large must the radius of the bob be for the error to be 1 percent?

12. A 2-kg mass is attached to a spring of force constant 10 N/m and rests on a smooth horizontal surface. A second mass of 1 kg slides along the surface toward the first at 6 m/sec. (a) Find the amplitude of oscillation if the masses make a perfectly inelastic collision and remain together on the spring. What is the period of oscillation? (b) Find the amplitude and period of oscillation if the collision is perfectly elastic. (c) For each case, write down the position x as a function of time t for the mass attached to the spring assuming that the collision occurs at time $t = 0$. What is the impulse given to the 2-kg mass in each case?

13. In this problem you are asked to derive Equation 14-1 from the application of Newton's laws of motion and the conservation of energy to the problem of a mass m which is influenced by a single force $-kx$, where k is a constant. (a) From Newton's second law write down the acceleration d^2x/dt^2 as a function of displacement from equilibrium x. (b) The solution of the differential equation found in part (a) requires two integrations. The first results in an equation which is equivalent to the conservation of energy. From the conservation of energy, write an equation relating the speed v to the displacement x and the total energy E. Show that the total energy can be written $E = \frac{1}{2}m\omega^2A^2$, where $\omega = \sqrt{k/m}$ and A is the maximum value of x. (c) In terms of the quantities defined in part (b) show that the speed v can be written $v = \omega\sqrt{A^2 - x^2}$. Using $v = dx/dt$, obtain the equation

$$\frac{dx}{\sqrt{A^2 - x^2}} = \omega\, dt$$

(d) Using the substitution $x = A \sin \theta$, show that the equation obtained in part (c) becomes $d\theta = \omega \, dt$, which has the solution $\theta = \omega t + \theta_0$. Compare your solution for $x(t)$ with Equation 14-1.

14. A pendulum clock that has run down to a very small amplitude gains 5 min/d. What is the proper (angular) amplitude for the pendulum to keep correct time?

15. A simple pendulum of length L is released from rest from an angle of θ_0. (a) Assuming the motion to be simple harmonic, find the velocity of the pendulum as it passes through $\theta = 0$. (b) Using conservation of energy, find this velocity exactly. (c) Show that your results for parts (a) and (b) are the same when θ_0 is small. (d) Find the difference in your result for $\theta_0 = 10°$ and $L = 1$ m.

16. Derive the equation $T = 2\pi \sqrt{mL/m_G g}$ for a simple pendulum where m_G is the gravitational mass, defined by $w = m_G g$, and w is the weight of the bob. Discuss the possibility of detecting m/m_G if the gravitational and inertial masses are proportional.

17. An object has moment of inertia I about its center of mass. When pivoted at point P_1 (Figure 14-23), it oscillates about the pivot with period T. There is a second point P_2 on the opposite side of the center of mass about which the object can be pivoted and for which the period of oscillation is also T. Show that $h_1 + h_2 = gT^2/4\pi^2$.

18. Figure 14-24 shows a tube of constant cross section A open to the atmosphere. It is filled to the level shown by a dashed line with an incompressible liquid which flows through the tube with negligible friction. The total length of the liquid column is L. Show that if the liquid surface is depressed on one side and then released, the liquid level will oscillate about the equilibrium position in simple harmonic motion with a period given by $T = 2\pi \sqrt{L/2g}$.

19. The following expression is sometimes used to represent the intermolecular potential energy:

$$U(x) = \tfrac{1}{2} U_0 x_0^6 \left(\frac{x_0^6}{x^{12}} - \frac{2}{x^6} \right)$$

(a) Show that there is an equilibrium point at $x = x_0$. (b) What is the value of $U(x_0)$? (c) What is the frequency of small oscillations about the equilibrium point if the oscillating mass is m?

20. Figure 14-25 shows two point masses m_1 and m_2 at their equilibrium positions. The period of oscillation of each mass is 4 sec. The two masses are pulled to the point $x = 25$ cm and released. If m_1 is released at time $t = 0$ and m_2 is released at time $t = t_0$, describe the motion of m_1 relative to m_2 for (a) $t_0 = 0$, (b) $t_0 = 1$ sec, (c) $t_0 = 2$ sec. Find the distance of closest approach and the first time it occurs (after $t = 0$) in each case.

21. A simple pendulum 50 cm long is suspended from the roof of a cart accelerating in the horizontal direction with $a = 7$ m/sec² (Figure 14-26). Find the period of small oscillations of the pendulum about its equilibrium angle.

Figure 14-23
Problem 17.

Figure 14-24
Problem 18.

Figure 14-25
Problem 20.

Figure 14-26
Problem 21.

CHAPTER 15 Damped and Forced Oscillations

In all real oscillatory motion, mechanical energy is dissipated because of some kind of frictional force. Left to itself, a mass on a spring or a pendulum will eventually stop oscillating. When the mechanical energy of oscillatory motion decreases with time, the motion is said to be *damped*. If the frictional or damping forces are small, the motion is nearly periodic except that the amplitude decreases slowly with time, as in Figure 15-1.

A forced oscillator is one that is driven by an external force. A simple example is a swing given a push once each period. Here the external force is a periodic impulsive force. Its effect is to increase the amplitude of oscillation until a steady state is reached, at which time the work done by the external force during each cycle equals the energy lost due to damping during the cycle. In Sections 15-2 and 15-3 we shall study the effects of an external simple harmonic driving force of angular frequency ω on an oscillator of natural frequency ω_0. We shall see that in the steady state, the amplitude and therefore the energy of the oscillator depend on the frequency of the driving force. The amplitude and energy are large when the frequency of the driving force is close to the natural frequency. This phenomenon is called *resonance*.

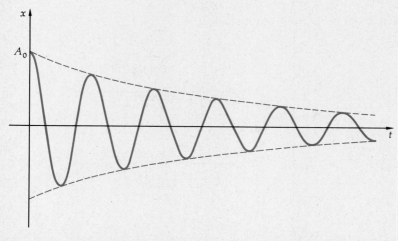

Figure 15-1
Displacement versus time for a slightly damped oscillator. The amplitude decreases slowly with time.

15-1 Damped Oscillations

In Figure 15-2 the oscillation of the mass is damped because of the motion of the plunger in the liquid. Mechanical energy of the mass-spring system is dissipated into heat in the liquid. The rate of energy loss can be varied by changing the size of the plunger or the viscosity of the liquid. Although the detailed analysis of such a damping force is usually complicated, often we can represent such a force by an empirical expression for which the mathematics is comparatively simple and which is in reasonable accord with experiment. The simplest and most common representation of such a force is one proportional to the velocity of the mass but in the opposite direction,

$$\mathbf{F}_d = -b\mathbf{v} \tag{15-1}$$

where b is a constant which describes the degree of damping. Many rather complicated phenomena can be approximately described with such a force. This force is clearly nonconservative because it depends on the velocity. Since it is always directed opposite the direction of motion, the work done by the force is always negative; thus it always decreases the mechanical energy of the system. We can also see this by computing the power input of this force:

$$P = \mathbf{F}_d \cdot \mathbf{v} = -bv^2 \tag{15-2}$$

Newton's second law, $\Sigma \mathbf{F} = m\mathbf{a}$, applied to the motion of the mass on a spring of force constant k and with damping force $-bv$ is

$$\Sigma F_x = -kx - bv = m\frac{dv}{dt} \tag{15-3}$$

The total mechanical energy of the system is

$$E = \tfrac{1}{2}mv^2 + \tfrac{1}{2}kx^2$$

The rate of change of mechanical energy is

$$\frac{dE}{dt} = \tfrac{1}{2}m\left(2v\frac{dv}{dt}\right) + \tfrac{1}{2}k\left(2x\frac{dx}{dt}\right) = v\left(m\frac{dv}{dt} + kx\right) \tag{15-4}$$

using $dx/dt = v$. But from Equation 15-3 we see that $m\,dv/dt + kx = -bv$. Thus

$$\frac{dE}{dt} = -bv^2 \tag{15-5}$$

The rate of change of mechanical energy is just the power input by the damping force, which is always negative.

We can get some understanding of the behavior of a damped oscillator without solving Equation 15-3 in detail. If the damping is small, we expect the mass to oscillate with a frequency ω' which is approximately equal to the *natural frequency* of undamped motion ω_0:

$$\omega' \approx \omega_0 = \sqrt{\frac{k}{m}} \tag{15-6}$$

We expect the amplitude of the oscillation to decrease slowly. The energy change in one period T is

$$\Delta E = \int_0^T \frac{dE}{dt}\,dt = \int_0^T -bv^2\,dt = -b\int_0^T v^2\,dt = -bT(v^2)_{av} \tag{15-7}$$

where the average value of v^2 over one period is defined by

$$(v^2)_{av} = \frac{1}{T}\int_0^T v^2\,dt \tag{15-8}$$

Figure 15-2
Physical arrangement of a damped oscillator. The motion of the mass is damped by the plunger immersed in the liquid. The damping can be varied by varying the size of the plunger or the viscosity of the liquid.

In simple harmonic motion, the energy oscillates between potential and kinetic energy. The average value of either the kinetic or the potential energy is one-half the total energy. Thus

$$\tfrac{1}{2}m(v^2)_{av} = (E_k)_{av} = \tfrac{1}{2}E \qquad\qquad 15\text{-}9$$

or

$$(v^2)_{av} = \frac{E}{m} \qquad\qquad 15\text{-}10$$

Combining Equations 15-7 and 15-10, we obtain for the energy loss per period,

$$-\frac{\Delta E}{T} = \frac{b}{m}E \qquad\qquad 15\text{-}11$$

A reasonable criterion for small damping is that the energy loss in one period be a small fraction of the total energy:

$$-\Delta E \ll E$$

or

$$-\frac{\Delta E}{E} = \frac{bT}{m} \ll 1 \qquad\qquad 15\text{-}12$$

In terms of the angular frequency $\omega' = 2\pi/T$ this criterion for small damping can be written

$$\frac{b}{m} \ll \frac{\omega'}{2\pi} \qquad\qquad 15\text{-}13$$

We can use Equation 15-11 to guess the time dependence of the energy. Let us write Δt for the time interval T in Equation 15-11. Then

$$\frac{\Delta E}{\Delta t} = -\frac{b}{m}E$$

Since the energy loss in one period is a small fraction of the total energy, the loss of energy per period cannot differ much from the instantaneous rate of energy loss. We assume therefore that the differences in the last equation can be replaced by differentials:

$$\frac{dE}{dt} = -\frac{b}{m}E \qquad\qquad 15\text{-}14$$

The function whose derivative is proportional to the function itself is the exponential. The solution of Equation 15-14 is

$$E(t) = E_0 e^{-(b/m)t} \qquad\qquad 15\text{-}15$$

where E_0 is the energy at time $t = 0$. We can use this equation to find the time dependence of the amplitude since the energy is proportional to the square of the amplitude. If $A(t)$ is the amplitude at time t and A_0 is that at $t = 0$, we have

$$\frac{E(t)}{E_0} = \frac{A^2(t)}{A_0{}^2}$$

Thus from Equation 15-15

$$\frac{A^2(t)}{A_0{}^2} = e^{-(b/m)t}$$

or

$$A(t) = A_0 e^{-(b/2m)t} \qquad\qquad 15\text{-}16$$

The exact solution of Equation 15-3 can be found by standard methods for solving differential equations. The solution for the case of small damping, $b < 2m\omega_0$, is

$$x = A_0 e^{-(b/2m)t} \cos(\omega' t + \delta) \qquad \text{15-17}$$

where A_0 is the original amplitude and the frequency ω' is the angular frequency with which the oscillator passes through its equilibrium position ($x = 0$); ω' is given by

$$\omega' = \omega_0 \sqrt{1 - \left(\frac{b}{2m\omega_0}\right)^2} \qquad \text{15-18}$$

in which $\omega_0 = \sqrt{k/m}$ is the angular frequency without damping, the natural frequency. We see that our qualitative observations were correct. For small damping, the frequency is very nearly equal to the natural frequency, and the time dependence of the amplitude is given by Equation 15-16, as expected.

Example 15-1 If the energy loss per cycle is one-tenth the total energy, by how much does the frequency differ from the natural frequency?

According to Equation 15-11, we have

$$-\frac{\Delta E}{E} = \frac{b}{m} T = \frac{b2\pi}{m\omega'} = \frac{1}{10}$$

or

$$\left(\frac{b}{2m\omega'}\right)^2 = \left(\frac{1}{40\pi}\right)^2 = \frac{1}{16,000}$$

using $\pi^2 \approx 10$. Since ω' is so close to ω_0, we can use this in Equation 15-18, to give

$$\omega' = \omega_0 \sqrt{1 - \frac{1}{16,000}}$$

For small ϵ, $\sqrt{1 - \epsilon} \approx 1 - \frac{1}{2}\epsilon$. Thus

$$\omega' \approx \omega_0 \left(1 - \frac{1}{32,000}\right) \qquad \text{and} \qquad \omega' - \omega_0 \approx \frac{-\omega_0}{32,000}$$

or

$$\frac{\omega' - \omega_0}{\omega_0} \approx -\frac{1}{32,000} = -0.003\%$$

We see that for this rather large damping, the frequency decreases by only about 0.003 percent. Such a small change in frequency is difficult to observe. Even when the damping is large enough to reduce the amplitude by half in each oscillation, the frequency is shifted by only 0.6 percent from the natural frequency ω_0. Hence the distinction between ω' and ω_0 can usually be ignored.

Figure 15-1 shows a plot of x given by Equation 15-17 versus t. This solution is valid if b is less than $2m\omega_0$. The value

$$b_c = 2m\omega_0 \qquad \text{15-19}$$

is called the *condition for critical damping*. If b is greater or equal to this critical value, the system does not oscillate at all but merely returns to its equilibrium position. The greater the damping the longer it takes for the system to return to equilibrium. When $b = b_c$, the system is said to be *critically damped*. The mass returns to its equilibrium posi-

Critical damping

tion in the shortest possible time with no oscillation. When b is greater than b_c, the system is *overdamped*. Figure 15-3 shows the displacement versus time for a critically damped and overdamped oscillator.

In many practical applications critical damping or nearly critical damping is used to avoid oscillations and yet have the system return to equilibrium quickly. One example is the use of shock absorbers to damp the oscillations of an automobile on its wheels. Such a system is usually slightly underdamped (b slightly less than the critical value); you can see this by pushing down on the front or back of the car and observing that one or two oscillations occur before the system comes to rest.

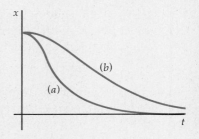

Figure 15-3
Displacement versus time for (a) critically damped and (b) overdamped oscillator.

Questions

1. Two oscillators have the same mass and the same original amplitude and are subject to the same damping force. One, however, has twice the frequency of the other. Which will be damped to half the original amplitude first?

2. Explain qualitatively why you would expect the frequency of an oscillator to decrease because of the presence of a damping force.

15-2   The Forced Oscillator

In many cases an oscillator is subject to an applied force or external force in addition to the damping force and the restoring force. The external force increases the mechanical energy of the oscillator if it acts in the direction of motion of the mass, and it absorbs energy from the oscillator if it acts opposite to the direction of motion. We saw a simple example of this in Chapter 14, a mass on a vertical spring. Here the external force is the weight, which is constant in magnitude and direction. The work done by this force is positive when the mass is moving down and negative when the mass is moving up. The net work done during one cycle is zero, and on the average this constant force does not change the energy of the mass-spring system. A constant force merely changes the position of equilibrium of the system.

A particularly important kind of external force is one which varies harmonically with time such as

$$F_{\text{ext}} = F_0 \sin \omega t \qquad\qquad 15\text{-}20$$

where ω is the angular frequency of the force, which is generally not related to the natural angular frequency of the system $\omega_0 = \sqrt{k/m}$. A mass m attached to a spring of force constant $k = m\omega_0{}^2$ subject to a damping force $-bv$ and to an external force $F_0 \sin \omega t$ then obeys the equation of motion given by

$$\Sigma F = -m\omega_0{}^2 x - bv + F_0 \sin \omega t = m\frac{dv}{dt}$$

or

$$m\frac{d^2x}{dt^2} + b\frac{dx}{dt} + m\omega_0{}^2 x = F_0 \sin \omega t \qquad\qquad 15\text{-}21$$

We first consider the special case of no damping because it is easier to solve. Equation 15-21 becomes, for $b = 0$,

$$m\frac{d^2x}{dt^2} + m\omega_0{}^2 x = F_0 \sin \omega t \qquad\qquad 15\text{-}22$$

We can show by substitution that we can satisfy Equation 15-22 with the function

$$x = A \sin \omega t$$

Then

$$\frac{d^2x}{dt} = -\omega^2 A \sin \omega t$$

Substituting this into Equation 15-22, we obtain

$$m(-\omega^2 A \sin \omega t) + m\omega_0^2 A \sin \omega t = F_0 \sin \omega t$$

which is satisfied for any time if A is given by

$$A = \frac{F_0}{m(\omega_0^2 - \omega^2)}$$

It is customary to write the position function $x(t)$ in terms of an amplitude A which is intrinsically positive. We can do this by introducing a phase angle δ. We write

$$x = A \sin(\omega t - \delta) \qquad\qquad 15\text{-}23$$

where

$$A = \frac{F_0}{m|\omega_0^2 - \omega^2|} \qquad\qquad 15\text{-}24$$

and the phase angle δ is 0 if $\omega < \omega_0$ and $\pm\pi$ if $\omega > \omega_0$.

The mass oscillates in phase with the driving force if ω is less than ω_0 and 180° out of phase with the driving force if ω is greater than ω_0. The amplitude of the oscillation is large if the frequency of the external force is near the natural frequency of the oscillator. For the case of no damping, Equation 15-24 implies that A approaches infinity as ω approaches ω_0. In all real situations there is some damping, and the amplitude is finite when $\omega = \omega_0$. Since the energy of the oscillator is proportional to A^2, the energy is large when ω is near ω_0. (For no damping the energy is infinite at $\omega = \omega_0$.) This phenomenon, called *resonance*, will be discussed more fully in the next section.

15-3 The Forced Oscillator with Damping

The solution of Equation 15-21 with damping is more complicated. We shall discuss the result first and then show that it is a solution of this equation. Equation 15-21 can be satisfied by the function $x(t)$ given by

$$x(t) = A \sin(\omega t - \delta) \qquad\qquad 15\text{-}25$$

where the amplitude A is given by

$$A = \frac{F_0}{\sqrt{m^2(\omega_0^2 - \omega^2)^2 + b^2\omega^2}} \qquad\qquad 15\text{-}26$$

and the phase constant δ by

$$\tan \delta = \frac{b\omega}{m(\omega_0^2 - \omega^2)} \qquad\qquad 15\text{-}27$$

The phase angle δ is shown in Figure 15-4, from which we see that

$$\sin \delta = \frac{b\omega}{\sqrt{m^2(\omega_0^2 - \omega^2)^2 + b^2\omega^2}} = \frac{b\omega A}{F_0} \qquad\qquad 15\text{-}28$$

Figure 15-4
The phase angle δ in Equation 15-25.

When the driving frequency equals the natural frequency, $\omega = \omega_0$, the amplitude A is large, but it is not infinite because of the presence of the damping constant b in the denominator of Equation 15-26.

The function $x(t)$ given by Equation 15-25 is not the complete solution of Equation 15-21 for a forced oscillator with damping. There are no constants of integration in this solution, which can be adjusted to satisfy the initial conditions, i.e., the initial position and velocity of the mass on the spring. The complete solution of Equation 15-21 is

$$x(t) = A'e^{-(b/2m)t} \cos (\omega' t + \delta') + A \sin (\omega t - \delta) \qquad \text{15-29}$$

where A' and δ' are arbitrary constants which can be adjusted to meet the initial conditions and ω' is the frequency of the damped but unforced oscillator given by Equation 15-18.

The first term is just the solution of the unforced damped oscillator given by Equation 15-17. This part of the solution is called the *transient solution*. After a long time, so that $bt/2m \gg 1$, this part of the entire solution becomes negligible because the amplitude has decreased exponentially with time. The second term, given by Equation 15-25, is called the *steady-state solution*. The amplitude A, given by Equation 15-26, does not decrease with time. After a long time ($bt/2m \gg 1$) we can neglect the transient solution. The position is then given by Equation 15-25 no matter what the initial conditions were.

The velocity of the particle in the steady state is obtained from the position function (Equation 15-25) by differentiation:

$$v = \frac{dx}{dt} = A\omega \cos (\omega t - \delta) \qquad \text{15-30}$$

The power input of the driving force in the steady state is

$$\begin{aligned} P &= Fv = (F_0 \sin \omega t)\, A\omega \cos (\omega t - \delta) \\ &= A\omega F_0 \sin \omega t \cos (\omega t - \delta) \end{aligned}$$

Using the identity $\cos (\omega t - \delta) = \cos \omega t \cos \delta + \sin \omega t \sin \delta$, we can write this as

$$P = \omega A F_0 \sin \delta \sin^2 \omega t + \omega A F_0 \cos \delta \sin \omega t \cos \omega t \qquad \text{15-31}$$

The power input varies with time over a cycle. During one cycle, the second term in Equation 15-31 is negative as often as it is positive and has an average value of zero. The average value of $\sin^2 \omega t$ over one cycle is $\frac{1}{2}$ (see Figure 15-5). The average power is therefore

$$P_{\text{av}} = \tfrac{1}{2}\omega A F_0 \sin \delta$$

Figure 15-5
Plot of $\sin^2 \omega t$ versus ωt. The average value over a cycle is $\frac{1}{2}$. This result can be obtained from the fact that $\cos^2 \omega t$ has the same average value over a cycle and from $\sin^2 \omega t + \cos^2 \omega t = 1$.

Using $\sin \delta = b\omega A/F_0$ from Equation 15-28, we can eliminate either $\sin \delta$ or A. We have

$$P_{\text{av}} = \tfrac{1}{2}b\omega^2 A^2 = \frac{1}{2}\frac{F_0^2}{b}\sin^2 \delta \qquad \text{15-32}$$

Alternatively, we can write either A or $\sin \delta$ in terms of the driving frequency ω:

$$P_{av} = \frac{1}{2} \frac{b\omega^2 F_0^2}{m^2(\omega_0^2 - \omega^2)^2 + b^2\omega^2}$$ 15-33

Figure 15-6 shows plots of the average power input versus driving frequency for two different values of the damping constant b. These curves are called *resonance curves*. The maximum power input occurs at the resonance frequency $\omega = \omega_0$. We can see this from Equations 15-32 and 15-27 since $\sin \delta$ has its maximum value of 1 at $\delta = 90°$. But according to Equation 15-27, when $\delta = 90°$, $\omega = \omega_0$ because $\tan 90°$ is infinite. The value of the maximum average power input is

$$P_{av} = \frac{1}{2} \frac{F_0^2}{b} \sin^2 90° = \frac{1}{2} \frac{F_0^2}{b}$$ 15-34

At resonance the displacement is 90° out of phase with the driving force, but the velocity is in phase with the driving force. Thus at resonance the particle is always moving in the direction of the driving force, as would be expected for maximum power input. When the damping is small, the power input at resonance is large and the resonance is sharp; i.e., the resonance curve is narrow, indicating that the power input is large only near the resonance frequency. When damping is large, the power input at resonance is small and the resonance curve is broad.

For any driving frequency the total energy is the sum of the potential and kinetic energies,

$$E = \tfrac{1}{2}kx^2 + \tfrac{1}{2}mv^2$$

Using $k = m\omega_0^2$ and Equations 15-25 and 15-30 for x and v, we have for the total energy in the steady state,

$$E = \tfrac{1}{2}m\omega_0^2 A^2 \sin^2(\omega t - \delta) + \tfrac{1}{2}m\omega^2 A^2 \cos^2(\omega t - \delta)$$ 15-35

Except at resonance, the total energy is not constant in time but varies during each cycle. The average total energy is large near resonance when the amplitude A is large. At the resonance frequency $\omega = \omega_0$ the total energy is constant in the steady state and has the value

$$E = \tfrac{1}{2}m\omega_0^2 A^2 = \tfrac{1}{2}m\omega_0^2 \frac{F_0^2}{\omega_0^2 b^2} = \frac{1}{2} \frac{mF_0^2}{b^2}$$ 15-36

At resonance the total energy varies inversely with the square of the damping constant.

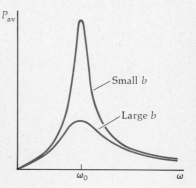

Figure 15-6
Plot of the average power input of the forcing term versus driving frequency ω for different values of the damping constant b. P_{av} is maximum in each case when $\omega = \omega_0$. The smaller the damping the greater the value of P_{av} at resonance and the narrower the resonance curve, i.e., the sharper the resonance.

Optional

Let us now show that $x = A \sin(\omega t - \delta)$, with A given by Equation 15-26 and δ by Equation 15-27, is indeed a solution of Equation 15-21. We have

$$x = A \sin(\omega t - \delta)$$

$$\frac{dx}{dt} = \omega A \cos(\omega t - \delta) \qquad \frac{d^2x}{dt} = -\omega^2 A \sin(\omega t - \delta)$$

Putting these into Equation 15-21 gives

$$m(\omega_0^2 - \omega^2) A \sin(\omega t - \delta) + b\omega A \cos(\omega t - \delta) = F_0 \sin \omega t$$ 15-37

This equation must be satisfied for all values of the time t. This is possible only if the constants A and δ have certain values. We can find them by choosing the convenient values $t = 0$ and $t = \delta/\omega$ for the time.

For example, when $t = 0$, Equation 15-37 becomes

$$m(\omega_0^2 - \omega^2) A \sin(-\delta) + b\omega A \cos(-\delta) = 0$$

or since $\sin(-\delta) = -\sin \delta$ and $\cos(-\delta) = \cos \delta$, we have

$$\tan \delta = \frac{b\omega}{m(\omega_0^2 - \omega^2)}$$

in agreement with Equation 15-27. Similarly, when $\omega t = \delta$ in Equation 15-37, we have

$$\sin(\omega t - \delta) = 0 \qquad \cos(\omega t - \delta) = 1 \qquad \sin \omega t = \sin \delta$$

Thus

$$b\omega A = F_0 \sin \delta \qquad \text{or} \qquad A = \frac{F_0 \sin \delta}{b\omega}$$

Using Equation 15-28 for $\sin \delta$ obtained from Figure 15-4, we have

$$A = \frac{F_0}{\sqrt{m^2(\omega_0^2 - \omega^2)^2 + b^2\omega^2}}$$

Questions

3. Give several examples of common situations which might be described as an oscillator driven by a sinusoidal driving force.

4. Under what conditions will the resonance curve of an oscillator have a high, narrow peak at $\omega = \omega_0$? Under what conditions will it have a broad, low peak?

5. When you push a swing, resonance occurs when the driving frequency equals the natural frequency and also when it is $\frac{1}{2}$, $\frac{1}{3}$, . . . times the natural frequency, i.e., if you push every other swing, every third swing, etc. Explain how this differs from a harmonic driving force, for which resonance occurs only at the natural frequency.

Review

A. Define, explain, or otherwise identify:

Damped oscillations, 380
Resonance, 380
Critical damping, 383

Transient solution, 386
Steady-state solution, 386

B. True or false:

1. The frequency of a slightly damped (unforced) oscillator is nearly equal to the undamped frequency.

2. The frequency of a damped (unforced) oscillator decreases as the amplitude decreases.

3. The amplitude of a damped (unforced) oscillator decreases exponentially with time.

4. In the steady state, the frequency of a forced oscillator equals the frequency of the forcing term.

5. In the steady state the motion of a forced oscillator is independent of the initial conditions.

6. At resonance, the displacement of a forced oscillator is in phase with the forcing term.

7. At resonance, the velocity of a forced oscillator is in phase with the forcing term.

8. The resonance frequency of a forced oscillator depends on the damping.

9. The sharpness of the resonance of a forced oscillator depends on the damping.

10. In a forced oscillator, the power input of the forcing term is maximum when $\omega = \omega_0$.

Exercises

Section 15-1, Damped Oscillations

1. Show that the SI units of the damping constant b are kilograms per second.

2. From the equation $x = A \cos \omega t$ for an undamped oscillator and the fact that the average value of either $\sin^2 \omega t$ or $\cos^2 \omega t$ over a cycle is $\frac{1}{2}$, show that $v_{av}^2 = \frac{1}{2}A^2\omega^2 = E/m$.

3. A 2-kg mass oscillates on a spring of force constant $k = 400$ N/m with initial amplitude of 3 cm. (a) Find the period and the total initial energy. (b) If the energy decreases by 1 percent per period, find the damping constant b.

4. An oscillator has a mass of 50 gm and period of 2 sec. Its amplitude decreases by 5 percent each cycle. (a) What is the damping constant b? (b) What fraction of the oscillator's energy is dissipated in each cycle?

5. The amplitude of a damped oscillator decreases by 50 percent each cycle. (a) By what fraction does the energy decrease during each cycle? (b) Use Equation 15-16 to show that $bT/2m = \ln 2$ and $b/2m = (\ln 2)\omega/2\pi$, where T is the period of the oscillator and ω is the angular frequency. (c) Using this result in Equation 15-18, show that the fractional decrease in the frequency is about 0.006.

6. Show that the ratio of amplitudes for two successive oscillations is constant in a damped oscillator.

Section 15-2, The Forced Oscillator

7. A 1-kg mass is attached to a spring of force constant 500 N/m. The oscillator is driven by an external force $F = 10 \sin 2\pi t$ N, where t is in seconds. Assuming negligible damping, find the period and the amplitude of the oscillations of the system.

8. A 5-lb weight is attached to a spring of force constant $k = 100$ lb/ft. It is driven by a force $F = F_0 \sin 2\pi ft$. It oscillates at frequency of 5 Hz and with amplitude of 2 ft. Find F_0 and f_0. (Assume negligible damping.)

9. A mass m rests on a frictionless horizontal table. It is acted on by a single force $F = F_0 \cos \omega t$. (a) Find the acceleration $a(t)$ and the velocity $v(t)$ assuming the mass to be at rest at time $t = 0$. (b) Find the position $x(t)$ assuming that $x = 0$ at time $t = 0$. Show that the amplitude of this simple harmonic motion is $A = F_0/m\omega^2$. (c) This mass is now attached to a spring of force constant k and is again driven by the above force. Compare its motion with that when it was not attached to the spring.

10. Find the resonant frequencies for the three systems in Figure 15-7.

11. The resonant (angular) frequency of a certain system is 60π rad/sec. This system is forced to oscillate at $\omega_1 = 40\pi$ rad/sec and at $\omega_2 = 80\pi$ rad/sec. Find the ratio A_1/A_2. (Assume the same maximum force in each case.)

Figure 15-7
Exercise 10.

$k = 400$ N/m

10 kg

(a)

$k = 800$ N/m

5 kg

(b)

L θ

$L = 2$ m

$m = 4$ kg

(c)

12. If an oscillator is driven by a force $F = F_0 \sin \omega t$, show that the power input of the external force is

$$P = F_0 A \omega \sin \omega t \cos \omega t = \frac{F_0^2 \omega}{2m(\omega_0^2 - \omega^2)} \sin 2\omega t$$

assuming no damping and $\omega < \omega_0$.

13. Show that the maximum value of the kinetic energy of a forced oscillator with no damping is not the same as the maximum value of the potential energy but is less or greater depending on whether ω is less or greater than ω_0. Explain this qualitatively by considering the relative directions of the external force and the velocity when the particle is moving toward its equilibrium position for (a) $\omega < \omega_0$ and (b) $\omega > \omega_0$. *Hint:* Note that x and F are in phase if $\omega < \omega_0$ and 180° out of phase if $\omega > \omega_0$.

Section 15-3, The Forced Oscillator with Damping

14. Show that at resonance ($\omega = \omega_0$, $\delta = \pi/2$) the driving force is equal in magnitude to the damping force at all times and 180° out of phase.

15. A 2-kg mass oscillates on a spring of force constant $k = 400$ N/m. The damping constant is $b = 2.00$ kg/sec. It is driven by a sinusoidal force of maximum value 10 N and angular frequency 10 rad/sec. (a) What is the amplitude of the oscillations? (b) If the frequency of the driving force is varied, at what frequency will resonance occur? (c) Find the amplitude of the vibrations at resonance.

16. Show that the average power dissipated in the damping material is equal to the average power delivered by the external force at all frequencies of the external force.

Problems

1. A damped oscillator loses one-twentieth of its energy during each cycle. How many cycles elapse before half the original energy is dissipated? During this time, by how much is the amplitude reduced? (Use the approximation of Equation 15-15).

2. Show that for a weakly damped oscillator, the maximum value of the damping force in any cycle is approximately $b/m\omega_0$ times the maximum value of the restoring force during that cycle.

3. Suppose that the amplitude of an oscillator decreases by a factor R each cycle. That is, if A_1 is the amplitude after the first cycle, $A_2 = RA_1$ is that after the second cycle, etc. A driving force $F = kB \sin \omega t$ is applied to the oscillator, where k is the force constant of the oscillator. Show that if ω is the resonant frequency, the amplitude is given by

$$A = \frac{\pi B}{\ln (1/R)}$$

4. A 1-kg mass attached to a certain spring is critically damped by an external viscous force. Describe the resultant motion if the same viscous force damps a 2-kg mass attached to the same spring.

5. A 3-kg sphere dropped in air has a terminal velocity of 25 m/sec (see Equation 5-38). It is attached to a spring of force constant $k = 400$ N/m and oscillates in air with an initial amplitude of 20 cm. (a) When will the amplitude be 10 cm? (b) How much energy will have been lost when the amplitude is 10 cm?

6. Show that the value of the driving frequency for which the amplitude A is maximum is $\omega = \sqrt{\omega_0^2 - b^2/2m^2}$. *Hint:* Find ω for which the denominator of Equation 15-26 is a minimum.

7. A 0.5-kg mass oscillates on a spring of force constant $k = 300$ N/m. During the first 10 sec it loses 0.5 J to friction. If the initial amplitude was 15 cm, (a) how long before the energy is reduced to 0.1 J? (b) What is the frequency of oscillation?

8. Show by direct substitution that Equation 15-17 is an exact solution of Equation 15-3.

9. A damped oscillator oscillates with frequency ω', which is 10 percent less than its undamped frequency. By what factor is its amplitude decreased in each cycle? By what factor is its energy reduced in each cycle?

10. Let ω_1 and ω_2 be the angular frequencies for which A^2 is half its value at resonance. Show that for small damping $|\omega_1 - \omega_2| \approx b/m$.

CHAPTER 16   Gravity

Gravity is one of the four basic interactions, discussed briefly in Chapter 6. Although of negligible importance in the interactions of elementary particles, gravity is of primary importance in the interactions of large objects. It is gravity that binds us to the earth and that binds the earth and the other planets to the solar system. The gravitational force plays an important role in the evolution of stars and in the behavior of galaxies. In a sense, it is gravity that holds the universe together.

In this chapter we shall study the force of gravity in some detail. In particular we shall show how Newton's law describing the gravitational force exerted by one particle on another can be applied to the description of the force exerted by one extended body on another. In doing this we shall introduce the concepts of a field and of lines of force, concepts used again later in the discussion of electric and magnetic forces.

16-1   Kepler's Laws

The gravitational force exerted by a particle of mass m_1 on another particle of mass m_2 is given by Newton's law of gravitation, discussed briefly in Chapter 6:

$$\mathbf{F}_{12} = -\frac{Gm_1m_2}{r_{12}^2}\hat{\mathbf{r}}_{12} \qquad 16\text{-}1$$

where $\mathbf{r}_{12}$ is the vector from mass m_1 to m_2 and $\hat{\mathbf{r}}_{12} = \mathbf{r}_{12}/r_{12}$ is a unit vector.

Newton justified this law of gravitation primarily by demonstrating that with it he could derive Kepler's laws of planetary motion, which summarize the kinematics of the motion of planets about the sun. These laws were deduced between 1600 and 1620 by Johannes Kepler, who used the precise astronomical observations of the planets made in the late 1500s by Tycho Brahe. Kepler's laws are:

Castle in the Pyrenees, by René Magritte. (*Collection of Harry Torczyner, New York; photograph by G. D. Hackett.*)

1. All planets move in elliptical orbits with the sun at one focus.

2. A line joining any planet to the sun sweeps out equal areas in equal times.

3. The square of the period of any planet is proportional to the cube of the planet's mean distance from the sun.

We have already discussed the relation between law 2 and angular momentum in Chapter 13. The rate of area swept out by a planet is proportional to the angular momentum of the planet about the sun. Thus Kepler's second law is equivalent to the statement that the angular momentum of a planet is constant. This implies that there is no torque exerted on the planet about the sun, i.e., that any force exerted on the planet is a central force. That is, the force is along the radial line from the planet to the sun, as with Newton's law of gravitation.

Newton showed that the general path of a planet moving under the influence of an inverse-square-law force is an ellipse with the center of force at one focus if the path is closed. (For a comet which does not return, the path is a parabola or hyperbola.) We shall consider the simpler special case of a circular orbit to show that Kepler's third law implies that the force varies inversely with the square of the distance.

Consider a planet moving with speed v about the sun in a circle of radius r. In the time of one period T the planet travels a distance of $2\pi r$. Thus

The Granger Collection

Johannes Kepler (1571–1630).

$$T = \frac{2\pi r}{v} \qquad\qquad 16\text{-}2$$

For a circular orbit, the mean distance from the sun is just the radius r. (For a general elliptical path with the sun at one focus, the mean distance equals the semimajor axis of the ellipse.) Kepler's third law for this case is then

$$T^2 = Cr^3 \qquad\qquad 16\text{-}3$$

where C is a proportionality constant which may depend on the properties of the sun but is the same for all planets. We have then

$$T^2 = \left(\frac{2\pi r}{v}\right)^2 = Cr^3 \qquad\qquad 16\text{-}4$$

or

$$v^2 = \frac{4\pi^2}{Cr} \qquad\qquad 16\text{-}5$$

Since the planet is in a circular orbit, it has centripetal acceleration v^2/r. If we call the mass of the planet m_p, Newton's second law applied to the planet is

$$F = m_p a = \frac{m_p v^2}{r} \qquad\qquad 16\text{-}6$$

where F is the central force exerted on the planet by the sun. Substituting v^2 from Equation 16-5 into Equation 16-6, we have

$$F = \frac{m_p(4\pi^2/Cr)}{r} = \frac{4\pi^2}{C}\frac{m_p}{r^2} \qquad\qquad 16\text{-}7$$

The force on the planet is proportional to the mass of the planet and inversely proportional to the square of the distance from the sun. By the law of action and reaction, this equals in magnitude the force ex-

NASA

Earth rise as seen from the moon.

erted on the sun by the planet. Since the force exerted by the planet on the sun is proportional to the mass of the planet, symmetry suggests that the force exerted by the sun on the planet is proportional to the mass M_s of the sun.[1] Writing $4\pi^2/C = GM_s$, where G is a constant independent of the mass of the sun or the planets we have

$$F = \frac{Gm_pM_s}{r^2} \qquad\qquad 16\text{-}8$$

As discussed in Section 6-1, Newton compared the acceleration of the moon in its orbit with the acceleration of objects near the surface of the earth for further confirmation of the inverse-square law of gravitation.

Questions

1. The sun, as seen from the earth, moves more rapidly against the background of stars in the winter than in the summer. On the basis of this fact and Kepler's laws, what can you say about the relative distances of the earth from the sun during these two seasons?

2. The distance from the center of the earth to the moon is 3.84×10^5 km and the period of the moon 27.3 d. How could you use these data to determine the period of a satellite just above the earth's surface (orbit radius 6400 km)?

3. Two of Jupiter's moons have orbit radii which differ by a factor close to 2. How do their periods compare?

---

[1] If the law of gravity derived from these laws of planetary motion were a special law applying only to the force between the sun and each planet, there would be no reason why the force should be proportional to M_s. Newton, however, argued that the same law should apply to any two masses in the universe. He supported this idea by noting that Kepler's third law also applies to such motions as the moons of Jupiter except that the constant of proportionality is different. This of course would be the case if the gravitational force is proportional to the masses of both bodies and the constant G is a universal constant of nature.

Comets

Stephen P. Maran
NASA-Goddard Space Flight Center

Our present knowledge of comets indicates that if we set out to make an artificial comet and launch it into space, we might well begin with a huge lump of ice embedded with extremely fine sand. Indeed, a small version of such an experiment was contemplated for the final manned Skylab flight in 1973–1974 but not executed. It appears that the solid part of a comet, called the *nucleus,* is nothing more than a large ball of ice and other frozen gases, interspersed with rock particles, most of which are microscopic. Physical and chemical characteristics of the various parts of a comet are summarized in Table 1.

As a comet approaches the sun, solar heating sublimates the frozen matter at the surface of the nucleus, releasing gas that flows outward. This gas forms a large cloud, the *coma,* known popularly as the *head* of the comet. The gases also blow off some of the rock particles, or dust. Close to the nucleus, the gases retain the same molecular form they exhibited in the frozen state, but as these *parent molecules* diffuse outward, they are gradually broken up into *daughter products,* i.e., smaller molecules and individual atoms, by ultraviolet radiation from the sun. This radiation also ionizes some of the molecules and atoms, producing the *cometary plasma,* electrified material that is influenced by the solar wind pervading interplanetary space. The wind consists of charged particles that are constantly streaming away from the outermost region of the sun, the *corona.* The wind sweeps the cometary plasma out of the coma in a direction away from the sun, forming the *ionic,* or *plasma, tail,* which stretches for tens of millions of miles.

Table 1
Physical and chemical characteristics of comets

Part of comet	Physical characteristics	Chemical composition
Nucleus	Typical diameter 0.3–30 km Mass 10^{13}–10^{19} gm	No observations but many theories; the most probable major constituents are frozen water and carbon monoxide, but other substances must be present
Coma	Diameter 10^4–10^6 km (and $>10^7$ km when observed in the ultraviolet light emitted by hydrogen atoms of the coma)	Parent molecules include water vapor† (H_2O), methyl cyanide† (CH_3CN), and hydrogen cyanide† (HCN), all as gases
		Silicate particles‡
		Daughter products: C, C_2, C_3, H, O, OH, CH, CN, NH, NH_2
Tail	Widths up to 10^6 km	
Dust	Length up to 10^7 km	Silicate particles‡
Plasma	Length up to 10^8 km	OH^+, H_2O^+, CO^+, CO_2^+, CH^+, N_2^+

† Found in only one comet as of late 1974.

‡ The presence of silicate particles is shown by infrared spectra of dust in the coma and tail.

Comet Kohoutek (1973), photographed with a wide-angle Schmidt telescope at the Joint Observatory for Cometary Research. Streaming back from the bright coma are the smooth-looking dust tail (below) and a striking plasma tail (above). Note the large disturbance in the plasma tail near the right edge of the picture; it was observed to move rapidly down the tail in the direction opposite the sun. On the original photographic plate a short "antitail," believed to consist of relatively large dust particles, extends to the left from the coma and appears (due to a perspective effect) to point toward the sun. (*Courtesy of the Joint Observatory for Cometary Research.*)

The visible light of the sun plays a similar role; its radiation pressure exerts a significant force on the dust particles of the coma, also in a direction away from the sun. The acceleration of a dust particle away from the sun depends on its surface area and mass, whereas acceleration toward the sun, due to solar gravity, is the same for all particles. Thus the less dense dust has a large component of motion away from the sun, while the largest particles have only a small component and tend to stream out roughly back along the orbit of the nucleus. The total effect is usually to form a smooth, curved yellow dust tail, which contrasts strikingly with the kinks, wave patterns, and rayed formations of the highly structured plasma tail. The color of the dust tail comes from the reflection of sunlight. The plasma tail looks blue, due to molecular band emission by the carbon monoxide ion (CO^+). The plasma tail acts as a sort of cosmic wind sock, allowing earth-bound astronomers to infer the speed and direction of the solar wind at various places in the solar system by observing the plasma tails of comets.

Since the material in the coma, dust tail, and plasma tail of a comet is not gravitationally bound to the small mass of the nucleus, it escapes into space. Thus, on each new approach to the sun, a comet evolves a new coma and tails.

Nearly all the comets that have been observed follow elliptical orbits that take them well within the orbit of Mars, and some go inside that of Mercury. Indeed, we rarely detect comets beyond Jupiter because they are so dim. When one tries to calculate how much material a comet loses each time it nears the sun and forms a coma, a problem arises. In a typical case, a bright comet like Halley's will vanish as a result of the sublimation process in a time (say, less than 1 million years) that is very short compared with the age of the solar system (5 billion years). Why then do we see any comets at all? Why weren't they all eliminated before man evolved on earth?

Two obvious possibilities are that new comets are continuously being formed, presumably on the outskirts of the solar system, or that huge numbers of comets were left over from the origin of the solar system and are stored somewhere on the outskirts. (This second hypothesis is actually the leading idea at present.) A third possibility, namely, that comets come to us from distant regions of the galaxy, seems to be excluded by the fact (old books to the contrary) that no confirmed hyperbolic orbits have been observed among comets approaching the sun.

The *Oort cloud* is the name given to the region, extending more than 2 light-years from the sun, in which perhaps 100 billion comets are thought to exist. In orbit around the sun, but usually never coming closer to it than the orbit of Jupiter, they are not significantly heated and can remain indefinitely in celestial cold storage. However, the cross-sectional area of the cloud is so great that occasionally stars must move through it on their way around the galaxy.

Indeed, roughly 3000 stars must have passed through the inner cloud (radius 4.7×10^{12} mi) since the solar system formed. The gravitation of a passing star perturbs cometary orbits. Some comets are accelerated and may escape from the cloud into interstellar space. Others are sent into the inner solar system, where, thanks to additional gravitational perturbations (especially by Jupiter), they are sometimes trapped in much smaller orbits that return them repeatedly to the vicinity of the sun. This is the source of the periodic comets well known to astronomers, such as Halley's (76 years) and Encke's (3.3 years), and it presumably explains why we still see comets near the sun billions of years after solar heat ought to have dissipated them.

SECTION 16-2 The Cavendish Experiment   397

16-2 The Cavendish Experiment

The first measurement of the gravitation constant G was made by Henry Cavendish in 1798. Figure 16-1 shows a schematic sketch of the apparatus he used to measure the gravitational force between two known masses.

The two small masses m_2 are at the ends of a light rod suspended by a fine fiber. A torque is required to turn the two masses through the angle θ from their equilibrium position because the fiber must be twisted. Careful measurement shows that the torque required to turn the fiber through a given angle is proportional to the angle. The constant of proportionality can be determined, and the fiber and the suspended masses can be used to measure very small torques. This arrangement, called a *torsion balance*, was invented in the eighteenth century, by John Michell. The French physicist Charles Augustin de Coulomb used a torsion balance in 1785 to determine the law of electric force known by his name. Cavendish used a refined and especially sensitive torsion balance in his determination of G.

In Cavendish's experiment two large masses m_1 are placed near the small masses m_2, as shown in Figure 16-1. The apparatus is allowed to come to equilibrium in this position; because the apparatus is so sensitive and because the gravitational force is so small, this takes hours. Instead of measuring the deflection angle directly, Cavendish reversed the positions of the large masses, as shown by the dashed lines in the figure. If the balance is allowed to come to equilibrium again, it will turn through angle 2θ in response to the reversal of the torque. From the measurement of the angle and of the torsion constant, the forces between the masses m_1 and m_2 can be determined. When their masses and their separations are known, G can be calculated. Cavendish obtained a value for G within about 1 percent of the present value:

$$G = 6.67 \times 10^{-11} \ \text{N-m}^2/\text{kg}^2$$

(a)

(b)

Figure 16-1
Schematic drawing of the Cavendish apparatus for determining the gravitational constant G. (a) Because of the gravitational attraction of the large masses m_1 for the nearby small masses m_2, the fiber is turned through a very small angle θ from its equilibrium position. (b) The large masses are reversed so that they are at the same distance from the equilibrium position of the balance but on the other side. The fiber then turns through the angle 2θ. Measurement of this angle and of the torsion constant of the fiber makes it possible to determine the force exerted by m_1 on m_2, which in turn allows the constant G to be determined.

Original drawing of Cavendish's apparatus. (*Courtesy of the Deutsches Museum, Munich.*)

Questions

4. Cavendish presented his result in a paper entitled Weighing the Earth. Explain how the earth's mass can be calculated from the values of G, g, and R_E.

16-3   The Gravitational Field

The gravitational force exerted by two masses m_1 and m_2 on a third mass m_0 at some point is just the (vector) sum of the forces exerted by m_1 and m_2 individually; i.e., the presence of a second mass m_2 has no effect on the force exerted by m_1 on m_0. (We could imagine, for example, that the second mass m_2 might shield m_0 from the force exerted by m_1 or influence it in some other way, but no such effects are observed.) If there are several masses, as in Figure 16-2, the gravitational force they exert on a mass m_0 at some point P is given by

$$\mathbf{F} = -\frac{Gm_1 m_0}{r_{10}^2}\,\hat{\mathbf{r}}_{10} - \frac{Gm_2 m_0}{r_{20}^2}\,\hat{\mathbf{r}}_{20} - \cdots \frac{Gm_i m_0}{r_{i0}^2}\,\hat{\mathbf{r}}_{i0} + \cdots \qquad 16\text{-}9$$

where $\hat{\mathbf{r}}_{i0}$ is the unit vector directed from the ith mass to point P. The force per unit mass acting on a mass at point P is called the *gravitational field* at that point:

$$\mathbf{g} = \frac{\mathbf{F}}{m_0} = \sum\left(-\frac{Gm_i}{r_{i0}^2}\,\hat{\mathbf{r}}_{i0}\right) \qquad 16\text{-}10$$

The gravitational force on mass m_0 at point P can be written

$$\mathbf{F} = m_0 \mathbf{g} \qquad 16\text{-}11$$

The gravitational field is a vector function of position (and of time if the positions of the other masses vary with time). By moving the test mass m_0 from point to point and measuring the force on it we can map out this function.

As we discussed in Chapter 4, the gravitational field is a particularly useful concept in dealing with the action-at-a-distance problem. We consider the interaction of the masses m_i with the mass m_0 in Figure 16-2 as a two-step process. The masses m_i set up a condition in space, the gravitational field, and this field in turn exerts the force on m_0. Similarly, m_0 contributes to the gravitational field at the location of

Henry Cavendish (1731–1810).

Gravitational field defined

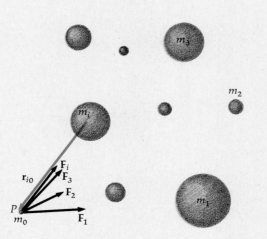

Figure 16-2
The force on the test mass m_0 is the vector sum of the forces exerted by each mass in the system. The resultant force on m_0 divided by m_0 is the gravitational field $\mathbf{g}$ at point P. The force on any other mass placed at point P is then the product of the mass and the gravitational field $\mathbf{g}$.

each mass m_1. If we suddenly move one of the masses such as m_3, the field at point P does not change immediately. There must be time for the propagation of the disturbance from m_3 to m_0. The change in the field due to a change in position of m_3 propagates as a gravitational wave with the speed 3×10^8 m/sec, the same as the speed of light. These statements, of course, do not follow from Newton's theory of gravitation but are features of the modern theory developed by Einstein in our own century. Newton's theory can be thought of as an approximation valid when the propagation time is negligible. In fact, it is sufficient for almost all known purposes.

Example 16-1 Two equal point masses are located on the y axis at points $y = +a$ and $y = -a$, as shown in Figure 16-3. Find the gravitational field on the x axis.

At a general point (x,y,z), not necessarily on the x axis, the gravitational field has three components each of which is a function of x, y, and z: $g_x(x,y,z)$, $g_y(x,y,z)$, and $g_z(x,y,z)$. Figure 16-3 illustrates the calculation of the field at a point in the xy plane. Here the field has only two components, $g_x(x,y)$ and $g_y(x,y)$; the z component is zero. In this example, we restrict our attention to the calculation of the field on the x axis, as in Figure 16-4. By symmetry, the y component of the field is zero. Since the point P is equidistant from each mass, the magnitudes of the contributions from each mass are equal. If we call this magnitude g_1, the x component of the field is

$$g_x = -2g_1 \cos \theta = -2 \frac{Gm}{r^2} \frac{x}{r} = -2Gm \frac{x}{(x^2 + a^2)^{3/2}} \qquad 16\text{-}12$$

using $r^2 = x^2 + a^2$ and $\cos \theta = x/r$. The minus sign is included because for positive values of x the field is toward the left.

Figure 16-5 is a sketch of the field $g_x(x)$ versus x. It is left for you to show (Problem 1) that as $x \to \infty$, $g_x \to -2Gm/x^2$ and that the field is maximum at $x = a/\sqrt{2}$.

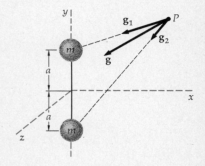

Figure 16-3
The gravitational field at point P in the xy plane due to the two masses on the y axis generally has both x and y components.

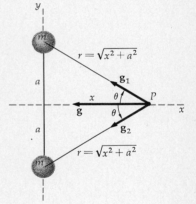

Figure 16-4
The gravitational field at a point P on the x axis due to the two masses on the y axis has only an x component because the y components of $\mathbf{g}_1$ and $\mathbf{g}_2$ cancel.

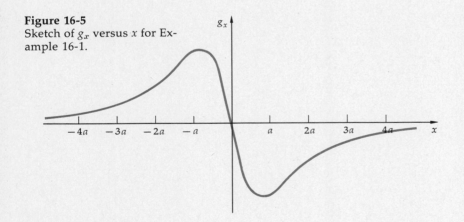

Figure 16-5
Sketch of g_x versus x for Example 16-1.

The gravitational field of an extended body (Figure 16-6) can be calculated from Equation 16-10 by treating the body as consisting of a great number of parts, each small enough to be considered a particle. In Figure 16-6 the body has been divided into N parts each of volume ΔV_i and mass $\Delta m_i = \rho \, \Delta V_i$, where ρ is the mass per unit volume. The gravitational field at point P is then approximately

$$\mathbf{g} \approx \sum \left(-\frac{G\,\Delta m_i}{r_{io}^{2}}\,\hat{\mathbf{r}}_{io} \right) \qquad\qquad 16\text{-}13$$

As N goes to infinity and Δm_i goes to zero, the sum becomes an integral:

$$\mathbf{g} = \int \left(-\frac{G\,dm}{r'^{2}}\,\hat{\mathbf{r}}' \right) \qquad\qquad 16\text{-}14$$

where r' is the distance from the mass element dm to the point where the field is to be calculated. The integral in Equation 16-14 ranges over all mass in the system.

Questions

5. What are the dimensions of the gravitational field?

6. If a mass m_0 is placed on the x axis at the point $x = 0$ in Example 16-1, it will be in equilibrium because $g_x = 0$ at that point. Is this equilibrium stable or unstable?

16-4   Gravitational Potential

The potential energy of a mass m_0 in the presence of a distribution of masses is usually easier to calculate than the force on m_0 because the potential energy is a scalar quantity whereas the force is a vector. Consider again the distribution of masses shown in Figure 16-2. In Chapter 8 we found the gravitational potential energy of a mass m_0 a distance r_{io} from a mass m_i to be $-Gm_im_0/r_{io}$ (see Equation 8-14). The total gravitational potential energy of the mass m_0 in Figure 16-2 is then

$$U = -\frac{Gm_1m_0}{r_{10}} - \frac{Gm_2m_0}{r_{20}} - \cdots \frac{Gm_im_0}{r_{io}} - \cdots \qquad\qquad 16\text{-}15$$

The potential energy of the mass m_0 divided by the mass m_0, called the *gravitational potential*, is a scalar function of position

$$V = \frac{U}{m_0} = \sum \left(-\frac{Gm_i}{r_{io}} \right) \qquad\qquad 16\text{-}16$$

Since, in general, the force is the negative derivative of the potential-energy function, the gravitational field is the negative derivative of the potential function. When the distribution of masses has perfect spherical symmetry, the gravitational potential depends only on the radial coordinate r. Then the gravitational field has only a radial component given by[1]

$$g_r = -\frac{dV(r)}{dr} \qquad\qquad 16\text{-}17$$

For a continuous distribution of mass, the gravitational potential is

$$V = \int \left(-\frac{G\,dm}{r'} \right) \qquad\qquad 16\text{-}18$$

[1] For the general case in which V depends on all three coordinates x, y, and z, the rectangular components of the gravitational field are related to the partial derivatives of the potential function (Section 8-10).

Figure 16-6
Calculation of the gravitational field at point P due to an extended body. The body is considered to consist of small mass elements m_i each of which is treated as a point mass. The field at P is then the sum of the fields due to the mass elements. This sum is found by integration.

Gravitational potential defined

16-5 Lines of Force

It is convenient to picture a field by drawing *lines of force* to indicate the direction of the field at each point. The field vector is tangent to the line at each point. Of course, there is an infinite number of points in space, and so only a few representative lines are drawn. Since we could choose any point to indicate the direction of the field by a line, the lines need not be continuous, but it is both customary and useful to draw continuous lines ending at a point mass. (The lines end rather than begin at the mass because the field near a point mass points toward the mass.)

Figure 16-7 shows the lines of force for a single point mass. They are equally spaced because of spherical symmetry. Consider a spherical surface a distance r from the mass. For a fixed number of lines, the number of lines per unit area of the sphere is inversely proportional to the area of the sphere $4\pi r^2$. Thus the *density of lines* (lines per unit area) decreases with distance as $1/r^2$, just as the magnitude of the field does, and the strength of the gravitational field is indicated by the density of lines.

If we have more than one point mass, we can indicate the field strength by choosing the number of lines to each mass to be proportional to the mass. Figure 16-8 shows the lines of force for two equal point masses separated by a distance $2a$. Without calculating the field at each point, we can construct this pattern as follows. Since the masses are equal, we choose an equal number of lines to each mass. At points very near one of the masses, the field is approximately due to the nearby mass only, since the field varies inversely as the square of the distance. Thus the lines through the surface of a sphere of very small radius ϵ ($\epsilon \ll a$) about one mass are equally spaced. At a very large distance from the masses $D \gg a$, the field should look like that from a single point mass of strength $2m$; the lines from the two masses are equally spaced through the surface of a sphere of very large radius. We can see by merely looking at Figure 16-18 that the gravitational field in the space between the masses is weak because there are few lines in this region compared with the region just to the right or left of the masses, where the lines are more closely spaced. This information can of course also be obtained by direct calculation of the field at points in these regions.

We can apply the above reasoning to drawing the lines of force for any system of point masses. Let d be the greatest separation between any two masses in the system. If we are very far from the system, the

Figure 16-7
Lines of force indicating the gravitational field near a point mass. The direction of the lines indicates the direction of the field at any point; the density of the lines indicates the magnitude of the field.

How to sketch lines of force

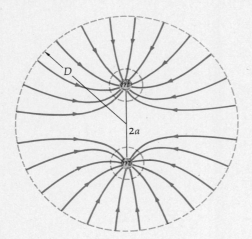

Figure 16-8
Lines of force indicating the gravitational field produced by two point masses. Very near either mass the lines are the same as if there were a single point mass m. Very far from the two masses, the lines are the same as if the two masses were together as a single mass $2m$.

detailed structure of the system cannot be important. The gravitation field is thus the same as that due to a single point mass equal to the total mass of the system. On a sphere of radius r, where r is much greater than d, the lines of force are equally spaced and point in toward the system. The number of lines is chosen to be proportional to the total mass of the system. At each point mass in the system, a number of lines proportional to the mass converge symmetrically. The lines cannot intersect at a point in space where there is no mass because there can be only one direction for the gravitational field at such a point. There are no points like that in Figure 16-9 from which the lines of force diverge. If such a point existed, a test mass placed anywhere near that point would experience a force away from the point, implying a negative mass at that point; however, negative mass which repels other mass has never been observed.[1] It is important to realize that *the convention indicating the field strength by lines of force works only because the gravitational field varies inversely as the square of the distance from a point mass.* Since the electric field of a point charge also varies inversely as the square of the distance, the concept of lines of force is also very useful in picturing the electrostatic field.

Figure 16-9
Lines of force diverging from a point in space. Such a situation is not observed in nature for the gravitational force. According to this pattern, a test mass placed near this point would be repelled from the point as if negative mass were at the point.

16-6   The Gravitational Field of a Spherically Symmetric Mass Distribution

A particularly important special mass distribution is one which is spherically symmetric. To a good approximation, the earth is such a distribution. We shall consider first a spherically symmetric shell of radius R and mass M (we calculate the field produced by such a system using integral calculus in Section 16-7). In this section, we shall investigate the properties of such a field by considering the lines of force. The only unique direction in a system with spherical symmetry is radial. The only possible direction for lines of force is along radii, either toward the center of symmetry or away from it. We choose the origin at the center of the shell. At very great distances compared with the shell radius R, the field must look like that of a point mass M. Thus the lines are radial and equally spaced far from the shell. Because of the symmetry of this system, the lines remain radial and equally spaced at all distances from the shell. The lines of force are shown for this system in Figure 16-10. Outside the shell the lines are exactly the same as those for a point mass M at the origin. Thus the field produced outside the shell is just

$$g_r = -\frac{GM}{r^2} \qquad\qquad 16\text{-}19$$

The lines end on the shell. There can be no lines inside the shell. If, for example, there were lines radially inward inside the shell, they would converge at the origin, but since there is no mass at the origin, they cannot converge there. If they were radially outward, they would have

[1] It has been proposed that antiparticles such as positrons or antiprotons may have negative gravitational mass and exhibit gravitational repulsion of ordinary mass. Because of the extreme weakness of the gravitational interaction compared with other interactions between particles, the validity of this proposal is difficult to test directly by experiment. There are theoretical reasons for expecting the gravitational mass to be positive for antiparticles as well as for ordinary particles.

$g_r = -\dfrac{GM}{r^2}$
for $r > R$

$g_r = 0$
for $r < R$

Figure 16-10
Lines of force for a spherical-shell mass distribution. Outside the shell the lines are the same as if there were a point mass at the center of the shell. Inside the shell there are no lines, indicating that the gravitational field is zero inside the shell.

to diverge from the origin, an impossibility, as we have already discussed. We thus have the remarkable result that a spherically symmetric shell of mass produces no gravitational field inside it:

$$g_r = 0 \qquad r < R \qquad\qquad\qquad 16\text{-}20$$

If a test mass m_0 is placed anywhere inside the shell, it will experience no gravitational attraction by the shell. This is easily understood for m at the center of the sphere, since then for any mass element of the sphere there is an equal mass element an equal distance on the opposite side. Their attractions for m_0 would cancel. That this is also true at every other point inside the sphere is not at first obvious. It is a consequence of the inverse-square character of the force.[1] As we shall see later, Franklin's discovery that the same thing occurs for the electric force led Priestley to conclude that the electric force is also an inverse-square force.

We can now use the results of Equations 16-19 and 16-20 to find the gravitational field inside and outside a solid sphere whose density depends only on the distance r from the center. We treat the solid sphere as a set of spherical shells. The gravitational field outside the sphere is just

$$g_r = -\frac{GM}{r^2} \qquad\qquad\qquad 16\text{-}21$$

where M is the total mass of the sphere since each shell acts as if it were a point mass at the center of the sphere. In other words, the field which any spherically symmetric mass produces outside its own surface is just the same as if all the mass were concentrated at the center of the sphere. It is this result which in Chapter 6 justified our calculating the force of gravity of the earth at its surface by treating the earth as a point mass concentrated at the center of the earth.

Derivation of the gravitational field inside the solid sphere is more complicated. The field inside the sphere depends upon how the density varies with r. Consider the case of constant density:

$$\rho = \rho_0 = \frac{M}{V} = \frac{M}{\frac{4}{3}\pi R^3}$$

[1] It is only because the force varies as $1/r^2$ that the field strength can be indicated by our system of lines of force.

We wish to find the field at a point a distance r from the center where $r < R$. As we have seen, a spherical shell produces no field at a point within the shell. Thus the only contribution to the field at this point is due to the mass M' within the radius r (see Figure 16-11). This mass produces a field which is the same as if this mass were at the origin. The mass within the distance r is

$$M' = \rho_0 \left(\tfrac{4}{3}\pi r^3\right) = \frac{M}{\tfrac{4}{3}\pi R^3} \tfrac{4}{3}\pi r^3 = M\,\frac{r^3}{R^3}$$

and the gravitational field at a point inside the sphere is

$$g_r = -\frac{GM'}{r^2} = -\frac{GMr^3/R^3}{r^2} = -\frac{GM}{R^3}\,r \qquad\qquad 16\text{-}22$$

The magnitude of the field increases with distance for $r < R$. Figure 16-12 is a plot of g_r versus r for a solid sphere of constant density.

Figure 16-11
Calculation of the gravitational field inside a uniform-solid-sphere mass distribution. At distance r, only the part of the mass M' contributes to the field. The field at r is proportional to M'/r^2, which is proportional to the distance r because M' is proportional to the volume $\tfrac{4}{3}\pi r^3$.

$M =$ total mass

Figure 16-12
Sketch of g_r versus r for a uniform-solid-sphere mass distribution. The magnitude of the field increases with r inside the sphere and decreases as $1/r^2$ outside the sphere, as indicated.

Example 16-2 A particle slides along a smooth straight tunnel dug through the earth (Figure 16-13). Show that the motion is simple harmonic and find the period.

Let the x axis be along the tunnel and choose the y axis through the center of the earth, as shown in Figure 16-13. When the mass is at position x, the gravitational force acting on it is, according to Equation 16-22,

$$\mathbf{F} = m\mathbf{g} = -m\,\frac{GM_E}{R_E^3}\,r\hat{\mathbf{r}}$$

where M_E is the mass of the earth and R_E is the radius of the earth. (We have assumed that the density of the earth is uniform.) The y component of this force is balanced by the normal force of the tunnel. The x component of this force is

$$F_x = -\frac{GM_E m}{R_E^3}\,r\sin\theta$$

But $\sin\theta = x/r$. Thus

$$F_x = -\frac{GM_E m r}{R_E^3}\,\frac{x}{r} = -\frac{GM_E m}{R_E^3}\,x$$

Figure 16-13
Tunnel through the earth for Example 16-2. The y axis is chosen through the center of the earth and perpendicular to the tunnel, which is taken along the x axis. The x component of the gravitational force on a mass in the tunnel is proportional to x and toward $x = 0$.

The acceleration in the x direction is thus

$$a_x = \frac{F_x}{m} = -\frac{GM_E}{R_E^3}\,x = -\omega^2 x \qquad\qquad 16\text{-}23$$

where

$$\omega^2 = \frac{GM_E}{R_E^3} \qquad\qquad 16\text{-}24$$

Equation 16-23 is the equation for simple harmonic motion with angular frequency ω. We can write ω in terms of the acceleration of gravity near the earth's surface:

$$g = \frac{GM_E}{R_E^2}$$

Thus

$$\omega^2 = \frac{g}{R_E}$$

The period is

$$T = \frac{2\pi}{\omega} = 2\pi\,\sqrt{\frac{R_E}{g}} = 2\pi\,\sqrt{\frac{3960 \times 5280\ \text{ft}}{32.2\ \text{ft/sec}^2}} = 5.06 \times 10^3\ \text{sec} = 84.4\ \text{min}$$

The period of free fall through a straight tunnel is the same as that of a satellite orbiting near the surface of the earth. It is independent of the length of the tunnel, which means that a transit system working on this principle could provide trips from one city to any other city on earth, with every trip taking about 42 min regardless of the distance involved. (Although it still seems too expensive, serious proposals for a tunnel between New York and Washington, D.C. have been made.)

Optional

16-7   Derivation by Integral Calculus of the Gravitational Field of a Spherical Shell

We can calculate the gravitational field produced at any point by a spherically symmetric shell either directly, from Equation 16-14, or indirectly, by first calculating the gravitational potential from Equation 16-18 and then finding the field from $g_r = -dV/dr$. The second method is easier because the potential is a scalar function, whereas the gravitational field is a vector function.

Consider a spherical shell of radius R, thickness t much smaller than R, and mass M. We are interested in the gravitational potential produced by this shell at some point P which may be either inside or outside the shell. By symmetry, the potential can depend only on the radial distance r from the center of the shell to the point P. (The point P at which the field or potential is to be calculated is called the *field point*.) Nearly all the difficulty in this calculation is due to unfamiliar spherical geometry and the use of spherical coordinates r, θ, and ϕ to set up the integral in Equation 16-18. The actual evaluation of the integral is quite easy.

Let us first consider a field point outside the shell, as in Figure

Figure 16-14
Calculation of the gravitational field of a uniform spherical shell by integration. The area of the element indicated is $R^2 \sin \theta \, d\theta \, d\phi$. The distance from this element to the field point is related to r, R, and θ by the law of cosines: $s^2 = r^2 + R^2 - 2rR \cdot \cos \theta$.

Figure 16-15
The gravitational field $d\mathbf{g}$ at point P due to the mass element dm on the spherical shell. A direct calculation of the gravitational field due to the shell would require summing the vectors $d\mathbf{g}$ due to each element dm over the shell. It is easier to find the gravitational potential first because it is a scalar function.

16-14. A small area element indicated on the spherical shell has sides $R \, d\theta$ and $R \sin \theta \, d\phi$. Its area is

$$dA = R \, d\theta \; R \sin \theta \, d\phi = R^2 \sin \theta \, d\theta \, d\phi$$

The mass of this area element (which has thickness t) is

$$dm = \rho t \, dA = \rho t R^2 \sin \theta \, d\theta \, d\phi$$

where ρ is the mass per unit volume. Let s be the distance from this area element to the field point. The gravitational potential due to this element is

$$dV = -\frac{G \, dm}{s} = -\frac{G \rho t R^2 \sin \theta \, d\theta \, d\phi}{s} \qquad \text{16-25}$$

Note how much simpler this is than the gravitational *field* due to this element, which is a vector pointing along the line from the mass element to the field point (Figure 16-15). In order to calculate the gravitational *field* directly, we would have to resolve the field due to the element dm into components and calculate each component by integration over all mass elements. To calculate the scalar gravitational potential we need only sum the scalar contribution given by Equation 16-25 over all mass elements. We can immediately sum over angles ϕ since the distance s does not depend on ϕ. Figure 16-14 shows a circular strip of circumference $2\pi R \sin \theta$, width $R \, d\theta$, and thickness t. The area of this strip is thus $2\pi R^2 \sin \theta \, d\theta$ (which can also be obtained from the area $R^2 \sin \theta \, d\theta \, d\phi$ by integrating $d\phi$ from $\phi = 0$ to $\phi = 2\pi$). The gravitational potential at point P due to this strip is

$$dV = -\frac{G \, dm}{s} = -\frac{G t \rho 2\pi R^2 \sin \theta \, d\theta}{s} \qquad \text{16-26}$$

The total potential produced by the complete shell is obtained by summing over all the circular strips on the shell, i.e., by integrating from $\theta = 0$ to $\theta = 180°$. The quantities s and θ are related by the law of cosines:

$$s^2 = r^2 + R^2 - 2rR \cos \theta \qquad \text{16-27}$$

Computing the derivative with respect to θ of each term in Equation 16-27 gives

$$2 \frac{s \, ds}{d\theta} = -2rR(-\sin \theta)$$

or

$$\sin \theta \, d\theta = \frac{s}{rR} \, ds \qquad \text{16-28}$$

Instead of substituting s from Equation 16-27 into Equation 16-26 and integrating over θ it is easier to substitute $\sin \theta \, d\theta$ from Equation 16-28 into Equation 16-26 and integrate from $s = r - R$ at $\theta = 0$ to $s = r + R$ at $\theta = 180°$. We then have

$$dV = -\frac{G t \rho 2\pi R^2 (s/rR) \, ds}{s} = -\frac{G t \rho 2\pi R}{r} \, ds$$

and

$$V = -\frac{G t \rho 2\pi R}{r} \int_{r-R}^{r+R} ds = -\frac{G t \rho 2\pi R}{r} \left[r + R - (r - R) \right]$$

$$= -\frac{G t \rho 2\pi R (2R)}{r} = -\frac{G (\rho t 4\pi R^2)}{r}$$

The area $4\pi R^2$ times the thickness t is the total volume of the shell. Then $\rho t 4\pi R^2$ is just the total mass M of the spherical shell. Thus we have

$$V = -\frac{GM}{r} \qquad \text{for } r > R \qquad\qquad 16\text{-}29$$

The gravitational potential due to a spherical shell is the same at a point *outside* the shell as it would be if there were only a point mass M at the center of the shell and the shell were absent.

The calculation of the potential at a field point *inside* the shell is the same except that now s varies from $s = R - r$ at $\theta = 0$ to $s = R + r$ at $\theta = 180°$. Thus for a point inside the shell,

$$V = -\frac{Gt\rho 2\pi R}{r} \int_{R-r}^{R+r} ds = -\frac{Gt\rho 2\pi R}{r} [R + r - (R - r)]$$

$$= -\frac{Gt\rho 2\pi R}{r} 2r = -G(\rho t 4\pi R) = -\frac{G(\rho t 4\pi R^2)}{R}$$

Again, $\rho t 4\pi R^2 = M$, and thus

$$V = -\frac{GM}{R} \qquad \text{for } r < R \qquad\qquad 16\text{-}30$$

The gravitational potential *inside* the shell is constant, independent of r. Equations 16-29 and 16-30 both give the same result for the point $r = R$.

We can now easily calculate the gravitational field:

$$g_r = \begin{cases} -\dfrac{dV}{dr} = -\dfrac{d}{dr}\left(-\dfrac{GM}{r}\right) = -\dfrac{GM}{r^2} & r > R \\[2ex] -\dfrac{dV}{dr} = -\dfrac{d}{dr}\left(-\dfrac{GM}{R}\right) = 0 & r < R \end{cases} \qquad 16\text{-}31$$

Review

A. Define, explain, or otherwise identify:

Kepler's laws, 393
Gravitational constant, 394
Torsion balance, 397

Gravitational field, 398
Gravitational potential, 400
Lines of force, 401

B. True or false:

1. Kepler's law of equal areas implies that gravity varies inversely with the square of the distance.

2. The planet closest to the sun on the average has the shortest period of revolution about the sun.

3. Kepler's laws can be derived from Newton's law of gravitation combined with Newton's laws of motion.

4. The force on a test mass m_0 in a gravitational field is the product of m_0 and the gravitational field at that point.

5. The gravitational potential energy of a test mass m_0 at some point is the product of m_0 and the gravitational potential at that point.

6. A spherically symmetric shell produces no gravitational field anywhere.

7. Both the magnitude and direction of the gravitational field are indicated by lines of force.

8. There are no lines of force inside a spherically symmetric shell.

9. Lines of force cannot begin at some point in space and radiate outward in all directions from it.

10. The gravitational field propagates instantaneously through space.

Exercises

Section 16-1, Kepler's Laws

1. Suppose a small planet were discovered with a period of 5 y. What would be its mean distance from the sun?

2. Halley's comet has a period of about 76 y. What is its mean distance from the sun?

3. The comet Kohoutek has a period estimated to be at least 10^6 y. What is its mean distance from the sun?

4. The mean distance of Jupiter from the sun is 5.22 times that of the earth. What is the period of Jupiter?

5. The radius of the earth's orbit is 1.49×10^{11} m and that of Uranus is 2.87×10^{12} m. What is the period of Uranus?

6. Use Kepler's law $T^2 = Cr^3$ for satellites orbiting the earth to find the period for a satellite just above the surface of the earth from the knowledge that the period of the moon is 27.3 d and the distance to the moon is 60 times the radius of the earth. What should the radius be for a satellite which orbits the earth with a period of 1 d?

Section 16-2, The Cavendish Experiment

7. If the value of G is known, it is possible to find the mass of the earth from the radius of the moon's orbit and its period T. Calculate the mass of the earth using $r_m = 3.84 \times 10^5$ km and $T = 27.3$ d.

8. The masses in a Cavendish apparatus are $m_1 = 10$ kg and $m_2 = 10$ gm, the separation of their centers is 5 cm, and the rod separating the two small masses is 20 cm long. What is the force of attraction between the large and small spheres? What torque must be exerted by the suspension to balance these forces?

Section 16-3, The Gravitational Field

9. A point mass m is on the x axis at $x = +a$ and another equal mass is on the x axis at $x = -a$. (a) What is the gravitational field halfway between the masses at $x = 0$? (b) Find the gravitational field on the x axis at points $x > a$.

10. At what point on the line from the earth to the moon is the gravitational field due to these two bodies zero? The distance from the earth to the moon is 3.84×10^5 km, and the mass of the moon is 0.0123 times the mass of the earth. Are there other points for which the gravitational field due to the earth and the moon is zero?

11. The gravitational field at some point in space is $\mathbf{g} = 2\mathbf{i} + 3\mathbf{j}$ N/kg. (a) What is the magnitude of the force exerted on a 3-kg mass placed at that point? (b) What is the direction of the force? (c) Write an expression for the gravitational force on a 5-kg mass placed at that point.

12. What is the magnitude and direction of the gravitational field due to the earth at the surface of the earth?

13. A 1-gm point mass is moving in a circle of radius 100 m. Its speed is 0.5 m/sec. The only force on the mass is due to gravity. What is the gravitational field at the position of the mass due to other masses?

Section 16-4, Gravitational Potential

14. If the potential energy of a particle depends on x only, the force is given by $F_x = -dU/dx$. From this fact, show that in this situation the gravitational field is related to the gravitational potential by $g_x = -dV/dx$.

15. Two point masses m are situated on the y axis at $y = +a$ and $y = -a$. (a) Find the gravitational potential $V(x)$ for points on the x axis. (b) Sketch $V(x)$ versus x. (c) Find the gravitational field $g_x = -dV/dx$ from your result in part (a). At what point is $g_x = 0$?

16. For the two-point mass distribution in Exercise 15, find the work required to bring a test mass m_0 from $x = \infty$ to the point $x = 0$.

17. A uniform thin ring of mass M and radius r lies in the yz plane with its center at the origin. (a) Find the gravitational potential $V(x)$ for points on the x axis (which is the axis of the ring). (b) Sketch $V(x)$ versus x. (c) At what point does $V(x)$ have maximum magnitude? What is the gravitational field at that point?

18. Two point masses m are situated on the x axis at $x = +a$ and $x = -a$. Sketch the gravitational potential $V(x)$ versus x for points on the x axis. At the point $x = 0$ the gravitational field is zero. Does the potential function $V(x)$ have a maximum or minimum point at $x = 0$?

Section 16-5, Lines of Force

19. Two point masses $m_1 = m$ and $m_2 = 2m$ are a distance D apart. Sketch the lines of force for this configuration.

20. Figure 16-16 shows lines of force in the xy plane due to a disk mass. What information about the gravitational field due to the disk can be obtained from the fact that (a) the lines are much more dense near the disk than far from the disk and (b) in the region near the center of the face of the disk the lines are uniformly spaced?

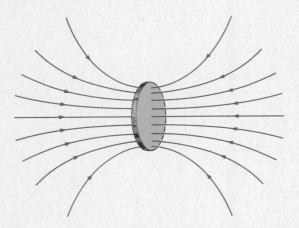

Figure 16-16
Lines of force for a uniform disk mass (Exercise 20). Only the lines in the plane of the axis are shown.

21. Explain why the lines of force shown in Figure 16-17a to c are not possible representations of any gravitational field.

(a)

(b)

(c)

Figure 16-17
Exercise 21.

Section 16-6, The Gravitational Field of a Spherically Symmetric Mass Distribution

22. (a) Use Equation 16-17 to show that the gravitational potential $V(r)$ is constant inside a spherical-shell mass distribution. (b) How does $V(r)$ vary with r outside a spherical-shell mass distribution? (c) Sketch $V(r)$ versus r for such a distribution, using the fact that the potential must be continuous at $r = R$, where R is the radius of the shell.

23. A spherical shell has a radius $R = 2$ m and mass 12 kg. What is the gravitational field (a) just outside and (b) just inside the shell?

24. Find the gravitational potential V just inside and just outside the spherical-shell mass distribution of Exercise 23.

25. (a) Show that the gravitational potential $V(r)$ outside a solid spherical mass of constant density is given by $V(r) = -GM/r$, where M is the total mass of the sphere. (b) Show that the gravitational potential just outside the earth's surface $V(R_E)$ can be written $V(R_E) = -gR_E$, where g is the acceleration of gravity and R_E is the radius of the earth. (c) Evaluate the gravitational potential energy just outside the earth's surface in joules per kilogram. (d) The kinetic energy needed for a mass m to escape from the earth is just $m|V(R_E)|$, where $V(R_E)$ is the gravitational potential near the earth's surface. Find the energy needed for an 80-kg astronaut to escape from the earth's gravitational field. At 3 cents per kilowatt-hour, how much would this energy cost?

Problems

1. For the mass distribution in Example 16-1 show that g_x is approximately $-2GMm/x^2$ when x is much greater than a. Show also that the maximum value of $|g_x|$ occurs at the point $x = a/\sqrt{2}$.

2. The gravitational potential $V(x)$ was found for points along the x axis for a ring mass in Exercise 17. (a) Calculate the gravitational field from $g_x = -dV/dx$. (b) At what points is the magnitude of the gravitational field maximum? (c) Calculate the gravitational field on the axis of a ring directly from Equation 16-14 by first finding g_x due to some element of the ring Δm_i and then summing over all the elements.

3. Two planets of equal mass orbit a much more massive star. Planet m_1 moves in a circular orbit of radius 1×10^8 km and period 2 y. Planet m_2 moves in an elliptical orbit with closest distance $r_1 = 1 \times 10^8$ km and farthest distance $r_2 = 1.8 \times 10^8$ km, as shown in Figure 16-18. (a) Using the fact that the mean radius of an elliptic orbit is the length of the semimajor axis, find the period of m_2's orbit. (b) What is the mass of the star? (c) Which planet has the greater speed at point P? Which has the greater total energy? (d) How does the speed of m_2 at point P compare with that at A? *Hint:* Use conservation of angular momentum.

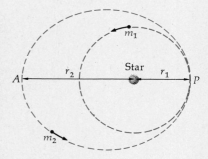

Figure 16-18
Problem 3.

4. The restoring torque for a torsional balance is proportional to the angular displacement $\tau = -k\theta$, where k is the torque constant. (a) From the equation $\tau = I\alpha$, where I is the moment of inertial for rotation about the axis of suspension, show that twisting motion of the balance is simple harmonic motion with period $T = 2\pi\sqrt{I/k}$. (b) A Cavendish apparatus uses two 25-gm metal spheres attached to the ends of a 40-cm rod with negligible mass. The rod is suspended by a fine fiber attached to its center. When the fiber is twisted, the rod oscillates with simple harmonic motion with a period of 1000 sec. Find the torsion constant of the fiber. (c) When two large masses m are placed near the smaller masses, the fiber twists through an angle $\theta = 2$ mrad. What is the force of attraction between each large mass m and the nearby 25-gm mass?

5. (a) Show that the gravitational field of a uniform ring of mass is zero at the center of the ring. (b) Figure 16-19 shows a point P in the plane of the ring but not at the center. Consider two elements of the ring of length s_1 and s_2 (in-

dicated in the figure) at a distance r_1 and r_2 from point P, respectively. What is the ratio of the masses of these elements? Which produces the greater field at point P? What is the direction of the field at point P due to these elements? (c) What is the direction of the gravitational field at point P? (d) Suppose that the gravitational field due to a point mass varied as $1/r$ rather than $1/r^2$. What then would be the resultant gravitational field at point P due to the elements shown? (e) How would your answers to parts (b) and (c) differ if point P were inside a spherical shell of mass rather than a plane circular ring?

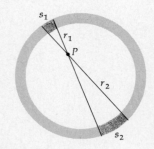

Figure 16-19
Problem 5.

6. A uniform thin disk has mass M and radius R. (a) What is the density of the disk in terms of M and R? (b) What is the gravitational potential on the axis of the disk a distance x from its center produced by a ring element of the disk of radius r and width dr? (c) Integrate your result for part (b) to obtain the potential for the whole disk. (d) From the potential, find the gravitational field strength at any point on the axis of the disk.

7. A mass m slides through the tunnel discussed in Example 16-2, starting at rest at the surface of the earth. Show that the maximum speed m reaches is given by $x\sqrt{g/R_E}$, where x is the initial displacement from equilibrium shown in Figure 16-13. Evaluate this speed for a tunnel joining two cities 200 mi apart. Use the approximation $2x = 200$ mi.

8. A thick spherical shell has an inner radius R_1 and an outer radius R_2. It has mass M and uniform density. Find the gravitational field g_r as a function of distance r from the center of the sphere for the ranges $0 \leqslant r \leqslant R_1$, $R_1 \leqslant r \leqslant R_2$, and $R_2 \leqslant r < \infty$.

9. A uniform rod of mass M and length L lies along the x axis with center at the origin. Consider an element of length dx a distance x from the origin. Show that this element produces a gravitational field at a point on the axis x_0 (x_0 greater than $\frac{1}{2}L$) given by

$$\frac{-GM\ dx/L}{(x_0 - x)^2}$$

Integrate this result over the rod to find the total gravitational field at the point x_0 due to the rod.

10. Calculate the gravitational potential at point x_0 due to the uniform rod of Problem 9. Use your result to find the gravitational field from $g_x = -dV/dx$.

11. A straight, smooth tunnel is dug through a spherical planet whose mass density ρ_0 is constant. The tunnel passes through the center of the planet and is perpendicular to the planet's axis of rotation, which is fixed in space. The planet rotates with an angular velocity so that objects in the tunnel have no acceleration relative to the tunnel. Find the relation between ρ_0 and ω for this to be true.

CHAPTER 17   Temperature

Thermodynamics is the study of energy transfers involving temperature between macroscopic bodies. In the following three chapters we
shall define the concepts of temperature, heat, and internal energy just
as we carefully defined such concepts as mass, force, potential energy,
etc., in our study of mechanics. Until we do however, we shall use the
words temperature and heat in their ordinary meanings: temperature
is what we measure with an ordinary thermometer; heat is energy
which is transferred because of a temperature difference.

17-1   Macroscopic State Variables

Consider a body of gas enclosed in some volume V and at some pressure P. There are two different approaches to the description of such a
system. One way, the *microscopic* method, involves a description in
terms of the many particles, the molecules, composing the gas. It
requires many assumptions about the particles which are very difficult
to test directly. For example, we assume that the gas is composed of N
molecules each moving about in a random way making elastic collisions with other molecules and with the walls of the container. Because of the huge size of N (for example, 1 mole, or 32 gm, of oxygen
contains Avogadro's number $N_A \approx 6 \times 10^{23}$ molecules), it is impossible to apply Newton's laws of motion separately to each molecule or
even to list the coordinates of each molecule. Entering just one coordinate for each molecule of 1 mole of material into a computer at the
rate of 1 μs per molecule would take 6×10^{17} sec $\approx 2 \times 10^{10}$ y, which
is the same order of magnitude as the age of the universe. However,
just because N is so large, statistical methods of treatment are very
accurate. In Chapter 11 we showed by a simple analysis that the pressure exerted by a gas on the wall of its container is proportional to the
average kinetic energy of the molecules in the gas. This type of calculation is an example of a microscopic calculation of a macroscopic variable, the pressure P.

Microscopic description

In the *macroscopic* approach characteristic of thermodynamics, the system is described by only a few variables, e.g., pressure, temperature, volume, and internal energy. These variables (except internal energy) are closely related to our senses and are easily measured. (Compare these few variables with the $6N$ coordinates and velocity components of the molecules and additional variables describing rotation or oscillation of molecules like O_2 which contain more than one atom.) Few assumptions are made in the macroscopic description of matter. The laws of thermodynamics, which, like Newton's laws of motion, are elegant and compact generalizations of the results of experience, are therefore quite general and independent of any particular molecular assumptions made in the microscopic approach. In fact, much of thermodynamics was developed before the molecular model of matter was completely accepted.

The minimum number of macroscopic variables needed to describe a system depends on the kind of system, but it is always a small number. Usually we must specify the composition (if the system is not homogeneous, e.g., a mixture of two or more gases), the mass of each part, and only two more variables such as the pressure P and the volume V of a gas. If we restrict our discussion to homogeneous systems of constant mass, we usually need only two variables.

We cannot say that a gas is at pressure P and temperature t unless the system is in *thermal equilibrium* with itself. Consider, for example, a gas in an enclosure of volume V, isolated from its surroundings. If we stir the gas rapidly in one corner of the container, we cannot assign a pressure and temperature to the whole gas until the gas settles down. If we measure the temperature at various parts of the gas just after stirring, we get different results, which change with time. *When the macroscopic properties of an isolated system become constant in time, the system is in thermal equilibrium with itself.* We can then describe some property such as pressure with a single variable P for the whole system.

Suppose we have a fixed mass of gas originally at some pressure P_0 and volume V_0. Let the temperature of the gas be t_0 (measured in any familiar way). We now do various things to the gas, e.g., compress it, heat it, let it expand against a piston, and cool it, but finally return it to the original pressure P_0 and volume V_0. When the gas is again at equilibrium with itself at the original pressure and volume, we find that its temperature is again t_0. Every other macroscopic property which we can measure is also the same as it was originally. The variables P and V thus specify a *macroscopic state* of the system. We could also specify the state of this system using the variables P and t. For a constant-mass gas system, an equilibrium state is specified by any two macroscopic variables.

There are many other kinds of macroscopic systems whose states can be described by two variables (assuming constant mass). For example, a long rod can be described by its length L and the pressure P (which is usually atmospheric pressure unless the rod is enclosed in some way). Similarly, the state of a conducting wire can be described by the pressure and its electric resistance. Even such a complicated system as an electric cell can often be described quite well in terms of only two variables, such as the emf[1] of the cell and the charge. In the following chapters we shall define temperature carefully and other mac-

Macroscopic description

---

[1] We will discuss emf in Chapter 34.

roscopic variables, e.g., internal energy and entropy, which are also *state variables*. We repeat the meaning of the concept of a macroscopic equilibrium state: if a system is in a given equilibrium state at some time and after various processes it is brought back to that equilibrium state, all the macroscopic properties of the system will be the same as they were originally. Note that a *macroscopic* equilibrium state is quite different from a *microscopic* state, which is specified by the positions, velocities, and internal coordinates of all the molecules in the system. In a simple gas in thermal equilibrium with itself the microscopic state is continually changing because the molecules are changing position and making collisions which change their velocities; but in equilibrium, the macroscopic state remains the same. There are many different microscopic states which correspond to a single macroscopic state.

State variables

17-2   Adiabatic and Diathermic Walls

Before we give a rigorous definition of temperature, let us consider some common experiences with properties of materials using temperature as measured by a common thermometer. Consider, for example, a given mass of gas with volume V and at pressure P. If we heat the gas (say with a bunsen burner), the pressure or volume of the gas will change. If the volume is kept constant, the pressure increases as the temperature is raised. Alternatively, if the pressure is kept constant by allowing the gas to expand against a piston, as in Figure 17-1, the volume increases as the temperature is raised. An increase in the temperature of the gas is indicated by an increase in either the pressure P or the volume V when the other variable is kept constant.

Let us consider some simple experiments with constant-volume gas systems. We place two systems, originally at different temperatures, in close contact by separating them only by a thin metal wall. The temperature of each system changes until the two systems reach a common temperature between the original temperatures. The pressure of one system increases as its temperature increases, and the pressure of the other decreases as its temperature decreases, until eventually the pressures reach steady values when the systems reach their final equilibrium temperature. When the pressures stop changing, the systems are in *thermal equilibrium* with each other. The time it takes to reach equilibrium depends on the masses and types of the gases, on the original temperatures, and on the kind of contact made between the two systems. If we replace the thin metal wall with a thick asbestos wall, the time is very long. Over rather long periods of time with this separation, the two systems remain at nearly their original pressures and temperatures. (We are assuming that both systems are otherwise isolated from other systems.) If we heat one system, stir it, or do anything to it, very little if anything happens to the other system.

We can do similar experiments with other types of systems. For example, instead of constant-volume gas systems, we might use long metal rods at constant pressure. In that case, the increase or decrease in the length of a rod indicates an increase or decrease in its temperature. From these experiments, we can define two kinds of ideal separations *without any prior reference to temperature*. Two systems are said to be separated by an *adiabatic wall* if we can arbitrarily change the variables of one system without having any effect on the other. For example, if two constant-volume gas systems are separated by an adiabatic wall, we can increase the pressure of one by heating it, or by

Figure 17-1
By confining a gas in a cylinder with a movable piston it is possible to heat the gas at constant pressure. As the gas is heated, the piston moves to the right against a constant force, which equals the pressure times the area.

Adiabatic and diathermic walls

some other means, and the other system will not be affected. (The common name for an adiabatic wall is a perfectly insulating wall. An adiabatic wall does not allow heat flow. However, we do not need to define heat or temperature in order to define an adiabatic wall.) The opposite extreme is a *diathermic wall*. If two systems are connected by a diathermic wall, a change in one of the thermodynamic variables of one system will influence the variables of the other system. For example, if two constant-volume gas systems are connected by a diathermic wall, heating one gas will cause an increase in pressure in the other gas (as well as in the one heated directly). The common name for a diathermic wall is, of course, a perfect heat conductor. Systems connected by a diathermic wall are said to be in *thermal contact*. In practice thin metal walls make excellent approximations to a perfect diathermic wall. Similarly, an adiabatic wall can be approximated with thick asbestos.

Thermal contact

17-3   The Zeroth Law of Thermodynamics

We now use our definitions of adiabatic and diathermic walls to define temperature. Suppose that two systems, originally separated, are put in contact by a diathermic wall and isolated from their surroundings by adiabatic walls (Figure 17-2). In general, when the systems are put in thermal contact, the thermodynamic variables will change from their original values. For example, the pressures P_1 and P_2 of two gas systems held at constant volume will change. One will increase, and the other will decrease. When the pressures reach their final equilibrium values, the two systems are said to be in *thermal equilibrium with each other*.

Suppose that when the two systems (originally separated) are put in contact by a diathermic wall, no change is observed in any of the variables of either system. The connected systems are in equilibrium, and they are said to be in thermal equilibrium even if they are separated. We thus generalize the concept of thermal equilibrium to include systems which are not in contact by a diathermic wall but which would be in equilibrium if they were so connected.

Figure 17-2
Systems 1 and 2 are connected to each other by a diathermic wall but separated from their surroundings by adiabatic walls. In general the thermodynamic variables of the systems will change when they are in thermal contact (connected by a diathermic wall). When the variables cease to change, the systems are in thermal equilibrium with each other.

Figure 17-3
(*a*) Systems *A* and *B* are in thermal contact with system *C*. When system *A* and system *B* are in thermal equilibrium with system *C*, they are in thermal equilibrium with each other. This can be checked by putting them in contact with each other, as in (*b*). This experimental result is known as the zeroth law of thermodynamics.

Suppose system *A* is in thermal equilibrium with system *C* and system *B* is also in thermal equilibrium with system *C*, as in Figure 17-3*a*. If we now place system *A* and *B* in thermal contact, i.e., connect them by a diathermic wall (Figure 17-3*b*), we find that they are in thermal equilibrium with each other. This result is known as the zeroth law of thermodynamics:

If two systems are in thermal equilibrium with a third system, the two systems are in thermal equilibrium with each other.

Zeroth law

The zeroth law of thermodynamics, which is an experimental law, shows that the relation between two systems implied by the statement that they are in thermal equilibrium is a *transitive relation*. That is, if A is in thermal equilibrium with C and B with C, then A is in thermal equilibrium with B. This transitive property is needed in order to define temperature.

The first step in defining temperature is to determine a rule for saying when two systems in equilibrium have the same temperature. This resembles our procedure in mechanics, where the first law of motion defined the condition of motion without force. We adopted the rule that there is no force when velocity does not change. In the case of temperature, we shall say that two systems have the same temperature if none of their macroscopic variables change when they are connected with a diathermic wall. This definition of temperature equality is more succinctly expressed as follows:

Two systems in thermal equilibrium with each other are at the same temperature.

Two systems which are not in equilibrium with each other are at different temperatures. Suppose the two systems are constant-volume gas systems and that P_1 decreases and P_2 increases when they are put in thermal contact. We could arbitrarily define either system to be at a higher temperature and still have a self-consistent concept of temperature. However, since it is important to make scientific definitions of quantities as close to common usage as possible, we want a system which feels hot to the touch to be at a higher temperature than one which feels cold. (It is not always possible to distinguish the relative hotness or coldness of two objects by sense of touch, but there is a quite general agreement for a wide choice of systems such as ice water and water at 80°F.) In our example of two gas systems, system 1 is originally "warmer" than system 2. We associate *decreasing pressure* of a constant-volume gas system with *decreasing temperature* and *increasing pressure* with *increasing temperature*. If we place a constant-volume gas system in thermal contact with a metal rod when the systems are not in thermal equilibrium, we find that if the pressure of the gas increases, the length of the rod decreases and vice versa. Thus increasing rod length at constant pressure indicates that the temperature of the rod is increasing.

Questions

1. Consider the relation expressed by "A loves B." Is this relation transitive?

2. Suppose we define two countries to be in equilibrium with each other when they are at peace with each other. Is this kind of equilibrium situation transitive?

3. Give two other examples of relations between two objects which are transitive and two which are not.

4. As we have defined it, does temperature have any meaning applied to a system not in equilibrium with itself?

5. How could you determine whether two bodies have the same temperature if it is impossible to put them into contact with each other?

17-4   Temperature Scales and Thermometers

We have just defined a method for comparing any two systems and deciding whether they are at the same temperature or, if not, which system is at the greater temperature. We note that if A is at a greater temperature than B and B is at a greater temperature than C, it follows that A is at a greater temperature than C. If we have N systems, we can order them along a line such that all those to the right of a given system have a greater temperature than that system and all those to the left have a smaller temperature. We are now in position to define a *temperature scale,* which we can use to assign a number to each system so that greater numbers indicate greater temperatures.

We first choose a system to be our thermometer. We then define the temperature to be any monotonic function of one of the state variables of the system with the other held constant. For example, let us choose a given mass of mercury contained in a narrow glass tube. When we put this system in thermal contact with another, e.g., a constant-volume gas system, we note that the length of the mercury column increases when the temperature increases. Thus the mercury system behaves essentially the same as a rod at constant pressure. (The pressure on the mercury is usually not kept constant, but the compressibility of mercury is so small that even a rather large change in pressure has little effect on the volume or length of the mercury column.) The simplest functional relation between temperature and length of the mercury column that we can choose is a linear one. We define the temperature t to be related to the length L by

$$t = aL + b \qquad\qquad 17\text{-}1$$

The slope a and the intercept b can be determined by arbitrarily defining the temperature of two reproducible states of some standard system. Alternatively, we can choose the intercept b to be zero and determine a by arbitrarily defining the temperature of a single standard state.

The first method, which was universally used before 1954, is still of some practical use today. We choose for one of our states the ice point of water, i.e., water and ice in equilibrium with air at atmospheric pressure (also called the *normal melting point*), and define its temperature to be zero degrees Celsius,[1] written 0°C. Similarly we define the temperature of the steam point, i.e., water and water vapor in equilibrium at atmospheric pressure (also called the *normal boiling point*), to be 100°C. Let L_i be the length of the mercury column when it is in thermal equilibrium with a system at the ice point and L_s be that when it is in thermal equilibrium with a system at the steam point. We then have from Equation 17-1,

$$t_i = aL_i + b = 0°C \qquad \text{and} \qquad t_s = aL_s + b = 100°C \qquad 17\text{-}2$$

These equations can be solved for a and b in terms of L_i and L_s, giving

$$a = \frac{100°C}{L_s - L_i} \qquad \text{and} \qquad b = -\frac{(100°C)L_i}{L_s - L_i} \qquad 17\text{-}3$$

Having determined these constants, we can measure the temperature of any other system by noting the length L of the mercury when the

SCALA

Galileo's thermoscope, one of the earliest thermometers, used by Galileo to detect temperature changes. (*Courtesy of the Science Museum, Florence.*)

[1] The Celsius scale was formerly called the centigrade scale.

thermometer is in equilibrium with that system and using Equation 17-1. Figure 17-4 illustrates this temperature scale.

If we choose a different system to be our thermometer, we define the temperature measured by this thermometer in a similar way. For example, if we choose a constant-volume gas thermometer (Figure 17-5), we define the temperature to vary linearly with the pressure

$$t = aP + b \qquad \text{17-4}$$

Again we can find a and b in terms of the pressure P_i at the ice point and P_s at the steam point. We obtain equations similar to Equation 17-3:

$$a = \frac{100°C}{P_s - P_i} \quad \text{and} \quad b = -\frac{(100°C)P_i}{P_s - P_i} \qquad \text{17-5}$$

Other thermometers can be similarly calibrated. For example, we can use a copper rod at constant pressure and define the temperature to be a linear function of the length or a resistance thermometer at constant pressure, for which the temperature is defined to vary linearly with electric resistance. The constants a and b are different for different thermometers.

We now ask whether the various thermometers defined in this way will agree when measuring the temperature of some system other than at the ice point or steam point of water. For example, if we measure the normal boiling point of sulfur (at about 444°C), we get different numbers using different thermometers. The discrepancies are particularly bad at temperatures far from the two fixed points. Similarly, if we measure thermal properties of some material, the results depend on the particular thermometer used. For example, if we use a copper-rod thermometer to measure the length of another piece of copper versus temperature, we find of course that the length of the copper varies linearly with temperature because the temperature scale was defined by this property. But if we measure the length of the same rod versus temperature using a mercury thermometer, we find that the expansion of the copper is not quite linear with temperature.

There is one group of thermometers for which the measured temperatures are in very close agreement at all temperatures. These are the gas thermometers, either constant-volume thermometers (discussed above) or constant-pressure thermometers, for which the temperature is taken to vary linearly with volume. If we measure the temperature of a given state of some system with different gas thermometers, we get close agreement no matter what kind of gas is used as long as the pressure in the thermometer is not too high and the temperature is not too low. If we reduce the pressure in all the thermometers by using less gas, the agreement improves.

Let us consider the following procedure. We measure some temperature, say the normal boiling point of sulfur, with a constant-volume gas thermometer, choosing the amount of gas so that the pressure at the steam point of water is $P_s = 1000$ millimeters of mercury (mm Hg; common units of pressure are described in Section 17-5). We then remove some of the gas in the thermometer so that the steam-point pressure P_s is now only 500 mm Hg and again measure the temperature of the normal boiling point of sulfur. We repeat this process with smaller and smaller amounts of gas and plot the measured temperature versus P_s. Figure 17-6 shows such a plot for various gases used in a constant-volume thermometer. As the pressure approaches zero, all the thermometers approach the same value, $t = 444.60°C$. We obtain similar results with a constant-pressure thermometer using the volume of the gas to measure the temperature. As the mass of the gas is

Figure 17-4
Temperature scale based on two fixed points. The temperature is assumed to vary linearly with the length of a mercury column. L_i and L_s are the lengths when the column is at the ice point and steam point of water, respectively. The scale is then determined by defining these temperatures to be 0°C and 100°C.

Figure 17-5
A constant-volume gas thermometer. The temperature is chosen to be proportional to the pressure of the gas in the bulb B_1. The tube B_3 is open to the atmosphere at the top and connected to the tube B_2 by a flexible hose. The volume is maintained constant by raising or lowering B_3 until the mercury in B_2 is at the zero mark. The pressure of the gas is then determined from the height h.

Figure 17-6
Temperature of the boiling point of sulfur measured with constant-volume gas thermometers filled with various gases. P_s, the pressure at the steam point of water, is varied by varying the amount of gas in the thermometer. As the pressure is reduced, the measured temperatures approach the value 444.60°C for all thermometers.

reduced so that the pressure becomes smaller, the temperatures measured by different gas thermometers tend to a single limit.

This agreement of all gas thermometers at low pressures means that the intercept b in Equation 17-4 and given by Equation 17-5 is the same for all gas thermometers. Measurements of b at low pressures yield values of about $-273.15°C$. There is some disagreement between various laboratories where this number is measured because of the experimental difficulty in measuring the ice-point and steam-point temperatures. Both states are very difficult to duplicate experimentally. Because of these difficulties, a temperature scale based on a single fixed point with b defined to be zero was adopted in 1954 by the International Committee on Weights and Measures. A reference state which is much more easily reproduced than either the ice point or steam point is the *triple point of water,* the single temperature and pressure at which water, water vapor, and ice coexist in equilibrium. The triple-point pressure is 4.58 mm Hg, and the temperature is about 0.01°C. The temperature of this state is conventionally chosen to be 273.16° (note that this is not degrees Celsius). Setting b equal to zero in Equation 17-4, we have for a constant-volume thermometer,

$$t = aP \qquad\qquad\qquad 17\text{-}6$$

Let P_3 be the pressure when the thermometer is in equilibrium with a system containing water, water vapor, and ice; then

$$273.16° = aP_3 \qquad \text{or} \qquad a = \frac{273.16°}{P_3}$$

Thus

$$t = \frac{273.16°}{P_3} P \qquad\qquad\qquad 17\text{-}7$$

In Section 17-7 and in Chapter 18 we shall discuss the behavior of real gases at very low pressures in terms of a simple model called an *ideal gas*. The temperature scale defined by Equation 17-7 in the limit of very low pressures is called the *ideal-gas temperature* θ. For a constant-volume gas thermometer, the ideal-gas temperature is defined to be

$$\theta = 273.16° \lim_{P_3 \to 0} \frac{P}{P_3} \qquad \text{constant } V \qquad\qquad 17\text{-}8a$$

Similarly, for a constant-pressure thermometer the ideal-gas temperature is

$$\theta = 273.16° \lim_{P_3 \to 0} \frac{V}{V_3} \qquad \text{constant } P \qquad\qquad 17\text{-}8b$$ *Ideal-gas temperature*

This temperature scale has the following advantages: (1) the measured temperature of any state is the same no matter what kind of gas is used, and (2) the reference state (the triple point of water) is easily reproduced throughout the world, so that temperatures measured in various laboratories are in good agreement with each other. This temperature scale depends on the properties of gases but not on the properties of any particular gas. Any substance can be used as long as it remains a gas. The lowest temperature that can be measured with a gas thermometer is about 1° using helium for the gas. Below this temperature helium liquefies. All other gases liquefy at higher temperatures.

In Chapter 19 we show that we can define a temperature scale which is independent of the properties of any material, called the *Kelvin scale,* or *absolute temperature scale.* We shall show that for temperatures above 1° for which the ideal-gas scale can be defined, the ideal-gas and absolute temperature scales are identical. In anticipation of this, we write[1] K after temperatures defined by the ideal-gas scale, and we shall use the conventional symbol T for the absolute temperature scale even though we cannot define this scale until we study the second law of thermodynamics.

Figure 17-7 shows the temperature of the steam point of water measured with constant-volume gas thermometers using various gases at various pressures P_3. As P_3 is reduced to zero by reducing the amount of gas in the various thermometers, the measurements approach the common value of 373.15 K, the ideal-gas temperature, which is the same as the absolute temperature. The ice-point temperature measured in a similar way is 273.15 K.

The Bettmann Archive

Lord Kelvin (1824–1907) with his compass for use on board iron ships.

Figure 17-7
Temperature of the steam point of water measured with constant-volume gas thermometers filled with various gases. The temperature is plotted as a function of P_3, the pressure at the triple point of water, which is varied by varying the amount of gas in the thermometer. As the pressure approaches zero, the measured temperatures approach the value 373.15 K for all thermometers.

17-5 Units of Pressure

Pressure is defined as force per unit area and has SI units of newtons per square meter. As we showed in Chapter 5, the pressure difference between the top and bottom of a column of incompressible liquid is $P = \rho g h$. In other words, the pressure difference is proportional to the height of the liquid column. The height h thus can be used as a measure of pressure. For example, a pressure can be specified by saying it is the same as the pressure difference between the top and the bottom of a column of mercury 500 mm high. A pressure so specified could be expressed in newtons per square meter by using the relationship $P = \rho g h$ and the actual values of ρ and g.

In practice, pressure is often measured in millimeters of mercury (commonly called Torr, after the Italian physicist Torricelli) and in

---

[1] The name of the unit of temperature was changed by the 13th General Conference on Weights and Measures in 1967 from degree Kelvin (°K) to kelvin (K), defined to be 1/273.16 of the absolute temperature of the triple point of water.

inches and feet of water (written in H_2O and ft H_2O). Another common unit is the atmosphere (atm), which is approximately air pressure at sea level. The atmosphere, millimeters of mercury, and newton per square meter are related as follows:

$$1 \text{ atm} = 760 \text{ mm Hg} = 760 \text{ Torr} = 1.013 \times 10^5 \text{ N/m}^2$$

$$1 \text{ mm Hg} = 1 \text{ Torr} = 1.316 \times 10^{-3} \text{ atm} = 133.3 \text{ N/m}^2$$

Other units commonly used on weather maps are the bar and the millibar, defined by

$$1 \text{ bar} = 10^3 \text{ millibar} = 10^5 \text{ N/m}^2$$

A pressure of 1 bar is just slightly less than 1 atm.

Example 17-1 The pressure in a pipe in a water system is 50 ft H_2O. Express this pressure in millimeters of mercury, atmospheres, and newtons per square meter.

To say that the pressure is 50 ft H_2O means that the pressure is $P = \rho_w g h_w$, where ρ_w is the density of water and $h_w = 50$ ft. The same pressure is related to the height h_m of mercury column by $P = \rho_m g h_m$, where ρ_m is the density of mercury. Thus

$$\rho_m g h_m = \rho_w g h_w \qquad \text{or} \qquad h_m = \frac{\rho_w}{\rho_m} h_w$$

When we use $\rho_w = 1$ gm/cm³ and $\rho_m = 13.6$ gm/cm³, this gives for $h_w = 50$ ft,

$$h_m = 3.68 \text{ ft} = 1120 \text{ mm}$$

Thus $P = 1120$ mm Hg. We can express P in other units using the conversion factors given above:

$$P = 1120 \text{ mm Hg} \frac{1.316 \times 10^{-3} \text{ atm}}{1 \text{ mm Hg}} = 1.47 \text{ atm}$$

and

$$P = 1120 \text{ mm Hg} \frac{133.3 \text{ N/m}^2}{1 \text{ mm Hg}} = 1.49 \times 10^5 \text{ N/m}^2$$

Otto von Guericke's demonstration of the large forces due to atmospheric pressure. The force exerted by the horses was not great enough to separate the two hollow hemispheres, which had been placed together and evacuated. (*Courtesy of the Deutsches Museum, Munich.*)

Most pressure gauges read the difference between the absolute pressure and atmospheric pressure. This difference is called *gauge pressure*. Absolute pressure is obtained from gauge pressure by adding the atmospheric pressure P_{atm}:

$$P = P_{gauge} + P_{atm}$$

17-6 Celsius, Rankine, and Fahrenheit Scales

The Celsius temperature scale (formerly called the centigrade scale) is defined as follows. The temperature t_C on the Celsius scale is related to a temperature T on the Kelvin, or absolute, scale by

$$t_C = T - 273.15 \qquad\qquad 17\text{-}9$$

The size of the degree on the Celsius scale is the same as that on the Kelvin scale. That is, a temperature difference of 10 kelvins is the same as a temperature difference of 10 Celsius degrees. The difference between the Kelvin and Celsius scales lies only in the choice of zero temperature.

The Celsius temperatures of the ice point and steam point are found by subtracting 273.15 from the Kelvin temperatures (273.15 K for the ice point and 373.15 K for the steam point). The results are 0.00°C for the ice point and 100.00°C for the steam point. The triple-point temperature of water (273.16 K) is 0.01°C. Table 17-1 lists the normal-boiling-point (NBP) and normal-melting-point (NMP) temperatures on the Celsius scale for several substances. These temperatures can be used to calibrate practical thermometers.

Two other scales in use in this country and Great Britain are the Rankine scale, defined by

$$T_R = \tfrac{9}{5}T \qquad\qquad 17\text{-}10$$

and the Fahrenheit scale, which has the same size degree as the Rankine scale but its zero is shifted:

$$t_F = T_R - 459.67°R \qquad\qquad 17\text{-}11$$

The Fahrenheit and Celsius scales can be related by eliminating T_R from Equations 17-10 and 17-11 and then eliminating T from the result and Equation 17-9. The result is

$$t_F = \tfrac{9}{5}t_C + 32°F \quad\text{or}\quad t_C = \tfrac{5}{9}(t_F - 32°F) \qquad 17\text{-}12$$

The temperatures of the ice point and steam point on the Fahrenheit scale are 32 and 212°F, respectively. The temperature 0°F is roughly the coldest temperature that can be obtained with a salt-water solution before freezing, and the temperature 100°F is roughly that of the human body. The Fahrenheit degree is smaller than the Celsius degree. The difference in temperature between the steam point and ice point is 180 Fahrenheit degrees, which equals 100 Celsius degrees.

In specifying a temperature it is important, of course, to say what scale is used. Temperatures specified on the absolute scales (Kelvin or Rankine) are customarily indicated with the letter T. Their numerical values are followed by K (kelvins) or °R (degrees Rankine). For example, the triple point of water is 273.16 K = 491.69°R. Temperatures

Table 17-1

Normal melting-point (NMP) and normal boiling-point (NBP) temperatures for various substances

	NMP, °C	NBP, °C
Alcohol, ethyl	−114	78
Bismuth	271	920
Bromine	−7	60
Gold	1063.00	2600
Lead	330	1170
Lithium	186	1336
Mercury	−39	358
Nitrogen	−210	−196
Oxygen	−219	−182.97
Silver	960.80	1950
Sulfur	119.0	444.60
Sulfuric acid	8.6	326
Water	0.00	100.00
Zinc	420	918

expressed on the Celsius or Fahrenheit scales generally are indicated with the letter t. Their numerical values are followed by °C (degrees Celsius) or °F (degrees Fahrenheit). For example, the steam point of water is 100.00°C = 212.0°F.

The Celsius and Fahrenheit scales are the ones in everyday use. The absolute scales, as we shall see, are much more convenient for scientific purposes, partly because many formulas are more simply expressed when absolute scales are used and partly because the absolute temperature can be given a more fundamental interpretation.

Example 17-2 What is the Kelvin temperature corresponding to 70°F?
From Equation 17-12 the Celsius temperature equal to 70°F is

$$t_C = \tfrac{5}{9}(70°F - 32°F) = \tfrac{5}{9}(38) = 21°C$$

From Equation 17-9,

$$T = t_C + 273.15 \text{ K} = 21 + 273 = 294 \text{ K}$$

Example 17-3 At what temperature do t_C and t_F have the same numerical value?
Setting $t_F = t_C$ in Equation 17-12 gives

$$t_C = \tfrac{9}{5}t_C + 32$$

Solving for t_C gives

$$t_C = -40°C$$

In other words, −40°C and −40°F are the same temperature.

Questions

6. Do the temperature scales we have defined allow negative temperatures?

7. Can you suggest why the Celsius and Fahrenheit scales are considered more convenient for ordinary nonscientific purposes?

8. Are there any circumstances in which the Kelvin and Celsius temperatures are not significantly different? The Kelvin and Rankine temperatures? The Rankine and Fahrenheit temperatures?

17-7 Equations of State; Ideal Gases

According to Equation 17-8, the absolute temperature (or ideal-gas temperature) of a gas at low pressures is proportional to the pressure at constant volume and to the volume at constant pressure. Thus at low pressures, the product PV is approximately proportional to the temperature T,

$$PV \approx CT$$

where C is a constant of proportionality appropriate to a particular body of gas. Since we expect the pressure (see Chapter 11) to be proportional to the amount of gas, it is convenient to write C as

$$C = Nk$$

where N is the number of molecules of gas and k is a constant which is found experimentally to have the same value for any kind or amount

of gas. We then have

$$PV = NkT \quad \text{or} \quad \frac{PV}{N} = kT \qquad\qquad 17\text{-}13$$

It is often convenient to write the amount of gas in terms of the number of moles. A mole of any substance is the amount of that substance that contains Avogadro's number of molecules, where Avogadro's number N_A (approximately 6.022×10^{23}) is defined to be the number of carbon atoms in 12 gm of ^{12}C. The mass of 1 mole is called the *molecular weight M*. The molecular weight of ^{12}C is, by definition, 12 gm $= 12 \times 10^{-3}$ kg. If we have n moles of a substance, the number of molecules is

Mole defined

$$N = nN_A \qquad\qquad 17\text{-}14$$

Equation 17-13 can also be written

$$\frac{PV}{n} = N_A kT = RT \qquad\qquad 17\text{-}15$$

where

$$R = kN_A \qquad\qquad 17\text{-}16$$

Figure 17-8 shows plots of PV/nT versus pressure P for several gases. We see that as the pressure approaches zero, the quantity PV/nT approaches the same value R, called the *universal gas constant*, for all gases. The numerical value of R depends of course on the units chosen. In addition to the international system, in which the pressure is expressed in newtons per square meter, the volume in cubic meters, and thus PV in newton-meters, i.e., joules, we often express P in atmospheres and V in liters (1 $\ell = 10^3$ cm$^3 = 10^{-3}$ m^3). The values of R in these units are

Universal gas constant

$$R = 8.31 \text{ J/mole-K} = 0.0821 \text{ } \ell\text{-atm/mole-K} \qquad\qquad 17\text{-}17$$

In terms of the heat-energy unit, the calorie (cal), which we define in the next chapter, the gas constant is

$$R = 1.99 \text{ cal/mole-K} \qquad\qquad 17\text{-}18$$

The constant k, called *Boltzmann's constant*, can be thought of as the gas constant per molecule,

Boltzmann's constant

$$k = \frac{R}{N_A} = 1.38 \times 10^{-23} \text{ J/K} \qquad\qquad 17\text{-}19$$

From Figure 17-8 we see that for real gases, PV/nT is very nearly constant over a rather large range of pressure. We define an *ideal gas* to

Figure 17-8
Plot of PV/nT versus P for real gases. As the pressure approaches zero, PV/nT approaches the value $R = 8.31$ J/mole-K for all gases. The ideal-gas equation $PV = nRT$ is a good approximation for all real gases for low pressures up to a few atmospheres.

be one for which PV/nT is constant for all pressures. Thus for an ideal gas, the pressure, volume, and temperature are related by

$$PV = nRT \qquad\qquad\qquad 17\text{-}20$$ *Ideal-gas law*

The concept of an ideal gas is an extrapolation of the behavior of real gases at low pressures to an ideal behavior. However, as can be seen from Figure 17-8, many gases differ little from an ideal gas at reasonably low pressures. Thus Equation 17-20, called an *equation of state*, is *Equation of state* quite useful in describing properties of real gases. By our definition of temperature, to every state $P_0 V_0$ there corresponds a temperature T_0. Thus there must be some function $T(P,V)$ for every gas, even at high pressures. Instead of thinking of T as a function of the two variables P and V, we could think of P as a function of T and V or V as a function of P and T. In any case, there is always a functional relationship between these three variables; given any two, the third is determined. However, it is not usually easy to find the relationship, and it is not possible to write down any single equation like Equation 17-20 which describes real gases over all ranges of the variables. For other thermodynamic systems, such as a metal rod, the state can be specified by the pressure P and length L. Thus the temperature T is a function of P and L. The equation which relates these variables over some range is also called an equation of state. Equations of state of systems are often found by fitting experimental data empirically. For example, there have been hundreds of equations of state proposed for various ranges of pressure for various gases. In thermodynamics, knowing that an equation of state exists is often sufficient to relate various measurable quantities such as the coefficient of thermal expansion and the compressibility even though the form of the equation is not known.

Example 17-4 What volume is occupied by 1 mole of gas at standard temperature of 0°C and normal atmospheric pressure?

From Equation 17-9, the absolute temperature corresponding to 0°C is 273 K. Using this and $P = 1$ atm, we find for the volume

$$V = \frac{nRT}{P} = \frac{(1 \text{ mole})(0.0821 \text{ } \ell\text{-atm/mole-K})(273 \text{ K})}{1 \text{ atm}}$$
$$= 22.4 \text{ } \ell$$

Example 17-5 How many molecules are there in 1 cm³ of gas at 0°C and atmospheric pressure?

Here $P = 1$ atm, $V = 1$ cm³ $= 10^{-3}$ ℓ, and $T = 273$ K. From Equation 17-15,

$$n = \frac{PV}{RT} = \frac{(1 \text{ atm})(10^{-3} \text{ } \ell)}{(0.0821 \text{ } \ell\text{-atm/mole K})(273 \text{ K})}$$
$$= 4.46 \times 10^{-5} \text{ mole}$$

From Equation 17-14,

$$N = nN_A = (4.46 \times 10^{-5} \text{ mole})(6.02 \times 10^{23} \text{ molecules/mole})$$
$$= 2.68 \times 10^{19} \text{ molecules}$$

Questions

9. How does the pressure of an ideal gas change when any one of the following quantities is doubled while the others are kept fixed: (*a*) the absolute temperature, (*b*) the volume, (*c*) the number of molecules?

10. A certain rod has length L_0 at temperature T_0. Its length is found to increase linearly with temperature and to be practically independent of pressure. Write an approximate equation of state for the rod.

17-8 Molecular Interpretation of Temperature

In Chapter 11 we calculated the pressure exerted by gas molecules making elastic collisions with the walls of their container. Using the fact that the number of molecules that hit a wall in the yz plane in a given time is proportional to the x component of velocity v_x and to the number of molecules per unit volume N/V and that the change in momentum of each molecule is $2mv_x$, we found that the average pressure on the wall is proportional to N/V and $mv_x{}^2$. The relation we derived is

$$P = \frac{N}{V}\, m(v_x{}^2)_{\text{av}}$$

or

$$PV = 2N(\tfrac{1}{2}mv_x{}^2)_{\text{av}} \qquad\qquad 17\text{-}21$$

Comparing this with the equation of state for an ideal gas,

$$PV = nRT = NkT$$

we have

$$(\tfrac{1}{2}mv_x{}^2)_{\text{av}} = \tfrac{1}{2}kT \qquad\qquad 17\text{-}22$$

The average kinetic energy associated with translational motion in the x direction is $\tfrac{1}{2}kT$. Since x was an arbitrary direction, we could write similar equations for $(\tfrac{1}{2}mv_y{}^2)_{\text{av}}$ and $(\tfrac{1}{2}mv_z{}^2)_{\text{av}}$:

$$(\tfrac{1}{2}mv_y{}^2)_{\text{av}} = \tfrac{1}{2}kT \qquad (\tfrac{1}{2}mv_z{}^2)_{\text{av}} = \tfrac{1}{2}kT$$

Adding these and writing $v^2 = v_x{}^2 + v_y{}^2 + v_z{}^2$, we have

$$(\tfrac{1}{2}mv^2)_{\text{av}} = \tfrac{3}{2}kT \qquad\qquad 17\text{-}23$$

The absolute temperature is thus a measure of the average translational kinetic energy of the molecules. (We include the word translational because a molecule may have other kinds of kinetic energy, e.g., rotational or vibrational. Only the translational kinetic energy comes into the calculation of the pressure exerted on the walls of the container.) The total translational kinetic energy of n moles of a gas containing N molecules is

$$E_k = N(\tfrac{1}{2}mv^2)_{\text{av}} = \tfrac{3}{2}NkT = \tfrac{3}{2}nRT \qquad\qquad 17\text{-}24$$

The translational kinetic energy is $\tfrac{3}{2}kT$ per molecule, or $\tfrac{3}{2}RT$ per mole.

We can use these results to estimate the order of magnitude of the kinetic energies and speeds of the molecules in a gas. The average kinetic energy of translation of a molecule is $\tfrac{3}{2}kT$. At a temperature $T = 300$ K $= 27°$C $(= 81°$F$)$, $\tfrac{3}{2}kT$ has the value

$$\tfrac{3}{2}kT = 6.21 \times 10^{-21} \text{ J} = 0.0388 \text{ eV}$$

Thus the average kinetic energy of a molecule in a gas at this temperature is about 0.04 eV. The square root of $(v^2)_{\text{av}}$ is the root-mean-square (rms) speed. The average value of v^2 is, by Equation 17-23,

$$(v^2)_{av} = \frac{3kT}{m} = \frac{3N_A kT}{N_A m} = \frac{3RT}{M}$$

where $M = N_A m$ is the mass of 1 mole, or the molecular weight. Thus the rms speed is

$$v_{rms} = \sqrt{(v^2)_{av}} = \sqrt{\frac{3kT}{m}} = \sqrt{\frac{3RT}{M}} \qquad 17\text{-}25$$

For oxygen gas at $T = 300$ K we have, using $M = 32 \times 10^{-3}$ kg/mole,

$$v_{rms} = \sqrt{\frac{3(8.31 \text{ J/mole-K})(300 \text{ K})}{32 \times 10^{-3} \text{ kg/mole}}} = 483 \text{ m/sec}$$

Questions

11. How does the average translational kinetic energy of a molecule in a gas change if the pressure is doubled while the volume is kept constant? If the volume is doubled while the pressure is kept constant?

12. By what factor must the absolute temperature of a gas be increased to double the rms speed of its molecules?

13. Would you expect all the molecules in a body of gas to have the same speed?

14. Two bodies of gas have the same temperature. Do their molecules necessarily have the same rms speeds? Explain.

17-9 Thermal Expansion

When the temperature of a body increases, it usually expands (one exception to this is water between 0 and 4°C, which contracts when the temperature increases). Let us first consider a long rod. Let its length be L_0 when the temperature is T_0 and $L = L_0 + \Delta L$ when the temperature is $T = T_0 + \Delta T$. We define the average coefficient of linear expansion for the interval ΔT to be the ratio of the fractional change in length divided by the temperature change when the pressure is constant:

$$\bar{\alpha} = \frac{\Delta L/L_0}{\Delta T} \qquad 17\text{-}26$$

Coefficient of linear expansion

Thus $\Delta L = \bar{\alpha} L_0 \Delta T$. The coefficient of linear expansion at temperature T_0 is the limit of Equation 17-26 as ΔT approaches zero:

$$\alpha = \lim_{\Delta T \to 0} \frac{\Delta L/L_0}{\Delta T} \qquad 17\text{-}27$$

The coefficient of expansion of a solid or liquid usually does not vary much with pressure, but it does vary appreciably with temperature. Thus the expression

$$\Delta L = \alpha L_0 \Delta T \qquad 17\text{-}28$$

where α at the initial temperature is used in place of $\bar{\alpha}$, holds approximately if the temperature interval is so small that α and its average value do not differ appreciably.

The coefficient of volume expansion β, sometimes called the expansivity, is defined similarly as the limit of the ratio of the fractional change in volume to the temperature interval as the temperature interval approaches zero at constant pressure:

$$\beta = \lim_{\Delta T \to 0} \frac{\Delta V/V_0}{\Delta T} \qquad\qquad \text{17-29}$$

Coefficient of volume expansion

For a given material, the coefficient of volume expansion is just 3 times the coefficient of linear expansion. Consider a box of dimensions L_1, L_2, and L_3. The volume at temperature T is

$$V_0 = L_1 L_2 L_3$$

At temperature $T + \Delta T$ the volume is $V_0 + \Delta V$, where

$$\begin{aligned} V_0 + \Delta V &= (L_1 + \Delta L_1)(L_2 + \Delta L_2)(L_3 + \Delta L_3) \\ &= (L_1 + \alpha L_1\,\Delta T)(L_2 + \alpha L_2\,\Delta T)(L_3 + L_3\,\Delta T) \\ &= L_1 L_2 L_3 (1 + \alpha\,\Delta T)^3 \\ &= V_0[1 + 3\alpha\,\Delta T + 3(\alpha\,\Delta T)^2 + (\alpha\,\Delta T)^3] \end{aligned}$$

Thus

$$\Delta V = V_0[3\alpha\,\Delta T + 3(\alpha\,\Delta T)^2 + (\alpha\,\Delta T)^3]$$

and

$$\frac{\Delta V/V_0}{\Delta T} = 3\alpha + 3\alpha^2\,\Delta T + \alpha^3(\Delta T)^2$$

Hence

$$\beta = \lim_{\Delta T \to 0} \frac{\Delta V/V}{\Delta T} = 3\alpha \qquad\qquad \text{17-30}$$

Figure 17-9, which shows the volume occupied by 1 gm of water versus temperature, illustrates that β is in general a function of temperature. The increase in size of any part of a body for a given temperature change is proportional to the original size of that part of the body. If we increase the temperature of a steel ruler, for example, the effect will be similar to that of a (very slight) photographic enlargement. Previously equally spaced lines will still be equally spaced but with correspondingly larger spaces. Values of α and β for various substances are given in Table 17-2.

Table 17-2

Approximate values of thermal expansion coefficients

Material	α, per °C	Material	β, per °C
Aluminum	24×10^{-6}	Acetone	1.5×10^{-3}
Brass	19×10^{-6}	Alcohol	1×10^{-3}
Carbon, diamond	1.2×10^{-6}	Mercury	0.18×10^{-3}
graphite	7.9×10^{-6}	Air	3.67×10^{-3}
Glass, ordinary	9×10^{-6}		
Pyrex	3.2×10^{-6}		
Ice	51×10^{-6}		
Invar	1×10^{-6}		
Steel	11×10^{-6}		

Figure 17-9
Volume of 1 gm of water at atmospheric pressure versus temperature. The minimum volume corresponding to maximum density occurs at 4°C. Since the variation in volume is only about 4 percent from $t = 0°C$ to $t = 100°C$, the thermal expansion or contraction of water can often be neglected.

Example 17-6 The temperature of a metal sphere is changed by a small amount ΔT. Using differentials to approximate small changes, show that $\beta = 3\alpha$.

The volume of a sphere of radius r is

$$V = \tfrac{4}{3}\pi r^3$$

Let Δr and ΔV be the changes in the radius and volume associated with the temperature change ΔT. Approximating these changes by differentials, we have

$$dV = \frac{dV}{dr}\, dr = 4\pi r^2\, dr$$

$$\frac{dV}{V} = \frac{4\pi r^2\, dr}{\tfrac{4}{3}\pi r^3} = 3\,\frac{dr}{r}$$

The coefficient of volume expansion is then

$$\beta = \frac{dV/V}{dT} = 3\,\frac{dr/r}{dT} = 3\alpha$$

Example 17-7 Find the coefficient of expansion of an ideal gas.

For a given temperature change, a gas at constant pressure expands by much more than a liquid or solid. We can compute β for any system if we know its equation of state. For an ideal gas we have

$$PV = nRT \qquad \text{or} \qquad V = \frac{nR}{P}\,T$$

Since P is constant, we can easily find dV/dT,

$$\frac{dV}{dT} = \frac{nR}{P} \qquad \text{and} \qquad \beta = \frac{1}{V}\frac{dV}{dT} = \frac{nR}{PV} = \frac{nR}{nRT} = \frac{1}{T}$$

The expansivity is thus just the reciprocal of the absolute temperature.

Questions

15. If a metal sheet with a hole in it expands, does the hole get larger or smaller?

16. If mercury and glass had the same coefficient of expansion, could a mercury thermometer be built?

17. What are the dimensions of α? Of β?

18. Near the bottom of a very deep lake, the water is compressed to its maximum density by the weight of the water above it. What value do you expect for the water temperature near the bottom of a deep lake?

19. If the maximum density of water occurred at 0°C, would you expect ice to form first at the top or bottom of a lake?

Review

A. Define, explain, or otherwise identify:

Microscopic description, 412
Macroscopic description, 413
System in thermal equilibrium with itself, 413
Macroscopic state of a gas, 413
State variables, 414
Adiabatic wall, 414
Diathermic wall, 415
Thermal contact, 415
Thermal equilibrium, 415
Zeroth law of thermodynamics, 415
Two systems at the same temperature, 416
Normal boiling point, 417
Normal melting point, 417

Triple point of water, 419
Ideal-gas temperature, 419
Pressure, 420
Kelvin temperature scale, 420
Gauge pressure, 422
Celsius temperature scale, 422
Rankine temperature scale, 422
Fahrenheit temperature scale, 422
Mole, 424
Universal gas constant, 424
Boltzmann's constant, 424
Ideal-gas law, 425
Equation of state, 425
Coefficient of linear expansion, 427

B. True or false:

1. An adiabatic wall is an insulating wall.

2. A diathermic wall is a heat-conducting wall.

3. The zeroth law of thermodynamics results from logical deduction rather than from experiment.

4. Two objects in thermal equilibrium with each other must be in thermal equilibrium with any third object.

5. All thermometers give the same result when measuring the temperature of any particular system.

6. The absolute temperature of a gas is a measure of the average translational kinetic energy of the gas molecules.

Exercises

Section 17-1, Macroscopic State Variables; Section 17-2, Adiabatic and Diathermic Walls; and Section 17-3, The Zeroth Law of Thermodynamics

1. A thermometer and pressure gauge are placed in the corner of a 25-ℓ flexible container of gas. At time $t = 0$, the system begins to expand, so that at $t = 5$ sec, when the volume is 30 ℓ, the pressure reading is 1.8 atm and the thermometer reads 20.0°C. At $t = 10$ sec, the system begins to contract, so that at $t = 14$ sec the volume is again 30 ℓ; the reading is then 1.8 atm, and the thermometer reads $t = 19$°C. If P and V define a state, explain the discrepancies in the temperature readings.

2. A 75-gm gaseous system is in thermal equilibrium with itself in the state $T = 30$°C, $V = 10$ ℓ, and $P = 3$ atm. The volume is increased to 15 ℓ while the pressure is held at 3 atm. Can the temperature be maintained at 30°C? If so, what must be done?

3. In each of the cases below, systems A and B are initially in thermal equilibrium with each other and are connected by a wall. Explain in each case whether the wall must be diathermic or adiabatic or if it may be either. (a)

When P_A is increased at constant volume, P_B and V_B do not change. (b) When P_A is increased at constant volume, V_B increases at constant pressure. (c) When P_A is increased while V_A is decreased, P_B and V_B do not change.

4. A class of 30 students meets in a classroom with 30 numbered seats. The teacher gives a macroscopic description of the room one day by saying that 28 of the seats are occupied. Discuss possible microscopic descriptions of the classroom on that day, and show that there are many microscopic "states" corresponding to the macroscopic state of 28 seats occupied.

5. If system A is not in thermal equilibrium with B, and B is not in thermal equilibrium with C, what conclusions, if any, can be drawn about the temperatures T_A, T_B, and T_C? In particular, can you conclude that T_A and T_C are not equal?

6. If system A is not in thermal equilibrium with system B and system B is in thermal equilibrium with system C, what conclusions can be drawn about the temperatures T_A, T_B, and T_C?

Section 17-4, Temperature Scales and Thermometers

7. The length of the column of a mercury thermometer is 4.0 cm when the thermometer is immersed in ice water and 24.0 cm when the thermometer is placed in boiling water. (a) What should the length be at room temperature of 22.0°C? (b) The mercury column is 25.4 cm long when the thermometer is placed in a boiling chemical solution. What is the temperature of the solution?

8. The pressure of a constant-volume gas thermometer is 0.400 atm at the ice point and 0.546 atm at the steam point. (a) When the pressure is 0.100 atm, what is the temperature? (b) What is the pressure at the boiling point of sulfur (444.6°C)?

9. A constant-volume gas thermometer reads 50 mm Hg pressure at the triple point of water. (a) What will the pressure be when the thermometer measures a temperature of 300 K? (b) What ideal-gas temperature corresponds to a pressure of 68 mm Hg?

10. A constant-volume gas thermometer has a pressure of 30 mm Hg when it reads a temperature of 373 K. (a) What is its triple-point pressure P_3? (b) What temperature corresponds to a pressure of 0.175 mm Hg?

Section 17-5, Units of Pressure

11. (a) Find the height in feet of a water column corresponding to a pressure of 1 atm. (b) Find the pressure in atmospheres and in millimeters of mercury which supports a water column of height 30.0 ft.

12. Compute a conversion factor for pressure in atmospheres to pounds per square inch.

13. What is normal atmospheric pressure in inches of mercury?

14. The lowest atmospheric pressure recorded at sea level was 25.9 in Hg in a hurricane in 1958. (a) What was the pressure in pounds per square inch? (b) A bottle of wine was stoppered on the day before the hurricane, when the barometer read 30.0 in Hg. If the diameter of the cork was 1 in, what frictional force was necessary to hold the cork in during the hurricane?

15. (a) What is the pressure on a swimmer 20 ft below the surface of water? (b) What is the gauge pressure at that depth?

16. Water flows through a pipe at sea level under a gauge pressure of 40 lb/in². What is the absolute pressure (a) in pounds per square inch and (b) in inches of mercury?

17. A tabletop is 3 by 6 ft. What is the force on the table due to the air pressure down on it? Give your answer in pounds.

Section 17-6, Celsius, Rankine, and Fahrenheit Scales

18. The boiling point of O_2 is $-182.86°C$. Express this temperature in (a) kelvins, (b) in degrees Fahrenheit, (c) in degrees Rankine.

19. The boiling point of tungsten is $5900°C$. Find this temperature in (a) kelvins and (b) degrees Fahrenheit.

20. The highest and lowest temperature ever recorded in the United States are $134°F$ (in California in 1913) and $-80°F$ (in Alaska in 1971). Express these temperatures on the Celsius scale.

21. What is the Celsius temperature corresponding to the normal temperature of the human body of $98.6°F$?

22. In Portugal, in September 1933, the temperature rose to $70°C$ for 2 min. What is that temperature in degrees Fahrenheit?

23. The temperature of the interior of the sun is about 10^7 K. What is this temperature (a) on the Celsius scale, (b) on the Rankine scale, and (c) on the Fahrenheit scale?

Section 17-7, Equations of State; Ideal Gases

24. One mole of a gas occupies a volume of 10 ℓ at a pressure of 1 atm. (a) What is the temperature of the gas? (b) The container is fitted with a piston so that the volume can change. The gas is heated at constant pressure and expands to a volume of 20 ℓ. What is its temperature in kelvins? In degrees Celsius? (c) The volume is now fixed at 20 ℓ and the gas is heated at constant volume until its temperature is 350 K. What is its pressure?

25. One mole of gas is in a container fitted with a piston and the initial pressure and temperature are 2 atm and 300 K. (a) What is the initial volume of the gas? (b) The gas is allowed to expand at constant temperature until the pressure is 1 atm. What is the new volume? (c) The gas is now compressed and heated at the same time until it is back to its original volume, at which time the pressure is 2.5 atm. What is its temperature then?

26. A cylindrical container has a cross-sectional area of 3 in^2 and height of 8 in and is open at the top. It contains air at 1 atm pressure. A tightly fitting piston weighing 2.0 lb is inserted and gradually lowered until the increased pressure in the container supports the weight of the piston. (a) What is the force exerted on the top of the piston due to atmospheric pressure? (b) What is the force that must be exerted by the gas in the container on the bottom of the piston to keep it in equilibrium? What is the pressure in the container? (c) Assuming that the temperature of the gas in the container does not change, what is the height of the equilibrium position of the piston?

27. A gas is kept at constant pressure. If its temperature is changed from 50 to $100°C$, by what factor does its volume change?

28. A pressure as low as 1×10^{-8} mm Hg can be achieved by an oil-diffusion pump. How many molecules are there in 1 cm^3 at this pressure if the temperature is 300 K?

29. A cubic metal box, of side 20 cm, contains air at pressure of 1 atm and temperature 300 K. It is sealed so that the volume is constant and heated to a temperature of 400 K. Find the net force on each wall of the box.

30. The mass of Avogadro's number of ^{12}C atoms is 12 gm. Each ^{12}C atoms contains six protons and six neutrons. Since the proton and neutron have approximately equal mass, the mass of Avogadro's number of protons or neutrons is 1 gm. The mass of the proton or neutron (in grams) is thus approximately the reciprocal of Avogadro's number. Calculate this mass and compare your answer with the mass given in Appendix Table B-1.

31. A 10-ℓ vessel contains gas at 0°C and a pressure of 4 atm. How many moles of gas are there in the vessel? How many molecules?

Section 17-8, Molecular Interpretation of Temperature

32. Show that $\sqrt{3RT/M}$ has the correct units meters per second if R is in joules per mole-kelvin, T in kelvins, and M in kilograms per mole.

33. Find v_{rms} of an argon atom if 1 mole of the gas is confined to a 1-ℓ container at 10 atm. ($M = 40 \times 10^{-3}$ kg/mole.) Compare this with that of helium gas under the same conditions (the molecular weight of helium is 4×10^{-3} kg/mole).

34. Find the total translational kinetic energy of 1 ℓ of oxygen gas held at a temperature of 0°C and at atmospheric pressure.

35. At what temperature will the rms speed of an H_2 molecule equal 332 m/sec?

Section 17-9, Thermal Expansion

36. A steel ruler has a length of 1 ft at 20°C. What is its length at 100°C?

37. Use Table 17-2 to find the coefficient of volume expansion for steel.

38. A 100-m-long bridge is built of steel. If it is built as a single continuous structure, how much will its length change from the coldest winter days (−30°C) to the hottest summer days (40°C)?

39. The experimental value of β for N_2 gas at 0°C and 1 atm is 0.003673/°C. Compare this with the theoretical value $\beta = 1/T$, assuming that N_2 is an ideal gas.

40. Define a coefficient of area expansion. Calculate it for a square and a circle, and show that it is 2 times the coefficient of linear expansion.

Problems

1. Gas is confined in a steel cylinder at 20°C and at a pressure of 5 atm. (a) If the cylinder is surrounded by boiling water and allowed to come to thermal equilibrium, how great will the gas pressure be? (b) If the gas is then allowed to escape until the pressure is again 5 atm, what fraction of the original gas (by weight) will escape? (c) If the temperature of the remaining gas in the cylinder is returned to 20°C, what will be its final pressure?

2. A constant-volume gas thermometer with a triple-point pressure of $P_3 = 500$ mm Hg is used to measure the boiling point of some substance. When it is placed in thermal contact with the boiling substance, its pressure is 734 mm Hg. Some of the gas in the thermometer is then allowed to escape so that its triple-point pressure is 200 mm Hg. When it is placed in thermal contact with the boiling substance, its pressure is 293.4 mm Hg. Again, some of the gas is removed from the thermometer so that its triple-point pressure is 100 mm Hg. Its pressure when in contact with the boiling substance is then 146.65 mm Hg. Find the ideal-gas temperature of the boiling substance to one place beyond the decimal point.

3. An automobile tire is filled to a gauge pressure of 28 lb/in² when it is at an air temperature of 70°F. After the car has been driven at high speed, the tire temperature has increased to 120°F. (a) Assuming that the volume of the tire has not changed, find the gauge pressure of the air in the tire (assume air to be an ideal gas). (b) Calculate the gauge pressure if the tire expands so that the volume increases by 10 percent.

4. An open steel 10-ℓ container is filled with acetone. The temperature rises from 0 to 40°C. How much acetone overflows from the container?

5. (*a*) If 2 moles of hydrogen gas (1 mole = 2 gm) are at atmospheric pressure and room temperature (20°C), what is the average translational kinetic energy of a hydrogen molecule in this gas? (*b*) What is v_{rms} for the hydrogen molecules? (*c*) What is the total kinetic energy of translation of all the molecules in this amount of hydrogen gas? (*d*) If a solid object of the same mass had this kinetic energy, what would its speed be?

6. At the surface of the sun the temperature is about 6000 K, and all materials are gaseous. From data given by the spectrum of light it is known that most elements are present on the sun. (*a*) What is the average kinetic energy of translation of an atom at the surface of the sun? Express your answer in both joules and electron volts. (*b*) What is the range of v_{rms} at the surface of the sun if the atoms present range from hydrogen ($M = 1$ gm/mole) to uranium ($M = 238$ gm/mole)?

7. In Chapter 9 it was shown that the escape velocity for a planet of radius R and acceleration of gravity g at the surface is given by $v_e^2 = 2Rg$. (*a*) At what temperature does v_{rms} for O_2 equal the escape velocity for the earth? (*b*) At what temperature is v_{rms} for H_2 the escape velocity for the earth? (*c*) Temperatures in the upper atmosphere reach about 1000 K. Can this account for the low abundance of hydrogen in the earth's atmosphere? (*d*) Compute the corresponding temperatures for the moon, where g has about one-sixth its value on the earth and $R = 1738$ km. Can you account in this way for the absence of an atmosphere on the moon?

8. One way to construct a device with two points whose separation remains the same in spite of temperature changes is to use rods with different coefficients of expansion, in the arrangement shown in Figure 17-10. The two rods are bolted together at one end. Show that the distance L will not change with temperature if the lengths L_A and L_B are chosen so that $L_A/L_B = \alpha_B/\alpha_A$. If material B is steel, material A is brass, and $L_A = 250$ cm at 0°C, what is the value of L? If both rods had been made of brass, how much would L increase when the rods are heated to 100°C?

Figure 17-10
Problem 8.

9. A steel tube has an outside diameter of 3.000 cm at room temperature (20°C). A brass tube has an inside diameter of 2.997 cm at the same temperature. To what temperature must the ends of the tubes be heated if the steel tube is to be inserted into the brass tube?

10. A clock pendulum is made of brass and has a period of 1.00 sec at a winter temperature 16°C. How much will the same clock gain or lose each day in summer if the average temperature then is 26°C?

11. Ten objects have the speeds tabulated:

Speed, m/sec	2	5	6	8
Number of objects	3	3	3	1

Calculate the rms speed for these objects.

12. At 127°C, 2.4 moles of a certain gas occupy a 4-ℓ container at a density of 1.68×10^{-2} gm/cm³. (*a*) Find the total translational kinetic energy. (*b*) Find the average kinetic energy per molecule. (*c*) What is the pressure of the gas? (*d*) What is the molecular weight of the gas? (*e*) What diatomic gas could this be?

CHAPTER 18 Heat, Work, and the First Law
of Thermodynamics

When two systems at different temperatures are placed in thermal contact, heat flows from the hotter system to the colder one until the two systems reach equilibrium at a common temperature. In the seventeenth century, Galileo, Newton, and other scientists generally supported the theory of the ancient Greek atomists, who considered heat to be a manifestation of molecular motion. In the next century, methods were developed for making quantitative measurements of the amount of heat that leaves or enters the body, and it was found that often when two bodies are in thermal contact, the amount of heat that leaves one body equals the amount of heat that enters the other body. An apparently successful theory of heat as a conserved material substance developed, in which heat, believed to be an invisible, weightless fluid, called *caloric,* was neither created nor destroyed but merely transferred from one body to another. The caloric theory of heat served quite well in the description of heat transfer but eventually was discarded when it was observed that caloric apparently could be created endlessly by friction with no corresponding disappearance of caloric somewhere else. In other words, the principle of conservation of caloric, which had been the experimental foundation of this theory of heat, proved to be false.

The first clear experimental observations showing that caloric cannot be conserved were made at the end of the eighteenth century by Benjamin Thompson, an American loyalist who emigrated to Europe, became the director of the Bavarian Arsenal, and was given the title Count Rumford. Thompson supervised the boring of cannon for Bavaria. Because of the heat generated by the boring tool, water was used for cooling. It had to be replaced continuously because it boiled away during the boring. According to the caloric theory, as the metal from the bore was cut into small chips, its ability to retain caloric was decreased. Therefore it released caloric to the water, heating it and causing it to boil. Thompson noticed, however, that even when the drill was too dull to cut the metal, the water still boiled away as long as the drill was turned. Apparently caloric was produced merely by friction and could be produced endlessly. He suggested that

Rumford's apparatus. Figure 3 shows a close-up of the borer (dotted blunt shape at left) within the metal being bored. The vertical dotted lines indicate a hole for the insertion of a thermometer. The box in Figures 3 and 4 contained water and was placed around the metal and borer. It was used in later experiments to counteract the criticism that air somehow had caused the temperature increase. (*From* Philosophical Transactions of the Royal Society, *vol. 88, 1798.*)

heat is not a substance that is conserved but some form of motion communicated from the bore to the water. He showed, in fact, that the heat produced is approximately proportional to the work done by the boring tool.

The caloric theory of heat continued to be the leading theory for some 40 years after Thompson's work, but it was gradually weakened as more and more examples of nonconservation of heat were observed. Not until the 1840s did the modern mechanical theory of heat emerge. In this view heat is another form of energy, exchangeable at a fixed rate with the various forms of mechanical energy already discussed. The most varied and precise experiments demonstrating this were performed, starting in the late 1830s, by James Joule (1818–1889), after whom the metric unit of energy is named. Joule showed that the appearance or disappearance of a given quantity of heat is always accompanied by the disappearance or appearance of an equivalent quantity of mechanical energy. The experiments of Joule and others showed that neither heat nor mechanical energy is conserved independently but that the mechanical energy lost always equals the heat produced (measured in the same units). What is conserved is the total of mechanical energy and heat energy.

18-1   Heat Capacity and Specific Heat

Although we do not need a special unit for heat once we recognize that heat is a form of energy and can be measured in joules, foot-pounds, electron volts, or any other energy unit, the historical unit of heat, the calorie, is still used. The calorie was originally defined to be the amount of heat energy needed to raise the temperature of one gram of water one Celsius degree. After careful measurement showed that this energy depends slightly on the temperature of the water, the calorie was defined[1] more precisely to be the amount of energy needed to raise the temperature of one gram of water from 14.5 to 15.5°C. The

Historical definition of calorie

---

[1] The calorie is now defined in terms of mechanical energy units, as discussed in Section 18-3. It differs slightly from the historical calorie discussed here, but the difference can usually be neglected in practice.

amount of heat energy needed to raise the temperature of one kilogram of water from 14.5 to 15.5°C is the *kilocalorie* (1 kcal = 10³ cal).
(The "calorie" used in measuring the energy equivalent of foods is
actually the kilocalorie.)

Using this definition of the calorie, we can measure the amount of
heat energy needed to raise the temperature of any object by any
amount. The amount of heat energy needed to raise the temperature of
an object one Celsius degree (or one kelvin since the kelvin and the
Celsius degree are the same size) is called the *heat capacity C* of the object. The heat capacity of one gram of water at 15°C is, by definition, 1
cal/°C = 1 cal/K. The heat capacity of an object is proportional to its
mass. The ratio of the heat capacity to the mass is the *specific heat c*,

Heat capacity

$$c = \frac{C}{m} \qquad\qquad 18\text{-}1$$

Specific heat

The heat capacity per mole is called the *molar heat capacity C'*,

$$C' = \frac{C}{n} \qquad\qquad 18\text{-}2$$

Molar heat capacity

where *n* is the number of moles. Since the mass of 1 mole is the molecular weight *M*, the molar heat capacity and specific heat are related by

$$C' = \frac{C}{n} = \frac{mc}{n} = Mc \qquad\qquad 18\text{-}3$$

Specific heats and molar heat capacities have been determined for
many substances and are listed in tables. The heat energy *Q* involved
in a temperature change Δ*T* of a system of mass *m* is

$$Q = C\,\Delta T = mc\,\Delta T \qquad\qquad 18\text{-}4$$

The temperature change is positive for heat put into the system and
negative for heat taken out of the system.

Suppose we wish to measure the specific heat of water at 80°C. We
need only place a given mass of water m_1 at 80°C in thermal contact
with a second mass of water m_2 at 14.5°C and isolate the two systems
from their surroundings by an adiabatic wall. When the temperature
of the second mass of water has risen to 15.5°C, the amount of heat
transfered is m_2 cal/gm. The specific heat of the water originally at

The complete arrangement of
Joule's original apparatus for
demonstrating the equiva-
lence of heat and mechanical
energy (see Figure 18-2, page
441, for a schematic diagram).
(*Crown copyright; courtesy of
the Science Museum, London.*)

80°C can then be calculated from Equation 18-4 using the measured temperature change ΔT. This method measures the *average* specific heat over the temperature interval ΔT. If we suspect that the specific heat varies appreciably over the interval ΔT, we can reduce the temperature change by adjusting the masses in the experiment (either increasing m_1 or decreasing m_2). The specific heat of water varies by only about 1 percent from 0 to 100°C at a pressure of 1 atm. We can usually neglect this variation and take the specific heat of water to be 1.00 cal/gm-°C over the whole range 0 to 100°C.

Because the specific heat of water varies so slightly with temperature, the heat capacity or specific heat of an object can be conveniently measured by heating it to some easily measurable temperature, placing it in a water bath of known mass and temperature, and measuring the final equilibrium temperature. If the whole system is isolated from its surroundings, the heat which leaves the body equals the heat which enters the water. Let m be the mass of the body, c be its specific heat, and T_1 its initial temperature. Let m_w be the mass of the water bath, $c_w = 1$ cal/gm-K be its specific heat, T_0 its initial temperature, and T_f the final equilibrium temperature of the system. The heat absorbed by the water is $m_w c_w (T_f - T_0)$, and that lost by the body is $mc(T_1 - T_f)$. Since these amounts of heat are equal, c can be calculated from

$$mc(T_1 - T_f) = m_w c_w (T_f - T_0) \qquad \text{18-5}$$

Because only differences in temperature are important in Equation 18-5, and because the kelvin and the Celsius degree are the same size, the temperatures can be measured on either the Celsius or Kelvin scale without affecting the result.

Closeup view of the water-containing section of Joule's apparatus showing the paddle wheel (right) and its adiabatic container (left). (*Loaned to the Science Museum, London, by Dr. Joule, Manchester.*)

Example 18-1 When 100 gm of aluminum shot is heated to 100°C and placed in 500 gm of water initially at 18.3°C, the final equilibrium temperature of the mixture is 21.7°C. What is the specific heat of aluminum?

The temperature change of the water is 21.7°C − 18.3°C = 3.4°C. Thus the heat absorbed by the water is

$$Q_w = m_w c_w \, \Delta T_w = (500 \text{ gm})(1 \text{ cal/gm-°C})(3.4°C) = 1700 \text{ cal}$$

The temperature change of the aluminum is 100°C − 21.7°C = 78.3°C. Its average specific heat over this interval is

$$c_{\text{Al}} = \frac{Q_w / \Delta T_{\text{Al}}}{m_{\text{Al}}} = \frac{1700 \text{ cal}}{(100 \text{ gm})(78.3°C)} = 0.217 \text{ cal/gm-°C}$$

The specific heat of aluminum (and of most materials) is considerably less than that of water. In practice, it is useful to choose the initial temperature of the water bath (using a rough knowledge of the specific heat to be measured) so that the final and initial temperatures of the water differ from room temperature by about the same amount. Then, even if the water is not perfectly isolated from its surroundings, it will gain about as much heat from the surroundings when it is below room temperature as it loses when it is above room temperature. For this example, the initial temperature was chosen for a room temperature of 20°C = 68°F.

In general, the amount of heat needed to raise the temperature of a body at constant pressure is not the same as the amount needed at constant volume. We must therefore distinguish between the specific heat at constant pressure c_p and the specific heat at constant volume c_v. For solids and liquids this difference amounts to a few percent or less and can be ignored except in the most precise experiments. Since it is quite easy to keep the pressure on a solid or liquid constant whereas it is extremely difficult to adjust the pressure to keep the volume constant, it is c_p that is measured for a solid or liquid. (This is somewhat unfortunate since it is c_v that is most easily related to the theory of solids and liquids. However, if c_p is known, c_v can be calculated from it by methods of thermodynamics which are too complicated to discuss here.) Table 18-1 lists the specific heat and molar heat capacity for several metals. Heat capacity per mole is about 6 cal/mole-K for most of these metals, a result known as the *Dulong-Petit law*. At sufficiently high temperatures, the molar heat capacity for all metals is about $3R \approx 6$ cal/mole-K. Later we shall discuss the significance of the Dulong-Petit law and the fact that at low temperatures the heat capacities of metals are all less than this value. Figure 18-1 shows the temperature dependence of C_v' for iron. The shape of this curve is similar for all solids. The temperature at which C_v' approaches the Dulong-Petit limit differs for different materials.

Table 18-1

Specific heat and molar heat capacity for various metals at room temperature

	Specific heat, cal/ gm-K	Molar heat capacity, cal/ mole-K
Aluminum	0.215	5.82
Bismuth	0.0294	6.15
Copper	0.0923	5.85
Gold	0.0301	6.11
Lead	0.0305	6.32
Silver	0.0558	6.02
Tungsten	0.0321	5.92
Zinc	0.0925	6.03

Figure 18-1
Molar heat capacity versus temperature for iron. All solids show this characteristic behavior, the values of the temperature scale varying from one material to another. At sufficiently high temperatures, the heat capacity is $3R \approx 6$ cal/mole-K, the Dulong-Petit law. Iron obeys the Dulong-Petit law for temperatures above about 350 K.

Questions

1. A large body of water, such as a lake or an ocean, tends to moderate the variations of temperature near it. Why? Would this be true if the specific heat of water had a value closer to that of other common substances?

2. Explain the circumstances under which the following situations could arise. (*a*) A massive body at high temperature is brought into thermal contact with a light object at low temperature. The final equilibrium temperature is closer to the original temperature of the massive body. (*b*) A massive body at high temperature is brought into thermal contact with a light body at a low temperature. The final temperature is closer to the original temperature of the light body.

3. Body *A* has twice the mass and twice the specific heat of body *B*. If they are supplied with equal amounts of heat, how do their temperature changes compare?

18-2   Latent Heat

In most circumstances, when heat is supplied to a body at constant pressure, the result is an increase in the temperature of the body. Sometimes, however, a body may absorb large amounts of heat without any change in temperature. This happens when the physical condition, or *phase*, of the material is changing from one form to another, e.g., from liquid to gas, from solid to liquid, or from one crystalline form to another. Thus the effect of heat is not only to change the temperature of a body but sometimes also to change the phase without any temperature change.

Phase

These phenomena are easily understood in terms of the mechanical or molecular theory of heat. When the temperature of a body increases because of heat added, it reflects an increase of the kinetic energy of motion of the molecules. When a material changes from liquid to gaseous form, the molecules, which originally were held together by their natural attractions, are moved far apart from each other. This requires that work be done against the attractive forces; i.e., it requires that energy be supplied to the molecules to separate them even though their kinetic energies (and the temperature) do not increase in the process. From this model we would expect the change in phase from liquid to gas to require heat even though there is no rise in temperature. Similarly, other changes, e.g., from solid to liquid or from one solid form to another, are rearrangements of molecules and involve work done against the forces they exert on each other. It is not surprising that heat energy may be required to accomplish these rearrangements at constant temperature.

For pure substances, changes of phase occur, for any given pressure, only at particular temperatures. For example, pure water at atmospheric pressure changes from solid to liquid at 0°C and from liquid to gas at 100°C. The first temperature is called the *melting point*, the second the *boiling point*.

For pure substances, a specific quantity of heat is required to change the phase of given amount of the substance. The required heat is proportional to the mass of the material,

$$Q = mL \qquad\qquad\qquad 18\text{-}6$$

where L is a constant characteristic of the substance and the kind of phase change involved. If the phase change is from solid to liquid, L_f is called the *latent heat of fusion* of the substance. For water at atmospheric pressure, the latent heat of fusion is 79.7 cal/gm. If the phase change is from liquid to gas, L_v is called the *latent heat of vaporization*. For water at atmospheric pressure, the latent heat of vaporization is 540 cal/gm.

Latent heat defined

Example 18-2 If 500 gm of ice at 0°C is heated at atmospheric pressure until all the ice is turned to gas, how much heat is required?

The amount of heat required to melt the ice is

$$Q_1 = mL_f = (500 \text{ gm})(79.7 \text{ cal/gm}) = 3.98 \times 10^4 \text{ cal}$$

The amount of heat required to raise the temperature of the liquid from 0 to 100°C is

$$Q_2 = mc\,\Delta T = (500 \text{ gm})(1 \text{ cal/gm-°C})(100°C) = 5.00 \times 10^4 \text{ cal}$$

Finally, the amount of heat required to vaporize the liquid is

$$Q_3 = mL_v = (500 \text{ gm})(540 \text{ cal/gm}) = 27.0 \times 10^4 \text{ cal}$$

The total heat required is

$$Q = Q_1 + Q_2 + Q_3 = 36.0 \times 10^4 \text{ cal}$$

Most of the heat supplied in this process was needed to change the phase of the water, not to increase its temperature.

18-3   The First Law of Thermodynamics

If we add heat to water, we raise its temperature, but we can also raise the temperature of water by stirring it or doing work on it in some other way without adding heat. Figure 18-2 is a schematic illustration of Joule's most famous experiment to determine the amount of work required to produce a given amount of heat. (Once the experimental equivalence of heat and energy has been established, one can describe Joule's work as determining the size of the calorie in energy units.) The water is enclosed by adiabatic walls so that its surroundings cannot affect its temperature by heat conduction. The weights, falling at constant speed, turn a paddle wheel, which does work against the water. If no energy is lost through friction in the bearings, etc., the work done by the paddle wheel against the water equals the loss in mechanical energy. The latter is just the potential energy $2mgh$ lost as the weights fall through height h.

The work needed to raise the temperature of 1 gm of water 1 Celsius degree when no heat is conducted was first measured accurately by Joule. Figure 18-3 shows the variation in this work with temperature. This figure is essentially a plot of the specific heat of water in joules per gram-kelvin versus temperature. As mentioned in Section 18-1, the specific heat of water varies by only about 1 percent from 0 to 100°C. At 15°C it has the value 4.186 J/gm-K. Thus the calorie defined as the heat energy needed to raise 1 gm of water from 14.5 to 15.5°C is equivalent to 4.186 J. Once it is recognized that the calorie is just another unit of energy, there is no need to define it experimentally. It is much more convenient to define the calorie in terms of other energy units already defined. The calorie (called the *thermochemical calorie*) is now defined to be exactly 4.184 J:

$$1 \text{ cal} = 4.184 \text{ J} \qquad\qquad 18\text{-}7$$

The calorie defined by Equation 18-7 differs slightly from the historical calorie (sometimes called the 15-degree calorie). It is approximately the energy needed to raise the temperature of water from 16.5 to 17.5°C. This difference is negligible in most applications. The size of the calorie in mechanical-energy units is called the *mechanical equivalent of heat.*

Figure 18-2
Schematic diagram of one of Joule's experiments to determine the amount of work required to produce a given increase in the temperature of water. The work done on the system is determined by the loss in gravitational potential energy of the masses.

Mechanical equivalent of heat

Figure 18-3
Specific heat of water versus temperature.

Figure 18-4
Another method of doing
work on an adiabatically
shielded system consisting of
water plus resistor. Electrical
work is done on the system
by the generator, which is
driven by the falling weight.
The amount of work needed
to raise the temperature a
given amount is the same no
matter how the work is done.

There are other ways of doing work on a system. In Figure 18-4 an
electrical resistor is placed in a water bath and connected to a generator driven by a falling weight. (This is another of Joule's early experiments.) The water as a system is not thermally insulated because it is
in thermal contact with the resistor and can absorb heat from it. If we
consider the resistor plus water as the thermodynamic system, this
system is shielded from its surroundings by an adiabatic wall. No heat
can be conducted into this system. The electrical work needed to raise
the temperature of the water by some amount is the same as the
mechanical work needed to raise the temperature by the same amount.
This type of experiment can be performed on various thermodynamic
systems such as gases, solids, etc. We find that if the system is adiabatically shielded from its surroundings, the work required to change the
system from state 1 to state 2 is *independent of how the work is performed* (stirring, compressing and expanding, electrical work, etc.) and
depends only on the initial and final states. This experimental result
expresses one form of the first law of thermodynamics.

Radio Times/Hulton Picture Library

James Prescott Joule
(1818–1889).

First law (first version)

*The adiabatic work done on a system in taking the system from state 1 to
state 2 is independent of the manner of doing the work and depends only on
the initial and final states of the system.*

Adiabatic work means work done on a system which neither gains
nor loses heat to its surroundings while the work is done; i.e., it is
work done on a system surrounded by adiabatic walls. Since the
adiabatic work depends on the initial and final states of the system,
we can define a function U of the state of the system such that the
change in U equals the adiabatic work done. This new state function is
called the *internal energy* of the system:

$U_2 - U_1 =$ adiabatic work done *on* the system bringing it
from state 1 to state 2   18-8

Internal energy defined

If the system is not adiabatically shielded from its surroundings, the
work done on the system as it goes from state 1 to state 2 does depend
on the process involved. For example, a given temperature increase of
the system might be accomplished with no work done by placing the
system in thermal contact with another system at a higher temperature. However, if we also measure the heat put into the system, the
sum of the net heat put in plus the work done on the system going

from state 1 to state 2 is the same for all processes and equal to the adiabatic work necessary to bring the system from state 1 to state 2 (assuming, of course, that the heat is expressed in energy units). Thus the sum of the heat put into a system plus the work done on the system equals the increase in internal energy of the system for any process. It is customary to write W for the work done *by* the system on its surroundings. Then $-W$ is the work done *on* the system by the surroundings. For example, if a gas expands against a piston, W is positive; if the gas is compressed, W is negative. Also, the heat put *into* a system is usually written Q. Then we have

$$Q + (-W) = \Delta U \qquad \text{18-9}$$

usually written

$$Q = \Delta U + W \qquad \text{18-10} \qquad \textit{First law}$$

This equation is the generalization of our first statement of the first law to include nonadiabatic work. It is another way of stating the first law of thermodynamics.

Equation 18-10 is sometimes taken to be the definition of heat. This point deserves elaboration, because, like Newton's laws of motion, the first law of thermodynamics is often misunderstood. From experiments with adiabatic work alone, we can define a state function, the internal energy of the system. We can thus prove the existence of the function U with no reference to heat at all. (Recall that we have already defined what is meant by an adiabatic wall without having to define temperature.) The first law of thermodynamics states that the state function U exists. This statement of the first law is analogous to our statement of the zeroth law, namely, that a state function called the temperature exists. Having shown that U exists, and given a method of measuring ΔU for any two states (one must shield the system adiabatically from its surroundings and measure the work needed to bring the system from state 1 to state 2), we find that if the system is not adiabatically shielded, the work done on the system does not equal the change in U. We can then define the heat put into the system as the difference between the change in U and the work done *on* the system. We find that heat defined in this way has all the characteristics we have already discussed. For example, 4.186 J of heat will raise the temperature of 1 gm of water from 14.5 to 15.5°C if no work is done.

We shall usually refer to Equation 18-10 as the statement of the first law of thermodynamics. However, we should always keep in mind that the real "content" of this law is that a state function U exists and can be found from Equation 18-10 or by the method as discussed above.

Questions

4. The experiments of Joule discussed in this section involved the conversion of mechanical energy into heat. Can you give examples in which heat is converted into mechanical energy?

5. Can a system absorb heat with no change in its internal energy?

6. The first law of thermodynamics is sometimes stated as follows: the total energy, including heat energy, of an isolated system is conserved. How is this statement related to $Q = \Delta U + W$?

18-4 Work and the *PV* Diagram for a Gas

Consider a gas which can be expanded or compressed by the motion of a tightly fitting frictionless piston, as shown in Figure 18-5. When the piston moves, the volume of the gas changes and either the pressure or temperature or both must change since these three variables are related by an equation of state (such as $PV = nRT$ for an ideal gas). If the piston moves suddenly, the gas will not be in an equilibrium state just afterward. For example, if we suddenly push the piston in to compress the gas, the pressure near the piston will be greater than that far from the piston initially. Until the gas settles down, we cannot define equilibrium macroscopic state variables for the gas such as T, P, or U. However, if we move the piston slowly in small steps, waiting after each step for equilibrium to be reestablished, we can compress or expand the gas in such a way that the gas is never far from an equilibrium state. This kind of a process is called a *quasi-static process*. In a quasi-static expansion, the piston moves infinitely slowly with no acceleration, so that the gas moves through a series of equilibrium states. In practice, it is possible to approximate quasi-static processes fairly well.

Let us begin with a gas at a fairly high pressure and let it expand quasi-statically. The force exerted by the gas on the piston is PA, where A is the area of the piston and P is the gas pressure, which in general changes as the gas expands (the pressure could be kept constant by heating the gas as it expands). Since in a quasi-static expansion the piston does not accelerate, there must be an external force pushing against the piston also equal to PA. The piston does work on the agent providing this external force. If the piston moves a distance dx, the work done *by the gas* is

$$dW = F\,dx = PA\,dx = P\,dV \qquad\qquad 18\text{-}11$$

where $dV = A\,dx$ is the increase in volume of the gas. Equation 18-11 holds also for a quasi-static compression. Then dV is negative, indicating that the gas does negative work. In order to calculate the work done by the gas for an expansion from volume V_1 to volume V_2 we need to know how the pressure varies during the expansion; i.e., we cannot integrate $P\,dV$ to find the total work unless we know the function $P(V,T)$, which in general is not constant. The states of the gas can be represented on a P-versus-V diagram as in Figure 18-6. Since any point (P_0, V_0) determines the thermodynamic state of the gas, each point on this diagram corresponds to a definite state. For example, the set of states corresponding to a constant pressure of 1 atm is represented by a horizontal line parallel to the V axis. *The work done by the gas in expanding a small amount dV is P dV represented by the area under the P-versus-V curve as shown.*

Consider the gas initially in the state P_1V_1 and expanding to the final state P_2V_2. Let us suppose that these two states are at the same temperature. (If the gas is ideal, $P_1V_1 = P_2V_2$.) Several possible kinds of expansion are illustrated in Figure 18-7 by different curves connecting these states. Along path A (Figure 18-7*a*), the pressure is kept constant until the gas reaches the volume V_2, and then the volume is kept constant while the pressure is reduced to its final value P_2. The work done along this path is $P_1(V_2 - V_1)$ for the horizontal (constant-pressure) part of the path and zero along the constant volume. This work is indicated by the shaded area under the curve. (In order to reduce the

Figure 18-5
Gas confined in adiabatically shielded cylinder with movable piston. When the piston moves a distance dx, the volume changes by $dV = A\,dx$. The work done by the gas is $PA\,dx = P\,dV$, where P is the pressure.

Quasi-static process

Figure 18-6
A particular state P_0V_0 is represented by a point on a PV diagram. The area $P\,dV$ on this diagram represents the work done by the gas as it expands.

The heat capacities are then

$$C_v = \frac{dU}{dT} = \tfrac{3}{2}nR \qquad\qquad 18\text{-}22$$

and

$$C_p = C_v + nR = \tfrac{5}{2}nR \qquad\qquad 18\text{-}23$$

Table 18-2 lists the measured heat capacities per mole for several gases. The ideal-gas prediction $C_p - C_v = nR$ holds quite well for all gases ($R = 1.99$ cal/mole-K), and the prediction $C_v = \tfrac{3}{2}nR$ holds quite well for most monatomic gases but not for other types.

In Section 18-5 we mentioned that we expect other kinds of kinetic energy, e.g., rotational energy, also to depend on the temperature. We discussed qualitatively how we might expect some kind of equilibrium between various kinds of energy, e.g., rotational and translational kinetic energy of a dumbbell molecule, to be established as a result of molecular collisions. Let us explore this equilibrium further.

Consider a smooth hard-sphere model of a monatomic gas. Suppose that at some time all the molecules are moving in the x direction only; that is, v_y and v_z are zero, and the kinetic energy of each is $\tfrac{1}{2}mv_x^2$. Such an unusual state is not an equilibrium state. Because of off-center collisions the molecules will acquire components v_y and v_z. On the average, such a collision at first will tend to increase the average value of v_y^2 and v_z^2 until these quantities have the same average values as v_x^2. When equilibrium is established, the average values of the energies associated with each kind of translation, $\tfrac{1}{2}mv_x^2$, $\tfrac{1}{2}mv_y^2$, and $\tfrac{1}{2}mv_z^2$, will be equal to each other. Since we have seen that the average translational energy per molecule is $\tfrac{3}{2}kT$, where $k = R/N_A$ is Boltzmann's constant, each of these terms must have an average value of $\tfrac{1}{2}kT$ in equilibrium. (The assumption of smooth-sphere molecules rules out any exchange of rotational energy since the forces in a collision will be along the line of centers of the molecules and will not change the angular momentum of the molecules.)

The example we have just considered is somewhat artificial because it is very unlikely that all the molecules would be moving only in the x

Table 18-2

Molar heat capacities of various gases, cal/mole-K

	C_v'	C_p'	$C_p' - C_v'$	$\gamma = C_p'/C_v'$
Monatomic gases:				
Helium	3.00	4.98	1.98	1.66
Neon				1.64
Argon	3.00	5.00	2.00	1.67
Krypton				1.68
Xenon				1.66
Diatomic gases:				
N_2	4.96	6.95	1.99	1.40
O_2	4.96	6.95	1.99	1.40
CO	4.93	6.95	2.02	1.41
HCl	5.02	7.08	2.06	1.41
Polyatomic gases:				
CO_2	6.74	8.75	2.01	1.30
H_2O	6.46	8.46	2.00	1.31
CH_4	6.48	8.49	2.01	1.31

direction at one time. However, there are similar situations in which the average value of the kinetic energy associated with motion in the x direction is momentarily greater than that associated with motion in the y or z direction. Consider a gas which is being compressed by a piston moving with a very slow speed in the negative x direction, so that the compression is approximately quasi-static. Suppose further that the gas is insulated so that the compression is adiabatic. From the molecular point of view, the energy of the gas increases because of the elastic collisions of the molecules with the moving piston. If v_x is the x component of a molecule moving toward the piston and u is the speed of the piston, the x component of velocity of the molecule after colliding with the piston will be $v'_x = -|v_x + 2u|$. (The molecule moves with speed $v_x + u$ relative to the piston; the motion is toward the piston before the collision and away from the piston after the collision.) The energy associated with motion in the x direction after the collision is $\frac{1}{2}mv'^2_x = \frac{1}{2}m(v_x + 2u)^2 \approx \frac{1}{2}mv_x^2 + 2muv_x$ (neglecting u^2 compared with v_x^2). The moving piston directly increases the energy associated with motion in the x direction but has no effect on that associated with motion in the y or z directions (assuming the piston to be smooth). But immediately after colliding with the piston, molecules collide with other nearby molecules and a new equilibrium is established, $\frac{1}{2}mv_x^2$, $\frac{1}{2}mv_y^2$, and $\frac{1}{2}mv_z^2$ each having the same average value of $\frac{1}{2}kT$, which is increased by the work done on the gas by the moving piston. (See Problem 13 for the completion of this analysis in showing that the increase in molecular energy is indeed equal to the work done by the moving piston.)

Sharing the energy equally between the three terms in the translational energy is a special case of the *equipartition theorem*, a result which can be derived from more advanced statistical mechanics. Each coordinate, velocity component, angular-velocity component, etc., which appears in the expression for the energy of a molecule is called a *degree of freedom*. The equipartition theorem states that

In equilibrium, there is associated with each degree of freedom an average energy of $\frac{1}{2}kT$ per molecule.

Equipartition theorem

For example, take a rigid-dumbbell model of a molecule (Figure 18-11) which can translate in the x, y, and z directions and can rotate about axes x' and y' through the center of mass perpendicular to the z' axis along the line joining the two masses.[1] The kinetic energy for this dumbbell-model molecule is then

$$E_k = \tfrac{1}{2}mv_x^2 + \tfrac{1}{2}mv_y^2 + \tfrac{1}{2}mv_z^2 + \tfrac{1}{2}I_{x'}\omega_{x'}^2 + \tfrac{1}{2}I_{y'}\omega_{y'}^2 \qquad 18\text{-}24$$

The equipartition theorem states that the average energy associated with each of the five degrees of freedom is $\frac{1}{2}kT$, so that the total energy for N molecules is

$$U = N(5)(\tfrac{1}{2}kT) = \tfrac{5}{2}NkT \qquad 18\text{-}25$$

Writing $N = nN_A$, where n is the number of moles, N_A is Avogadro's

Figure 18-11
Rigid-dumbbell model of a diatomic gas. The motion can be described as translation of the center of mass along the x, y, or z axis plus rotation about the x', y', or z' axis. If the spheres are smooth or points, rotation about the z' axis can be neglected because this energy cannot be changed by collisions.

[1] We rule out rotation about the z' axis of the dumbbell by assuming either that the atoms are points and the moment of inertia about this axis is therefore zero or that the atoms are hard smooth spheres, in which case rotation about this axis cannot be changed by collisions and therefore does not participate in the absorption of energy. Either of these assumptions also rules out the possibility of rotation of a monatomic molecule.

number, and $N_A k = R$, we have

$U = \frac{5}{2}nRT$

The heat capacity at constant volume is then

$$C_v = \frac{dU}{dT} = \frac{5}{2}nR \qquad\qquad 18\text{-}26$$

and

$$C_p = C_v + nR = \frac{7}{2}nR \qquad\qquad 18\text{-}27$$

From the observation that C_v/n for nitrogen and oxygen is approximately $\frac{5}{2}R$, Clausius speculated (about 1880) that these gases must be diatomic gases which can rotate about two axes as well as translate.

If a diatomic molecule can vibrate as well as rotate and translate, there are two more degrees of freedom, corresponding to the kinetic and potential energy of vibration along the line joining the atoms. The equipartition theorem thus predicts that the internal energy per mole will be $\frac{7}{2}RT$. According to Table 18-2, diatomic gases apparently do not vibrate. The calculation of the number of degrees of freedom for a molecule with more than two atoms is more complicated if all possible vibrations are allowed.

Although the equipartition theorem is quite successful in relating the molar heat capacities of a gas to its atomic structure, it fails in several ways. There is no hint from the equipartition theorem why diatomic molecules do not vibrate or why the heat capacities vary with temperature. According to the equipartition theorem, there should be no temperature variation. The equipartition theorem fails because classical mechanics itself breaks down when applied to atomic and molecular systems and must be replaced by quantum mechanics. In the quantum-mechanical theory of motion, the possible energies of an atom or molecule are quantized. In particular there is a gap between the lowest possible energy and the next lowest. For the vibrational energies of a diatomic molecule, this energy gap is of the order of several tenths of an electron volt, which is much higher than $kT \approx 0.026$ eV (the value at ordinary temperatures). A collision between molecules having energies of the order of kT cannot increase their energy from the lowest possible energy to the next allowed energy, and consequently vibrational energy does not play a role in the internal energy at low temperatures.

The rotational energy of a molecule is also quantized, spacing between possible energies depending inversely on the moment of inertia. For rotation of monatomic molecules and rotation of diatomic molecules about the line joining the atoms the moment of inertia is so small that the energy spacing is large compared with kT at ordinary temperatures. For these cases, rotational energy plays no role in the internal energy at ordinary temperatures. On the other hand, the moment of inertia for rotation of diatomic molecules about axes perpendicular to the line joining the atoms is so large that the spacing of possible energies is small compared with kT at ordinary temperatures. In this case, energy quantization is not important, and the predictions of the classical equipartition theory are correct.

Using the equipartition theorem and a simple model of a solid, we can understand the Dulong-Petit law for the heat capacities of a solid. (We need not distinguish between C_v and C_p here because for a solid they are almost equal.) Let us assume that a solid consists of a regular

Figure 18-12
Model of a solid consisting of atoms connected to each other by springs. The internal energy of the solid then consists of kinetic and potential vibrational energy.

array of molecules each having a fixed equilibrium position and being connected by springs to each of its neighbors, as in Figure 18-12. Each molecule can oscillate in the x, y, and z directions. Its total energy is thus

$$E_k = \tfrac{1}{2}mv_x^2 + \tfrac{1}{2}mv_y^2 + \tfrac{1}{2}mv_z^2 + \tfrac{1}{2}Kx^2 + \tfrac{1}{2}Ky^2 + \tfrac{1}{2}Kz^2$$

where K is the effective force constant of the springs. The molecule thus has six degrees of freedom and an average energy of $6 \times \tfrac{1}{2}kT$ according to the equipartition theorem. Thus the total energy of 1 mole of a solid is

$$U = 3RT$$

and the molar heat capacity is $C_v' = dU/dT = 3R$, which is the Dulong-Petit law. This result holds for many solids but not for all at room temperature. Again, the reason for disagreement between this prediction and experiment is the breakdown of classical physics in the atomic realm.

Example 18-5 One mole of oxygen gas is heated from room temperature of 20°C and pressure of 1 atm to a temperature of 100°C. How much heat must be supplied if the volume is kept constant during the heating? How much heat must be supplied if the pressure is kept constant? How much work is done if the pressure is constant? (Assume that oxygen is an ideal gas.)

The heat capacity at constant volume of oxygen is

$$C_v = \tfrac{5}{2}nR = 5 \text{ cal/K}$$

using $n = 1$ mole and $R = 2$ cal/mole-K. The heat added to raise the temperature from 293 to 373 K is then

$$Q_1 = C_v \, \Delta T = (5 \text{ cal/K})(80 \text{ K}) = 400 \text{ cal}$$

Since no work is done when the volume is constant, this is also the increase in the internal energy of the gas $\Delta U = 400$ cal. Since the internal energy depends only on the temperature, this is the increase in internal energy when the gas temperature changes from 293 to 373 K for any process.

If we keep the pressure constant, the heat that must be added is

$$Q_2 = C_p \, \Delta T = \tfrac{7}{2}nR \, \Delta T = (7 \text{ cal/K})(80 \text{ K}) = 560 \text{ cal}$$

again using $R = 2$ cal/mole-K. This is greater because although the internal energy change is again 400 cal, work is done when the gas expands. The work done at constant pressure is

$$W = P\,dV = P(V_2 - V_1)$$

We can find the initial and final volumes from the result of Example 17-4 that the volume at 1 atm and 273 K is 22.4 ℓ. Since $PV = nRT$, the volume at constant pressure is just proportional to the temperature. The volumes V_1 and V_2 are thus

$$V_1 = (22.4\ \ell)(\tfrac{293}{273}) = 24.0\ \ell \qquad V_2 = (22.4\ \ell)(\tfrac{373}{273}) = 30.6\ \ell$$

The work done is thus

$$W = P(V_2 - V_1) = (1\ \text{atm})(30.6 - 24.0\ \ell) = 6.6\ \ell\text{-atm}$$

We can convert this energy unit to calories or joules using the fact that 1 atm = 1.013×10^5 N/m² and $1\ \ell = 10^3$ cm³ = 10^{-3} m³. Then

$$1\ \ell\text{-atm} \times \frac{1.013 \times 10^5\ \text{N/m}^2}{1\ \text{atm}}\,\frac{10^{-3}\ \text{m}^3}{1\ \ell} = 101.3\ \text{N-m} = 101.3\ \text{J}$$

or

$$1\ \ell\text{-atm} = 101.3\ \text{J} = 24.2\ \text{cal}$$

Thus

$$W = 6.6\ \ell\text{-atm} \times \frac{24.2\ \text{cal}}{1\ \ell\text{-atm}} = 160\ \text{cal}$$

The heat added at constant pressure, 560 cal, equals the change in internal energy, 400 cal, plus the work done, 160 cal. These two processes are illustrated on a PV diagram in Figure 18-13.

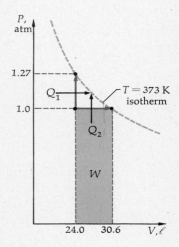

Figure 18-13
Example 18-5. Two methods of raising the temperature of a gas from 293 to 373 K. The dashed gray line is the isotherm at 373 K. The internal energy of the two different final states is the same because they have the same temperature. The heat added at constant pressure Q_2 is therefore greater than that added at constant volume Q_1 by the amount of work done W.

Question

11. Between 0 and 4°C water contracts as its temperature increases. Which is larger for water in this temperature range, C_p or C_v?

18-8 Quasi-static Adiabatic Expansion of an Ideal Gas

In a quasi-static adiabatic expansion of an ideal gas, the gas expands slowly against a piston, doing work on it. The gas is insulated from its surroundings so that no heat enters or leaves the gas. The work done by the gas equals the decrease in internal energy of the gas, and the temperature of the gas decreases. The curve representing this process on a PV diagram is shown in Figure 18-14. This curve is steeper than for an isothermal expansion; i.e., when the volume increases by dV, the pressure in an adiabatic expansion decreases by more than it does in an isothermal expansion because the temperature decreases.

The work done by a gas undergoing a quasi-static adiabatic expansion equals the area under the curve shown in Figure 18-14. The calculation of this work is important in determining efficiencies of heat engines (Chapter 19), and for this purpose we need to know the relation between P and V for this curve. This relation can be found by applying the first law to the adiabatic process and using the equation

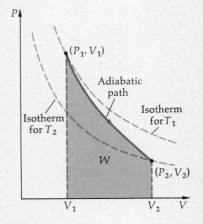

Figure 18-14
Quasi-static adiabatic expansion of an ideal gas. The curve on the PV diagram connecting the initial and final states (called an adiabatic path) is steeper than the isotherms because the temperature drops during the adiabatic expansion. This curve is given by $PV^\gamma =$ constant.

of state for an ideal gas. From the first law we have

$$dQ = dU + dW = dU + P\ dV = 0 \qquad\text{18-28}$$

According to Equation 18-17, the change in internal energy of the gas is related to the change in temperature by

$$dU = C_v\ dT \qquad\text{18-29}$$

(Although this result was obtained considering a constant-volume process, it relates the state variables U and T and is therefore valid independent of the process.) Then

$$C_v\ dT + P\ dV = 0 \qquad\text{18-30}$$

From the equation of state $PV = nRT$ we have (Equation 18-20)

$$P\ dV + V\ dP = nR\ dT$$

Using $dT = -\,(P/C_v)\ dV$ from Equation 18-30, we have

$$P\ dV + V\ dP = nR\left(-\frac{p\ dV}{C_v}\right)$$

or

$$C_vP\ dV + C_vV\ dP = -nRP\ dV$$

Rearranging gives

$$(C_v + nR)P\ dV + C_vV\ dP = 0$$

But $C_v + nR$ is just C_p. Using this fact and dividing each term by C_vPV, we obtain

$$\frac{C_p}{C_v}\frac{dV}{V} + \frac{dP}{P} = 0$$

or

$$\gamma\frac{dV}{V} + \frac{dP}{P} = 0 \qquad\text{18-31}$$

where

$$\gamma = \frac{C_p}{C_v} \qquad\text{18-32}$$

is the ratio of heat capacities. Integrating each term gives

$$\gamma \ln V + \ln P = \text{constant} \qquad \ln PV^\gamma = \text{constant}$$

or

$$PV^\gamma = \text{constant} \qquad\text{18-33}$$

This is the equation relating P and V in a quasi-static adiabatic expansion. This equation also applies to a quasi-static adiabatic compression in which the piston does work on the gas.

Example 18-6 A quantity of air expands adiabatically and quasi-statically from an initial pressure of 2 atm and volume 2 ℓ at room temperature (20°C) to twice its original volume. What are the final pressure and temperature? For air, $\gamma = 1.4$.

According to Equation 18-33, the quantity PV^γ remains unchanged during a quasi-static adiabatic expansion. Thus, if P_1 and V_1 are the initial pressure and volume and P_2 and V_2 are the final pressure and volume, we have

$$P_2 V_2{}^\gamma = P_1 V_1{}^\gamma \quad \text{or} \quad P_2 = P_1 \left(\frac{V_1}{V_2}\right)^\gamma$$

For the given values we have

$$P_2 = (2 \text{ atm}) \left(\frac{2\ \ell}{4\ \ell}\right)^{1.4} = 0.758 \text{ atm}$$

Since we always have $PV = nRT$ or $PV/T = nR$, we must have for this fixed number of moles of gas

$$\frac{P_2 V_2}{T_2} = \frac{P_1 V_1}{T_1}$$

or

$$T_2 = T_1 \frac{P_2 V_2}{P_1 V_1} = (293 \text{ K}) \frac{(0.758 \text{ atm})(4\ \ell)}{(2 \text{ atm})(2\ \ell)} = 222 \text{ K}$$

The corresponding Celsius temperature is

$$t_C = 222 \text{ K} - 273 \text{ K} = -51°\text{C}$$

Review

A. Define, explain, or otherwise identify:

Calorie, 437
Heat capacity, 437
Specific heat, 437
Molar heat capacity, 437
Phase, 440
Latent heat of fusion, 440
Latent heat of vaporization, 440
Adiabatic work, 442
Internal energy, 442
Heat, 443

Quasi-static process, 444
PV diagram, 444
Isothermal process, 446
Ideal gas, 448
Free adiabatic expansion
  of a gas, 448
Equipartition theorem, 452
Quasi-static adiabatic expansion
  of a gas, 455

B. True or false:

1. The heat capacity of a body is the amount of heat it can store at a given temperature.

2. A quasi-static process is one in which no work is done.

3. When a system goes from state 1 to state 2, the heat added is the same for all processes.

4. When a system goes from state 1 to state 2, the work done by the system is the same for all processes.

5. When a system goes from state 1 to state 2, the change in internal energy of the system is the same for all processes.

6. The internal energy of an ideal gas depends only on the temperature.

7. C_p is greater than C_v for any material which expands when heated.

8. In a free adiabatic expansion of an ideal gas the final state is the same as the initial state.

9. In an isothermal expansion of an ideal gas the work done by the gas equals the heat absorbed.

10. Equipartition of energy says that in equilibrium all molecules of a gas have the same energy.

Exercises

Section 18-1, Heat Capacity and Specific Heat

1. How many calories of heat energy are required to raise the temperature of 20 kg of water from 10 to 20°C?

2. A man typically consumes food with a total energy value of 3000 kcal each day. (a) How many joules of energy is this? (b) Calculate his power output in watts assuming this energy is dissipated at a steady rate during 24 h.

3. A common unit of heat energy is the British thermal unit (Btu), defined to be the amount of energy needed to raise the temperature of one pound of water one Fahrenheit degree. (a) Find the number of calories in 1 Btu. (b) Find the number of joules in 1 Btu. (c) Find the number of Btu needed to raise the temperature of 1 gal of water from 32 to 212°F (1 gal contains 8 pints; 1 pint of water weighs 1 lb).

4. A 200-gm piece of lead is heated to 90°C and dropped into 500 gm of water initially at 20°C. Neglecting the heat capacity of the container, find the final temperature of the lead and water.

5. The specific heat of a certain metal is determined by measuring the temperature change which occurs when a heated piece of the metal is placed in an insulated container made of the same material and containing water. The piece of metal has mass 100 gm and an initial temperature of 100°C. The container has a mass of 200 gm and contains 500 gm of water at an initial temperature of 17.3°C. The final temperature is 22.7°C. What is the specific heat of the metal?

Section 18-2, Latent Heat

6. How much heat must be removed when 100 gm of steam at 150°C is cooled and frozen into 100 gm of ice at 0°C? (Take the specific heat of steam to be 0.48 cal/gm-°C.)

7. A 200-gm piece of ice at 0°C is put into 500 gm of water at 20°C. The system is in a container of negligible heat capacity and insulated from its surroundings. (a) What is the final equilibrium temperature of the system? (b) How much of the ice melts?

8. A 50-gm piece of ice at 0°C is placed in 500 gm of water at 20°C, as in Exercise 7. What is the final temperature of the system assuming no heat loss to the surroundings?

9. Liquid nitrogen boils at −196°C and has a heat of vaporization of 48 cal/gm. A 50-gm piece of aluminum at 20°C is cooled to −196°C by placing it in a large container of liquid nitrogen. How much nitrogen is vaporized? (Assume that the specific heat of aluminum is constant and equal to 0.22 cal/gm-°C.)

Section 18-3, The First Law of Thermodynamics

10. (a) How much work must be done on 1 kg of water to raise its temperature from 20 to 25°C assuming the water is adiabatically shielded from its surroundings? (b) In an actual experiment, the work done is 2.25×10^4 J. How much heat escapes to the surroundings? Express your answer both in joules and in calories.

11. (a) Express the heat capacity of water in joules per kilogram-kelvin. (b) Express the latent heat of fusion of water in joules per kilogram.

12. A 1-kg piece of ice is dropped from a height of 40 m into a box of wood shavings. (a) Assuming that all the mechanical energy lost goes into internal energy of the ice, how much ice is melted? (b) Does the fraction of the mass of ice that is melted in this experiment depend on the original mass of ice?

13. A box of lead shot is thrown vertically into the air to a height of 4 m and allowed to fall to the floor in a lecture demonstration. The original temperature

of the lead is 20°C. Five such throws are made, and the temperature is then measured. What result do you expect?

14. A lead bullet with speed 200 m/sec is stopped in a block of wood. Assuming that all the energy goes into heating the bullet, find the final temperature of the bullet if the initial temperature is 20°C.

15. At Niagara Falls, water drops a distance of 162 ft. (a) If all the change in potential energy goes into internal energy of the water, compute the increase in temperature. (b) Do the same for Yosemite Falls, where the water drops 2.42×10^3 ft.

16. A body of water is heated at constant pressure from 20 to 40°C. Explain carefully why it is incorrect to say that the water at 40°C contains more heat than it did at 20°C. Is it correct to say that the water has more internal energy at 40°C than at 20°C? Why, or why not?

Section 18-4, Work and the PV Diagram for a Gas

17. Use the values of the gas constant R to find conversion factors for energy in liter-atmospheres to joules and to calories.

In Exercises 18 to 21, 1 mole of a gas is originally in state $P_1 = 3$ atm, $V_1 = 1$ ℓ, and $U_1 = 456$ J. Its final state is $P_2 = 2$ atm, $V_2 = 3$ ℓ, and $U_2 = 912$ J. All processes are quasi-static.

18. The gas is allowed to expand at constant pressure to a volume of 3 ℓ. It is then cooled at constant volume until its pressure is 2 atm. (a) Indicate this process on a PV diagram and calculate the work done by the gas. (b) Find the heat added during the entire process.

19. The gas is first cooled at constant volume until its pressure is 2 atm. It is then allowed to expand at constant pressure until its volume is 3 ℓ. (a) Indicate this process on a PV diagram and calculate the work done by the gas. (b) Find the heat added during this process.

20. The gas is allowed to expand isothermally until its volume is 3 ℓ and its pressure is 1 atm. It is then heated at constant volume until its pressure is 2 atm. (a) Indicate this process on a PV diagram and calculate the work done by the gas. (b) Find the heat added during this process.

21. The gas expands and heat is added such that the gas follows a straight-line path on the PV diagram from its initial state to its final state. (a) Indicate this process on a PV diagram and calculate the work done by the gas. (b) Find the heat added for this process.

Section 18-5, Internal Energy of a Gas

22. An ideal gas is originally at pressure $P_1 = 2$ atm, volume $V_1 = 1$ ℓ, and temperature $T_1 = 300$ K. It is allowed to expand at constant pressure until its volume is 4 ℓ. (a) How much work is done during this expansion? (b) What is the temperature of the gas after this expansion? (c) The gas is now cooled at constant volume until its pressure is 0.5 atm. What is its temperature now? (d) What is the net amount of heat added to the gas during the complete process of expansion and cooling?

23. A certain ionized gas is composed of ions which repel each other. The gas undergoes a free adiabatic expansion. How does the temperature of the gas change? Why?

Section 18-6, Heat Capacities of an Ideal Gas, and Section 18-7, The Equipartition of Energy

24. The heat capacity at constant volume of a certain monatomic gas is $C_v = 11.9$ cal/K. (a) Find the number of moles of the gas. (b) What is the in-

ternal energy of this gas at $T = 300$ K? (c) What is the heat capacity at constant pressure?

25. For a certain gas, the heat capacity at constant pressure is greater than that at constant volume by 5.97 cal. (a) How many moles of the gas are there? (b) If the gas is monatomic, what are C_v and C_p? (c) If the gas molecules are diatomic molecules which rotate but do not vibrate, what are C_v and C_p?

26. For air, $\gamma = C_p/C_v = 1.40$. Which is the best model for an air molecule: (a) an elastic sphere, (b) a rigid dumbbell, or (c) a nonrigid dumbbell which vibrates and rotates? Explain.

27. Find the molar heat capacities C_v' and C_p' and the ratio $\gamma = C_p/C_v$ for ideal gases which are: (a) elastic spherical atoms, (b) rigid dumbbell-shaped molecules, (c) nonrigid dumbbell-shaped molecules which vibrate and rotate.

28. For each of the gases with the following $\gamma = C_p/C_v$ give a possible physical model of the molecule: (a) $\gamma = 1.29$, (b) $\gamma = 1.40$, (c) $\gamma = 1.67$.

29. One mole of an ideal monatomic gas is heated at constant volume from $T = 300$ K to $T = 600$ K: (a) find the increase in internal energy, the work done W, and the heat added Q. (b) Find these same quantities if this same gas is heated from 300 to 600 K at constant pressure. (c) For the constant-pressure heating in part (b), calculate the work done by the gas directly from $W = \int P\, dV = P\, \Delta V$ for $P = 1$ atm. *Hint:* Use the equation of state to find the initial and final volume of the gas.

30. Repeat each part of Exercise 29 for a gas containing diatomic molecules which rotate but do not vibrate.

31. The specific heat of helium at constant pressure is measured to be 1.248 cal/gm-K. Use the fact that helium is a monatomic gas to calculate the molecular weight of helium from this result.

32. (a) Show that when an ideal gas undergoes a temperature change, its internal-energy change is $U = C_v\, \Delta T$ no matter what the process is. (b) Show explicitly that this expression holds for the expansion of an ideal gas at constant pressure. Do this by calculating the work done and showing that it can be written $W = nR\, \Delta T$, where ΔT is the temperature change, and subtracting this from the heat added, $Q = C_p\, \Delta T$.

Section 18-8, Quasi-static Adiabatic Expansion of an Ideal Gas

33. Show that during a quasi-static adiabatic expansion of an ideal gas, $TV^{\gamma-1} = $ constant, where T is the temperature.

34. Show that during a quasi-static adiabatic expansion of an ideal gas, $T^\gamma/P^{\gamma-1} = $ constant.

35. One mole of an ideal gas ($\gamma = \frac{5}{3}$) expands adiabatically from a pressure of 10 atm and temperature 0°C to a final state of pressure 2 atm. Find (a) the initial and final volume and (b) the final temperature.

36. An ideal gas at room temperature (20°C) is compressed quasi-statically and adiabatically to half its original volume. (a) If the gas is monatomic, find its final temperature. (b) If the gas is diatomic (but the molecules do not vibrate), find its final temperature.

Problems

1. A piece of ice is dropped from a height H. Find the minimum value of H such that the ice melts when it makes an inelastic collision with the ground. Is it reasonable to neglect the variation in the acceleration of gravity in doing this problem? Comment on the reasonableness of neglecting air resistance. What effect would air resistance have on your answer?

2. An insulated cylinder with a movable piston (to maintain constant pressure) initially contains 100 gm of ice at $-10°C$. Heat is supplied to the cylinder at a constant rate by a 100-W heater. Make a graph showing the temperature of the cylinder contents as a function of time starting at time $t = 0$, when the temperature is $-10°C$, and ending when the temperature is 110°C. (Use $c = 0.50$ cal/gm-°C for the average specific heat of ice from -10 to 0°C and for steam from 100 to 110°C.)

3. Compare the specific heat of ice with that calculated from the Dulong-Petit law. How might you account for the difference in these values on the basis of a mechanical model of ice? Explain on the basis of the equipartition theorem how the specific heat of steam (at constant pressure) can be about 0.50 cal/gm-°C.

4. One mole of water at 100°C is vaporized at a constant pressure of 1 atm. (a) Find the amount of heat added. (b) Find the change in volume and the work done by the system in expanding against atmospheric pressure (treat the steam as an ideal gas). (c) Find the change in internal energy of the water. (d) If 1 mole of ice at 0°C and 1 atm is completely liquefied, is the internal-energy change greater or less than $18L_f$? Explain.

5. A 200-gm aluminum calorimeter can contains 500 gm of water at 20°C; 300 gm of aluminum shot is heated to 100°C and placed in the calorimeter. Using the value of the specific heat given in Table 18-1, find the final temperature of the system (assuming no heat losses to the surroundings). If this calorimeter is to be used to make an accurate measurement of the specific heat of aluminum, what should the initial temperature of the water and container be to minimize the error due to heat transfer to and from the surroundings if the room temperature is 20°C?

6. (a) A 200-gm aluminum calorimeter can contains 500 gm of water at 20°C. A 100-gm piece of ice cooled to $-20°C$ is placed in the can. Find the final temperature of the system assuming no heat losses (assume the specific heat of ice is 0.50 cal/gm-°C). (b) A second 200-gm piece of ice at $-20°C$ is added. How much ice remains in the system after it reaches equilibrium? (c) Would your answer to part (b) be different if both pieces were added at the same time?

7. An ideal gas at initial pressure P_1 and volume V_1 expands quasi-statically and adiabatically to volume V_2 and pressure P_2. Show by direct integration of $P\,dV$, using $PV^\gamma = $ constant, that the work done is

$$W = \frac{P_1V_1 - P_2V_2}{\gamma - 1}$$

Show that this is consistent with the general result that the internal-energy change is $\Delta U = C_v\,\Delta T$.

8. Using the ideal-gas law and $PV^\gamma = $ constant for an adiabatic expansion, show that the slope of the adiabatic-expansion curve at any point on the PV diagram is steeper (greater magnitude) than the slope of the isothermal-expansion curve.

9. A solid material has a density ρ, coefficient of linear expansion α, and mass m. (a) Show that at pressure P the heat capacities C_p and C_v are related by $C_p - C_v = 3\alpha mP/\rho$. (b) Find the difference (in calories per mole-kelvin) in the molar heat capacities of aluminum at atmospheric pressure using $\alpha = 23 \times 10^{-6}$ per kelvin, $M = 27$ gm/mole, and $\rho = 2.7$ gm/cm^3.

10. One mole of an ideal gas is in an initial state of $P = 2$ atm and $V = 10$ ℓ indicated by point a on the PV diagram of Figure 18-15. It expands at constant pressure to point b, where its volume is 30 ℓ, and is then cooled at constant volume until its pressure is 1 atm at point c. It is then compressed at constant pressure to its original volume at point d and finally heated at constant volume until it is back at its original state. (a) Find the temperature of each state $a, b, c,$

Figure 18-15
PV diagram for Problem 10.

and d. (b) Assuming that the gas is monatomic, find the heat added along each path of the cycle. (c) Calculate the work done along each path. (d) Find the internal energy of each state a, b, c, and d. (e) What is the net work done by the gas for the complete cycle? How much heat is added during the complete cycle?

11. One mole of N_2 gas is maintained at room temperature (20°C) and at a pressure of 5 atm. It is allowed to expand adiabatically and quasi-statically until its pressure equals the room pressure of 1 atm. It is then heated at constant pressure until its temperature is again 20°C. During this heating, the gas expands. After it reaches room temperature, it is heated at constant volume until its pressure is 5 atm. It is then compressed at constant pressure until it is back in its original state. (a) Construct an accurate PV diagram showing each process in the cycle. (b) *From your graph* determine the work done by the gas during the complete cycle. (c) How much heat was added or subtracted from the gas during the complete cycle? (d) Check your graphical determination of the work in part (b) by calculating the work done during each process of the cycle.

12. An ideal gas of n moles is at pressure P_1, volume V_1, and temperature T_h. It undergoes an isothermal expansion until its pressure and volume are P_2 and V_2. It then expands adiabatically until its temperature is T_c and its pressure and volume are P_3 and V_3. It is then compressed isothermally until it is at volume V_4, which is related to its initial volume V_1 by $T_c V_4{}^{\gamma-1} = T_h V_1{}^{\gamma-1}$. It is then compressed adiabatically until it is in its original state, $P_1 V_1$ and T_h. (a) Assuming that each process is quasi-static, plot this cycle on a PV diagram (this cycle is known as a Carnot cycle for an ideal gas, to be discussed in the next chapter). (b) Show that the heat added during the isothermal expansion at T_h is $Q_h = nRT_h \ln (V_2/V_1)$. (c) Show that the heat rejected by the gas during the isothermal compression at T_c is $Q_c = nRT_c \ln (V_3/V_4)$. (d) Using the result of Exercise 33 that for an adiabatic expansion or compression, $TV^{\gamma-1}$ is constant, show that $V_2/V_1 = V_3/V_4$. (e) The efficiency of such a cycle is defined to be the net work done divided by the heat absorbed Q_h. Show from the first law of thermodynamics that the efficiency is $1 - Q_c/Q_h$. Using your results of the previous parts of this problem, show that $Q_c/Q_h = T_c/T_h$.

13. In Section 18-7 the collisions of gas molecules with a piston moving at a small speed u along the x axis were discussed. It was shown that in colliding with the moving piston, each molecule gains energy equal to $2m|v_x|u$, where m is the mass of the molecule and v_x is its x component of velocity. Suppose that the gas has molecular weight M, density ρ, and temperature T. The area of the piston is A. (a) Show that the number of molecules which collide with the piston in a short time dt is given by $(N_A \rho A |v_x| dt)/2M$. (Assume that all molecules have the same magnitude of v_x, half moving to the left and half to the right.) (b) What is the total kinetic energy gained by all the molecules that hit the piston during the time dt? (c) From your result for part (b) show that the rate at which the internal energy of the gas increases because of collisions with the moving piston is

$$\frac{dU}{dt} = \tfrac{1}{2} m v_x{}^2 \frac{2 N_A \rho A}{M} u$$

(d) Show that the last result also can be written

$$\frac{dU}{dt} = \frac{\rho RT}{M} Au$$

(e) If $|dx|$ is the distance the piston moves in time dt, show that the increase in internal energy when the piston moves this distance is

$$dU = \frac{\rho RT}{M} A|dx|$$

(f) Use the last result, the gas law, and the fact that $dV = -A|dx|$ is the change in volume of the gas to show that $dU = -P\, dV$. This shows that the work done *on* the gas by the piston equals the increase in internal energy.

CHAPTER 19   The Availability of Energy

Our study of the first law of thermodynamics showed that it is possible to increase the internal energy of a body either by adding heat to the body or by doing work on it. In this sense, work and heat are equivalent: 10 J of either work or heat added to a system increases the internal energy of the system by 10 J. On the other hand, if we decrease the internal energy of a system and try to use this energy to do work on another system or to add heat to another system, we find an important difference between heat and work. There is no difficulty in taking internal energy out of a system in the form of heat, but it is impossible to convert this internal energy completely into work without any other change taking place in the surroundings. There is thus an asymmetry in the roles played by heat and work which is not evident from the first law.

It is quite easy to convert work completely into heat without any change in the surroundings (except in the body which absorbs the heat). A common example is the work done against friction, which can go completely into heat. This process can go on indefinitely as long as there is a supply of work but the reverse is often impossible. We cannot easily convert heat completely into work. One situation in which heat is converted into work is in the isothermal expansion of an ideal gas (or in an expansion of a real gas along a path of constant internal energy). If the expansion is allowed to proceed freely, the heat absorbed by the gas is completely converted into work until the pressure of the gas equals atmospheric pressure and the expansion stops. If the gas system is to be used again, however, work must be done on it to compress it.

Besides the conversion of heat into work, there are other conceivable processes which are consistent with the first law of thermodynamics but do not occur in nature. For example, heat does not go from a cold body to a hot body by itself. Processes which conserve energy but which never occur are all related to processes which are irreversible. For example, a block with initial kinetic energy slides along a rough table. The work against friction goes completely into heat, which increases the internal energy of the block and the table. The reverse process never occurs. The internal energy of the block and

Irreversible processes

table is never spontaneously converted into kinetic energy of the block, sending it sliding along the table while the table and block cool off. Similarly, heat can flow from a hot body to a cold body until the two bodies are at the same temperature. The reverse never happens. Two bodies in thermal contact at the same temperature remain at the same temperature. Heat is never spontaneously conducted from a cold body to a hot body. A third type of irreversible process not involving heat is the free adiabatic expansion of a gas. Whether or not the gas is ideal, the final energy equals the initial energy. Left to itself, a gas will never contract so that it fills only one of two connected compartments.

The second law of thermodynamics summarizes the fact that processes of this type do not occur. There are many different ways of stating the second law; we shall study several and show them to be equivalent. Before giving precise statements of the second law we shall consider heat engines and refrigerators briefly because the study of heat-engine efficiency gave rise to the first clear statements of the second law of thermodynamics.

19-1   Heat Engines and the Second Law of Thermodynamics

The first practical heat engine was the steam engine, invented in the seventeenth century for pumping water out of coal mines. Today the primary use of steam engines is in generating electric energy. We need not consider details of the operation of the steam engine or any other type because we can represent all types of engines—steam engines, internal-combustion engines, diesel engines—schematically. A substance or system, called the *working substance* (water in the case of the steam engine), absorbs a quantity of heat Q_h from a heat reservoir at temperature T_h. It does work W and rejects heat Q_c to a heat reservoir at a lower temperature T_c. The working substance then returns to its original state. (We use the subscripts h and c to indicate quantities associated with the hot and cold reservoirs.) The engine, therefore, is a cyclic device. At various parts of its cycle it absorbs or rejects heat, and it does work, the purpose being to gain some work at the expense of heat absorbed in each cycle.

Working substance

The Granger Collection

Early steam engine designed by James Watt in the mid-1700s.

Since the initial and final states of the engine are the same, the final internal energy must equal the initial internal energy. The first law of thermodynamics thus relates the heat absorbed Q_h, the heat rejected Q_c, and the work done W by

$$Q_h - Q_c = W \qquad\qquad 19\text{-}1$$

(In this discussion we temporarily abandon our convention that the heat is positive if absorbed by the system and negative if rejected. We shall use Q_h and Q_c to represent positive amounts of heat energy and use a minus sign, as in Equation 19-1. Later in this chapter we revert to the original convention and write $Q_h + Q_c$ for the net heat absorbed, allowing Q_c to be a negative number.)

Figure 19-1 shows a schematic representation of a heat engine. Heat Q_h enters from reservoir at temperature T_h (hot reservoir), and heat Q_c is rejected to the heat reservoir at temperature T_c (cold reservoir). Work W is done by the engine. When the cycle is completed, the process repeats. The efficiency ϵ of the engine is defined to be the ratio of the work done to the heat absorbed:

$$\epsilon = \frac{W}{Q_h} = \frac{Q_h - Q_c}{Q_h} = 1 - \frac{Q_c}{Q_h} \qquad\qquad 19\text{-}2$$

Since the heat Q_h is usually produced by burning coal, oil, or some other kind of fuel which must be paid for, one tries to design a heat engine with the greatest possible efficiency. We can see from Equation 19-2 that we want to reject as small a fraction of the heat absorbed as possible. For perfect efficiency ($\epsilon = 1 = 100$ percent), $Q_c = 0$ and no heat is rejected in a cycle. In that case, all the heat absorbed from the first reservoir would be converted into work done. None would be rejected or lost to the second reservoir.

Although the efficiency of heat engines has been greatly increased since the early steam engines, it is impossible to make a heat engine which is 100 percent efficient, i.e., which would reject no heat to a reservoir at a lower temperature. This experimental result is known as the *Kelvin-Planck statement of the second law of thermodynamics*:

It is impossible for an engine working in a cycle to produce no other effect than that of extracting heat from a reservoir and performing an equivalent amount of work.

Note the words "in a cycle"; it is possible to extract heat from a single reservoir and transform it completely into work. An ideal gas undergoing an isothermal expansion does just this, but after the expansion the gas is not in its original state. In order to bring the gas back to its original state, heat must be rejected to another reservoir at a lower temperature, or the original work obtained must be put back into the gas as in an isothermal compression, in which case the net heat absorbed and net work done are both zero. If the Kelvin-Planck statement were not true, it would be possible to design a heat engine for a ship which would extract heat from the ocean (a convenient heat reservoir) and use it to power the ship without using a second heat reservoir at a lower temperature to receive any of the heat.

Figure 19-2 is a schematic representation of a refrigerator, which is similar to a heat engine but absorbs heat from a cold reservoir and rejects heat to a hot one. In order to do this, work W must be done *on* the refrigerator. If Q_c is the heat absorbed and W the work done on the

Figure 19-1
Schematic representation of a heat engine which removes heat energy Q_h from a hot reservoir at temperature T_h, does work W, and rejects heat energy Q_c to a cold reservoir at temperature T_c.

Second law (Kelvin-Planck statement)

Figure 19-2
Schematic representation of a refrigerator which removes heat energy Q_c from a cold reservoir, rejects heat energy Q_h to the hot reservoir, and absorbs work W, which must be done on the refrigerator.

refrigerator, the heat rejected is

$$Q_h = W + Q_c$$

The purpose of a refrigerator is to transfer heat from a cold body to a hot body. It is desirable to do this with the least possible work. It is found from experience that some work W must always be done. This result is the Clausius statement of the second law of thermodynamics:

It is impossible for a refrigerator working in a cycle to produce no other effect than the transfer of heat from a colder body to a hotter body.

   If the Clausius statement were not true, it would be possible in principle to cool our homes in the summer with a refrigerator which pumped heat to the outside without using any electricity or other energy.

   A measure of the performance of a refrigerator is the ratio Q_c/W, called the *coefficient of performance* η:

$$\eta = \frac{Q_c}{W} \qquad\qquad 19\text{-}3$$

The greater the coefficient of performance the better the refrigerator. Typical refrigerators have coefficients of performance of about 5 or 6. In terms of this ratio, the Clausius statement of the second law is that the coefficient of performance of a refrigerator cannot be infinite.

Questions

1. What plays the role of the high-temperature reservoir in the steam engine? The low-temperature reservoir? What plays these roles in an internal-combustion engine?

2. How does friction in an engine affect its efficiency?

Refrigerators

Second law (Clausius statement)

Rudolf Julius Emanuel Clausius (1822–1888).

Brown Brothers

19-2 Equivalence of the Kelvin-Planck and Clausius Statements

Although the two statements of the second law we have given may seem to be quite different, they are in fact equivalent; i.e., if either statement is true, the other must be true also. We can prove this by showing that if either statement is false, the other must be false also. This is sufficient to prove equivalence.

We first assume that the Clausius statement is false, i.e., that it is possible to transfer heat from a cold reservoir to a hot reservoir without any other effects. Suppose an ordinary engine removes 100 J of energy from a hot reservoir, does 40 J of work, and exhausts 60 J of energy to the cold reservoir. This engine has an efficiency of 40 percent. If the Clausius statement were not true, we could use a perfect refrigerator to remove 60 J of energy from the cold reservoir and transfer it to the hot reservoir, doing no work in the process. The net effect of our perfect refrigerator working along with the ordinary engine would be to remove 40 J from the hot reservoir and do 40 J of work, with no energy rejected (Figure 19-3). This violates the Kelvin-Planck statement of the second law. Thus if the Clausius statement were false, the Kelvin-Planck statement would be too, as illustrated in Figure 19-4 for general values of Q_h and Q_c used by the ordinary engine.

We now assume that the Kelvin-Planck statement is false and show that this implies the Clausius statement is false. Consider an ordinary refrigerator which removes 100 J of energy from a cold reservoir, uses 50 J of work, and rejects 150 J to the hot reservoir (Figure 19-5). If the Kelvin-Planck statement were false, we could remove energy from a single reservoir and convert it completely into work with 100 percent efficiency. We could thus use such a perfect engine to remove 50 J of energy from the hot reservoir and do 50 J of work (Figure 19-5b). The net result of the ordinary refrigerator combined with the perfect engine would be to transfer 100 J from the cold reservoir to the hot reservoir without any work being done, contradicting the Clausius statement. (Figure 19-6 illustrates this combination of an ordinary refrigerator and perfect engine for general values of Q_h, W, and Q_c used by the refrigerator.) Hence, if the Kelvin-Planck statement were false, the Clausius statement would be too. We have thus shown that these two statements of the second law of thermodynamics are equivalent.

Figure 19-3
(a) An ordinary heat engine which removes 100 J from a hot reservoir, performs 40 J of work, and rejects 60 J to the cold reservoir. If the Clausius statement of the second law were false, a perfect refrigerator (b) could remove 60 J from the cold reservoir and reject it to the hot reservoir without requiring any work. (c) The net effect of the ordinary engine and perfect refrigerator in (a) and (b) is a perfect engine which violates the Kelvin-Planck statement of the second law by removing 40 J from the hot reservoir and converting it completely into work with no other effects.

Hot reservoir at temperature T_h

100 J

Ordinary engine

40 J

60 J

60 J

Perfect refrigerator

60 J

40 J

40 J

Perfect engine

Cold reservoir at temperature T_c

(a)   (b)   (c)

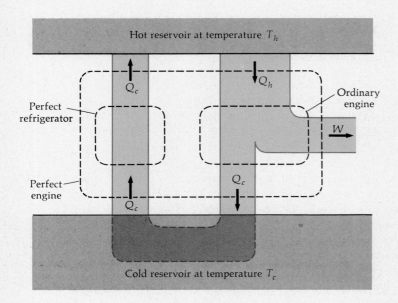

Figure 19-4
An ordinary heat engine combined with a perfect refrigerator, resulting in a perfect heat engine. The combination removes heat $Q_h - Q_c$ from the hot reservoir and converts it completely into work.

Figure 19-5
(a) An ordinary refrigerator which removes 100 J from a cold reservoir and rejects 150 J to a hot reservoir, requiring 50 J of work. If the Kelvin-Planck statement of the second law were false, a perfect engine (b) could remove 50 J from the hot reservoir and convert it completely into work with no other effects. (c) The net effect of the ordinary refrigerator and perfect engine in (a) and (b) is a perfect refrigerator which violates the Clausius statement of the second law.

Figure 19-6
Ordinary refrigerator combined with a perfect heat engine, resulting in a perfect refrigerator which removes heat Q_c from the cold reservoir and transfers it to the hot reservoir without requiring any work.

19-3 Reversibility

Consider the simple process of conduction of a certain amount of heat Q from a hot reservoir to a cold reservoir. According to the Clausius statement of the second law of thermodynamics, it is impossible to transfer this heat back to the hotter reservoir without other changes in the surroundings. We could use a refrigerator to remove the heat Q from the lower reservoir and transfer heat $Q + W$ to the upper reservoir, where W is the work done on the refrigerator, but then energy W has been lost by the surroundings and an extra amount of heat W is in the upper reservoir. According to the Kelvin-Planck statement, we cannot remove this heat from the hot reservoir and convert it completely into work. In any cycle some heat must be rejected to the surroundings. The process of heat conduction from a hot body to a cold body is *irreversible:* we cannot bring the system back to its original state without making a permanent change in the surroundings.

We define any process to be irreversible if the system and surroundings cannot be brought back to their initial states. Irreversibility is intimately connected with the second law of thermodynamics. We can find many irreversible processes in nature. Any process that converts mechanical energy into internal energy is irreversible; e.g., the process of a block sliding along a rough table until it stops due to friction is irreversible because we cannot extract the increased internal energy of the block and table and convert it completely back into mechanical energy. Similarly, if we drop a block of wood into a lake, mechanical energy mgh is converted into internal energy of the lake (and block). We cannot reverse this process without doing work. Another irreversible process we have discussed is the free adiabatic expansion of a gas from one compartment into an evacuated compartment. Although no work is done, no heat is transferred, and the internal energy does not change, it is impossible to reverse the process.

This irreversibility is also related to the second law of thermodynamics. Let us suppose that the gas at temperature T freely expands from volume V_1 of the original compartment to the final volume V_2. As we have mentioned, the final temperature is also T since the internal energy of the ideal gas did not change. We can bring this gas back to its original volume by isothermal compression, in which we do work W and an equal amount of heat $Q = W$ is rejected into a heat reservoir at temperature T. Such an isothermal compression is itself reversible, but the combination of the free expansion plus the isothermal compression puts the gas back in its original state, with an amount of work W converted into energy in the heat reservoir. Since it is impossible to convert this energy back into work with no other changes, the complete process is irreversible. Thus the free adiabatic expansion is irreversible (Figure 19-7). The gas, once expanded, will never spontaneously contract to its original volume.

From these considerations and our statements of the second law of thermodynamics, we can list some conditions necessary for a process to be reversible:

1. There must be no work done by friction, viscous forces, or other dissipative forces which produce heat.

2. There can be no heat conduction due to a temperature difference.

3. The process must be quasi-static so that the system is always in an equilibrium state (or infinitesimally near an equilibrium state).

Irreversibility defined

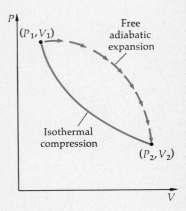

Figure 19-7
A free adiabatic expansion of an ideal gas is indicated by the arrows. It cannot be represented by a curve on the PV diagram because the process is not quasi-static and the gas does not pass through equilibrium states. The gas can be returned to its original state by a reversible isothermal compression during which work is converted completely into heat. The combined cycle cannot be reversed because heat cannot be converted completely into work with no other change. The free adiabatic expansion is therefore irreversible.

Conditions for reversibility

Any process which violates any of the above conditions is irreversible. Most processes in nature are irreversible. In order to have a reversible process, great care must be taken to eliminate frictional and other dissipative forces and to make the process quasi-static. Since this can never be done completely, a reversible process seems impossible in practice. Nevertheless, one can come very close to a reversible process, and the concept is very important in theory.

Consider, for example, a quasi-static expansion of a gas from volume V_1 to volume V_2 at constant pressure, shown in Figure 19-8. If this process is to be reversible, the heat must be absorbed isothermally so that there is no heat conduction across a finite temperature difference. We can approximate the constant-pressure path by an alternate reversible path consisting of the series of isotherms and quasi-static, adiabatic paths indicated. Heat is then absorbed along each isotherm from a reservoir at the temperature of the isotherm. With a very large number of heat reservoirs, we can make this alternate path approximate the constant-pressure path as closely as we wish. Similarly, any quasi-static process represented by a curve in the PV diagram can be approximated by a reversible path consisting of a series of isotherms and quasi-static, adiabatic paths.

In the next sections, we shall see how the investigation of reversible processes leads to a theoretical limit on the efficiency of a heat engine operating between two reservoirs of fixed temperatures and to the definition of an absolute temperature scale which does not depend on the properties of any material.

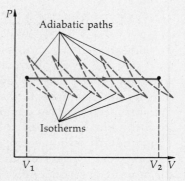

Figure 19-8
Quasi-static expansion at constant pressure. This process can be considered reversible because it can be approximated as closely as desired by a series of reversible isothermal and adiabatic curves as shown. Any quasi-static process can be performed approximately reversibly using a large number of heat reservoirs so that the heat is absorbed or rejected approximately isothermally.

Questions

3. Give several examples of irreversible processes in everyday life.

4. If a system changes from state A to state B by an irreversible process, does that mean it can never be returned to state A again?

5. A bottle of ink is slowly, carefully, and thoroughly mixed with a tub of water. Is this a reversible or an irreversible process?

19-4 The Carnot Engine

In 1824, before the first law of thermodynamics was established, a young French engineer, Carnot, described an ideal reversible engine working in a simple cycle between two heat reservoirs and found the theoretical limit for the efficiency of an engine in terms of the temperatures of the heat reservoirs. Such an ideal engine is now called a *Carnot engine* and its cycle a *Carnot cycle*. Carnot's results are given in a simple but important theorem, called the *Carnot theorem*:

No engine working between two given heat reservoirs can be more efficient than a reversible engine working between those reservoirs.

This theorem is easily proved by using the second law of thermodynamics. Consider a *reversible* engine working between two reservoirs. Let it remove 100 J of energy from the hot reservoir, do 40 J of work, and reject 60 J of energy into the cold reservoir (Figure 19-9a). Its efficiency is thus 40 percent. Since the engine is reversible, it can be operated in reverse, absorbing 60 J of energy from the cold reservoir

Drawing by L. L. Boilly of Nicolas Léonard Sadi Carnot (1796–1832), aged seventeen.

Carnot's theorem

Hot reservoir at temperature T_h

(a) 100 J / 40 J / 60 J

(b) 100 J / 40 J / 60 J

(c) 100 J / 45 J / 55 J

(d) 5 J / 5 J

Cold reservoir at temperature T_c

(a)   (b)   (c)   (d)

Figure 19-9
Illustration of the Carnot theorem. (a) A reversible heat engine with 40 percent efficiency. (b) The same heat engine run backward as a refrigerator. (c) An assumed heat engine working between the same two reservoirs with efficiency of 45 percent. (d) The combination of the two engines with the reversible engine operating as a refrigerator results in a perfect heat engine, violating the second law.

and rejecting 100 J into the hot reservoir while work of 40 J is done on it (Figure 19-9b). We now consider a second engine, which may or may not be reversible, and wish to show that if its efficiency is greater than that of the first engine, the second law can be violated. Suppose we use this engine to remove 100 J of energy from the hot reservoir. Since we are assuming that its efficiency is greater than 40 percent, it does more than 40 J of work and rejects less than 60 J to the cold reservoir. Suppose it has an efficiency of 45 percent. Then 45 J of work is done, and 55 J of energy is rejected (Figure 19-9c). The net effect of these two engines working together (with the reversible engine operating as a refrigerator) is that 5 J of energy has been removed from the cold reservoir and changed completely into work (Figure 19-9d). This violates the Kelvin-Planck statement of the second law. Figure 19-10 illustrates this proof for general quantities of heat removed and rejected and work done. In this figure we choose the heat removed by the second engine Q_h' to be equal to that rejected by the first engine operating as a refrigerator. If the efficiency of the second engine is greater than that of the first, the work done W' is greater than the work W needed to operate the reversible engine as a refrigerator and the heat rejected Q_c' is less than that absorbed from the cold reservoir by the reversible engine. Thus the net effect of the two engines is that heat $Q_c - Q_c'$ is removed from the cold reservoir and changed completely into work. (On the other hand, if the efficiency of the second

Hot reservoir at temperature T_h

Q_h' Q_h

Ordinary engine
$\epsilon = \dfrac{W'}{Q_h'}$ W Reversible engine as refrigerator
$\epsilon = \dfrac{W}{Q_h}$

W'

$W' - W$

Q_c' Q_c

Cold reservoir at temperature T_c

Figure 19-10
Illustration of the Carnot theorem for arbitrary amounts of heat and work. The reversible engine on the right is run backward as a refrigerator, removing heat Q_c from the cold reservoir and rejecting heat Q_h to the hot reservoir while requiring work W. If the engine on the left has a greater efficiency than the reversible one, it can remove heat $Q_h' = Q_h$ and perform work W' which is greater than W. If part of this work is used to run the refrigerator, the net effect of both engines is the removal of heat $Q_c - Q_c'$ from the cold reservoir and complete conversion of this heat into work.

engine is less than that of the reversible engine, there is no contradiction of the second law of thermodynamics. The net result is that net work has been converted into internal energy in the cold reservoir.) We have shown that the efficiency of the reversible engine must be greater than or equal to the efficiency of any other engine working between the same reservoirs, which is the Carnot theorem.

A corollary to the Carnot theorem reads

All reversible engines working between the same two reservoirs have the same efficiency.

This follows from Carnot's theorem because for any two reversible engines, the theorem requires that each have an efficiency greater than or equal to the efficiency of the other. Since they cannot both have greater efficiency than the other, their efficiencies must be equal.

Carnot's theorem and corollary can also be expressed in terms of refrigerators:

No refrigerator working between two given heat reservoirs can have a greater coefficient of performance than a reversible refrigerator working between those reservoirs.

Similarly,

All reversible refrigerators working between the same two reservoirs have the same coefficient of performance.

The proof that these statements follow from the second law of thermodynamics is left as an exercise.

It is not hard to see what the cycle of a Carnot engine must be. Since the cycle is reversible, heat cannot be transferred at a temperature difference, because this is always irreversible. The engine must therefore absorb and reject heat isothermally. Figure 19-11 shows a Carnot cycle for a gas used as the working substance of a Carnot engine. We assume that the gas is originally at the temperature of the hot reservoir T_h. (If not, we can always perform an adiabatic expansion or compression until the gas is at this temperature.) The gas first expands isothermally to position 2 on the PV diagram. During this expansion the gas does some work and absorbs heat Q_h from the hot reservoir. Since this heat is absorbed isothermally and quasi-statically, the expansion is reversible (assuming no friction). If the gas were

Carnot cycle

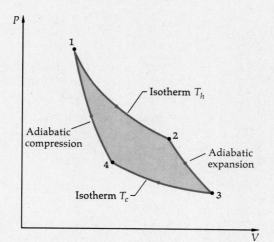

Figure 19-11
A Carnot cycle for a gas. The gas first expands isothermally from state 1 to state 2, absorbing heat from the reservoir at T_h and performing work. It then expands adiabatically until its temperature is T_c in state 3. Work is performed but no heat is absorbed or rejected. The gas is then compressed isothermally to state 4 and adiabatically back to its original state. All parts of the cycle are quasi-static. The net work performed during the cycle is indicated by the enclosed area.

ideal, the work done would equal the heat absorbed, but this is not generally true of a real gas. After the gas is removed from contact with the hot reservoir, it undergoes a quasi-static adiabatic expansion until the temperature of the gas is that of the cold reservoir T_c at position 3. Some work is done, but no heat is transferred. The gas then is compressed isothermally while it is in contact with the lower-temperature reservoir to state 4. During this compression, work is done on the gas, and heat Q_c is rejected to the reservoir. Finally, the gas is compressed adiabatically and quasi-statically until it reaches its original temperature T_h at state 1, and the cycle is completed. The net work done is indicated by the enclosed area in Figure 19-11, i.e., the area defined by the two isothermal curves and two adiabatic curves, and is equal to $Q_h - Q_c$ by the first law of thermodynamics. The efficiency of the engine can be computed if the equation of state is known so that the work can be computed under the curves in the PV diagram. We shall compute the efficiency for an ideal gas in the next section.

19-5 The Absolute Temperature Scale

The efficiency is the same for all reversible engines working between the same two heat reservoirs, whatever the working substance — ideal gas, real gas, or water. As long as the engine performs in a reversible cycle, which means absorbing and rejecting the heat isothermally (and quasi-statically) and changing its temperature adiabatically (and quasi-statically), the efficiency is the same no matter what the system is. Since the only characteristic of a heat reservoir is its temperature, the efficiency of a Carnot engine must depend only on the temperatures of the two heat reservoirs. The heats absorbed and rejected by a Carnot engine are related to the efficiency by Equation 19-2, which can be written

$$\frac{Q_c}{Q_h} = 1 - \epsilon_R$$

where we have added the subscript R to indicate that ϵ_R is the efficiency of a reversible engine. Thus Q_c/Q_h must also be a function only of the temperatures of the reservoirs. We use this result to define an absolute temperature scale, defining the ratio of absolute temperatures of the heat reservoirs by

$$\frac{T_c}{T_h} = \frac{Q_c}{Q_h} \qquad\qquad 19\text{-}4$$

Absolute temperature defined

To use this definition to measure the ratio of two temperatures we would have to set up a reversible engine to operate between two reservoirs with the two temperatures and carefully measure the heats absorbed from or rejected to those reservoirs in each cycle of the engine.

Equation 19-4 defines only the ratio of two absolute temperatures. The temperature scale is completely determined by choosing one fixed point, as was done for the other temperature scales. We define the absolute temperature of the triple point of water to be 273.16 K. In terms of the absolute temperatures of the heat reservoirs the efficiency of a Carnot engine is

$$\epsilon_R = 1 - \frac{T_c}{T_h} \qquad\qquad 19\text{-}5$$

Efficiency of a Carnot engine

This definition of an absolute temperature scale is completely independent of the properties of any materials. Although such a scale
might seem impossible to use in practice, that is not the case. At very
low temperatures, where the ideal-gas scale cannot be defined, temperatures are actually measured by performing a Carnot cycle as carefully as possible between the two heat reservoirs and measuring the
heats Q_h and Q_c. In the temperature range in which the ideal-gas temperature scale can be defined, the absolute and ideal-gas temperature
scales are identical, as will be shown in Example 19-1.

Example 19-1 The Carnot cycle shown in Figure 19-11 is performed
using an ideal gas. Show that the ratio of the heat rejected to the heat
absorbed equals the ratio of the ideal-gas temperatures of the heat reservoirs.

The equation of state of an ideal gas is $PV = nR\theta$, where we now
use θ for the ideal-gas temperature to avoid assuming the result we
wish to prove. We want to show that $Q_c/Q_h = \theta_c/\theta_h$. We first consider
the isothermal expansion from state 1 to state 2. Since the internal
energy of an ideal gas does not change if the temperature is constant,
the work done by the gas in this isothermal expansion equals the heat
absorbed Q_h. The work done is

$$W_{1-2} = \int_1^2 P \, dV = \int_1^2 \frac{nR\theta_h}{V} \, dV = nR\theta_h \ln \frac{V_2}{V_1}$$

Then

$$Q_h = nR\theta_h \ln \frac{V_2}{V_1}$$

Similarly, the heat rejected to the cold reservoir Q_c equals the work
done *on* the gas in the isothermal compression at temperature θ_c from
state 3 to state 4. This work is of the same magnitude as that done *by*
the gas if it expands from state 4 to state 3. The heat rejected is thus

$$Q_c = nR\theta_c \ln \frac{V_3}{V_4}$$

The ratio of these heats is then

$$\frac{Q_c}{Q_h} = \frac{\theta_c \ln (V_3/V_4)}{\theta_h \ln (V_2/V_1)} \qquad\qquad 19\text{-}6$$

We can relate the volumes V_1, V_2, V_3, and V_4 using the equation for the
adiabatic expansion and compression derived in Section 18-8. Along
these curves we have

$$PV^\gamma = \text{constant}$$

If we eliminate the pressure using the equation of state, we have

$$\frac{nR\theta}{V} V^\gamma = \text{constant}$$

or

$$\theta V^{\gamma-1} = \text{constant} \qquad\qquad 19\text{-}7$$

Applying Equation 19-7 to states 2 and 3 connected by the adiabatic
expansion, we have

$$\theta_h V_2^{\gamma-1} = \theta_c V_3^{\gamma-1} \qquad\qquad 19\text{-}8$$

Similarly for the states 4 and 1 connected by the adiabatic compression,

$$\theta_h V_1^{\gamma-1} = \theta_c V_4^{\gamma-1} \qquad\qquad 19\text{-}9$$

Dividing Equation 19-8 by Equation 19-9 gives

$$\left(\frac{V_2}{V_1}\right)^{\gamma-1} = \left(\frac{V_3}{V_4}\right)^{\gamma-1} \qquad\qquad 19\text{-}10$$

and so $V_2/V_1 = V_3/V_4$ and $\ln (V_2/V_1) = \ln (V_3/V_4)$. After canceling the logarithmic terms in Equation 19-6, our result is proved:

$$\frac{Q_c}{Q_h} = \frac{\theta_c}{\theta_h} \qquad\qquad 19\text{-}11$$

Comparing this result with Equation 19-4, we see that the ratio of the ideal-gas temperatures of the two reservoirs is the same as the ratio of the absolute temperatures. Since both temperature scales have the same fixed value, 273.16 K for the temperature of the triple point of water, the ideal-gas and absolute temperatures are equal everywhere the ideal-gas temperature scale is defined.

Example 19-2 An engine works between reservoirs at 400 and 300 K, extracting 100 cal from the hot reservoir during each cycle. What is the greatest efficiency possible for this engine, and how much work can it perform during each cycle?

A Carnot engine working between these reservoirs has efficiency

$$\epsilon_R = 1 - \frac{T_c}{T_h} = 1 - \frac{300 \text{ K}}{400 \text{ K}} = 0.25 = 25\%$$

The work done by a Carnot engine in one cycle is found from $\epsilon_R = W/Q_h$. Then $W = \epsilon_R Q_h = (0.25)(100 \text{ cal}) = 25$ cal. Any other engine working between these two reservoirs will have efficiency less than 25 percent because of irreversibility due to friction, non-quasi-static processes, etc.

Example 19-3 What is the greatest possible coefficient of performance of a refrigerator working between reservoirs at 400 and 300 K?

From Example 19-2 we saw that a Carnot engine performed 25 cal of work for each 100 cal of heat removed from the upper reservoir. It must therefore reject 75 cal to the lower-temperature reservoir. When this engine is run as a refrigerator, it removes 75 cal from the reservoir at 300 K and rejects 100 cal to the reservoir at 400 K. The coefficient of performance of a Carnot refrigerator between these reservoirs is thus

$$\eta = \frac{Q_c}{W} = \frac{75 \text{ cal}}{25 \text{ cal}} = 3$$

Any other refrigerator will have a smaller coefficient of performance because of irreversibility due to friction, non-quasi-static processes, etc.

Questions

6. Why do power-plant designers try to increase the temperature of the steam fed to engines as much as possible?

7. Will the efficiency of the engines in a power plant be improved if more cooling water is used so that the temperature rise in the cooling water is smaller?

Power Plants and Thermal Pollution

Laurent Hodges
Iowa State University

The scientist's interest in a heat engine is focused primarily on the work obtained from a given heat input. Society, however, is also interested in the waste heat output. When it leads to undesirable effects, it is called *thermal pollution*.

The largest heat engines in modern society—those from which thermal pollution can be the most damaging—are the steam engines used in electric power plants to drive an ac generator and produce electricity. About 85 percent of the electricity in the United States is produced by such steam engines, the other 15 percent being generated by water power in hydroelectric plants.

The operation of a steam electric power plant is explained in Figure 1. The *heat source* is usually either the combustion of a fossil fuel (coal, oil, or natural gas) or the fission of uranium 235; occasionally geothermal power or the combustion of solid wastes are used. The *boiler* heats water, converting it into high-temperature, high-pressure steam. A nuclear power plant has a reactor core in which water is heated into steam (boiling-water reactor, or BWR) or into pressurized water (pressurized-water reactor, or PWR); in the PWR, heat is then transferred to a steam cycle in a heat exchanger. Steam expands and cools as it passes through the *turbine,* converting heat energy into the mechanical energy of a rotating shaft. A *generator* converts the mechanical energy into electric energy (alternating current). The *condenser* cools the steam exhausted from the turbine and reduces its pressure, thereby increasing the efficiency of the power plant.

Typical temperatures and efficiencies for steam electric plants are shown in Table 19-1. The average efficiency for all power plants in the United States is about 34 percent, but the best fossil-fuel plants have about 40 percent efficiency and many smaller or older plants have efficiencies of 25 percent or

Figure 1
Major components of a steam electric power plant (schematic).

Table 19-1

Typical higher and lower temperatures and efficiencies for steam electric power plants

	Temperature, °C		Efficiency, %	
	High	Low	Carnot	Actual
Large fossil-fuel plant	380	40	52	40
Boiling-water reactor	285	40	44	34
Pressurized-water reactor	315	40	47	34

less. The efficiencies of BWR and PWR nuclear plants are about 34 percent, but those of some experimental nuclear plants (cooled by gas or liquid sodium) are closer to 40 percent.

Existing power plants must dispose of waste heat amounting to twice the electrical energy generated. A popular method, *once-through cooling*, involves passing water from a river or lake through the condenser once and then returning it at a warmer temperature. This works well only if adequate water is present. Many plants of 1000 MW_e (e = electric power) are being built today, sometimes several at one location. Even on a large river the resulting temperature rise may be significant: a 3000 MW_e–9000 MW_t (t = thermal power) installation using a flow of 120 m^3/sec (the average yearly minimum flow of the Missouri River at its mouth) would cause a 12°C rise by its 6000 MW of waste heat.

Thermal pollution is the assortment of undesirable effects resulting from waste heat. Although the temperature changes produced in a river by once-through cooling may not be as large as natural daily or seasonal fluctuations, possible adverse ecological effects include greater growth of bacteria, pathogens, or undesirable blue-green algae or physiological and behavioral effects on aquatic life (such as fish). As an example, large-mouth bass acclimated to 30°C show a 50 percent mortality rate within 72 h if the water is warmed to 34°C.

Warmer water also contains less dissolved oxygen necessary for aquatic life or for the decomposition of organic wastes; e.g., the dissolved oxygen at saturation in water is 11.3 mg/ℓ at 10°C and 6.6 mg/ℓ at 40°C. Warmer water is also less viscous, permitting faster deposition of the sediment load, which can affect aquatic food supplies.

Most of the cooling water used in the United States is used by electric power plants. The rapid growth of electric energy consumption, averaging 7 percent annually for many decades, has led to greater use of alternatives to once-through cooling. One of these is the cooling pond, really a private lake, but the land requirements for such a pond are often too expensive to consider.

The most common alternative, the cooling tower, transfers the waste heat to the atmosphere (Figure 2). Usually these are evaporative towers, which use the heat to evaporate water. Evaporative cooling towers are either large hyperbolic types, with a natural draft, or mechanical-draft (fan) types. Nonevaporative cooling towers, which transfer heat to the air by heat exchangers, are expensive but may be needed in moist climates. At ordinary temperatures the evaporation of water requires 580 cal/gm, and so the water requirements are much less than in once-through cooling, although the water is consumed in the process. The evaporated water can cause fog, increased precipitation, and (in certain climates) icing of nearby roads, and the cooling tower and its plume may be blots on the landscape, so that evaporative towers are not a completely satisfactory answer to the problem of thermal pollution.

Figure 2
Hyperbolic natural-draft evaporative cooling towers at the Fort Martin Power Station, Fairmont, West Virginia. (*The Marley Company, Mission, Kansas.*)

19-6 Entropy

We used the zeroth law of thermodynamics to define a new thermodynamic state function, the temperature, which is a measure of the hotness or coldness of a system. In the molecular picture, the temperature measures the average kinetic energy of translation of the molecules. Similarly the first law allowed us to define the internal-energy function U. Now we consider a new thermodynamic state function, the entropy S, related to the second law of thermodynamics. The existence of this state function is less obvious than that of T and U, and it is less easily related to the second law than they were to the zeroth and first laws. The reason is that the second law is more complicated than the first and zeroth laws in that it describes processes that do *not* occur. We shall first look at the special case of an ideal gas. With this simple system it is easy to show that there is a new state function which is related to the heat absorbed by the system and to the temperature at which the heat is absorbed.

Consider an arbitrary quasi-static reversible process in which an ideal gas absorbs an amount of heat dQ. According to the first law, dQ is related to the internal-energy change dU and the work done $dW = P\,dV$ by

$$dQ = dU + P\,dV$$

For our ideal gas we can substitute nRT/V for P from the equation of state and write the change in internal energy in terms of the heat capacity $dU = C_v\,dT$:

$$dQ = C_v\,dT + nRT\,\frac{dV}{V} \qquad \text{19-12}$$

When the system goes from state 1 to state 2, we must know the path followed in order to calculate the total heat added Q. This is clear mathematically from the fact that we cannot integrate Equation 19-12. There is no problem with the first term because $C_v = dU/dT$ is a function of temperature only. The integration of this term gives the change in internal energy. The problem is with the second term, the work done by the gas. This point was discussed in Chapter 18. Both the heat added and the work done depend on the path. Thus neither is a state function. However, if we divide each term in Equation 19-12 by T, we can integrate both terms on the right-hand side:

$$\frac{dQ}{T} = C_v\,\frac{dT}{T} + nR\,\frac{dV}{V} \qquad \text{19-13}$$

Even if C_v is not constant, it can depend only on T, so that whatever function of T it is, the first term can be integrated. Thus if the system is carried from state 1 to state 2 along any quasi-static path, we can find the sum (integral) of dQ/T. It is in fact given by

$$\int_1^2 \frac{dQ}{T} = C_v\,\ln\frac{T_2}{T_1} + nR\,\ln\frac{V_2}{V_1} \qquad \text{19-14}$$

assuming C_v to be constant. The right side of Equation 19-14 depends only on the states 1 and 2 and not on the path. If in addition the path is reversible, we get the same magnitude for the sum of dQ/T by reversing the path and going from state 2 to 1, except that the sum is the negative of that obtained from state 1 to state 2. Thus if we travel along one reversible path from 1 to 2 and back along another reversible path from state 2 to 1, the sum of dQ/T is zero. This implies that there is a state function whose change is given by dQ/T. We call this function the *entropy S*:

$$\Delta S = S_2 - S_1 = \int_1^2 \frac{dQ_R}{T} \qquad\qquad 19\text{-}15$$

or

$$dS = \frac{dQ_R}{T} \qquad\qquad 19\text{-}16$$

We have used the subscript R on dQ to remind us that the heat must be absorbed reversibly.

A Carnot cycle is an example of a reversible closed path. During the isothermal expansion the entropy change of the gas is

$$\int_1^2 \frac{dQ_R}{T_h} = \frac{1}{T_h} \int dQ = \frac{Q_h}{T_h} \qquad\qquad 19\text{-}17$$

During the reversible adiabatic expansion and compression the entropy change is zero because no heat is absorbed or rejected by the gas. During the isothermal compression the entropy change is

$$\int \frac{dQ_R}{T_c} = \frac{1}{T_c} \int dQ_R = \frac{Q_c}{T_c} \qquad\qquad 19\text{-}18$$

This is negative because, according to our sign convention, dQ is negative when heat leaves the system. (We now return to our original sign convention, in which the heat out of a system is negative, and use Q_c for the heat *absorbed* from the cold reservoir. Since heat is actually rejected, Q_c is negative.) Since the total entropy change must be zero for a complete cycle, we have

$$\frac{Q_h}{T_h} + \frac{Q_c}{T_c} = 0 \qquad\qquad 19\text{-}19$$

or

$$\frac{-Q_c}{Q_h} = \frac{T_c}{T_h}$$

This is the same as the defining equation (19-4) for the ratio of absolute temperatures except for the sign of Q_c because now the symbols Q_h and Q_c stand for heat absorbed and are negative if heat is rejected.

Although we have been considering a special system, the ideal gas, it can be shown that the sum of dQ_R/T for any system undergoing a *reversible* change is independent of path and depends only on the initial and final states. (See the general proof in Section 19-10.) Thus Equations 19-15 and 19-16, which define the entropy function, are general. It is important to understand, however, that only for a reversible process is $\int dQ/T$ independent of path. For an irreversible process, change in the entropy of the system will not be given by $\int dQ/T$. However, since entropy is a state function, we can find the entropy change in the system undergoing an irreversible process from state 1 to state 2 by considering any *reversible* process connecting the same two states and computing $\int dQ_R/T$.

Example 19-4 An ideal gas undergoes a free adiabatic expansion from volume V_1 to volume V_2. What is the change in entropy of the gas?

As we have discussed previously, the final energy of the gas is the same as the initial energy, and the final temperature is the same as the initial temperature. *During the free expansion,* we cannot describe the gas as having a temperature or internal energy since the gas does not pass through equilibrium states. In this process no heat is absorbed or rejected, so that $\Delta Q = 0$ for the whole process. We might expect, therefore, that there is no entropy change, but this is not correct. The change in entropy is *not* given by the sum of dQ/T because this process is not reversible. We cannot even define T during the process. However, changes in a state function are independent of the process. The entropy change, $S_2 - S_1$, is independent of the process connecting states 1 and 2. We can compute $S_2 - S_1$ by considering a *reversible* process connecting these two states. Any reversible process will do since the entropy change does not depend on the process. The convenient process for this example is a quasi-static isothermal expansion from volume V_1 to V_2. Since the temperature is constant for this reversible process, the entropy change is just Q/T, where Q is the total heat absorbed. This heat absorbed equals the work done by the gas (since the internal energy is constant). Thus

$$Q = W = \int_1^2 P\,dV = nRT \int_1^2 \frac{dV}{V} = nRT \ln \frac{V_2}{V_1} \qquad 19\text{-}20$$

The entropy change is

$$S_2 - S_1 = \frac{Q}{T} = \frac{nRT \ln (V_2/V_1)}{T} = nR \ln \frac{V_2}{V_1} \qquad 19\text{-}21$$

This same result is obtained by integrating Equation 19-13 with $dT = 0$. The entropy of the system increases even though no heat is transferred. In order for the entropy of a gas to decrease by a free adiabatic "expansion" the final volume would have to be less than the initial volume. An adiabatic free contraction never occurs in nature.

Example 19-5 The melting point of a substance is T_0, and its latent heat is L. What entropy change takes place when mass m of the substance melts at this temperature?

To compute the entropy change we must consider a reversible process for the melting and calculate the integral of dQ_R/T for that process. Such a process would be the melting produced by putting the solid material into contact with a reservoir whose temperature is only very slightly higher so that melting would proceed very slowly. The process could be reversed by lowering the reservoir temperature very slightly, causing any molten material to freeze again. As we have seen, for heat conduction to be reversible the temperature difference must be vanishingly small.

From Equation 19-15,

$$\Delta S = \int \frac{dQ_R}{T} = \frac{1}{T_0} \int dQ_R = \frac{mL}{T_0}$$

The temperature T_0 is removed from the integral since the melting takes place at the constant temperature T_0. The remaining integral $\int dQ_R$ is just the heat required to melt mass m, or mL.

To illustrate our result numerically, we calculate the entropy increase when 100 gm of mercury melts at $-39°C$ ($= 234$ K) and atmospheric pressure. The latent heat of fusion is 2.8 cal/gm:

$$S = \frac{mL}{T_0} = \frac{(100 \text{ gm})(2.8 \text{ cal/gm})}{234 \text{ K}} = 1.2 \text{ cal/K}$$

Questions

8. Does the entropy change in a physical system passing from state 1 to state 2 depend on the path taken between those states?

9. Is it possible to choose the value of the entropy of a system at some particular state and thereafter assign a value to the entropy of the system for every other state?

10. Give an example of a system whose entropy decreases with time.

11. A gas undergoes a quasi-static adiabatic expansion to twice its original volume. How does its entropy change?

19-7 Entropy Change of the Universe

We have shown that the entropy state function exists for an ideal gas,[1] and we have seen how to calculate changes in entropy for a system, but it is not immediately evident what use this function is. In this section we calculate the entropy change of the universe for several processes, where by universe we mean the system and surroundings, e.g., heat reservoirs and other systems, which interact with the system. In these examples we shall often be calculating the entropy change of a heat reservoir, which is easy to do.

The state of a heat reservoir is determined by its internal energy and its temperature, which, by definition, is constant. If a heat reservoir absorbs heat Q by some reversible process, the entropy of the reservoir increases by Q/T, where T is the temperature of the reservoir. If it absorbs the heat in an irreversible process, we need only replace the irreversible process by a reversible process to calculate the change in entropy. Again the entropy increases by Q/T. If the reservoir gives up heat Q to the system or another reservoir, the entropy of the reservoir *decreases* by Q/T since Q is now leaving the reservoir.

Let us first consider the entropy change of the universe for a reversible process. A system absorbs heat Q from a reservoir at temperature T; since the process is reversible, the absorption must occur isothermally. The system has an increase in entropy of Q/T, and the reservoir has a decrease in entropy by the same amount. Thus the total change in the entropy of the system plus reservoir is zero. No matter how many systems and reservoirs take part in a reversible process, for each heat absorption or rejection the entropy change of the reservoir is exactly the negative of that for the system. Thus *the entropy change of the universe is zero for a reversible process.*

Example 19-6 Show that the entropy change of the universe is zero during a Carnot cycle.

The entropy change of the engine after a complete cycle must be zero because the engine is back in its original state. We thus have only to calculate the entropy change of the two heat reservoirs. The hot reservoir gives up heat Q_h at temperature T_h; its entropy therefore decreases. The entropy change of the hot reservoir is

$$\Delta S_h = -\frac{|Q_h|}{T_h} \qquad\qquad 19\text{-}22$$

---

[1] The proof for a general system is given in Section 19-10.

The cold reservoir absorbs heat Q_c at temperature T_c. Its entropy change is positive, given by

$$\Delta S_c = + \frac{|Q_c|}{T_c} \qquad \qquad \text{19-23}$$

Since this is a Carnot cycle, the heats $|Q_h|$ and $|Q_c|$ are related by Equation 19-4:

$$\frac{|Q_c|}{|Q_h|} = \frac{T_c}{T_h}$$

If we substitute $|Q_h|T_c/T_h$ for $|Q_c|$ in Equation 19-23, we have

$$\Delta S_c = + \frac{|Q_h|}{T_h}$$

Thus the sum of ΔS_c and ΔS_h is zero.

We now consider the entropy change of the universe for processes that are irreversible. In Section 19-10 we show that for a general irreversible process the entropy change of the universe must be positive. Here we shall merely investigate some typical irreversible processes and show in each case that the entropy change of the universe must be greater than zero.

Let us consider heat conduction from a hot reservoir to a cold reservoir; i.e., an amount of heat Q is conducted from a reservoir at temperature T_h to a reservoir at temperature T_c. The entropy of the hot reservoir decreases by Q/T_h, and that of the cold reservoir increases by Q/T_c. Since T_c is less than T_h, the increase in the entropy of the cold reservoir is greater in magnitude than the decrease in the entropy of the hot reservoir. Thus the total entropy change of the universe is greater than zero and is given by

$$\Delta S_u = \frac{Q}{T_c} - \frac{Q}{T_h} > 0 \qquad \qquad \text{19-24}$$

Next let us consider a process that is irreversible because mechanical energy is lost to internal energy due to friction or other dissipative forces—say a block with kinetic energy E_k sliding along a rough table until it is stopped by friction. We assume for simplicity that the table is large so that it can be considered a reservoir. (This is not important to the conclusion but it simplifies the calculation.) Because of the work done by friction, the internal energy of the table (and block if it is not much smaller than the table) and air surroundings increases by the amount E_k. The entropy change of the table and air surroundings is the same as if heat $Q = E_k$ were transferred reversibly. Thus the entropy change of the table and air is $+ E_k/T$. This is the entropy change of the universe:

$$\Delta S_u = + \frac{E_k}{T} > 0 \qquad \qquad \text{19-25}$$

Finally we consider the third kind of irreversible process discussed in Section 19-3, a non-quasi-static process, again taking the free adiabatic expansion of an ideal gas. Since no heat is transferred and no work done, the surroundings suffer no change whatsoever. We have already calculated the entropy change of the gas in Example 19-4. This is also the entropy change of the universe. According to Equation 19-21, the entropy change of the gas and universe is $nR \ln (V_2/V_1)$, which is positive because V_2 is greater than V_1.

In each of these typical irreversible processes the change in entropy of the universe is greater than zero. The reason is that a negative change in entropy of the universe would violate the second law. For example, in heat conduction, the entropy change of the universe could be negative only if the heat left the cold reservoir and entered the hot reservoir, violating the Clausius statement of the second law of thermodynamics. Similarly, in the conversion of internal energy into mechanical energy, the entropy change would be negative if heat were removed from the surroundings and converted completely into mechanical energy, violating the Kelvin-Planck statement of the second law. We have already discussed the fact that the irreversibility of the free adiabatic expansion is connected with the second law. If the entropy of the universe were to decrease in a free adiabatic "expansion," the gas would have to contract to a smaller volume by itself.

As a result we have a new statement of the second law of thermodynamics, equivalent to the other statements:

For any process, the entropy change of the universe must be greater than or equal to zero. The entropy change is equal to zero only if the process is reversible.
Second law (entropy form)

The entropy function gives us a numerical measure of the irreversibility of a given process. Suppose, for example, we consider a real attempt to produce an isothermal quasi-static reversible expansion of a gas. We can compute the entropy change of the heat reservoir by measuring the heat which leaves the reservoir. The entropy of the gas can be found in tables. If there is friction in the piston and some turbulence in the gas (because the piston has a slight acceleration or because the expansion happens too fast for the gas to remain near equilibrium states), the total entropy change will not be zero but some positive number. If we reduce the friction or make the process more nearly quasi-static, the total entropy change will be less. We thus have a numerical measure of the degree of irreversibility of any given process.

19-8 Entropy and the Availability of Work

Let us consider a single heat reservoir at temperature T. If there are no other heat reservoirs around and no systems at a lower temperature which can be used as heat reservoirs, we cannot use any of the internal energy of the reservoir for the performance of work. The internal energy of the reservoir is unavailable. To extract some of it and do work requires a lower-temperature reservoir or system to accept the heat rejected. The second law states that we cannot remove some of the internal energy and convert it completely into work; in other words, the conversion of some of the internal energy completely into work would decrease the entropy of the universe, which is not allowed.

Whenever an irreversible process occurs, some energy is made unavailable for use as work which was available before the process took place. For the block sliding along the rough table, if it were not for the mechanical energy lost because of friction, the original kinetic energy of the block could be used to do some useful work, e.g., lifting a weight or turning a generator. After the block's energy has been converted into internal energy of the surroundings, all this potential for doing work is lost. The entropy increase of the universe in this case is $E_k/T = \Delta S_u$. The energy which is made unavailable in this case is $T \, \Delta S_u$, where T is the temperature of the available reservoir and ΔS_u is the increase in entropy of the universe. This is a general result.

In an irreversible process in which the entropy change of the universe is ΔS_u *some energy becomes unavailable for use to perform work. The amount of energy made unavailable equals* $T \, \Delta S_u$, *where* T *is the temperature of the lowest-temperature reservoir available.*

In another example, the free adiabatic expansion of an ideal gas, we assume that we have one reservoir at the temperature of the gas, which is the same after the expansion as before. The entropy change when the gas expands freely from volume V_1 to volume V_2 is $nR \ln (V_2/V_1)$, as calculated in Example 19-4. Since there are no effects on the surroundings, this is the entropy change of the universe. According to the result stated above, the energy made unavailable for doing work is T times this entropy change, or $nRT \ln (V_2/V_1)$. This is just the work that could have been done if we had allowed the gas to expand isothermally and quasi-statically. During this reversible expansion, the gas does work $W = nRT \ln (V_2/V_1)$, as previously calculated, while absorbing an equal amount of heat from the reservoir. Thus the result of the irreversible adiabatic free expansion is the loss of the opportunity of converting this internal energy of the reservoir into work.

In our final example the loss of ability to do work occurs in the irreversible process of conducting heat Q from a hot reservoir to a cold reservoir. The entropy change of the universe for this process was computed in the previous section:

$$\Delta S_u = \frac{Q}{T_c} - \frac{Q}{T_h}$$

Q is *not* the amount of energy made unavailable for work because, according to the second law, we could not have removed this heat from the hot reservoir and changed it completely into work. However, some of this energy could have been converted into work, the amount depending on the efficiency of the heat engine used. The greatest amount of work that can be obtained from the heat energy Q is the amount done using a Carnot engine. The efficiency of a Carnot engine is

$$\epsilon_R = 1 - \frac{T_c}{T_h}$$

The work that can be done with heat Q entering a Carnot engine is thus

$$W = \epsilon_R Q = Q - \frac{QT_c}{T_h} = T_c \left(\frac{Q}{T_c} - \frac{Q}{T_h} \right)$$

Again the work that could have been done is just the temperature of the lowest-temperature heat reservoir available T_c times the entropy change of the universe.

19-9   Molecular Interpretation of Entropy

There is a fundamental difference between the internal energy of a system and the macroscopic mechanical energy of a system. Figure 19-12 shows a schematic illustration of the velocities of the molecules in a system whose center of mass is at rest. If the system is a solid, the molecules are vibrating about their equilibrium positions; if it is a gas, the molecules move throughout the volume. In either case, the velocity vectors $\mathbf{u}_i$ point in all directions. In a gas the velocity of any one molecule points in a direction unrelated to that of any other molecule unless the two molecules have just collided. The total linear momentum and the total angular momentum of the system are zero. The average kinetic energy associated with each degree of freedom is $\frac{1}{2}kT$ per molecule. Suppose we now add a velocity v in the x direction to the velocity of each molecule. The center of mass of the system then moves with speed v in the x direction, and the total kinetic energy is the sum of the center-of-mass energy $\frac{1}{2}Mv^2$ and the energy relative to the center of mass,

Figure 19-12
In a body at rest, the velocities of the molecules $\mathbf{u}_i$ are randomly directed.

$$E_k = \tfrac{1}{2}Mv^2 + \Sigma \tfrac{1}{2}m_i u_i{}^2 \qquad\qquad 19\text{-}26$$

where M is the total mass. The two terms in the expression for kinetic energy are quite different. The motion giving rise to the term $\frac{1}{2}Mv^2$ is an ordered motion. Each molecule has the same component v in the same direction. Thus all the molecules are moving together. The center of mass moves with velocity v. This *mechanical kinetic energy* has nothing to do with the internal energy or the temperature. On the other hand, the second term (the energy relative to the center of mass) is the original internal kinetic energy. It is associated with the random, or *disordered*, motion of the molecules. The ordered part of the total energy of the system, the mechanical kinetic energy, can easily be changed completely into other forms, e.g., potential energy or rotational kinetic energy (we could attach a string to the moving system and use it to lift a weight or turn a wheel, which could even generate electric energy).

On the other hand, the disordered part of the total energy, the internal energy, cannot easily be converted into mechanical energy. As we have seen, only part of this energy can be extracted and converted into work, which requires that some of the random motion be converted into ordered motion. We can do this with a heat engine, say with gas as the working substance. We place the gas system in contact with the system whose internal energy we want to convert into mechanical energy, calling this system the reservoir, in keeping with previous usage. If the gas is at a slightly lower temperature, some internal energy is transferred to the gas by conduction. In the molecular picture of conduction the molecules in the walls of the gas enclosure are vibrating with less average energy than those of the walls of the reservoir because the gas temperature is lower. When the two systems are in contact, some of the kinetic energy of vibration of molecules in the reservoir walls is transferred to kinetic energy of the molecules in the gas-container walls. (This energy is quickly brought to equilibrium with the potential energy of vibration of the wall molecules.) Now the gas container is not in equilibrium with the gas molecules, and when the gas molecules collide with the container walls, energy is transferred on the average to the gas molecules. These molecules in turn collide with others and transfer kinetic energy, until the temperature of the gas and wall has increased to that of the reservoir. The pressure of the gas is thus increased. This random internal energy can now be transferred into ordered mechanical energy by letting the gas at higher pressure expand against a piston. Since the piston can move in only one direction, the transfer of energy of the gas molecules to energy of the piston amounts to transfer of random kinetic energy of the gas molecules to ordered motion of the piston.

We have seen in this chapter that ordered mechanical energy is generally more useful than unordered internal energy. The second law of thermodynamics can be stated: The entropy of the universe always increases (or in reversible processes remains the same). This can be related to the fact that molecular motion always tends toward disordered rather than ordered motion. Imagine a block with mechanical kinetic energy $\frac{1}{2}Mv^2$ moving toward a wall and making an inelastic collision, thereby changing the kinetic energy into internal kinetic energy of disordered motion of the molecules in the block, wall, and air. Our experience and intuition tell us that the reverse will not happen. Disordered motion of the molecules will never spontaneously change into ordered motion. Thus entropy increase is an increase in the disordered motion of the molecules in the universe. When the entropy of the universe reaches its maximum value, no more processes can occur (except absolutely reversible processes). Heat will not be conducted because the whole universe will be at the same temperature. No more energy will be available to perform work.

Questions

12. When a gas is compressed isothermally, it gives up heat and its entropy decreases. In what sense is the motion of the gas molecules more orderly after compression?

13. When you pick up a spilled deck of cards and put them in a neat pile, you have increased the order of the universe. What compensating decrease in order accompanied your action?

14. One liter each of oxygen gas and nitrogen gas are initially in separate containers at room temperature and atmospheric pressure. Then the containers are connected, allowing the gases to mix. What happens to the entropy of the system consisting of the two gases?

Optional

19-10 Proof that Entropy Exists and that the Entropy of the Universe Can Never Decrease

The general proof of the existence of the entropy function is not difficult but rather abstract. It is interesting, however, because it shows that entropy and its increase are directly related to the second law of thermodynamics. We first state and prove the *Clausius inequality*.

Let a system undergo any cycle in which it absorbs and rejects heat from any number of different heat reservoirs, performs positive or negative work, and returns to its original state. Let ΔQ_i be the heat absorbed from the ith reservoir at temperature T_i. If heat is rejected to the reservoir, ΔQ_i will be negative. The Clausius inequality states that the sum of $\Delta Q_i/T_i$ is less than or equal to zero:

$$\sum \frac{\Delta Q_i}{T_i} \le 0 \qquad\qquad 19\text{-}27$$

To prove this inequality we use an auxiliary reservoir at temperature T_0 and as many Carnot cycles as we need. We run a Carnot engine between each reservoir and our auxiliary reservoir so that the original reservoir is returned to its original state. That is, if ΔQ_i was removed from the ith reservoir, we run a Carnot engine between it and the auxiliary reservoir to replace ΔQ_i in the ith reservoir. The heat extracted from the auxiliary reservoir when the engine runs between it and the ith reservoir is given by Equation 19-4,

$$\Delta Q_{0i} = \frac{T_0}{T_i} \Delta Q_i \qquad\qquad 19\text{-}28$$

We note that if ΔQ_i is positive, ΔQ_{0i} is positive, and if ΔQ_i is negative, ΔQ_{0i} is negative, indicating that heat was put into the auxiliary reservoir. The total heat *extracted* from the auxiliary reservoir is

$$\Delta Q_0 = \sum \Delta Q_{0i} = T_0 \sum \frac{\Delta Q_i}{T_i}$$

After this procedure all the original reservoirs are in their original state. The net result is that heat ΔQ_0 has been extracted from the auxiliary reservoir and, according to the first law of thermodynamics, an equal amount of work has been done. The second law of thermodynamics tells us that ΔQ_0 must be less than or equal to zero, so that either no heat was extracted or negative work was done and heat was put into the auxiliary reservoir. Thus $\Delta Q_0 \le 0$ and therefore

$$\sum \frac{\Delta Q_i}{T_i} \le 0$$

The Clausius inequality has thus been proved. If the system undergoes a reversible cycle, absorbing heat ΔQ_i from the ith reservoir, the equality in Equation 19-27 holds. We can see this by merely reversing the cycle, putting ΔQ_i into each reservoir, which merely changes the sign of ΔQ_i, giving

$$-\sum \frac{\Delta Q_i}{T_i} \le 0$$

The only possibility for a reversible cycle is thus

$$\sum \frac{\Delta Q_i}{T_i} = 0 \qquad \text{reversible cycle} \qquad 19\text{-}29$$

We are now in position to define entropy for a general system. We let the system move reversibly from state A to state B along one path and move back to state A along a different *reversible* path. Any number of reservoirs can be used. According to Equation 19-29, we have

$$\underset{\substack{A \\ \text{path 1}}}{\overset{B}{\sum}} \frac{\Delta Q_i}{T_i} + \underset{\substack{B \\ \text{path 2}}}{\overset{A}{\sum}} \frac{\Delta Q_i}{T_i} = 0$$

Since each path is reversible, we have

$$\sum_{\substack{B \\ \text{path 2}}}^{A} \frac{\Delta Q_i}{T_i} = -\sum_{\substack{A \\ \text{path 2}}}^{B} \frac{\Delta Q_i}{T_i}$$

so that

$$\sum_{\substack{A \\ \text{path 1}}}^{B} \frac{\Delta Q_i}{T_i} - \sum_{\substack{A \\ \text{path 2}}}^{B} \frac{\Delta Q_i}{T_i} = 0 \quad \text{or} \quad \sum_{\substack{A \\ \text{path 1}}}^{B} \frac{\Delta Q_i}{T_i} = \sum_{\substack{A \\ \text{path 2}}}^{B} \frac{\Delta Q_i}{T_i}$$

Thus the sum $\Sigma(\Delta Q_i/T_i)$ is the same for all reversible paths connecting state A to state B. Figure 19-13 shows an arbitrary quasi-static process for a gas. In order to make this process reversible, we must absorb heat isothermally. We do so by using a very large number of heat reservoirs at different temperatures and following the alternative path, consisting of a series of isotherms and adiabatic paths. In the limit of an infinite number of reservoirs, we can make this alternate path approach the original path as closely as desired. Thus for a general reversible path we need a large number of heat reservoirs, and the heat absorbed from each is very small. We thus write dQ_R for ΔQ_i and indicate the sum by an integral sign, leaving off the subscripts i

$$\int_{\text{path 1}} \frac{dQ_R}{T} = \int_{\text{path 2}} \frac{dQ_R}{T}$$

Since the integral of dQ_R/T is independent of path between two states, it can depend only on the states. We thus can define a new function of state, the entropy S, by

$$S_B - S_A = \int_A^B \frac{dQ_R}{T}$$

where again we put a subscript R on dQ to remind us that the process must be reversible. For a very small change we can write

$$dS = \frac{dQ_R}{T}$$

These are the same as Equations 19-15 and 19-16.

We now consider a system which undergoes an *irreversible* change from state A to state B and then is brought back to state A by a reversible process. This cycle is indicated in Figure 19-14, where the wiggly line indicates the irreversible process, for which we cannot plot a curve because the system is not in equilibrium. According to the Clausius inequality, we have for the complete cycle

$$\underset{\substack{\text{Irreversible} \\ \text{path}}}{\int_A^B \frac{dQ}{T}} + \int_B^A \frac{dQ_R}{T} < 0 \qquad\qquad \text{19-30}$$

or

$$\underset{\substack{\text{Irreversible} \\ \text{path}}}{\int_A^B \frac{dQ}{T}} < -\int_B^A \frac{dQ_R}{T} = \int_A^B \frac{dQ_R}{T}$$

where we have used

$$\int_A^B \frac{dQ_R}{T} = -\int_B^A \frac{dQ_R}{T}$$

Figure 19-13
An arbitrary path can be approximated as accurately as desired by a series of alternating quasi-static adiabatic and isothermal paths.

Figure 19-14
An irreversible transition from A to B followed by a reversible transition from B to A.

for the *reversible* path. By our definition of entropy we have

$$S_B - S_A = \int_A^B \frac{dQ_R}{T}$$

Thus

$$\int_A^B \frac{dQ}{T} < S_B - S_A$$

Irreversible
path

In particular, if a system is isolated from its surroundings, no heat can enter or leave. When an isolated system changes from state A to state B, $dQ = 0$. Then if the process is irreversible,

$$0 < S_B - S_A \qquad S_B > S_A$$

We can consider the universe to be an isolated system. We have thus shown that the entropy of the universe always increases for any irreversible process. The defining equation (19-15) for entropy when applied to the universe with $dQ_R = 0$ shows that for reversible processes the entropy change of the universe is zero.

Review

A. Define, explain, or otherwise identify:

Heat engine, 464

Efficiency of a heat engine, 465

Kelvin-Planck statement of the
   second law, 465

Clausius statement of the
   second law, 466

Coefficient of performance, 466

Equivalent statements, 467

Reversible and irreversible
   processes, 469

Carnot engine, 470

Carnot cycle, 472

Absolute temperature scale, 473

Carnot efficiency, 473

Entropy, 478

Available energy, 483

Ordered and disordered motion, 485

B. True or false:

1. Work can never be converted completely into heat.

2. Heat can never be converted completely into work.

3. All heat engines have the same efficiency.

4. It is impossible to transfer a given quantity of heat from a cold reservoir to a hot reservoir.

5. The coefficient of performance of a refrigerator cannot be greater than 1.

6. All reversible processes are quasi-static.

7. All quasi-static processes are reversible.

8. All Carnot cycles are reversible.

9. The entropy of a system can never decrease.

10. The entropy of the universe can never decrease.

Exercises

Section 19-1, Heat Engines and the Second Law of Thermodynamics

1. An engine with 20 percent efficiency does 100 J of work in each cycle. (*a*) How much heat is absorbed in each cycle? (*b*) How much heat is rejected?

2. An engine absorbs 100 cal of heat and does 120 J of work in each cycle. (*a*) What is its efficiency? (*b*) How much heat is rejected in each cycle?

3. An engine absorbs 100 cal and rejects 60 cal in each cycle. (*a*) What is its efficiency? (*b*) If each cycle takes 0.5 sec, find the power output of this engine in watts.

4. A refrigerator absorbs 5000 cal from a cold reservoir and rejects 8000 cal. (*a*) Find the coefficient of performance Q_c/W of the refrigerator. (*b*) The refrigerator is reversible and is run as a heat engine ($Q_h = 8000$ cal; $Q_c = 5000$ cal). What is its efficiency?

5. An engine with an output of 200 W has an efficiency of 30 percent. It works at 10 cycles/sec. How much heat is absorbed and how much rejected in each cycle?

Section 19-2, Equivalence of the Kelvin-Planck and Clausius Statements

6. Suppose that there are two statements A and B, each of which may be either true or false. (*a*) List the four possible combinations of truth or falsity for the two statements. (*b*) What possibilities are left if it is shown that if A is true, B must also be true? Does this prove that the statements are equivalent? (*c*) Suppose that it is also shown that if A is false, B is false. Do these two results prove that the two statements are equivalent?

7. A certain engine running at 30 percent efficiency draws 200 cal of heat from a hot reservoir. Assume the Clausius statement to be false and show how this engine combined with a perfect refrigerator can violate the Kelvin-Planck statement of the second law.

8. A certain refrigerator takes in 500 J of heat from a cold reservoir and rejects 800 J to a hot reservoir. Assume that the Kelvin-Planck statement is false and show how a perfect engine working with this refrigerator can violate the Clausius statement.

Section 19-3, Reversibility

9. Show that the reversibility of the following processes would violate the second law of thermodynamics: (*a*) an object is dropped from a height H to the ground and comes to rest; (*b*) a car traveling at high speed brakes to a stop; (*c*) a hot object is placed in a cold-water bath, and the system comes to an equilibrium temperature.

Section 19-4, The Carnot Engine

10. A reversible engine working between reservoirs at temperatures T_h and T_c has efficiency of 30 percent. When working as a heat engine it rejects 140 cal of heat to the cold reservoir. A second engine working between the same two reservoirs also rejects 140 cal to the cold reservoir. Show that if the second engine has an efficiency of greater than 30 percent, the two engines can work together to violate the Kelvin-Planck statement of the second law.

11. A reversible engine working between reservoirs at temperatures T_h and T_c has an efficiency of 20 percent. When working as a heat engine, it does 100 J of work in each cycle. A second engine working between the same two reservoirs also does 100 J of work in each cycle. Show that if the efficiency of the second engine is greater than 20 percent, the two engines can work together to violate the Clausius statement of the second law.

12. A Carnot engine works between two heat reservoirs as a refrigerator. It removes 100 cal from the cold reservoir and rejects 150 cal to the hot reservoir during each cycle. Its coefficient of performance is $\eta = Q_c/W = 100/50 = 2$. (*a*) What is the efficiency of the Carnot engine when working as a heat engine

between the same two reservoirs? (*b*) Show that no other engine working as a refrigerator between the same two reservoirs can have a coefficient of performance greater than 2.

Section 19-5, The Absolute Temperature Scale

13. A Carnot engine works between two heat reservoirs at temperatures $T_h = 300$ K and $T_c = 200$ K. (*a*) What is its efficiency? (*b*) If it absorbs 100 cal from the hot reservoir during each cycle, how much work does it do? How much heat does it reject during each cycle? (*c*) What is the coefficient of performance of this engine when working as a refrigerator between these two reservoirs?

14. An engine works between the steam point 100°C and the ice point 0°C. What is its greatest possible efficiency?

15. Which has the greater effect on increasing the efficiency of a Carnot engine, a 5-K increase in the temperature of the hot reservoir or a 5-K decrease in the temperature of the cold reservoir (in each case keeping the other reservoir fixed)?

16. A refrigerator works between 0°C and room temperature of 20°C. (*a*) What is the greatest possible coefficient of performance? (*b*) If the refrigerator is to be cooled to −10°C, what is the greatest coefficient of performance assuming the same room temperature of 20°C?

17. An engine draws heat from a reservoir at a temperature of 100°C. If the engine is to be 40 percent efficient, what is the warmest possible temperature of the cold reservoir?

18. An engine is designed to exhaust heat to the atmosphere at $t = 20°C$. What is the least possible temperature of the upper reservoir if the engine is to have an efficiency of 20 percent?

Section 19-6, Entropy, and Section 19-7, Entropy Change of the Universe

19. Two moles of an ideal gas at $T = 400$ K expand quasi-statically and isothermally from an initial volume of 40 ℓ to a final volume of 80 ℓ. (*a*) Find the entropy change of the gas. *Hint:* Use Equation 19-21. (*b*) What is the entropy change of the universe for this process?

20. The gas in Exercise 19 is taken from the same initial state ($T = 400$ K, $V_1 = 40 \ell$) to the same final state ($T = 400$ K, $V_2 = 80 \ell$) by a non-quasi-static process. (*a*) Is the entropy change of the gas the same as, greater than, or less than that found in Exercise 19? (*b*) Is the entropy change of the universe greater than, less than, or the same as that found in Exercise 19?

21. A system absorbs 200 cal of heat reversibly from a reservoir at 300 K and rejects 100 cal reversibly to a reservoir at 200 K as it moves from state A to state B. During this process, which is quasi-static, 50 cal of work is done by the system. (*a*) What is the change in internal energy of the system? (*b*) What is the change in entropy of the system? (*c*) What is the change in entropy of the universe? (*d*) If the system went from state A to state B by a non-quasi-static process, how would your answers to parts (*a*), (*b*), and (*c*) differ?

22. A system absorbs 300 cal from a reservoir at 300 K and 200 cal from a reservoir at 400 K. It returns to its original state, doing 100 cal of work and rejecting 400 cal of heat to a reservoir at temperature T. (*a*) What is the entropy change of the system for the complete cycle? (*b*) If the cycle is reversible, what is the temperature T?

23. Two moles of an ideal gas originally at $T = 400$ K and $V = 40 \ell$ undergoes a free adiabatic expansion to twice its volume. What is (*a*) the entropy change of the gas and (*b*) the entropy change of the universe?

24. A 5-kg block is dropped from rest at a height of 6 m above the ground. It hits the ground and comes to rest. The block, ground, and atmosphere are all at 300 K initially. What is the entropy change of the universe for this process?

25. If 500 cal of heat is conducted from a reservoir at 400 K to one at 300 K, what is the entropy change of the universe?

26. A 200-kg block of ice at 0°C is placed in a large lake. The temperature of the lake is just slightly higher than 0°C, and the ice melts. (a) What is the entropy change of the ice? (b) What is the entropy change of the lake? (c) What is the entropy change of the universe (ice plus lake)?

27. Calculate the entropy change of 1 gm of water at 100°C when it changes to steam under standard conditions.

Section 19-8, Entropy and the Availability of Work

28. A heat engine works in a cycle between reservoirs at 400 and 200 K. The engine absorbs 1000 cal of heat from the hot reservoir and does 200 cal of work in each cycle. (a) What is the efficiency of this engine? (b) Find the entropy change of the engine, each reservoir, and of the universe for each cycle. (c) What is the efficiency of a Carnot engine working between the same two reservoirs? How much work could be done by a Carnot engine in each cycle if it absorbed 1000 cal from the hot reservoir? (d) Show that the difference in the work done by the Carnot engine and the original engine is $T_c \Delta S_u$, where ΔS_u is that calculated in part (b).

29. A refrigerator works between two reservoirs at 200 and 400 K. In each cycle it absorbs 200 cal from the cold reservoir and rejects 600 cal to the hot reservoir. (a) How much work is put into the refrigerator in each cycle? (b) What is the entropy change of the universe in each cycle? (c) If a Carnot engine is used as a refrigerator between these two reservoirs, how much heat would be rejected if it absorbed 200 cal from the cold reservoir? How much work is needed? *Hint:* The easiest way to find these is to use the fact that the entropy change of the universe is zero for a reversible process. (d) Show that the additional work required by the first refrigerator is $T_h \Delta S_u$, where ΔS_u is that found in part (b). (e) The additional work required by the first engine is not completely wasted because the energy is stored in the hot reservoir. Find how much of this additional work could be recovered using a Carnot engine between the reservoirs and show that the amount of work completely wasted by the first engine is equal to $T_c \Delta S_u$.

30. How much of the 500 cal of heat taken from a reservoir at 400 K in Exercise 25 could have been converted into work using a cold reservoir at 300 K?

31. One mole of an ideal gas first undergoes an adiabatic free expansion from $V_1 = 12.3 \, \ell$, $T_1 = 300$ K to $V_2 = 24.6 \, \ell$, $T_2 = 300$ K. It is then compressed isothermally and quasi-statically back to its original state. (a) What is the entropy change of the universe for the complete cycle? (b) How much work is wasted in this cycle? (c) Show that the work wasted is $T \Delta S_u$.

32. Which process is more wasteful: (a) a block moving with 500 J of kinetic energy being slowed to rest by friction (temperature of the atmosphere = 300 K) or (b) 1000 J of heat conducted from a reservoir at 400 K to one at 300 K? *Hint:* How much of the 1000 J of heat could be converted into work in an ideal situation? (c) Compute the entropy change of the universe in each case.

Section 19-9, Molecular Interpretation of Entropy

33. Air consists mainly of diatomic molecules (N_2 and O_2) which can rotate about two axes. The total kinetic energy of 1 mole of air can be written $E_k = \frac{1}{2}Mv_{CM}^2 + \frac{5}{2}RT$, where $M = 29.0$ gm/mole is the molecular weight and v_{CM} is

the velocity of the center of mass. Which has more total energy, 1 mole of air at rest at 25°C or 1 mole of air at 20°C with a wind speed of 10 m/sec (about 22.4 mi/h)? Which could be used to run a windmill?

Problems

1. An engine operates with a working substance which is 1 mole of an ideal gas with $C_v = \frac{3}{2}R$ and $C_p = \frac{5}{2}R$. The cycle begins at $P_1 = 1$ atm and $V_1 = 24.6\ \ell$. The gas is heated at constant volume to $P_2 = 2$ atm. It then expands at constant pressure until $V_2 = 49.2\ \ell$. During these two steps, heat is absorbed. The gas is then cooled at constant volume until its pressure is again 1 atm. It is then compressed at constant pressure back to its original state. During the last two steps heat is rejected. All steps are quasi-static and reversible. (a) Indicate this cycle on a PV diagram. Find the work done, the heat added, and the internal-energy change for each step of the cycle. (b) Find the efficiency of this cycle.

2. An engine using 1 mole of an ideal gas with $C_v = \frac{5}{2}R$ and $C_p = \frac{7}{2}R$ performs a cycle consisting of three steps: (1) an adiabatic expansion from initial pressure of 2.64 atm and volume 10 ℓ to a final pressure of 1 atm and volume 20 ℓ, (2) a compression at constant pressure to its original volume of 10 ℓ, (3) heating at constant volume to its original pressure of 2.64 atm. Find the efficiency of this cycle.

3. The behavior of a gasoline engine can be approximated by an ideal cycle called an *Otto cycle* (Figure 19-15). The steps are tabulated. (a) Compute the heat input and the heat output and show that the efficiency can be written

$$\epsilon = 1 - \frac{T_e - T_b}{T_d - T_c}$$

where T_e is the temperature of state e, etc. (b) Using the relation for adiabatic expansion or compression $TV^{\gamma-1} = $ constant, show that $\epsilon = 1 - (V_1/V_2)^{\gamma-1}$, where $V_1 = V_c = V_d$ and $V_2 = V_b = V_e$. (c) The ratio V_2/V_1 is called the *compression ratio*. Find the efficiency of this cycle for a compression ratio of 8 (use $\gamma = 1.5$ for ease in calculation). (Compression ratios much greater than this cannot be achieved in real engines because of preignition problems.) (d) Explain why the efficiency of a real gasoline engine might be much less than that calculated in part (c).

Figure 19-15
Otto cycle for Problem 3.

No.	Step	Action	Comment
1	$a \rightarrow b$	Air intake at constant pressure	Number of moles varies from 0 to n; volume varies from 0 to V_b, given by $P_0V_b = nRT_b$, where T_b = temperature of outside air
2	$b \rightarrow c$	Adiabatic compression to pressure P_c, temperature T_c, and volume V_c	
3	$c \rightarrow d$	Heating at constant volume	To approximate effect of explosion in gasoline engine
4	$d \rightarrow e$	Adiabatic expansion to volume $V_e = V_b$	The power stroke in the cycle
5	$e \rightarrow b$	Cooling at constant volume until pressure is again atmospheric pressure P_0	
6	$b \rightarrow a$	Exhaust of gas at constant pressure	

4. An engine using 1 mole of an ideal gas initially at $V_1 = 24.6\ \ell$ and $T = 400$ K performs in a cycle which consists of four steps: (1) isothermal expansion at $T = 400$ K to twice its volume, (2) cooling at constant volume to $T = 300$ K, (3) isothermal compression to its original volume, and (4) heating at constant volume to its original temperature of 400 K. Assume that $C_v = 5$ cal/K. Sketch the cycle on a PV diagram and calculate its efficiency.

5. A steam engine takes in superheated steam at 270°C and discharges condensed steam from its cylinder at 50°C. Its efficiency is 30 percent. (a) How does this efficiency compare with the best efficiency possible for these temperatures? (b) If the useful power output of the engine is 200 kW, how much heat does the engine discharge to the surroundings in 1 h?

6. One mole of an ideal gas for which $\gamma = 1.4$ is carried through a Carnot cycle. The high temperature and pressure are 400 K and 4 atm; the low temperature and pressure are 300 K and 1 atm. (a) What is the volume when $T = 400$ K and $P = 4$ atm? (b) What are the values of PV and PV^γ for the isothermal and adiabatic lines through this point? (c) What is the volume when $T = 300$ K and $P = 1$ atm? (d) What are the values of PV and PV^γ for the isothermal and adiabatic lines through this point? (e) Make an accurate plot of the Carnot cycle.

7. If two adiabatic curves on a PV diagram intersected, a cycle could be completed using an isothermal path between the two adiabatics, as shown in Figure 19-16. Show that such a cycle could violate the second law of thermodynamics.

Figure 19-16
Problem 7.

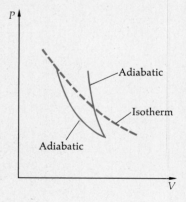

8. (a) Show that the coefficient of performance of a Carnot refrigerator working between two reservoirs at temperatures T_h and T_c is related to the efficiency of a Carnot engine by $\eta = T_c/\epsilon T_h$. (b) Show that the coefficient of performance of a Carnot refrigerator can be written

$$\eta = \frac{T_c}{T_h - T_c}$$

(c) Which gives the greater increase in coefficient of performance of a refrigerator, increasing the temperature of the cold reservoir by 5 K or decreasing the temperature of the hot reservoir by 5 K?

9. The cooling compartment of a refrigerator and its contents are at 5°C. Their heat capacity is 20 kcal/°C. The refrigerator exhausts heat to the room at 25°C. What is the smallest power motor which could be used to operate the refrigerator if it is to reduce the temperature of the interior and the contents by 1°C in 1 min?

10. (a) Show that if the Clausius statement of the second law were not true, the entropy of the universe could decrease. (b) Show that if the Kelvin-Planck statement of the second law were not true, the entropy of the universe could decrease. (c) An alternative statement of the second law is that the entropy of the universe cannot decrease. Have you just proved that this statement is equivalent to the Clausius and Kelvin-Planck statements?

11. Equation 19-14 gives the entropy change of an ideal gas when the volume and temperature increase reversibly. Use this equation and the relation $TV^{\gamma-1}$ = constant to show explicitly that the entropy change is zero for an adiabatic expansion from state V_1T_1 to state V_2T_2.

12. A substance is heated reversibly at constant pressure from temperature T_1 to temperature T_2. Show that the entropy of the substance increases by the amount $\Delta S = C_p \ln (T_2/T_1)$, where C_p is the heat capacity at constant pressure. Is this also the entropy change of the substance if the heating is done irreversibly?

13. A 100-gm piece of ice at 0°C is placed in an insulated container with 100 gm of water at 100°C. (a) When equilibrium is established, what is the

final temperature of the water? (*b*) Find the entropy change of the universe for this process (see Problem 12). (Ignore the heat capacity of the container.)

14. A block of metal has a heat capacity $C_p = 100$ cal/K. It is to be heated from $T_1 = 200$ K to $T_2 = 400$ K. In Problem 12 it was shown that the entropy increase of the metal is $\Delta S = C_p \ln (T_2/T_1) = 100 \ln 2 = 69.3$ cal/K. In this problem you are to investigate the entropy change in the universe when the block is heated in several different ways. (*a*) The block originally at 200 K is placed in contact with a reservoir at temperature 400 K. How much heat is needed to raise the temperature of the block to 400 K? What is the entropy change in the reservoir when it loses this much heat? What is the entropy change of the universe for this process? (*b*) The block originally at 200 K is first placed in contact with a reservoir at 300 K until it comes to thermal equilibrium. It is then placed in contact with a reservoir at 400 K until its temperature is 400 K. Compute the entropy change of each reservoir and of the universe and compare your result with the process in part (*a*). (*c*) The block originally at 200 K is heated by first placing it in contact with a reservoir at 250 K until it comes to equilibrium. It is heated to 300 K, then to 350 K, and finally to 400 K, using successively reservoirs at 300, 350, and 400 K. Compute the entropy change of each reservoir and the entropy change of the universe for this process. Explain how reversible heating can be approximately accomplished in practice.

CHAPTER 20   Wave Pulses

Wave motion can be thought of as the transport of energy and momentum from one point in space to another without the transport of matter. In mechanical waves, e.g., water waves, waves on a string, or sound waves, the energy and momentum are transported by means of a disturbance in the medium which is propagated because the medium has elastic properties. On the other hand, in electromagnetic waves, the energy and momentum are carried by electric and magnetic fields which can propagate through vacuum. (We shall define an electric field and magnetic field in later chapters. For our study of waves, we need only say that these fields are represented by vectors, are produced by electric charges, and exert forces on other charges. These fields are similar to the gravitational field, which is produced by masses and exerts forces on other masses.)

The variety of wave phenomena observed in nature is immense. Yet in this immense variety are many features common to all kinds of waves and others shared by a wide range of wave phenomena. In the next few chapters we shall study these general properties of waves, illustrating them with different wave phenomena observed in nature.

We first consider wave motion in one dimension. As we found in our study of mechanics, much can be learned before introducing the complications of two and three dimensions. In this chapter we shall study the motion of wave pulses with examples in waves on strings and sound waves. We shall calculate the speed of these waves in terms of properties of the transmitting media by applying the laws of mechanics. We shall study the properties of harmonic waves in Chapter 21 and of standing waves in Chapter 22. In Chapter 23 we consider the superposition of waves of different frequency. The general properties of waves in two and three dimensions will be considered in Chapters 24 and 25. Chapters 26 and 27 deal with the especially important topics of light and other electromagnetic waves. Chapter 28, a brief introduction to the special theory of relativity, is a revision of newtonian mechanics of special importance for motion at great speeds. It is discussed at that point because its discovery was intimately related to research on light waves.

20-1 Wave Pulses

When a string stretched under tension is given a flip, as in Figure 20-1, the shape of the string changes in time in a regular way. The bump which is produced at the end by the flip and which travels down the string is called a *wave pulse*. It is a disturbance in the string, i.e., a distortion of the shape of the string from its normal, or equilibrium, shape. The pulse travels down the string at a definite speed which depends on the nature of the string and the tension. As it moves, the pulse usually changes shape, gradually spreading out. This effect, called *dispersion*, occurs to some extent in all waves (except electromagnetic waves in vacuum), but in many important examples the dispersion is negligible and the wave pulse travels with approximately the same shape. The fate of the pulse at the other end of the string depends on how the string is fastened at that end. If it is tied to a rigid support, the pulse will be reflected and return inverted, as in Figure 20-2. If the support is not rigid, some or all of the pulse will be absorbed or it may be reflected without inversion.

Dispersion defined

A pulse traveling down a stretched string is only one example of a wave pulse: the report of a gunshot is a wave pulse of sound; a lightning flash is a wave pulse of light; a tidal wave is a wave pulse in water.

A chief characteristic of a wave pulse is that it has a beginning and an end. It is a disturbance of limited extent. At any instant only a limited region of space is disturbed. At any point, the wave pulse passes by in a limited time. We can produce a light pulse, for example, by quickly opening and closing a shutter in front of a continuous light source. Figure 20-3a shows such a pulse with an upward and a downward bump, easily produced on a string. A wave which has many oscillations up and down, as in Figure 20-3b, is usually not called a wave

Wave pulse

Figure 20-1
Wave pulse moving to the right on a string. The change in shape of the pulse as it moves is called dispersion.

Figure 20-2
A pulse arriving at the rigid support of a stretched string is reflected and inverted.

(a)   (b)

pulse. To a good approximation such a wave can be treated as an end-less series of alternate up and down disturbances. Unlike a wave pulse of limited extent, such a wave does not spread out as it travels. This kind of wave is also common in nature. We shall study it in Chapter 21.

We can demonstrate that energy and momentum are transported by a wave pulse by hanging a weight on a string under tension, as shown in Figure 20-4, and giving the string a flip at one end. When the pulse arrives at the weight, the weight will be lifted momentarily. The action of the hand in flipping one end of the string is transmitted along the string until the weight is lifted at the other end. This is usually described by saying that the momentum introduced by the hand flip-ping the end of the string is transmitted along the string and is received by the weight. Similarly, the work done by the hand in lifting the string goes into kinetic and potential energy of the string at the pulse. (We shall calculate this energy in the string later.) This energy is transmitted along the string and is converted into work lifting the weight. Thus *both energy and momentum are transmitted by such a wave pulse.*

It is not the mass elements of the string that are transported but the *disturbance in the shape* caused by flipping one end. The mass elements of the string, in fact, move in a direction perpendicular to the string and thus perpendicular to the direction of motion of the pulse. A wave in which the disturbance is perpendicular to the direction of the wave is called a *transverse wave.* Other examples of transverse waves are any electromagnetic wave (light, radar, radio, television, etc.) produced by a vibrating charge system which produces an alternating electric and magnetic field. The electric and magnetic field vectors are perpendic-ular to the direction of propagation of the electromagnetic wave (and, as we shall see later, perpendicular to each other). Sound waves in air, on the other hand, are not transverse waves. In sound waves, a distur-bance in the pressure and density of air is set up by the vibration of a body (say a tuning fork or a violin string), and the disturbance is propagated through the air by the collisions of air molecules. The mo-tion of the air molecules is in the same direction as the propagation. Any wave in which the disturbance is parallel to the direction of prop-agation is called a *longitudinal wave.* Sound consists of longitudinal waves. A longitudinal pulse in a spring analogous to a sound pulse can be produced by suddenly compressing the spring (Figure 20-5).

Water waves are neither completely transverse nor completely longitudinal but a combination of the two. Figure 20-6 shows the mo-tion of a water particle in a water wave. The water particle moves in a

Figure 20-3
(*a*) A wave pulse may include both positive and negative displacement. (*b*) A wave with many alternating posi-tive and negative displace-ments ordinarily is not called a pulse.

Figure 20-4
Wave pulses transmit both energy and momentum, in-dicated here by the upward motion of the weight when the pulse arrives.

Waves transmit momentum and energy

Transverse and longitudinal waves defined

Figure 20-5
Longitudinal wave pulse in a spring. In a longitudinal wave, the disturbance is in the direction of motion of the wave.

Figure 20-6
Surface waves on water. The water particles on the surface move in nearly circular paths having both longitudinal and transverse components.

nearly circular path, its motion having both transverse and longitudinal components.

Questions

1. Give examples of wave pulses in nature in addition to those mentioned in the text. In each case, explain what kind of disturbance from equilibrium occurs.

2. Consider a long line of cars equally spaced by one car length and moving with the same speed. One car suddenly slows to avoid a dog and then speeds up until it is again one car length behind the car ahead. Discuss how the space between cars propagates back along the line. How is this like a wave pulse? Is there a transport of energy and momentum? Is the wave transverse or longitudinal? What does the speed of propagation depend on? (It may be useful to consider this situation in a reference frame in which all the cars are initially at rest.)

20-2   The Wave Function; Interference

Consider a pulse on a string at $t = 0$, as in Figure 20-7. The shape of the string at time $t = 0$ can be represented by some function $y = f(x)$. At some later time, the pulse is farther down the string, so that the shape at that time is some other function of x. Let us assume that the pulse does not vary in shape, i.e., is not dispersed, and introduce a new coordinate system with origin O' which moves with the speed v of the pulse. In this reference frame the pulse is stationary. The shape of the string is $y' = f(x')$ for all time. The coordinates of the two reference frames are related by

$$y = y' \quad \text{and} \quad x = x' + vt$$

Thus the displacement of the string in frame O can be written

$$y = f(x - vt) \qquad \text{wave moving right} \qquad \text{20-1}$$

This same line of reasoning for a pulse moving to the left leads to

$$y = f(x + vt) \qquad \text{wave moving left} \qquad \text{20-2}$$

In each of these expressions v is the speed of propagation of the wave. The function $y = f(x - vt)$ is called the *wave function*. For waves on a string, the wave function is the vertical displacement of the string at point x and time t. This wave function is thus a function of two variables. Analogous wave functions for sound waves are the pressure $P(x - vt)$ or a related function, the displacement from the equilibrium position of gas molecules. The wave function for electromagnetic waves is the electric field vector $\mathbf{E}(x - vt)$ or the magnetic field vector $\mathbf{B}(x - vt)$, which is related to the electric field.

Wave function defined

Figure 20-7
A wave pulse moving in the positive x direction with speed v relative to the origin O. In the primed coordinate system moving with the same speed as the pulse, the wave function is $y' = f(x')$ for all time, assuming no change in the shape of the pulse. In the unprimed system, the wave function is $y = f(x - vt)$.

Consider two pulses on a string moving in opposite directions, as in Figure 20-8. The shape of the string when they meet can be found by adding the displacements produced by each pulse separately, as in the figure. For the special case of two pulses identical except that one is inverted relative to the other (Figure 20-9) there will be one time when the pulses exactly overlap and add to zero. At this time the string is horizontal, but it is not at rest. A short time later the pulses emerge, and each continues in its original direction. Combining separate waves to produce the resultant wave is called *interference*. Interference is the characteristic property of wave motion. It occurs whenever two waves meet in the same region of space. There is no analogous situation in particle motion. Two particles never overlap or add together in this way. Interference is unique to wave motion.

If we have two pulses on a string, as in Figures 20-8 and 20-9, we cannot write the shape of the string as a simple function of either $x - vt$ or $x + vt$ alone. However, the shape is still a function of the two variables x and t. Let us write $y(x,t)$ for the wave function of the string on which there are two pulses. That is, $y(x,t)$ is the vertical displacement of the point x at time t. We can treat the phenomenon of interference mathematically by noting that if we call the wave function for the single pulse moving to the right $y_1(x - vt)$ and that for the pulse moving to the left $y_2(x + vt)$, the total wave function is just the algebraic sum of the individual wave functions,

$$y(x,t) = y_1(x - vt) + y_2(x + vt) \qquad 20\text{-}3$$

For example, if we have two pulses of the same shape but one inverted, there will be some time $t = t_1$ when they overlap. At this time $y_1(x - vt_1) = -y_2(x + vt_1)$, so that $y(x,t_1) = 0$.

The mathematical addition of two wave functions to form the resulting wave function, as in Equation 20-3, is called *superposition*. The statement that the resultant wave function is the algebraic sum of the individual wave functions is called the *principle of superposition*. In most wave phenomena small wave pulses obey this principle. Electromagnetic waves in vacuum always obey it. For other wave phenomena, the principle of superposition does not hold for very large pulses; i.e., the wave function produced by the interference of two very large pulses is not merely the algebraic sum of the individual wave pulses. Such waves are called *nonlinear* and are not studied in this book.

If one of the two pulses is inverted relative to the other, as in Figure 20-9, the algebraic addition when the pulses meet amounts to an arithmetic subtraction. The resultant pulse is smaller than the larger pulse and perhaps smaller than either. The pulses tend to cancel each other when they overlap. Such interference is called *destructive interference*. (Complete cancellation occurs only if the shapes are identical.)

On the other hand, if the displacement of the two pulses is in the same direction, the resultant pulse when they overlap is greater than either pulse by itself. This is called *constructive interference*.

Figure 20-8
Two wave pulses moving in opposite directions on a string. The shape of the string when the pulses meet can be found by adding the displacements of each separate pulse. This kind of wave superposition is called constructive interference.

Figure 20-9
Two pulses having opposite displacements traveling in opposite directions on a string. Here the algebraic addition of the displacements of the separate pulses amounts to a subtraction of the magnitudes. This kind of wave superposition is called destructive interference.

Questions

3. When two waves moving in opposite directions interfere, does either impede the progress of the other?

4. Can you give an example where the principle of superposition is not obeyed in the interference of waves?

20. Calculate the speed of sound waves in helium gas ($M = 4$ gm/mole) and compare it with the rms speed of helium molecules. (Take $T = 300$ K and $\gamma = 1.67$ for helium.)

21. The speed of sound in mercury is 1450 m/sec. What is the bulk modulus for mercury ($\rho = 13.6 \times 10^3$ kg/m³)?

Section 20-5, Reflection and Transmission of Pulses

22. A pulse is moving 1 cm/sec to the right on a 10-cm string (Figure 20-16). Assume that the string is fixed at both ends and that there is no loss upon reflection. (*a*) When is the next time the string will have the shape shown? (*b*) Which way will the pulse be moving the next time the string has the shape shown?

23. The motion described in Exercise 22 is periodic, i.e., repeats itself after some time T. Write a general expression for the period in terms of the length of the string L and the pulse speed v. Does the period depend on the initial position of the pulse?

24. A pulse is moving at 1 cm/sec to the right on a 10-cm string with its maximum originally 2 cm from the left end (Figure 20-16). Assume that the left end of the string is fixed but the right end is attached to a very light thread so that it is free to move and there is no loss upon reflection. (*a*) When is the next time the string will have the shape shown? (*b*) Which way will the pulse be moving at that time? (*c*) When is the next time the string will have the shape shown *and* the pulse moving to the right?

25. The motion in Exercise 24 is periodic. Write a general expression for the period of this motion in terms of the length of the string L and the pulse speed v.

26. A pulse of the shape shown in Figure 20-18 is moving to the right at 1 cm/sec along a string which is fixed at the right end. Sketch the shape of the string at 5, 6, 7, 8, and 9 sec. *Hint:* At 5 sec the leading edge of the pulse has just reached the end of the string. Sketch an inverted image pulse to the right of the end of the string. After each additional second, the real pulse moves to the right 1 cm, and the image pulse moves 1 cm to the left. The shape of the string is found by algebraic addition of these pulses.

27. Repeat Exercise 26 for the right end of the string attached to a very light thread so that it is free to move. (In this case the image pulse is not inverted.)

Problems

1. A common rule of thumb for deciding the distance to a lightning flash is to begin counting when the flash is observed and stop when the thunder clap is heard. The number of seconds counted is then divided by 5 to get the distance in miles. Why is this justified? What is the velocity of sound in miles per second? How accurate is this procedure? Is the correction for the time taken for the light to reach you important? (The speed of light is about 3×10^8 m/sec.)

2. A method for measuring the speed of sound using an ordinary watch (with a second hand) is to stand some distance from a large flat wall and clap your hands rhythmically in such a way that the echo from the wall is heard halfway between each two claps. Show that the speed of sound is given by $v = 4LN$, where L is the distance to the wall and N is the number of claps per unit time. What is a reasonable value for L for this experiment to be feasible? (If you have access to a flat wall outdoors somewhere, try this method and compare your result with the standard value.)

3. A man drops a stone from a high bridge and hears it strike the water below exactly 4 sec later. (*a*) Estimate the distance to the water on the assumption that the travel time for the sound to reach the man is negligible. (*b*) Improve

your estimate by using your result from part (*a*) for this distance to estimate the time for sound to travel this distance. Then calculate the distance the rock falls in 4 sec minus this time. (*c*) Calculate the exact distance and compare with your previous estimates.

4. (*a*) Compute the derivative of the speed of a wave on a string with respect to the tension dv/dT and show that the differentials dv and dT obey $dv/v = \frac{1}{2}dT/T$. (*b*) A wave moves with speed 300 m/sec on a wire which is under tension of 500 N. Using dT to approximate the change in tension, find how much the tension must be changed to increase the speed to 312 m/sec.

5. Compute the derivative of the velocity of sound with respect to the absolute temperature and show that the differentials dv and dT obey $dv/v = \frac{1}{2}dT/T$. Use this to compute the percentage change in the velocity of sound when the temperature changes from 0 to 27°C. If the speed of sound is 331 m/sec at 0°C, what is it (approximately) at 27°C? How does this approximation compare with an exact calculation?

6. A coiled spring such as a Slinky is stretched to a length L. It has a force constant k and mass m. Show that the velocity of longitudinal compression waves along the spring is given by $v = L\sqrt{k/m}$. Show that this is also the velocity of transverse waves along the spring if the natural length of the spring is much less than L.

7. A heavy rope 3 m long is attached to the ceiling and allowed to hang freely. (*a*) Show that the speed of transverse waves in the rope is independent of its mass and length but does depend on the distance y from the bottom according to the formula $v = \sqrt{gy}$. (*b*) If the bottom end of the rope is given a sudden sideways displacement, how long does it take the resulting wave pulse to go to the ceiling, reflect, and return to the bottom of the rope?

8. If a loop of chain is spun at high speed, it will roll like a hoop without collapsing. Consider a chain of linear mass density μ which is rolling without slipping at a high speed v_0. (*a*) Show that the tension in the chain is $T = \mu v_0^2$. (*b*) If the chain rolls over a small bump, a transverse wave pulse will be generated in the chain. At what speed will it travel along the chain? (*c*) How far around the loop (in degrees) will a transverse wave pulse travel in the time the hoop rolls through one complete revolution?

CHAPTER 21   Harmonic Waves in One Dimension

An important special kind of wave function is a sine or cosine function, such as

$$y(x,t) = y_0 \sin k(x - vt) \qquad\qquad 21\text{-}1a$$

where k is called the *wave number* and y_0 is the *amplitude*. This function can also be written

$$y(x,t) = y_0 \sin (kx - kvt) = y_0 \sin (kx - \omega t) \qquad\qquad 21\text{-}1b$$

where

$$\omega = kv \qquad\qquad 21\text{-}2$$

is called the *angular frequency*. This type of wave, called a *harmonic wave,* can be produced, for example, by attaching one end of a stretched string to a tuning fork which vibrates with simple harmonic motion at angular frequency ω in a direction perpendicular to the string. In this case, $y(x,t)$ is the displacement of the string at position x and time t.

We can produce harmonic sound waves by vibrating a piston or loudspeaker cone with simple harmonic motion, causing the air molecules next to the piston or speaker to oscillate with simple harmonic motion about their equilibrium position. These molecules collide with neighboring molecules, causing them to oscillate. If we replace $y(x,t)$ and y_0 in Equation 21-1 with the displacement $s(x,t)$ and the maximum displacement s_0, the equation describes the displacement of the molecules from their equilibrium positions as a function of x and t. These displacements, however, are along the x axis, the direction of propagation of the wave.

Harmonic waves have one unusual property that makes them particularly important. As we mentioned in the last chapter, wave pulses change their shape as they propagate; i.e., they are dispersed, or spread out, as their energy and momentum are absorbed. Harmonic waves, however, do not change their shape even when they are propagated in a highly dispersive medium. The only thing that happens

Harmonic wave defined

No dispersion for harmonic waves

to a harmonic wave is that the amplitude y_0 may decrease as the wave is propagated.

The proof that harmonic waves do not change shape is beyond the scope of this text, but we can see why this is an important feature. In general, the shape of a wave changes as it progresses, and the definition of its speed becomes problematical. What point in the changing wave shape can be chosen as the typical one whose speed is the wave speed? There is no unambiguous answer. For harmonic waves, however, the shape is constant. Any point on the wave can be chosen as the one whose speed is the wave speed v. Indeed, it is only for harmonic waves that the wave speed v can be precisely defined.

For this reason any detailed treatment of waves with other shapes and propagating in dispersive media is carried out by resolving those waves into a superposition of harmonic waves. The mathematical technique used, called *Fourier analysis,* is applied in virtually every branch of physical science and engineering. Although we shall not discuss Fourier analysis in detail, we mention it because its frequent practical applications are a chief reason for studying harmonic waves. (The infinite train of alternating crests and valleys of a harmonic wave may otherwise seem rather artificial.)

Importance of harmonic waves

Harmonic waves are also important because many cases occur in nature where a harmonic wave shape is a good approximation to the true wave shape. For example, the waves corresponding to a single note played on a musical instrument may contain from around 30 up to several thousand successive crests and valleys. Over much of its length such a pulse wave is very much like a segment of a harmonic wave.

From our study of simple harmonic motion it should be clear that that we could just as well choose a cosine function in Equation 21-1 since the sine and cosine functions differ only in phase, $\sin \theta = \cos (\theta - \pi/2)$. We also could have reversed kx and ωt in Equation 21-1 since $\sin (kx - \omega t) = \sin (\omega t - kx + \pi)$. We have omitted a constant phase in Equation 21-1 for simplicity.

21-1   Wavelength, Frequency, and Velocity of Harmonic Waves

Figure 21-1 shows the shape of a harmonic wave at some instant t_0. This figure could be obtained by taking a snapshot of a harmonic wave on a string. The wavelength λ is the distance between two successive crests, i.e., the distance in space within which the wave function repeats itself at a given time. The shape of this curve is obtained from Equation 21-1 by setting the time equal to a constant t_0. Then

Wavelength defined

$$y = y_0 \sin (kx - \omega t_0) \qquad\qquad 21\text{-}3$$

Figure 21-1
Harmonic wave at some instant in time. λ is the wavelength and y_0 is the amplitude.

We can simplify the appearance of this equation by noting that the quantity ωt_0 is merely a phase constant; calling it δ, we have

$$y = y_0 \sin (kx - \delta) \qquad\qquad 21\text{-}4$$

We can use Equation 21-4 to relate the wavelength λ to the wave number k. Let the position of one wave crest be x_1 and the position of the next crest be x_2. In the distance $x_2 - x_1 = \lambda$ the wave function repeats itself. Thus the argument of the sine function $kx - \delta$ changes by 2π:

$$(kx_2 - \delta) - (kx_1 - \delta) = 2\pi$$

$$k(x_2 - x_1) = 2\pi$$

or

$$k\lambda = 2\pi$$

The wavelength λ and the wave number k are related by

$$k = \frac{2\pi}{\lambda} \qquad \lambda = \frac{2\pi}{k} \qquad\qquad 21\text{-}5$$

The wave number k is 2π times the number of waves per unit length.

If we look instead at the motion of one point on the string in time, we see that it is simple harmonic motion. Setting $x = x_0$ in Equation 21-1, we have

$$y(x_0,t) = y_0 \sin (kx_0 - \omega t) = y_0 \sin (\omega t - \delta_1)$$

where $\delta_1 = kx_0 + \pi$ is again just a phase constant. The amplitude of this simple harmonic motion is y_0, and the angular frequency is ω. The period T and the frequency f are related to the angular frequency in the usual way:

$$T = \frac{2\pi}{\omega} \qquad\qquad 21\text{-}6$$

and

Period and frequency defined

$$f = \frac{1}{T} = \frac{\omega}{2\pi} \qquad\qquad 21\text{-}7$$

There is a simple relation between the frequency f, the wavelength λ, and the velocity v of a harmonic wave. Consider, for example, vibrating the end of a string with frequency f for a time t. In this time the number of waves generated is $N = ft$. The first wave generated travels a distance vt. The ratio of this distance to the number of waves in this distance is the wavelength λ. Thus

$$\lambda = \frac{vt}{N} = \frac{vt}{ft} = \frac{v}{f}$$

or

$$v = f\lambda \qquad\qquad 21\text{-}8$$

This relation can also be obtained by combining Equation 21-2 with Equations 21-5 and 21-7:

$$\omega = kv \qquad 2\pi f = \frac{2\pi}{\lambda} v$$

or

$$v = f\lambda$$

Example 21-1 A stretched string is vibrated by a tuning fork which oscillates with a frequency of 60 Hz. Waves are produced with wavelength 10 cm. How far does a wave travel in 3 sec?

In 3 sec, $3 \times 60 = 180$ waves are produced with wavelength 10 cm. The first wave has traveled $180(10 \text{ cm}) = 18$ m. The velocity of the waves is

$$v = f\lambda = (60 \text{ sec}^{-1})(10 \text{ cm}) = 600 \text{ cm/sec} = 6 \text{ m/sec}$$

Questions

1. How do two harmonic waves of the same amplitude, frequency, and wavelength differ if their phase difference is π? 2π? 3π?

2. How is the wave number k of a harmonic wave related to the number of wave crests that lie in a length L along the direction of wave propagation?

3. In time Δt how many wave crests pass a given point if the wave frequency is f?

4. When a harmonic wave is transmitted across the boundary between two media with different wave speeds, the frequency of the wave does not change. Explain why.

5. A harmonic wave strikes a boundary and is both reflected and transmitted. The reflected wave is inverted. Is the wavelength of the transmitted wave greater or less than that of the original wave?

21-2 Polarization

In any transverse wave, the vibration is perpendicular to the direction of propagation of the wave and can therefore be resolved into rectangular components in the plane perpendicular to the direction of propagation. For example, in a wave propagating in the x direction along a string, the vibration of each element of the string is in the yz plane. If the vibration of each element of the string is along a line, the wave is said to be *linearly polarized.* The harmonic wave given by Equation 21-1 is linearly polarized in the y direction. In this wave, the string vibrates in the xy plane. Linear polarization is also called *plane polarization.* A harmonic wave propagating in the x direction and polarized in the z direction would be represented by an equation similar to 21-1 with y replaced by z.

Linear, or plane, polarization

There are other kinds of polarization of transverse waves. If one end of a string is moved with constant speed in a circle, a wave will be propagated along the string in which each element of the string moves in a circle. Such a wave is called a *circularly polarized wave.* A general harmonic wave propagating in the x direction has both y and z vibrational components, which can be written

Circular polarization

$$y = y_0 \sin (kx - \omega t)$$

$$z = z_0 \sin (kx - \omega t + \delta)$$

21-9

where δ is the phase difference between the two components. Such a wave is said to be polarized if the phase difference is constant. If the phase difference is zero, the wave is linearly polarized along the line making an angle θ with the z axis given by $\tan \theta = y/z = y_0/z_0$. If the phase is $\pi/2$, we can write $z = z_0 \sin (kx - t + \frac{1}{2}\pi) = z_0 \cos (kx - \omega t)$.

General definition of polarization

Then the y and z components of the vibration are related by

$$\frac{y^2}{y_0{}^2} + \frac{z^2}{z_0{}^2} = \sin^2{(kx - \omega t)} + \cos^2{(kx - \omega t)} = 1 \qquad \text{21-10}$$

This is the equation of an ellipse. Such a wave is said to be *elliptically polarized*. Circular polarization is a special case of elliptical polarization with $y_0 = z_0$.

Elliptical polarization

Most waves produced by a single source, e.g., those produced by vibrating one end of a string, are polarized. Waves produced by many sources are usually unpolarized. A light wave, for example, is usually produced by millions of atoms acting independently. The electric field for a light wave propagating in the x direction can be resolved into y and z components at any instant, but the phase difference δ varies in a random way because there is no correlation between the electric field vectors produced by the different atoms. Such a light wave is unpolarized.

Since there is only one possible direction of vibration for a longitudinal wave, namely, along the direction of propagation, polarization has no meaning for a longitudinal wave.

Questions

6. How could you produce unpolarized waves on a string?

7. Discuss the polarization of water waves on the surface of a lake.

21-3 Harmonic Sound Waves

We can produce harmonic sound waves in one dimension by vibrating a piston with simple harmonic motion against an air column enclosed in a long narrow tube. The motion of the piston produces in the nearby air mass a displacement which is transmitted to other air masses in the tube by molecular collisions. Let us write $s(x,t)$ for the displacement of a tiny volume of the gas from its equilibrium position. If the piston vibrates with simple harmonic motion of angular frequency ω, the displacement $s(x,t)$ will be a harmonic wave with the same angular frequency and with wave number k related to the angular frequency and the velocity of the wave by Equation 21-2. We can write the displacement function

$$s(x,t) = s_0 \sin{(kx - \omega t)} \qquad \text{21-11}$$

where s_0 is the maximum displacement of the gas from its equilibrium position. This displacement is along the direction of motion of the wave; sound is a longitudinal wave.

The displacement of the gas molecules causes the density of the gas at a point to increase or decrease, depending on whether the gas is displaced toward the point or away from it. If the density increases (or decreases) at some point, the pressure also increases (or decreases) at that point, giving a pressure wave which is related to the displacement wave. We can use Figure 21-2a, showing a sketch of the function $s(x,t)$ at some time t_0, to see that the pressure wave is 90° out of phase with the displacement wave. Points P_1 and P_3 are points of zero displacement at this time. Just to the left of point P_1 the displacement is negative, indicating that the gas is displaced to the left away from the point. Just to the right of P_1 the displacement is positive, indicating that the gas is displaced to the right, again away from this point. Thus

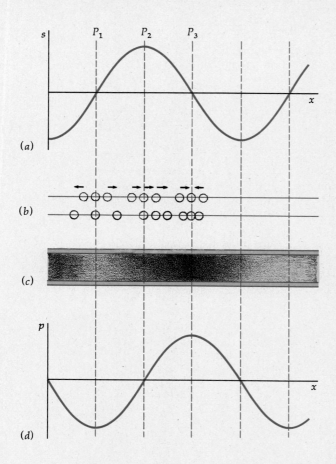

(a)

(b)

(c)

(d)

Figure 21-2
(a) The displacement from equilibrium s of air molecules in a harmonic sound wave at some instant. At P_1 and P_3 the air molecules are at their equilibrium positions. At P_2 they have maximum displacement. (b) Equilibrium position (*top*) and displacement (*bottom*) of three molecules near each of the points P_1, P_2, and P_3. (c) Density of molecules at this time. (d) Plot of pressure change versus position at this time. At the position of maximum displacement, the pressure change is zero. At points of zero displacement, the pressure change is either maximum or minimum. The pressure change is 90° out of phase with the displacement.

the density is a minimum at point P_1 because the gas is displaced away from this point on both sides. At point P_3 the density is a maximum because to the right of this point the displacement is negative, indicating displacement to the left toward the point, and to the left of the point the displacement is positive, indicating displacement to the right, toward the point. The displacements near these points are indicated in Figure 21-2b. At point P_2, the displacement function is a maximum. The displacements to the left and to the right of this point are both positive and of equal magnitude. Thus the density does not change near this point. Figure 21-2c indicates the change in density for this displacement wave. Since the pressure is maximum when the density is maximum, the pressure varies with distance at this time, as indicated in Figure 21-2d.

We shall show below that a displacement wave given by Equation 21-11 implies a pressure wave given by

Sound as a pressure wave

$$p = p_0 \sin (kx - \omega t - 90°) . \qquad \text{21-12}$$

where p stands for the *change* in pressure from the equilibrium pressure with no wave and the amplitude p_0 is the maximum value of this change. We shall also show that the pressure amplitude p_0 is related to the displacement amplitude s_0 by

$$p_0 = \rho \omega v s_0 \qquad \text{21-13}$$

where v is the speed of propagation and ρ is the equilibrium density of the gas. We can think of a sound wave as either a displacement wave or a pressure wave, the displacement and pressure being 90° out of phase with each other.

Derivation of Equations 21-12 and 21-13

We can relate the changes in pressure to the displacement by noting that a displacement changes the volume of a given mass of gas and that changes in pressure and volume are related by the bulk modulus defined by Equation 20-6. Since we are using the notation that p stands for a *change* in pressure here, we have

$$p = - B \frac{\Delta V}{V} \qquad \text{21-14}$$

We can express the bulk modulus in terms of the wave speed v and the gas density using Equation 20-5:

$$B = \rho v^2 \qquad \text{21-15}$$

Thus the change in pressure p is related to the change in volume V by

$$p = - \rho v^2 \frac{\Delta V}{V} \qquad \text{21-16}$$

Consider a given mass of gas initially between points x_1 and x_2 occupying a volume $V = A(x_2 - x_1) = A \, \Delta x$, where A is the area of the tube of gas and $\Delta x = x_2 - x_1$. This volume is shown in Figure 21-3. In general, a displacement of the gas causes a change in the volume of a given mass of gas. If the displacement is the same at points x_2 and x_1, there will be no change in the volume. For example, a positive displacement at point x_2 increases the volume, but a positive displacement at point x_1 decreases the volume. There will be a change in the volume of the gas only if there is a difference in displacement at these two points. Let us call the difference in displacement Δs:

$$\Delta s = s(x_2, t_0) - s(x_1, t_0) \qquad \text{21-17}$$

The change in volume of the gas equals this difference in displacement times the area A:

$$\Delta V = A \, \Delta s$$

This change in volume is related to the change in pressure p by Equation 21-16:

$$p = -\rho v^2 \frac{A \, \Delta s}{A \, \Delta x} = -\rho v^2 \frac{\Delta s}{\Delta x} \qquad \text{21-18}$$

In the limit of small Δx the ratio $\Delta s/\Delta x$ becomes the derivative of s with respect to x. This is a partial derivative because we are considering a single time t_0. Replacing $\Delta s/\Delta x$ by the notation for partial derivative $\partial s/\partial x$, we have

$$p = -\rho v^2 \frac{\partial s}{\partial x} \qquad \text{21-19}$$

Figure 21-3
Change in volume of a given mass of gas because of variation in displacement with position. The original equilibrium volume is $V = A \, \Delta x$, where A is the area of the tube and $\Delta x = x_2 - x_1$. The change in volume is $\Delta V = A(s_2 - s_1) = A \, \Delta s$, where s_2 and s_1 are the displacements at x_2 and x_1. The fractional change in volume is then $\Delta V/V = \Delta s/\Delta x$.

We compute $\partial s/\partial x$ from Equation 21-11:

$$s = s_0 \sin (kx - \omega t_0)$$

$$\frac{\partial s}{\partial x} = ks_0 \cos (kx - \omega t_0)$$

Thus

$$p = -\rho v^2 s_0 k \cos (kx - \omega t_0) = +k\rho v^2 s_0 \sin (kx - \omega t_0 - 90°)$$
$$= p_0 \sin (kx - \omega t_0 - 90°) \qquad\qquad 21\text{-}20$$

where

$$p_0 = k\rho v^2 s_0$$

But according to Equation 21-2, $kv = \omega$. Thus

$$p_0 = \rho \omega v s_0 \qquad\qquad 21\text{-}21$$

and Equations 21-20 and 21-21 are identical to Equations 21-12 and 21-13.

21-4   Superposition and Interference of Harmonic Waves

According to the principle of superposition, when there are two or more waves, the resultant wave is just the algebraic sum of the waves. We shall now show that the superposition of two harmonic waves of the same amplitude, frequency, and wavelength traveling in the same direction but differing in phase gives a harmonic wave of the same frequency and wavelength. The amplitude and phase of the resultant wave depend on the phase difference between the original two waves.

Let y_1 and y_2 be the wave functions for the two original waves:

$$y_1 = y_0 \sin (kx - \omega t) \qquad y_2 = y_0 \sin (kx - \omega t + \delta)$$

The resultant wave is the sum

$$y_3 = y_1 + y_2 = y_0 \sin (kx - \omega t) + y_0 \sin (kx - \omega t + \delta)$$

We can simplify this by using the relation

$$\sin A + \sin B = 2 \sin \tfrac{1}{2}(A + B) \cos \tfrac{1}{2}(A - B) \qquad\qquad 21\text{-}22$$

For this case $A = kx - \omega t$ and $B = kx - \omega t + \delta$, so that

$$\tfrac{1}{2}(A + B) = kx - \omega t + \tfrac{1}{2}\delta \qquad \text{and} \qquad \tfrac{1}{2}(A - B) = -\tfrac{1}{2}\delta$$

Thus

$$y_3 = 2y_0 \cos \tfrac{1}{2}\delta \sin (kx - \omega t + \tfrac{1}{2}\delta) \qquad\qquad 21\text{-}23$$

where we have used $\cos (-\tfrac{1}{2}\delta) = \cos \tfrac{1}{2}\delta$. We see that the resultant of these two waves is another harmonic wave with the same frequency and wavelength. It differs in phase from both the original waves, and its amplitude is $2y_0 \cos \tfrac{1}{2}\delta$.

If $\delta = 0$, the two waves are in phase, $\cos \tfrac{1}{2}\delta = 1$, and the resultant amplitude is just twice that of either wave. If $\delta = \pi$, $\cos \tfrac{1}{2}\delta = 0$ and the two waves cancel each other totally. These two extremes are *perfectly constructive interference* and *perfectly destructive interference*.

Length x_1

Figure 21-4
A wave enters from the left
and splits equally at point A.
At point B, where the waves
recombine, there is a phase
difference because of the path
difference. If λ is the wavelength and Δx the path difference, the phase difference
is $\delta = 2\pi\ \Delta x/\lambda$.

A common cause of phase difference between two waves is a difference in the path length traveled by two waves from the same
source. In Figure 21-4 we assume that the wave splits equally at point
A; that is, the amplitudes of the waves in the two tubes are equal.
When they recombine at point B, there will be a phase difference due
to the longer path traveled by the wave in the lower tube.

If the path difference is exactly 1 wavelength, the phase difference
between the two waves will be 2π, which is the same as no phase difference, and the two waves will interfere constructively. Perfectly constructive interference will also occur if the path difference is any integer times the wavelength. On the other hand, if the path difference is
exactly $\frac{1}{2}$ wavelength, $\frac{3}{2}$ wavelength, or any odd number of half
wavelengths, the phase difference will be π and the interference will
be destructive. For any other path difference Δx the phase difference
will be

$$\delta = 2\pi\ \frac{\Delta x}{\lambda} \qquad\qquad\qquad 21\text{-}24$$

21-5 Vector Method of Addition of Harmonic Waves

A simple geometric interpretation of harmonic wave functions leads to
a method of addition of harmonic waves of the same frequency by
geometric construction. This method lets us find the sum of two or
more harmonic waves geometrically without having to remember the
trigonometric identity of Equation 21-22. It is useful even if the amplitudes of the waves are different or if there are more than two waves.
The method is based on the fact that the y (or x) component of the
resultant of two vectors equals the sum of the y (or x) components of
the vectors.

Let $y_1 = A_1 \sin (kx - \omega t)$ and $y_2 = A_2 \sin (kx - \omega t + \delta)$ be the wave
functions of the two waves. We wish to add these waves at some point
x and some time t. We can simplify our notation by writing θ for the
quantity $kx - \omega t$. Our problem is then to find the sum

$$y_1 + y_2 = A_1 \sin \theta + A_2 \sin (\theta + \delta)$$

Consider a vector of magnitude A_1 making an angle θ with the x axis
(Figure 21-5). The y component of this vector is $A_1 \sin \theta$, which is the
wave function y_1. Similarly, the wave function $y_2 = A_2 \sin (\theta + \delta)$ is
the y component of a vector of magnitude A_2 making an angle $\theta + \delta$
with the x axis. By the laws of vector addition, the sum of these components equals the y component of the resultant vector, as shown in
Figure 21-5. The y component of the resultant vector, $A' \sin (\theta + \delta')$, is

Figure 21-5
The wave function $A_1 \sin \theta$ is the y component of the vector $\mathbf{A}_1$ making angle θ with the x axis. The wave function $A_2 \cdot \sin (\theta + \delta)$ is the y component of the vector $\mathbf{A}_2$ making angle $\theta + \delta$ with the x axis. The sum of these wave functions is $A' \cdot \sin (\theta + \delta')$, which is the y component of the resultant vector $\mathbf{A}' = \mathbf{A}_1 + \mathbf{A}_2$.

a harmonic wave function which is the sum of the two original wave functions,

$$A_1 \sin \theta + A_2 \sin (\theta + \delta) = A' \sin (\theta + \delta') \qquad 21\text{-}25$$

where $\theta = kx - \omega t$ and A' (the amplitude of the resultant wave) and δ' (the phase of the resultant wave relative to the first wave) are found by adding the vectors representing the waves, as in Figure 21-5. As time varies, θ varies. The vectors representing the two wave functions and the resultant vector representing the resultant wave function rotate in space, but their relative positions do not change because all the vectors rotate with the same angular velocity ω.

Example 21-2 Use the vector method of addition to derive Equation 21-23 for the superposition of two waves of the same amplitude.

Figure 21-6 shows the vectors representing two waves of equal amplitude A and the resultant wave of amplitude A'. These three vectors form an isosceles triangle in which the two equal angles are δ'. Since the sum of these angles equals the exterior angle δ, we have

$$\delta' = \tfrac{1}{2}\delta$$

The amplitude A' can be found from the right triangle shown in Figure 21-6b formed by bisecting the resultant vector. From this triangle we have

$$\cos \tfrac{1}{2}\delta = \frac{\tfrac{1}{2}A'}{A}$$

Therefore the amplitude is given by $A' = 2A \cos \tfrac{1}{2}\delta$, and the resultant wave is

$$A' \sin (\theta + \delta') = 2A \cos \tfrac{1}{2}\delta \sin (kx - \omega t + \tfrac{1}{2}\delta)$$

in agreement with Equation 21-23.

$$\cos \tfrac{1}{2}\delta = \frac{\tfrac{1}{2}A'}{A}$$

$$A' = 2A \cos \tfrac{1}{2}\delta$$

(b)

Figure 21-6
The vector addition for two waves of equal amplitude A having phase difference δ. (a) The vectors at a particular time at which $\theta = \omega t$. (b) Construction for finding the amplitude of the resultant wave. The amplitude A' is found from $\cos \tfrac{1}{2}\delta = \tfrac{1}{2}A'/A$, giving $A' = 2A \cos \tfrac{1}{2}\delta$.

Example 21-3 Find the resultant of the two waves

$$y_1 = 4 \sin (kx - \omega t) \qquad \text{and} \qquad y_2 = 3 \sin (kx - \omega t + 90°)$$

Figure 21-7 shows the vector diagram for this addition. The vectors make an angle of 90° with each other. The resultant of these two vectors has the magnitude 5 and makes an angle of 37° with the first vector, as shown. The sum of these two waves is

$$y_1 + y_2 = 5 \sin (kx - \omega t + 37°)$$

This vector method of addition will prove very useful in our study of waves in the following chapters.

Figure 21-7
Vector diagram for the addition of the two waves in Example 21-3.

21-6   Energy and Intensity of a Harmonic Wave on a String

An important property of waves is that they transport energy and momentum. The transport of energy in a wave ordinarily is described in terms of the *wave intensity*, defined to be the average rate at which the wave transmits energy per unit area normal to the direction of propagation. That is, the intensity at any point in a wave is the average incident energy per unit time per unit area. Since the energy per unit time is the power, the intensity is the average power incident per unit area[1]:

$$I = \frac{(\Delta E/\Delta t)_{av}}{A} = \frac{P_{av}}{A} \qquad\qquad 21\text{-}26$$

Wave intensity defined

Figure 21-8
Energy transmitted by a wave on a string. At time t_1 the wave has just reached point P_1. In an additional time Δt the wave travels a distance $v\,\Delta t$. The energy transmitted past point P_1 is $\eta A v\,\Delta t$, where η is the average energy per unit volume and A is the cross-sectional area of the string.

There is a simple relation between the intensity of a wave and the energy per unit volume in the medium carrying the wave. Suppose that a wave traveling to the right on a string has just reached point P_1 at time t_1, as shown in Figure 21-8. The part of the string to the left of P_1 contains energy because each segment is oscillating with simple harmonic motion. At this time t_1 there is no energy to the right of P_1 because the wave has not yet reached that part of the string. After a time Δt the wave moves past point P_1 a distance $v\,\Delta t$, where v is the wave velocity. The total energy of the string is thus increased by the amount of energy in the string past point P_1. This increase in energy can be written

$$\Delta E = \eta A v\,\Delta t$$

where η is the average energy per unit volume of the string, A the cross-sectional area, and $Av\,\Delta t$ the volume of the string past point P_1 which now contains energy.[2] The rate of increase of energy is the power passing point P_1. (The source of this energy is of course at the left end of the string, where there must be an external force doing

---

[1] For waves on a string, the area is just the cross-sectional area of the string. We use the term power per unit area even though it is somewhat artificial for a string because our discussion can then be carried over to any kind of waves.

[2] We assume that the amplitude of the wave is small so that $v\,\Delta t$ is approximately the length of string containing the wave beyond point P_1.

work on the end of the string.) Thus the average incident power is

$$P_{av} = \frac{\Delta E}{\Delta t} = \eta A v \qquad \text{21-27}$$

The intensity of the wave at a point is found by dividing the incident power by the area of the string:

$$I = \frac{P_{av}}{A} = \eta v \qquad \text{21-28}$$

Thus the *intensity equals the product of the wave velocity v and the average energy per unit volume, or the average energy density* η. This result is applicable to all waves.

To calculate the average energy density η for waves on a string, consider a harmonic wave of angular frequency ω and amplitude y_0 traveling along a stretched string. Each element of the string is undergoing simple harmonic motion of angular frequency ω and amplitude y_0. The energy of a segment of the string of mass Δm is of the same form as Equation 14-16 for the energy of a mass oscillating on a spring,

$$\Delta E = \tfrac{1}{2}(\Delta m)\omega^2 y_0^2 \qquad \text{21-29}$$

The mass of the segment is just the mass density ρ times the volume of the segment ΔV. Substituting $\Delta m = \rho\, \Delta V$ into Equation 21-29, we have

$$\Delta E = \tfrac{1}{2}\rho\omega^2 y_0^2\, \Delta V$$

The average energy density

$$\eta = \frac{\Delta E}{\Delta V} = \tfrac{1}{2}\rho\omega^2 y_0^2 \qquad \text{21-30}$$

Average energy density for waves on a string

is proportional to the square of the frequency and to the square of the amplitude. Substituting this result into Equation 21-28, we have for the intensity of a wave on a string,

$$I = \eta v = \tfrac{1}{2}\rho\omega^2 y_0^2 v \qquad \text{21-31}$$

This result, that the *intensity of a wave is proportional to the square of the frequency and to the square of the amplitude,* is a general property of all harmonic waves. For example, the amplitude of a light wave is the maximum value of the electric field E_0. The intensity of a light wave is proportional to E_0^2 and to the square of the frequency. Similarly, as we shall see in Section 21-7, the intensity of sound waves is proportional to the square of either the displacement amplitude or the pressure amplitude.

Questions

8. If the amplitude of harmonic waves is doubled, how does the rate at which energy is used to generate the waves change?

9. Transverse waves of the same frequency and amplitude are sent along two parallel stretched wires. The wires are of the same kind except that one has a greater tension than the other. Over a long time, which wire transmits the greater energy? For which wire is the wave intensity greater?

21-7 Energy and Intensity of Harmonic Sound Waves

Let Δm be the mass of a small portion of gas whose displacement is given by Equation 21-11. Since this motion is simple harmonic at any given time, the average energy of vibration of this gas is given by Equation 21-29,

$$\Delta E = \tfrac{1}{2}\Delta m \; \omega^2 s_0^2$$

where ω is the angular frequency and s_0 is the maximum displacement amplitude. If the element of gas has equilibrium volume ΔV, the average energy per unit volume, or average energy density, is

$$\eta = \frac{1}{2}\frac{\Delta m}{\Delta V}\; \omega^2 s_0^2 = \tfrac{1}{2}\rho\omega^2 s_0^2$$

Energy density for sound waves

where $\rho = \Delta m/\Delta V$ is the mass density. We can relate this to the pressure amplitude p_0 using Equation 21-13 relating p_0 to s_0. We have

$$\eta = \tfrac{1}{2}\rho\omega^2 \left(\frac{p_0}{\rho\omega v}\right)^2 = \frac{1}{2}\frac{p_0^2}{\rho v^2} \qquad\qquad 21\text{-}32$$

Thus, using Equation 21-31, we have for the intensity of a sound wave in a gas,

$$I = \eta v = \tfrac{1}{2}\rho v\omega^2 s_0^2 = \frac{1}{2}\frac{p_0^2}{\rho v} \qquad\qquad 21\text{-}33$$

Intensity of sound waves

The human ear can accommodate a rather large range of sound-wave intensities from about 10^{-12} W/m², which is usually taken to be the threshold of hearing, to about 1 W/m², which produces a sensation of pain in most people. The pressure amplitudes for these extreme sound intensities can be easily calculated from Equation 21-33. Taking $\rho = 1.29$ kg/m³ for the density of air and $v = 331$ m/sec for the speed of sound, we find for the pressure amplitude corresponding to the threshold of hearing intensity of 10^{-12} W/m²:

$$p_0^2 = 2\rho v I = 2(1.29)(331)(10^{-12}) = 8.54 \times 10^{-10}$$

and

$$p_0 = 2.92 \times 10^{-5} \text{ N/m}^2$$

Similarly for an intensity of 1 W/m² at the pain threshold, the pressure amplitude is

$$p_0 = \sqrt{2(1.29)(331)(1)} = 29.2 \text{ N/m}^2$$

These very small changes in pressure are superimposed on the normal constant atmospheric pressure level of about 1.01×10^5 N/m².

Because of the enormous range of intensities to which the ear is sensitive, and because the psychological sensation of loudness varies with intensity not directly but apparently more nearly logarithmically, a logarithmic scale is used to describe the intensity level of a sound wave. The intensity level β measured in *decibels* (dB) is defined by

$$\beta = 10 \log \frac{I}{I_0} \qquad\qquad 21\text{-}34$$

Decibel intensity level for sound waves

where I is the intensity corresponding to the level β and I_0 is a reference level which we shall take to be the threshold of hearing:

$$I_0 = 10^{-12} \text{ W/m}^2 \qquad\qquad 21\text{-}35$$

On this scale, the threshold of hearing is

$$\beta = 10 \log \frac{I_0}{I_0} = 10 \log 1 = 0 \text{ dB}$$
Threshold of hearing

Similarly, the pain threshold is

$$\beta = 10 \log \frac{1}{10^{-12}} = 10 \log 10^{12} = 10(12) = 120 \text{ dB}$$
Pain threshold

Table 21-1 lists the intensity level of some common sounds.

Table 21-1
Decibel intensity level of some common sounds

Source of sound	dB	Description
Large rocket engine (nearby)	180	
Jet takeoff (nearby)	150	
Pneumatic riveter; machine gun	130	
Rock concert with amplifiers (2 m); jet takeoff (60 m)	120	Pain threshold
Construction noise (3 m)	110	
Subway train	100	
Heavy truck (15 m); Niagara Falls	90	Constant exposure endangers hearing
Noisy office with machines; average factory	80	
Busy traffic	70	
Normal conversation (1 m)	60	
Quiet office	50	Quiet
Library	40	
Soft whisper (5 m)	30	Very quiet
Rustling leaves	20	
Normal breathing	10	Barely audible
	0	Hearing threshold

Questions

10. A source of sound waves oscillates with a fixed amplitude and frequency. Assuming the atmospheric pressure to remain constant, how does the rate at which sound waves carry energy away from the source change if the air temperature goes up?

11. Two tuning forks produce sound waves in air of the same amplitude. One has frequency 256 Hz and the other frequency 512 Hz. Which makes the louder sound, i.e., produces sound with the greater intensity?

Sonic Booms

Laurent Hodges
Iowa State University

One of the most common examples of a shock wave resulting from a source traveling faster than the wave-propagation speed is the sonic boom generated by an airplane whose speed exceeds the speed of sound. A common misconception is that a sonic boom is produced when the airplane first accelerates past the speed of sound ("crashes through the sound barrier"). In fact the shock wave exists during the whole time that the airplane is traveling supersonically, and a boom is heard every time the shock wave sweeps over a person with good hearing.

The airplane actually has two shock waves, associated with its front and back (Figure 1). These bow and tail shock waves have nearly the shape of cones (*Mach cones*) with apex at the aircraft's bow and tail, respectively. (Some deviation from perfect cone shape results from variations in sound speeds in different parts of the air.) The cones have a half angle θ given by $\sin \theta = v_s/v_a$, where v_s is the speed of sound and v_a is the speed of the airplane.

The air pressure in the region of overpressure between the two shock waves differs from normal atmospheric pressure, the bow and tail waves being associated with pressures higher and lower than normal, respectively. This pressure deviation produces the sensation of sound in an observer. As the bow wave sweeps over the observer, the pressure increases by the *overpressure* ΔP in a rise time τ. It then decreases to approximately ΔP below normal atmospheric pressure before suddenly returning to normal at the tail wave. A plot of the time dependence of the pressure at a point has the shape of a slanted N and is therefore called the *N signature* (Figure 2).

The major pressure changes experienced at the ear occur as the bow and tail shock waves reach the observer, each producing an explosive sound. This

Figure 1
Cross-sectional representation of a supersonic transport in flight, showing bow and tail shock waves, Mach cone angle 2θ, and a plot of the pressure at ground level. The deviations from normal atmospheric pressure occur in the region of overpressure between the two shock waves.

Figure 2
A plot of the N signature, or time dependence, of the pressure at a given point which experiences a sonic boom. Shown are the overpressure ΔP, the rise time τ, and the time duration T.

explains the double crack of a sonic boom. A supersonic bullet also has bow and tail shock waves, but its two booms are so close together in time that only one crack is heard.

The startling nature of a sonic boom and the resulting annoyance are a function of the rise time, the total duration of the N signature, and the overpressure. The rise time is of the order of 3 ms, and the time duration varies from about 0.1 sec for a supersonic fighter to about 0.4 sec for the British-French Concorde supersonic transport (SST). A typical overpressure for an SST 20 km overhead would be 100 N/m^2 (about 2 lb/ft^2). The overpressure is less at places on either side of the plane's path, but booms can be heard over a zone typically 80 km wide.

It is not possible to assign a decibel reading to a sonic boom because of its short duration and its highly nonsinusoidal form. A sinusoidal sound wave with a rms pressure of 100 N/m^2 would correspond to 134 dB, but the overpressure is not the only relevant parameter. Shorter rise times, for example, are associated with "louder" booms. U.S. Air Force studies have shown that an overpressure of 100 N/m^2 corresponds to 110 to 120 on the perceived-noise decibel scale. (This modification of the decibel scale incorporates the psychological effects of the frequency spectrum of aircraft noises.)

There have been several systematic studies of the effects of sonic-boom exposures, including some carried out by the U.S. Air Force, which has tried to make the sonic boom psychologically acceptable by referring to it as the "sound of freedom." Besides startling people and animals, sonic booms can rattle dishes, shatter glass, and even lead to structural damage to some buildings. Actual experience indicates that approximately $600 in damage claims would result from every million person-booms, and Shurcliff[1] has estimated that each SST might experience 1,000 claims totaling $500,000 annually.

Some people are not bothered much by sonic booms. Many others will presumably learn to tolerate them if supersonic flight becomes commonplace, but even they will suffer the adverse physiological effects that result from any loud noise. Perhaps 25 to 50 percent of the United States population will not be able to adapt to sonic booms, and frequent supersonic flights will doubtless encounter stiff public opposition.

Soviet Russia and a British-French consortium have SSTs for sale as of 1975, but only the state-owned airlines of the three producing countries have purchased the aircraft. The SST program ended in the United States in 1971 after Congress cut off federal funding, although there are occasional attempts to revive the project. Many countries have instituted restrictions, e.g., no supersonic flights over land, that may well make the SST highly uneconomical, so that its future is highly uncertain.

No aircraft design exists at present which permits supersonic flight without generating the shock waves responsible for sonic booms. Even if such a design were feasible, SSTs present other formidable problems:

[1] William A. Shurcliff, *S/S/T and Sonic Boom Handbook*, Ballantine Books, New York, 1970. For further information see Harvey H. Hubbard, Sonic Booms, *Physics Today*, vol. 21, p. 31, February 1968; Herbert A. Wilson, Jr., Sonic Boom, *Scientific American*, vol. 206, p. 36, January 1962; and Karl D. Kryter, Sonic Booms from Supersonic Transport, *Science*, vol. 163, p. 359, 1969.

1. They are extremely noisy apart from the boom (United States engineers tried for a noise limit of 120 perceived-noise decibels 3 mi away from the SST at the start of its takeoff).

2. Their exhaust pollutants (especially nitrogen oxides) may reduce the ozone concentration in the stratosphere, permitting an increase in harmful ultraviolet radiation at the earth's surface.

3. SSTs are very inefficient from the point of view of energy consumption.

Optional

21-8   The Wave Equation

A general wave function $y(x,t)$ is a solution of a differential equation called the *wave equation*. The wave equation relates the second derivative of the wave function with respect to x to the second derivative with respect to t. Because there are two variables, these are partial derivatives. We can obtain the wave equation by recalling that the function

$$y(x,t) = y_0 \sin (kx - \omega t)$$

is a particular solution for harmonic waves. It is useful to write the angular frequency ω in terms of the velocity v and wave number k, that is, $\omega = kv$. Then the harmonic wave function is

$$y(x,t) = y_0 \sin (kx - kvt) \qquad \text{21-36}$$

The derivative with respect to x, holding t constant, is

$$\frac{\partial y}{\partial x} = ky_0 \cos (kx - kvt)$$

Similarly, the second derivative with respect to x is

$$\frac{\partial^2 y}{\partial x^2} = -k^2 y_0 \sin (kx - kvt) = -k^2 y(x,t) \qquad \text{21-37}$$

The derivative of $y(x,t)$ with respect to t, holding x constant, is

$$\frac{\partial y}{\partial t} = -kvy_0 \cos (kx - kvt)$$

and

$$\frac{\partial^2 y}{\partial t^2} = -k^2 v^2 y_0 \sin (kx - kvt) = -k^2 v^2 y(x,t) \qquad \text{21-38}$$

Combining Equations 21-37 and 21-38, we obtain

Wave equation

$$\frac{\partial^2 y}{\partial x^2} = \frac{1}{v^2} \frac{\partial^2 y}{\partial t^2} \qquad \text{21-39}$$

the wave equation. If y is the displacement of a vibrating string, this equation describes string waves. If we interpret y as the increase or decrease in the pressure or density of a gas, this equation describes sound waves. The same equation also describes electromagnetic waves, in which y is the electric or magnetic field.

Equation 21-39 is satisfied by any wave in one dimension which is propagated without dispersion or change of shape. We showed earlier that in general such a wave has a wave function which can be expressed as a function of either $x + vt$ or $x - vt$. We can easily show that any function of $x - vt$ or of $x + vt$ satisfies Equation 21-39. Let $\theta = x - vt$ and consider any wave function

$$y = y(x - vt) = y(\theta)$$

The derivative of y with respect to θ we shall call y'. Then by the chain rule for derivatives

$$\frac{\partial y}{\partial x} = \frac{\partial y}{\partial \theta} \frac{\partial \theta}{\partial x} = y' \frac{\partial \theta}{\partial x} \quad \text{and} \quad \frac{\partial y}{\partial t} = \frac{\partial y}{\partial \theta} \frac{\partial \theta}{\partial t} = y' \frac{\partial \theta}{\partial t}$$

Since $\partial \theta / \partial x = 1$ and $\partial \theta / \partial t = -v$, we have

$$\frac{\partial y}{\partial x} = y' \quad \text{and} \quad \frac{\partial y}{\partial t} = -vy'$$

Taking the second derivatives, we obtain

$$\frac{\partial^2 y}{\partial x^2} = y''$$

$$\frac{\partial^2 y}{\partial t^2} = -v \frac{\partial y'}{\partial t} = -v \frac{\partial y'}{\partial \theta} \frac{\partial \theta}{\partial t} = +v^2 y''$$

Thus again

$$\frac{\partial^2 y}{\partial x^2} = \frac{1}{v^2} \frac{\partial^2 y}{\partial t^2}$$

Of course other equations relating the derivatives of these wave functions can be obtained by taking derivatives of the functions.

Equation 21-39 is important because it is a direct consequence of Newton's second law, $\Sigma \mathbf{F} = m\mathbf{a}$, applied to a segment of a string. For sound waves, the identical equation (with the reinterpretation of y mentioned) is derived from Newton's laws applied to fluids. Similarly, an equation of the same form can be derived for electromagnetic waves from Maxwell's equations for electric and magnetic fields. We discuss the case of string waves only, to illustrate that the wave equation is a consequence of newtonian mechanics.

In Figure 21-9 we have isolated one segment of a string. Our derivation will apply only if the wave is of small enough amplitude for the angle between the string and the horizontal (the original direction of the string with no wave) to be small, in which case the length of the segment is approximately Δx and the mass is $\mu \, \Delta x$. The string moves vertically with acceleration $\partial^2 y / \partial t^2$. The net vertical force is

$$\Sigma F = T \sin \theta_2 - T \sin \theta_1 \qquad \text{21-40}$$

where θ_2 and θ_1 are the angles indicated in Figure 21-9 and T is the tension in the string. Again, since the angles are assumed to be small, we can approximate $\sin \theta$ by $\tan \theta$. The tangent of the angle made by

Figure 21-9
The segment of a stretched string used for the derivation of the wave equation. The net vertical force on the segment is $T \sin \theta_2 - T \sin \theta_1$, where T is the tension. The wave equation is derived by setting this force equal to the mass of the segment times its acceleration.

the string with the horizontal is just the slope of the curve formed by the string,

$$\tan \theta = S = \frac{\partial y}{\partial x}$$

Thus the net force on the string segment can be written

$$\Sigma F = T(\sin \theta_2 - \sin \theta_1) \approx T(\tan \theta_2 - \tan \theta_1) = T(S_2 - S_1) = T \Delta S$$

where $S = \tan \theta = \partial y/\partial x$ is the slope and ΔS is the change in slope. Setting this resultant force equal to the mass times the acceleration gives

$$T \Delta S = \mu \, \Delta x \, \frac{\partial^2 y}{\partial t^2} \qquad T \frac{\Delta S}{\Delta x} = \mu \, \frac{\partial^2 y}{\partial t^2}$$

In the limit $\Delta x \to 0$, we have

$$\lim_{\Delta x \to 0} \frac{\Delta S}{\Delta x} = \frac{\partial S}{\partial x} = \frac{\partial}{\partial x} \left(\frac{\partial y}{\partial x} \right) = \frac{\partial^2 y}{\partial x^2}$$

Thus

$$\frac{\partial^2 y}{\partial x^2} = \frac{\mu}{T} \frac{\partial^2 y}{\partial t^2} \qquad\qquad 21\text{-}41$$

It is important to realize that this wave equation for a stretched string holds only for small angles and thus for small displacements $y(x,t)$. Comparing Equations 21-39 and 21-41, we see again that the velocity of the wave is

$$v = \sqrt{\frac{T}{\mu}}$$

An important property of the wave equation 21-39 is that it is linear; i.e., the function $y(x,t)$ and its derivatives occur only to the first power. There are no terms like y^2, $(\partial y/\partial x)^2$, $y \, \partial^2 y/\partial t^2$, or $(\partial^2 y/\partial t^2)^2$. An important property of linear equations is that if $y_1(x,t)$ and $y_2(x,t)$ are two solutions of the equation, the linear combination

$$y_3(x,t) = C_1 y_1(x,t) + C_2 y_2(x,t) \qquad\qquad 21\text{-}42$$

where C_1 and C_2 are any constants, is also a solution. This is easily shown by direct substitution of y_3 into the equation, using

$$\frac{\partial^2 (y_1 + y_2)}{\partial x^2} = \frac{\partial^2 y_1}{\partial x^2} + \frac{\partial^2 y_2}{\partial x^2} \qquad \text{and} \qquad \frac{\partial^2 (y_1 + y_2)}{\partial t^2} = \frac{\partial^2 y_1}{\partial t^2} + \frac{\partial^2 y_2}{\partial t^2}$$

Equation 21-42 is the mathematical statement of the superposition principle. If any two waves satisfy the wave equation 21-39, their sum also satisfies the same wave equation.

The superposition principle for waves on a string holds only if the amplitudes of the waves are small, so that the approximation used in deriving the wave equation $\sin \theta \approx \tan \theta$ holds. If the amplitudes are large, so that this approximation does not hold, the resulting equation relating the time derivatives and spatial derivatives of $y(x,t)$ is not linear. In that case, the sum of two solutions is not a solution and the principle of superposition does not hold.

A similar small-amplitude approximation must be made to derive the wave equation for sound waves from Newton's laws for a fluid. Thus the principle of superposition for sound waves is also limited to waves in which the amplitude of the pressure or displacement variations is small.

The wave equation for electromagnetic waves follows directly from the laws of electricity and magnetism without any small-amplitude approximation. Thus the principle of superposition holds for electromagnetic waves under all conditions.

Review

A. Define, explain, or otherwise identify:

Harmonic wave, 513	Circularly polarized wave, 516
Wave number, 513	Elliptically polarized wave, 517
Amplitude, 513	Intensity, 523
Angular frequency, 513	Energy density, 524
Wavelength, 514	Intensity level, 525
Polarization, 516	Decibel, 525
Linearly polarized wave, 516	Wave equation, 529

B. True or false:

1. The speed of a harmonic wave equals the frequency times the wavelength.

2. Harmonic waves are dispersionless.

3. Plane polarization means the same as linear polarization.

4. Sound waves can be polarized.

5. The displacement and pressure in a sound wave are 180° out of phase.

6. The sum of two harmonic waves of the same wavelength and frequency is itself a harmonic wave.

7. The energy in a harmonic wave is proportional to the square of the amplitude of the wave.

8. The units of intensity are watts per square meter.

9. The intensity of a wave equals the product of the energy density and the speed.

10. A 60-dB sound has twice the intensity of a 30-dB sound.

Exercises

Use the following data in these exercises and problems unless otherwise specified: speed of sound in air $= 340$ *m/sec* $= 1110$ *ft/sec; speed of sound in water* $= 1500$ *m/sec; speed of light* $c = 3 \times 10^8$ *m/sec.*

Section 21-1, Wavelength, Frequency, and Velocity of Harmonic Waves

1. Equation 21-1b expresses the displacement of a harmonic wave as a function of x and t in terms of the wave parameters k and ω. Write equivalent expressions which instead of k and ω contain the following pairs of parameters: (a) k and v, (b) λ and f, (c) λ and T, (d) λ and v, (e) f and v.

2. The ear is sensitive to sound frequencies in the range of about 20 to 20,000 Hz. (a) What are the wavelengths in air corresponding to these frequencies? (b) What are the wavelengths in water?

3. (a) Middle C in the musical scale has a frequency of 262 Hz. What is the wavelength of this note in air? (b) The frequency of the C an octave above middle C is twice that of middle C. What is the wavelength of this note?

4. The eye is sensitive to electromagnetic waves whose wavelengths are in the range of about 4×10^{-7} to 7×10^{-7} m. What are the corresponding frequencies of these light waves?

5. Typical frequencies of electromagnetic radio waves are 100 kHz for AM and 100 MHz for FM. Calculate the wavelengths corresponding to these frequencies. (All electromagnetic waves travel with the speed of light.)

6. The wave function for a harmonic wave in a string is $y(x,t) = 0.001 \cdot \sin (62.8x + 314t)$, where y and x are in meters and t is in seconds. (a) What direction does this wave travel, and what is its speed? (b) Find the wavelength, frequency, and period of this wave. (c) What is the maximum displacement of any string segment?

7. A wave travels to the right along a string with speed 10 m/sec. Its frequency is 60 Hz, and its amplitude is 0.02 m. (a) Write a suitable wave function for this wave. (b) Is this wave function the only function that could describe this wave? Explain.

Section 21-2, Polarization

8. One end of a long string moves with frequency f and amplitude A in random directions in a plane perpendicular to the string, thus setting up unpolarized waves in the string. The string passes through a long narrow vertical slot in a board. (a) Describe the wave that passes through the slot in the board. The string now passes through a second board with a long narrow slot. Describe the wave on the other side of the second board (b) if the slot is horizontal and (c) if the slot makes an angle of 45° with the vertical.

9. What kind of polarization results when the phase δ in Equation 21-9 is (a) 180° and (b) 270°?

10. Explain why sound waves cannot be polarized.

Section 21-3, Harmonic Sound Waves

11. A typical loud sound wave with a frequency of 1000 Hz would have a pressure amplitude of about 10^{-4} atm. (a) At $t = 0$, the pressure is maximum at some point x_1. What is the displacement at that point at $t = 0$? (b) What is the maximum value of the displacement at any time and place? (Take the density of air to be 1.29 kg/m³.)

12. What is the displacement amplitude for a sound wave of frequency 100 Hz and pressure amplitude 10^{-4} atm?

13. The displacement amplitude for a sound wave of frequency 300 Hz is 10^{-7} m. What is the pressure amplitude for this wave?

14. (a) Find the displacement amplitude for a sound wave of frequency 1000 Hz at the pain-threshold pressure amplitude of 29 N/m². (b) Find the displacement amplitude for a sound wave with the same pressure amplitude but of frequency 500 Hz.

15. (a) Find the displacement amplitude for a sound wave of frequency 500 Hz at the threshold-of-hearing pressure amplitude of 2.9×10^{-5} N/m². (b) Find the displacement amplitude for a wave of the same pressure amplitude but of frequency 1000 Hz.

Section 21-4, Superposition and Interference of Harmonic Waves, and Section 21-5, Vector Method of Addition of Harmonic Waves

16. Two waves with the same frequency, wavelength, and amplitude are traveling in the same direction. If they differ in phase by 90° and each has amplitude 0.05 m, find the amplitude of the resultant wave.

17. Two waves traveling on a string in the same direction have frequency 100 Hz, wavelength 2 cm, and amplitude 0.02 m. They differ in phase by 60°. What is the amplitude of the resultant wave?

18. Two sound sources oscillate in phase with the same amplitude. They are separated in space by $\frac{1}{3}\lambda$. What is the amplitude of the resultant wave from the two sources at a point on the line joining the sources if the amplitude due to each source separately is A? (Assume that the point is not between the sources.)

19. Two sound sources oscillate in phase with frequency 100 Hz. At a point 5.00 m from one source and 5.85 m from the other the amplitude of the sound from each source separately is A. (a) What is the difference in phase of the sound waves from the two sources at that point? (b) What is the amplitude of the resultant wave at that point?

20. Use the vector method of wave addition to find the wave function for the sum of the two waves $y_1 = 3 \sin (kx - \omega t)$ and $y_2 = 4 \sin (kx - \omega t + \delta)$ for (a) $\delta = 90°$ and (b) $\delta = 60°$. (Find the amplitude and phase of the resultant wave using a ruler and protractor or use trigonometry.)

21. Use the vector method of addition to find graphically the sum of the following three waves: $y_1 = 5 \sin (kx - \omega t)$, $y_2 = 5 \sin (kx - \omega t + 120°)$, and $y_3 = 5 \sin (kx - \omega t + 240°)$.

Section 21-6, Energy and Intensity of a Harmonic Wave on a String, and Section 21-7, Energy and Intensity of Harmonic Sound Waves

22. Show that the power passing a point on a string equals the product of the energy per unit length and the wave velocity.

23. A 20-m string has a mass of 0.06 kg and is under a tension of 50 N. Waves of frequency 200 Hz and amplitude 1 cm move along the string from left to right. (a) What is the total energy of the waves in the string? (b) What is the power transmitted past a given point in the string (see Exercise 22)?

24. Two parallel tubes with the same diameter are filled with gas at the same pressure and temperature. One tube contains H_2, and the other contains O_2. (a) If sound waves traveling in the tubes have the same displacement amplitude and frequency, how do the intensities compare? (b) If the waves have the same frequency and pressure amplitude, how do the intensities compare? (c) If the waves have the same frequency and intensity, how do the pressure amplitudes and displacement amplitudes compare?

25. A piston at one end of a long tube filled with air at room temperature and normal pressure oscillates with frequency 500 Hz and amplitude 0.1 mm. The area of the piston is 100 cm². (a) What is the pressure amplitude of the sound waves generated in the tube? (b) What is the intensity of the waves? (c) What average power is required to keep the piston oscillating (neglecting friction)?

26. What is the intensity level in decibels for a sound wave (a) of intensity of 10^{-10} W/m², (b) of intensity of 10^{-2} W/m²?

27. Find the intensity if (a) $\beta = 10$ dB and (b) $\beta = 3$ dB. (c) Find the pressure amplitude for sound waves in air at standard temperature and pressure for each of these intensities.

28. Show that if the intensity is doubled, the intensity level increases by $10 \log 2 = 3.0$ dB.

29. What fraction of the acoustic power of a noise would have to be eliminated to lower its sound intensity level from 90 to 70 dB?

Section 21-8, The Wave Equation

30. Show that the function $y_3(x,t)$ given by Equation 21-42 satisfies the wave equation if $y_1(x,t)$ and $y_2(x,t)$ do.

31. Show explicitly that the following functions satisfy the wave equation: (a) $y(x,t) = (x + vt)^3$; (b) $y(x,t) = Ae^{ik(x-vt)}$, where A and k are constant and $i = \sqrt{-1}$; (c) $y(x,t) = \ln k(x - vt)$.

32. (a) Show that the function $y = A \sin kx \cos \omega t$ satisfies the wave equation. (b) Use the trigonometric identity $\sin A + \sin B = 2 \sin \frac{1}{2}(A + B) \cos \frac{1}{2}(A - B)$ to show that the wave function in part (a) is the sum of a wave traveling to the right and a wave traveling to the left.

Problems

1. Derive the general relation given by Equation 21-24 between δ and Δx, where δ is the phase difference due to a path difference Δx. Do this by letting x_1 be the path length for one wave and $x_2 = x_1 + \Delta x$ be that for the other wave. Then show that $y_2 = y_0 \sin (kx_2 - \omega t)$ can be written $y_2 = y_0 \sin (kx_1 - \omega t + \delta)$, where δ is given by Equation 21-24.

2. For the wave function given in Exercise 6 find the maximum speed and acceleration experienced by any point on the string.

3. A tuning fork attached to a stretched wire generates transverse waves. The vibration of the fork is perpendicular to the string. Its frequency is 440 Hz, and its amplitude of oscillation is 0.50 mm. The wire has linear mass density of 0.01 kg/m and is under a tension of 1000 N. (a) Find the period and frequency of waves in the wire. (b) What is the speed of the waves? (c) What are the wavelength and wave number? (d) Write a suitable wave function for the waves on the wire. (e) Calculate the maximum speed and acceleration of a point in the wire. (f) At what average rate must energy be supplied to the fork to keep it oscillating at a steady amplitude?

4. Two loudspeakers oscillate in phase but are separated by a distance d. The speakers and a listener are in a straight line. The listener is a distance x from the nearer speaker (and $x + d$ from the farther speaker). The speakers put out a sound wave of frequency 500 Hz. The intensity at the listener for each speaker acting separately is I_0. (a) For what values of d will the listener hear no sound from the two speakers? (b) For what values of d will the listener hear the greatest sound intensity from the speakers? For these values, what will the intensity be? (Give your answer in terms of I_0.) (c) What intensity will be heard by the listener if $d = 17$ cm?

5. Two wires of different densities are soldered together end to end and then stretched under tension T (the same in both wires). The wave speed in the first wire is twice that in the second wire. When a harmonic wave traveling in the first wire is reflected at the junction of the wires, the reflected wave has half the amplitude of the transmitted wave. (a) Assuming no loss in the wire, what fraction of the incident power is reflected at the junction and what fraction is transmitted? (b) If the incident-wave amplitude is A, what are the reflected- and transmitted-wave amplitudes?

6. Power is to be transmitted along a stretched wire by means of transverse harmonic waves. The wave speed is 100 m/sec, and the linear density is 0.01 kg/m. The power source oscillates with amplitude of 0.50 mm. (a) What average power is transmitted along the wire if the frequency is 400 Hz? (b) The power transmitted can be increased by increasing the tension in the wire, the frequency of the source, or the amplitude of the waves. If just one of these quantities were changed, how would each quantity have to be changed to effect an increase in power by a factor of 100? (c) Which of the changes would probably be accomplished most easily?

7. (a) Use the vector model of addition to find the amplitude of the sum of three harmonic waves $y_1 = y_0 \sin \theta$; $y_2 = y_0 \sin (\theta + \delta)$, and $y_3 = y_0 \cdot \sin (\theta + 2\delta)$, where $\theta = kx - \omega t$ for $\delta = 30°$ and $y_0 = 2$ cm. (b) What is the smallest value of δ for which the resultant amplitude is 0? (c) If the inten-

sity of each wave separately is I_0, what is the intensity of the resultant wave when $\theta = 0$? For what values of δ other than 0 is the intensity again this value? (d) Find the other value of δ less than 360° for which the resultant intensity is 0. Make a sketch of the resultant intensity versus δ from $\delta = -4\pi$ to $\delta = +4\pi$.

8. This problem is essentially Problem 7 with four waves $y_1 = y_0 \sin \theta$, $y_2 = y_0 \cdot \sin (\theta + \delta)$, $y_3 = y_0 \sin (\theta + 2\delta)$, and $y_4 = y_0 \sin (\theta + 3\delta)$. (a) Find the values of δ for which the resultant amplitude is greatest, and find the intensity (in terms of I_0 the intensity of one wave separately) at these maxima. (b) Find the three values of δ between 0 and 360° for which the resultant amplitude is 0. (c) Make a sketch of the resultant intensity versus δ.

9. (a) Make a sketch of y versus θ for each of the three waves in Problem 7 for $\delta = 120°$. Add the wave functions graphically to show that the sum of the three waves is zero for all θ. (b) Make a similar sketch for $\delta = 180°$ and find the sum graphically.

10. Three noise sources produce intensity levels of 70, 73, and 80 dB when acting separately. When acting together, the intensities of the sources add. (There is no interference between the amplitudes from the different sources because the relative phase changes randomly.) Find the sound intensity level in decibels when the three sources act at the same time. Discuss the usefulness of eliminating the two least intense sources in order to reduce the intensity level of the noise.

11. An article on noise pollution claims that the sound intensity level in large cities has been increasing by about 1 dB annually. What percentage increase in intensity does this correspond to? Does this increase seem reasonable?

CHAPTER 22   Standing Waves

When waves are confined in space, like waves on a piano string or in an organ pipe, there are reflections at both ends and therefore waves traveling in both directions. These waves combine according to the general law of wave interference. For a given string or pipe, there are certain frequencies for which this interference results in a stationary vibration pattern called a *standing wave*. The study of standing waves has many applications in the field of music and in nearly all areas of science and technology.

22-1 Standing Waves on a String Fixed at Both Ends

Consider a string fixed at one end and tied at the other end to a tuning fork, which vibrates with frequency f and small amplitude. The waves produced by the tuning fork travel down the string, are inverted by reflection at the fixed end, and travel back to the fork. Since the fork is vibrating with a small amplitude, it acts essentially as a fixed end as far as reflection is concerned. The waves are thus inverted once again upon reflection at the fork and start back down the string.

Let us look at a particular wave crest generated at the left end of the string by the fork. It travels to the right end of the string, is reflected back, and is reflected again at the fork. Since it has been reflected twice, it has been inverted twice and now differs from the next wave crest coming from the fork only in that the first has already traveled a distance $2L$, where L is the length of the string. If this distance is exactly equal to the wavelength λ, the twice-reflected wave will be in phase with the second wave and the two will interfere constructively. The resultant wave has an amplitude twice that of either wave (assuming no loss by reflection). When this resulting wave travels the distance $2L$ to the fixed end and back and has been reflected twice, it will exactly overlap the third wave generated by the tuning fork. Thus each

Doug Fulton/Photo Researchers

Standing waves are produced on a violin string by bowing the string and sometimes by plucking the string.

new wave is in phase with the waves reflected at the tuning fork, and the amplitude continues to increase as the string absorbs energy from the tuning fork. This continues until a maximum amplitude is reached due to various damping effects, e.g., loss of energy due to reflection or imperfect flexibility of the string. This maximum amplitude is much larger than that of the tuning fork. Thus the tuning fork is in *resonance* with the string when the tuning-fork frequency is such that the wavelength in the string equals twice the length of the string.

When the wavelength just equals the length of the string, the distance $2L$ equals 2 wavelengths. When the first wave has traveled the distance $2L$ and is reflected at the fork, it will be exactly in phase with the third wave generated at the fork. Again a large amplitude builds up in the string. We can see, in general, that resonance will occur if the distance $2L$ is any integer times the wavelength. Thus the condition for resonance is

$$2L = n\lambda \qquad\qquad 22\text{-}1$$

Resonance, or standing-wave, condition for a string fixed at both ends

where n is any integer. In terms of the frequency of the waves $f = v/\lambda$, the condition for resonance is

$$2L = n\frac{v}{f}$$

or

$$f_n = n\frac{v}{2L} = nf_1 \qquad\qquad 22\text{-}2$$

where

$$f_1 = \frac{v}{2L} = \frac{1}{2L}\sqrt{\frac{T}{\mu}} \qquad\qquad 22\text{-}3$$

is the lowest resonance frequency, called the *fundamental frequency*, and we have used Equation 20-4 for the speed of waves on the string.

Fundamental frequency defined

It is sometimes convenient to think of the resonance condition in terms of the time necessary for the first wave to travel to the end and back. Since this distance is $2L$, the time will be $2L/v$, where v is the wave speed. If this time equals the period of vibration of the fork, the first wave will add constructively to the second wave. Resonance will also result if this time equals any integral number of periods. Thus we can write the resonance condition

$$\frac{2L}{v} = nT = \frac{n}{f} \qquad \text{or} \qquad f = n\frac{v}{2L}$$

which is the same as that found by fitting an integral number of wavelengths into the distance $2L$. The frequencies given by Equation 22-2 are called the *natural frequencies* of the string.

Example 22-1 A string is stretched between two fixed supports 1 m apart, and the tension is adjusted until the fundamental frequency of the string is 440 Hz. What is the speed of transverse waves on the string?

From the condition for resonance (Equation 22-1) the wavelength for the fundamental, or $n = 1$, resonance frequency is $\lambda = 2L = 2$ m. Hence, the wave speed is

$$v = \lambda f = (2 \text{ m})(440 \text{ sec}^{-1}) = 880 \text{ m/sec}$$

What happens when the frequency of the tuning fork is *not* equal to one of the natural frequencies of the string? When the first wave has traveled the distance $2L$ and is reflected from the fork, it differs in phase from the wave being generated at the fork (Figure 22-1). Suppose the phase difference is δ. As we saw in Section 21-4, if each wave has amplitude y_0, the resultant of the new wave and the twice-reflected wave is a wave of amplitude $2y_0 \cos \frac{1}{2}\delta$ differing in phase by $\frac{1}{2}\delta$ from either of the two waves. When this resultant wave travels a distance of $2L$ and is again reflected at the fork, it will differ in phase from the next wave from the fork by $\delta + \frac{1}{2}\delta = \frac{3}{2}\delta$. The incoming waves and reflected waves will have a phase difference which depends on the number of reflections. The interference is thus sometimes constructive, in which case the amplitude of the wave on the string will increase, and sometimes destructive, in which case the amplitude of the wave will decrease. On the average, the amplitude will not increase but remain that of the first wave generated; i.e., the amplitude of the resultant wave will equal that of the tuning fork, which is small. The string does not absorb energy on the average. Only when the frequency of the tuning fork equals one of the natural frequencies of the string given by Equation 22-2 will the waves add in phase and the amplitude build up.

This resonance phenomenon is analogous to the resonance of a simple harmonic oscillator with a harmonic driving force. If the frequency of the driving force equals the natural frequency of a simple harmonic oscillator, the oscillator absorbs the maximum amount of energy from the driving force. Note, however, that a string fixed at both ends has not just one natural frequency but a sequence of natural frequencies, which are integral multiples of the fundamental frequency. This series is called a *harmonic series*. The second frequency $f_2 = 2f_1$ is called the second harmonic; the nth is called the nth harmonic. In another terminology often used in music, the second harmonic is called the first overtone; the third harmonic is the second overtone; etc. Thus the nth harmonic is also the $(n-1)$st overtone.

When the string is vibrated at any one of its natural frequencies, it absorbs energy from the external force and the amplitude increases until it reaches a maximum value; then the rate at which energy is lost to damping effects equals the rate at which energy is absorbed. The wave produced is called a *standing wave*. The change in the shape of the

Figure 22-1
Waves on a string produced by a tuning fork whose frequency is not in resonance with the natural frequencies of the string. The wave leaving the tuning fork for the first time (*dashed line*) and the wave leaving for the second time after being reflected twice (*gray line*) are not in phase and do not interfere constructively. The resultant wave is indicated by the black line.

Harmonic series

Winds set up standing waves in the Tacoma Narrows Suspension Bridge, leading to its collapse on Nov. 7, 1940, only 4 months after it had been opened for traffic.

Wide World

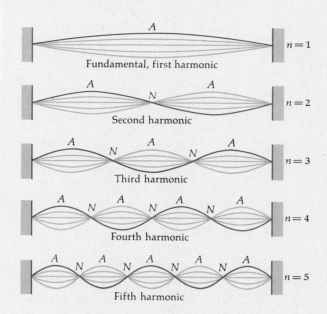

Figure 22-2
Standing waves on a string fixed at both ends. The points labeled A are antinodes, those labeled N are nodes. In general the nth harmonic has n antinodes and $n - 1$ nodes.

string is indicated in Figure 22-2 for the fundamental and the first few harmonics. The energy of the string is constant, but it oscillates from potential energy, when the string has its maximum displacement and is at rest, to kinetic energy, when the string is in its original shape but each segment has its maximum speed.

Questions

1. Give some examples of standing waves in one dimension other than on stretched strings.

2. The wires for low notes on a piano are wound with copper to increase their mass. Why?

3. When the tension in a string is increased without changing its length, how do the resonance frequencies change? How do the wavelengths corresponding to these frequencies change?

22-2 Standing-Wave Functions

We can find the mathematical form of the wave functions illustrated in Figure 22-2 and also rederive the resonance condition, or standing-wave condition (Equation 22-1), by considering the resultant wave formed by the addition of a wave traveling to the right and a wave traveling to the left. Let us call the displacement of the wave moving to the right y_R and that of the wave moving to the left y_L and assume that the amplitudes are equal. Then

$$y_R = y_0 \sin (kx - \omega t) \qquad \text{and} \qquad y_L = y_0 \sin (kx + \omega t)$$

where $k = 2\pi/\lambda$ is the wave number and $\omega = 2\pi f$ is the angular frequency. The sum of these two waves is

$$y(x,t) = y_R + y_L = y_0 \sin (kx - \omega t) + y_0 \sin (kx + \omega t)$$

or

$$y(x,t) = 2y_0 \cos \omega t \sin kx \qquad\qquad\qquad 22\text{-}4 \qquad Standing\text{-}wave\ function$$

where again we have used Equation 21-22 for the sum of two sine functions.[1]

If the string is fixed at $x = 0$ and $x = L$, we have the following *boundary conditions* on the wave functions:

$$y(x = 0, t) = 0 \qquad \text{22-5}$$

and

Boundary conditions

$$y(x = L, t) = 0 \qquad \text{22-6}$$

for all times t. The first boundary condition is automatically met because $\sin kx = 0$ at $x = 0$. The second boundary condition is met only for those particular values of the wave number which satisfy

$$\sin kL = 0 \qquad \text{22-7}$$

The values k_n which satisfy this equation are given by

$$k_n L = n\pi \qquad \text{22-8}$$

where n is any integer. In terms of the wavelength $\lambda = 2\pi/k$, Equation 22-8 is

$$\frac{2\pi}{\lambda_n} L = n\pi$$

or

$$n\lambda_n = 2L \qquad \text{22-9}$$

This is the same condition we derived earlier. Twice the length of the string must equal an integral number of wavelengths.

The standing-wave functions are sine functions whose wavelengths are given by Equation 22-9. The easiest way to remember the condition for standing waves is to draw a line of length L and fit sine waves so that the displacement is zero at each end. We note that in addition to $x = 0$ and $x = L$, there are other points which are at rest if n is greater than 1. For example, for the wave for the second harmonic, the midpoint of the string is at rest. Such a point is called a *node*. In the third harmonic there are two points at rest (Figure 22-2). In general there are $n - 1$ nodes (not counting $x = 0$ and $x = L$) for the nth harmonic.

Nodes and antinodes defined

The points where the amplitude of vibration is maximum are called *antinodes*. There is an antinode halfway between each pair of nodes, including the ends. There are n antinodes when the string is vibrating in its nth harmonic.

22-3   Standing Waves on a String Fixed at One End

We can also produce standing waves in a string with one end free instead of fixed. A nearly free end results if the string is tied to a very long light thread, as in Figure 22-3. The analysis differs only slightly.

---

[1] We might think that we should subtract the two waves since the wave is inverted by reflection. It makes no difference whether we add or subtract the waves. Using $\sin A - \sin B = 2 \sin\frac{1}{2}(A - B) \cos\frac{1}{2}(A + B)$, we have $y_L - y_R = 2y_0 \sin \omega t \cos kx$. This differs from Equation 22-4 only in the phases of the functions. Equation 22-4 is more convenient because we do not have to add a phase constant in order to meet the boundary conditions.

Figure 22-3
An approximation to a string
fixed at one end and free at
the other end can be pro-
duced by connecting the
"free" end of the string to a
very long, light thread. Since
the amplitude of the tuning
fork is small, the end attached
to the fork is approximately
fixed.

When the first wave is reflected at the free end, it is not inverted; however, it is inverted when it is reflected at the tuning fork. Thus if it arrives back at the fork in a time equal to *half* the period of the fork, it
will add constructively to the next wave (actually the last half of the
first wave). Constructive interference will also occur if the time taken
for the first wave to travel twice the length of the string equals $\frac{3}{2}$ times
the period, $\frac{5}{2}$ times the period, or any odd number of half periods.
Thus the resonance condition for a standing wave on a string of length
L fixed at one end (the tuning fork) and free at the other end is

$$\frac{2L}{v} = \frac{nT}{2} \qquad \text{where } n = 1, 3, 5, 7, \ldots \qquad\qquad 22\text{-}10$$

or, in terms of the frequency $f = 1/T$,

$$f = n\frac{v}{4L} \qquad n = 1, 3, 5, 7, \ldots \qquad\qquad 22\text{-}11$$

The natural frequencies of this system occur in the ratios $1:3:5:7$; that
is, the frequencies are given by

$$f_n = nf_1 \qquad \text{where } n = 1, 3, 5, 7, \ldots \qquad\qquad 22\text{-}12$$

where

$$f_1 = \frac{v}{4L} \qquad\qquad 22\text{-}13$$

is the fundamental frequency. The even harmonics are missing.

We can obtain the natural frequencies for this system and the wave
functions as we did for the string fixed at both ends from Equation
22-4:

$$y = 2y_0 \cos \omega t \sin kx$$

The boundary conditions are now that $y = 0$ at $x = 0$, which occurs
automatically, and that y is a maximum or minimum at $x = L$. That is,
the point $x = L$ is an antinode. This occurs if

$$\sin k_n L = \pm 1$$

or

$$k_n L = \frac{n\pi}{2} \qquad \text{where } n = 1, 3, 5, 7, \ldots \qquad\qquad 22\text{-}14$$

In terms of the wavelength $\lambda_n = 2\pi/k_n$, this condition is

$$\frac{2\pi}{\lambda_n} L = \frac{n\pi}{2}$$

or

$$n\lambda_n = 4L \qquad\qquad 22\text{-}15$$

This is the same as Equation 22-11 since the frequency is $f = v/\lambda$.
Again, the easiest way to remember the standing-wave condition is to
draw a string of length L and fit sine waves so that the end at $x = L$ is
an antinode. The first few standing-wave modes for a string fixed at
one end are shown in Figure 22-4.

Fundamental

Third harmonic

Fifth harmonic

Seventh harmonic

Ninth harmonic

Figure 22-4
Standing waves on a string fixed at only one end. The points labeled A are antinodes; those labeled N are nodes.

Margot Granitas/Photo Researchers

Standing waves are set up in a flute by blowing across the mouthpiece.

22-4   Standing Sound Waves

Much of what we have learned about standing waves on strings can be applied to standing sound waves. Figure 22-5 shows a tube of air closed at the right end and fitted with a movable piston at the left. Because the air cannot vibrate past the closed end at $x = L$, this point must be a displacement node. If the vibration of the piston at the left end is of small amplitude, that end is also approximately a displacement node. (This approximation is similar to that for the vibrating string.) Let us call the speed of sound v. The standing-wave condition for this system is the same as for the string fixed at both ends, and all the same equations apply. The distance $2L$ must contain an integral number of wavelengths:

$$n\lambda = 2L$$

The allowed wavelengths are those which can be fitted into the length of the tube with displacement nodes at each end. Since the pressure variation is 90° out of phase with the displacement, these displacement nodes are pressure antinodes.

Example 22-2 If the speed of sound is 340 m/sec, what are the allowed frequencies and wavelengths for standing waves in a closed tube 1 m long?

The fundamental frequency is the lowest allowed frequency and corresponds to the longest wavelength $\lambda = 2L = 2$ m. Thus the fundamental frequency is $f_1 = v/\lambda = (340 \text{ m/sec})/(2 \text{ m}) = 170$ Hz. The frequency and wavelength of the nth harmonic are

$$f_n = nf_1 = 170n \text{ Hz} \qquad \text{and} \qquad \lambda_n = \frac{2L}{n} = \frac{2}{n} \text{ m}$$

If the end of the tube at the right in Figure 22-5 is not closed but open to the atmosphere, the open end must remain at atmospheric pressure. The open end is therefore a pressure node and a displacement antinode. The condition for the resonant frequencies and wavelengths for this system are the same as those for a string with one

Air

Movable piston

Figure 22-5
Air confined to a tube closed at both ends. There is a displacement node at both ends if the amplitude of the piston is small. The standing-sound-wave condition is thus the same as for a string fixed at both ends.

end fixed and one end free. The wavelength of the fundamental node is 4 times the length of the tube, and only odd harmonics are present. For the tube of length 1 m (Example 22-2) the wavelength of the fundamental is 4 m, and its frequency is $f_1 = \frac{340}{4} = 85$ Hz. The other allowed frequencies are

$$f_3 = 3f_1 = 255 \text{ Hz} \qquad f_5 = 5f_1 = 425 \text{ Hz}$$

and so on.

The result that the open end of the tube is a pressure node and displacement antinode is based on the assumption that the sound wave in the tube is a one-dimensional wave, which is approximately true if the diameter of the tube is very small compared with the wavelength of the sound wave. In practice, the displacement antinode and pressure node are slightly beyond the open end of the tube. The effective length of the tube L_{eff} is thus somewhat longer than the true length L. We can write the effective length of the tube as the sum of the true length L and an end correction ΔL:

$$L_{\text{eff}} = L + \Delta L$$

The end correction ΔL is of the order of the radius R of the tube. Note that the distance between two successive nodes or antinodes is still $\frac{1}{2}\lambda$ even though the distance from the open end of the tube to the first displacement node is slightly less than $\frac{1}{4}\lambda$ because of the end correction.

Example 22-3 Figure 22-6 shows an apparatus for measuring the speed of sound in air. A narrow vertical tube is partially filled with water; its level can be adjusted, and therefore the length of the air column can be adjusted. A tuning fork of frequency f_0 vibrates at the top open end of the tube and sends sound waves down the tube, which are reflected at the adjustable bottom, the water level. When the water level is such that the standing-wave condition is met, resonance occurs and the increased energy in the sound wave can be detected by the ear. In this experiment, the wavelength is $\lambda_0 = v/f_0$, where v is the velocity of sound in air. It is fixed since v is determined by the air temperature and f_0 by the tuning fork. If ΔL is the correction term for the tube, the tube will resonate if its length is L_1, given by

$$L_1 + \Delta L = \tfrac{1}{4}\lambda_0$$

It will also resonate at lengths $L_3, L_5, \ldots, L_n$, given by

$$L_3 + \Delta L = \tfrac{3}{4}\lambda_0$$

$$L_5 + \Delta L = \tfrac{5}{4}\lambda_0$$

$$L_n + \Delta L = \frac{n}{4}\lambda_0 \qquad n = 1, 3, 5, 7, \ldots$$

The wavelength, and thus the speed of sound, can be measured by measuring the distance between two consecutive resonances, e.g.,

$$L_3 - L_1 = \tfrac{1}{2}\lambda_0 = \frac{v}{2f_0}$$

Figure 22-6
Apparatus for determining the speed of sound in air (Example 22-3). Sound waves of the frequency of the tuning fork are excited in the tube on the left. The length of the tube is varied by adjusting the water level. Resonance occurs when the effective length of the tube (length plus end correction) equals $\frac{1}{4}\lambda, \frac{3}{4}\lambda, \frac{5}{4}\lambda \ldots$, where λ is the wavelength of the sound. Measuring the difference in water level for two successive resonances gives $\frac{1}{2}\lambda$, from which the speed of sound can be found using $v = f\lambda$.

An organ pipe is a familiar example of the use of standing waves in air columns. In the flue-type organ pipe shown in Figure 22-7 a stream of air is directed against the sharp edge of an opening (point A

in the figure). The complicated swirling motion of the air near the edge sets up vibrations in the air column. The resonance frequencies of the pipe depend on the length of the pipe and on whether the other end is closed or open.

In a closed organ pipe there is a pressure antinode at the closed end and a pressure node near the opening (point A in Figure 22-7). The resonance frequencies for such a pipe are therefore those for a tube open at one end and closed at the other. The wavelength of the fundamental is approximately 4 times the length of the pipe, and only odd harmonics are present.

In an open organ pipe, there is a pressure node near both ends of the pipe. The resonance frequencies for a pipe open at both ends are the same as for one closed at both ends except that there is an end correction at each end. The wavelength of the fundamental is 2 times the effective length of the pipe, and all harmonics are present.

Figure 22-7
Flue-type organ pipe. A stream of air is blown against the edge, causing a swirling motion of the air near point A, which excites standing waves in the pipe. There is a pressure node near point A, which is open to the atmosphere. The resonance frequencies of the pipe depend on the length of the pipe and on whether the other end is open or closed.

Question

4. How do the resonance frequencies of an organ pipe change when the air temperature increases?

Review

A. Define, explain, or otherwise identify:

Fundamental frequency, 538	Overtone, 539
Standing wave, 539	Node, 541
Harmonic, 539	Antinode, 541
Harmonic series, 539	Boundary condition, 541

B. Sketch the wave functions for the fundamental and first three overtones for a string fixed at both ends. From your sketches, write down the wavelengths for these harmonics. Do the same for a string fixed at one end and free at the other end.

C. Sketch both the displacement and pressure standing-wave functions for the fundamental and first three overtones in an organ pipe open at both ends. Do the same for a pipe open at only one end.

D. True or false:

1. A standing wave can be considered to be the superposition of a wave traveling to the right plus one traveling to the left.

2. The frequency of the fifth harmonic is 5 times the frequency of the fundamental.

3. In a pipe open at one end and closed at the other end, the even harmonics cannot be excited.

4. Because of the end correction, the pressure antinodes are not separated by $\frac{1}{2}$ wavelength in an open pipe.

5. The fundamental frequency of an organ pipe open at one end and closed at the other is lower than that of a pipe of the same length open at both ends.

Exercises

Section 22-1, Standing Waves on a String Fixed at Both Ends

1. A 5-gm steel wire 1 m long is under tension of 968 N. (*a*) Find the speed of transverse waves in the wire. (*b*) Find the wavelength and frequency of the fundamental. (*c*) Find the frequency of the second and third harmonics.

2. Middle C on the equal-temperament scale used by modern instrument makers has a frequency of 261.63 Hz. If this is the fundamental frequency of a 7-gm piano wire 80 cm long, what should the tension in the wire be?

3. A piano string without windings has a fundamental frequency of 200 Hz. When it is wound with wire, its linear mass density is doubled. What is its fundamental frequency then?

4. A string fixed at both ends is 3 m long. It resonates in its second harmonic at a frequency of 60 Hz. What is the speed of transverse waves in the string?

5. The length of the B string on a certain guitar is 60 cm. It vibrates at 247 Hz. (a) What is the speed of transverse waves on the string? (b) If the linear mass density is 0.01 gm/cm, what should the tension be when it is in tune?

Section 22-2, Standing-Wave Functions

6. Show that the wave function for the nth harmonic on a string of length L fixed at both ends can be written $y(x,t) = y_0 \cos (n\pi vt/L) \sin (n\pi x/L)$, where v is the wave speed.

7. A string 3 m long fixed at both ends is vibrating in its third harmonic. The maximum displacement of any point on the string is 4 mm. The speed of transverse waves on this string is 50 m/sec. (a) What are the wavelength and frequency for this wave? (b) Write the wave function for this wave.

8. The wave function for a certain standing wave on a string fixed at both ends is $y(x,t) = 0.30 \sin 0.20x \cos 300t$, where y and x are in centimeters and t in seconds. (a) What are the wavelength and frequency of these waves? (b) What is the speed of transverse waves on this string? (c) If the string is vibrating in its fourth harmonic, how long is it?

9. The wave function for a certain standing wave on a string fixed at both ends is $y(x,t) = 0.5 \sin 0.025x \cos 500t$, where y and x are in centimeters and t in seconds. (a) Find the speed and amplitude of the two traveling waves which result in this standing wave. (b) What is the distance between successive nodes in the string? (c) What is the shortest possible length of the string?

10. A string 2.51 m long has the wave function given in Exercise 9. (a) Sketch the position of the string for the times $t = 0$; $t = \frac{1}{4}T$; $t = \frac{1}{2}T$; $t = \frac{3}{4}T$, where $T = 1/f$ is the period of the vibration. (b) Find T in seconds. (c) When the string is horizontal, what has become of the energy in the wave?

Section 22-3, Standing Waves on a String Fixed at One End

11. A 160-gm rope 4 m long is fixed at one end and tied to a light string at the other end. Its tension is 400 N. (a) What are the wavelengths of the fundamental and the first two overtones? (b) What are the frequencies of these standing waves?

12. A string fixed at one end only is vibrating in its fundamental mode. The wave function is $y(x,t) = 0.02 \sin 2.36x \cos 377t$, where y and x are in meters and t in seconds. (a) What is the wavelength of the wave? (b) What is the length of the string? (c) What is the speed of transverse waves on the string?

13. A string 5 m long fixed at one end only is vibrating in its fifth harmonic with frequency 400 Hz. The maximum displacement of any segment of the string is 3 cm. (a) What is the wavelength of this wave? What is the wave number k? (b) What is the angular frequency? (c) Write the wave function for this standing wave.

14. Three successive resonant frequencies for a certain string are 75, 125, and 175 Hz. (a) Find the ratios of each pair of successive resonant frequencies. (b) How can you tell that these frequencies are for a string fixed at one end only rather than for a string fixed at both ends? (c) What is the fundamental

frequency? (*d*) Which harmonics are these resonance frequencies? (*e*) If the speed of transverse waves on this string is 400 m/sec, find the length of the string.

Section 22-4, Standing Sound Waves

Unless otherwise specified, take the speed of sound to be 340 m/sec = 1115 ft/sec.

15. Calculate the fundamental frequency for a 32-ft organ pipe which is open at both ends and for one that is closed at one end.

16. The normal range of hearing is from about 20 Hz to about 20,000 Hz. What is the greatest length of an organ pipe that would have its fundamental note in this range: (*a*) if it is closed at one end; (*b*) if it is open at both ends?

17. The shortest pipes used in organs are about 3 in long. (*a*) What is the fundamental frequency of a pipe this long which is open at both ends? (*b*) What is the highest harmonic for such a pipe which is within the audible range (see Exercise 16)?

18. The space above the water in the tube shown in Figure 22-6 is 120 cm long. Near the open end is a loudspeaker driven by an audio oscillator whose frequency can be varied from 10 to 5000 Hz. (*a*) What is the lowest frequency of the oscillator which will resonate with the tube? (*b*) What is the greatest frequency which will resonate? (*c*) How many different frequencies of the oscillator will produce resonance?

Problems

1. The G string on a violin is 30 cm long. When played without fingering, it vibrates at frequency 196 Hz. The next higher notes on the scale are A (220 Hz), B (247 Hz), C (262 Hz), and D (294 Hz). How far from the end of the string must a finger be placed to play these notes?

2. A steel piano wire is 40 cm long, has a mass of 2 gm, and is under tension of 600 N. (*a*) What is the fundamental frequency? (*b*) What is the wavelength in air of sound produced when the wire vibrates at its fundamental frequency? (*c*) If the highest frequency a certain listener can hear is 14,000 Hz, what is the highest harmonic produced by the wire that he can hear?

3. An early method for determining the speed of sound in different gases was as follows. A cylindrical glass tube is placed horizontally, and a quantity of light powder or fine wood shavings is spread along the bottom of the tube. One end is closed by a piston which can be attached to an oscillator of known frequency *f* (such as a tuning fork). The other end is closed by a piston whose position can be varied. While the opposite piston is made to oscillate at frequency *f*, the movable piston's position is adjusted until resonance occurs. When this happens, the powder collects in piles equally spaced along the bottom of the tube. (This is known as *Kundt's method*.) (*a*) Explain why the powder collects in this way. (*b*) Derive a formula which gives the speed of sound in the gas in terms of *f* and the distance between piles of powder. (*c*) Give suitable values for the frequency *f* and the length *L* of the tube for which the speed of sound could be measured using either air or helium.

4. A string with mass density of 4×10^{-3} kg/m is under tension of 360 N and is fixed at both ends. One of its resonance frequencies is 375 Hz. The next higher resonance frequency is 450 Hz. (*a*) What is the fundamental resonance frequency? (*b*) Which harmonics are the ones given? (*c*) What is the length of the string?

5. A string fastened at both ends has successive resonances with wavelengths of 0.54 m for the *n*th harmonic and 0.48 m for the (*n* + 1)st harmonic. (*a*) Which harmonics are these? (*b*) What is the length of the string? (*c*) What is the wavelength of the fundamental?

6. Three successive resonance frequencies in an organ pipe are 1310, 1834, and 2358 Hz. (a) Is the pipe closed at one end or open at both ends? (b) What is the fundamental frequency? (c) What is the length of the pipe?

7. A wire of mass 1 gm and length 50 cm is stretched with a tension of 440 N. It is placed near the open end of the tube in Figure 22-6 and stroked with a violin bow so that it oscillates with its fundamental frequency. The water level in the tube is lowered until a resonance is first obtained, at 18 cm below the top of the tube. Use these data to determine the speed of sound in air. Why is this method not very accurate?

8. A 40-cm-long wire of mass 0.01 kg vibrates in its second harmonic. When it is placed near the open end of the tube in Figure 22-6, resonance with the fundamental of the tube occurs if the water level is 1 m below the top of the tube. Assuming the speed of sound in air to be 340 m/sec, find: (a) the frequency of oscillation of the air column in the tube, (b) the speed of waves along the wire, and (c) the tension in the wire.

9. With a tuning fork of frequency 500 Hz held above the tube in Figure 22-6, resonances are found when the water level is at distances 16, 50.5, 85, and 119.5 cm. Use these data to calculate the speed of sound in air. How far outside the open end of the tube is the pressure node?

10. In a lecture demonstration of standing waves, a string is attached to a tuning fork which vibrates at 60 Hz and sets up transverse waves of that frequency on the string. The other end of the string passes over a pulley, and the tension is varied by attaching weights to that end. The string has approximate nodes at the tuning fork and at the pulley. If the string has mass density 8 gm/m and is 2.5 m long (from tuning fork to pulley), what must the tension be for the string to oscillate in its fundamental mode? Find the tensions for vibration in the first three overtones.

11. (a) For the wave function given in Exercise 12, find the velocity of a string segment at some point x as a function of time. (b) Which point has the greatest speed at any time? What is the maximum speed of this point? (c) Find the acceleration of a string segment at some point x as a function of time. Which point has the greatest acceleration? What is the maximum acceleration of this point?

12. A 2-m string is fixed at one end and vibrating in its third harmonic. The greatest displacement of any segment of the string is 3 cm. The frequency of vibration is 100 Hz. (a) Write the wave function for this vibration. (b) Write an expression for the kinetic energy of a segment of the string of length dx at point x at some time t. At what time is this kinetic energy maximum? What is the shape of the string at this time? (c) Find the maximum kinetic energy of the string by integrating your expression over the total length of the string. (d) Find the potential energy of a segment of the string and compute the maximum potential energy of the string by integration. Hint: Remember that the potential energy of a mass m in simple harmonic motion of angular frequency ω is $\frac{1}{2}m\omega^2 y^2$, where y is the displacement.

13. Show that if the tension in a string fixed at both ends is changed by a small amount ΔT, the frequency of the fundamental is changed approximately by Δf, where $\Delta f/f = \frac{1}{2}\Delta T/T$. (Use the differential approximation.) Does this result apply to all harmonics? Use this to find the percentage change in tension needed to raise the frequency of the fundamental of a piano wire from 260 to 262 Hz.

14. Show that if the temperature changes by a small amount ΔT, the fundamental frequency of an organ pipe changes by approximately Δf, where $\Delta f/f = \frac{1}{2}\Delta T/T$. Suppose an organ pipe closed at one end has a fundamental frequency of 200 Hz when the temperature is 68°F. What will its fundamental frequency be when the temperature is 90°F? (Ignore any change in the length of the pipe due to thermal expansion.)

The following sections from Chapters 23 and 24, covering beats and the doppler effect, are included so that a more complete treatment of sound waves is available in Volume 1.

23-1 Superposition of Two Waves of Nearly Equal Frequency and Wavelength

Consider two waves of slightly different frequencies and wavelengths but having equal amplitudes and moving in the same direction. Let us choose the waves to be in phase at $t = 0$ and $x = 0$:

$$y_1 = y_0 \cos (k_1 x - \omega_1 t) \tag{23-1}$$

$$y_2 = y_0 \cos (k_2 x - \omega_2 t) \tag{23-2}$$

where $k = 2\pi/\lambda$ and $\omega = 2\pi f$. The resultant wave can be found by graphical addition or by algebraic addition of the functions using a trigonometric identity for the sum of two cosine functions. Figure 23-1a

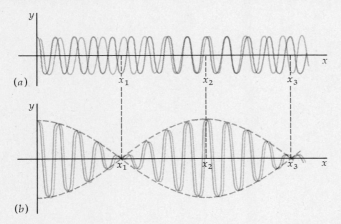

(a)

(b)

shows the waves at time $t = 0$, when the waves are in phase and add constructively at $x = 0$. Because of the difference in wavelength, they are out of phase at other places. At some distance x_1, the waves are 180° out of phase and add to zero. At an equal distance beyond this point, at x_2, the waves are in phase again. The greater the difference in wavelength, the shorter the distance x_1 in which they become out of phase. Figure 23-1 also could represent the time dependence of the waves at the fixed point $x = 0$. Initially they are in phase, but because of the difference in frequency, they are 180° out of phase and cancel at some time later t_1. Later they are again in phase and interfere constructively. The greater the difference in frequency, the sooner they will be out of phase and cancel.

We can add the waves algebraically by using $\cos A + \cos B = 2 \cos \frac{1}{2}(A - B) \cos \frac{1}{2}(A + B)$. Let $y(x,t)$ be the resultant wave function. Then

$$\begin{aligned} y(x,t) = y_2 + y_1 &= y_0 \cos (k_2 x - \omega_2 t) + y_0 \cos (k_1 x - \omega_1 t) \\ &= 2y_0 \cos [\tfrac{1}{2}(k_2 - k_1)x - \tfrac{1}{2}(\omega_2 - \omega_1)t] \cos [\tfrac{1}{2}(k_2 + k_1)x - \tfrac{1}{2}(\omega_2 + \omega_1)t] \end{aligned} \tag{23-3}$$

This result is simplified if we use the notation Δk and $\Delta \omega$ for the differences in wave number and frequency and $\bar{k}$ and $\bar{\omega}$ for their averages:

$$\Delta k = k_2 - k_1 \qquad \Delta \omega = \omega_2 - \omega_1 \qquad \bar{k} = \tfrac{1}{2}(k_2 + k_1) \qquad \bar{\omega} = \tfrac{1}{2}(\omega_2 + \omega_1) \tag{23-4}$$

Figure 23-1
(a) Two waves of different wavelengths at a time when they are in phase at $x = 0$. At x_1 they are 180° out of phase and cancel completely. At x_2 they are in phase again, and at x_3 they are 180° out of phase. (b) The resultant of the two waves shown in part (a). The wavelength of the rapid oscillation is about the same as that of the original waves, but the amplitude is modulated, as indicated by the dashed envelope. The amplitude is maximum at $x = 0$ and $x = x_2$ and zero at $x = x_1$ and $x = x_3$.

Then Equation 23-3 becomes

$$y = 2y_0 \cos (\tfrac{1}{2}\Delta k \, x - \tfrac{1}{2}\Delta\omega \, t) \cos (\bar{k}x - \bar{\omega}t) \qquad \text{23-5}$$

The resultant wave is sketched in Figure 23-1b for frequencies and wavelengths nearly equal so that $\Delta\omega$ and Δk are small and $\bar{\omega}$ and $\bar{k}$ nearly equal to the frequency and wave number of either wave. The result is a wave of about the same frequency and wavelength as the original waves but with the amplitude *modulated* by the factor $\cos (\tfrac{1}{2}\Delta k \, x - \tfrac{1}{2}\Delta\omega \, t)$. The velocity of the resultant wave $v = \bar{\omega}/\bar{k}$ is nearly the same as that of the individual waves. This velocity is called the *phase velocity*. The envelope (dashed curve in Fig. 23-2b) travels as a wave of wave number $\tfrac{1}{2}\Delta k$ and angular frequency $\tfrac{1}{2}\Delta\omega$. We can find the velocity of the envelope by considering the modulating factor in Equation 23-5,

Phase velocity

$$\cos (\tfrac{1}{2}\Delta k \, x - \tfrac{1}{2}\Delta\omega \, t) = \cos \tfrac{1}{2}\Delta k \left(x - \frac{\Delta\omega}{\Delta k} \, t \right) = \cos \tfrac{1}{2}\Delta k \, (x - v_g t)$$

where

$$v_g = \frac{\Delta\omega}{\Delta k} \qquad \text{23-6}$$

The velocity of the envelope $v_g = \Delta\omega/\Delta k$ is called the *group velocity*. The relation between the group velocity and phase velocity depends on the medium through which the wave is transmitted. We shall show in Section 23-5 that in a medium in which the phase velocity does not depend on the frequency of the wave, the group and phase velocities are equal. Such a medium is called a *dispersionless medium.* Examples are waves on a perfectly flexible string, sound waves in air, and light waves in vacuum. On the other hand, if the phase velocity does depend on the frequency or wavelength, the group velocity and phase velocity are not equal. Examples are water waves, light waves in glass or water, and waves on a string which is not perfectly flexible. A medium for which the phase velocity depends on the frequency is called a *dispersive medium.*

Group velocity

23-2   Beats

When two sound sources of comparable intensity have nearly equal frequencies, the interference of the sound waves at the ear alternates between constructive and destructive interference. The sound heard alternates between loud and soft. Each pulsation is called a *beat.* The frequency of oscillation between loud and soft, or *beat frequency,* is just equal to the difference between the frequencies of the two sound sources. We can see this from Equation 23-5, which gives the resultant interference pattern of the two waves. If we have two tuning forks of frequency f_1 and f_2 and let the ear be at some fixed point x_1, the quantities $\tfrac{1}{2}\Delta k \, x_1$ and $\bar{k}x_1$ in Equation 23-5 are just phase constants. If we ignore these phase constants, we can write for the wave at the ear,

$$y(t) = 2y_0 \cos (\tfrac{1}{2}\,\Delta\omega \, t) \cos \bar{\omega}t = 2y_0 \cos (2\pi\tfrac{1}{2}\,\Delta f \, t) \cos 2\pi\bar{f}t \qquad \text{23-7}$$

The ear thus hears the average frequency $\bar{f} = \tfrac{1}{2}(f_1 + f_2)$ with the amplitude $2y_0 \cos (2\pi\tfrac{1}{2}\,\Delta f \, t)$. Since the energy of the wave is proportional to the square of the amplitude, the sound is loud whenever the amplitude is either maximum or minimum, i.e., whenever $\cos 2\pi\frac{1}{2}\Delta f\,t$ is $+1$ or -1. Since the maximum amplitude occurs with frequency $\frac{1}{2}\Delta f$, the frequency of maximum and minimum amplitudes is just twice this, or Δf. For example, if the tuning forks have frequencies 241 and 243 Hz, the ear will hear the frequency 242 Hz and the sound will be loud twice each second.

The phenomenon of beats is often used to compare an unknown frequency with a known frequency, as in tuning a piano with a tuning fork. The ear can detect beats up to about 10 per second. Above this the fluctuations in loudness are too rapid to be heard. Beats are also used to detect small frequency changes like those produced in a radar beam reflected from a moving car. The shift in frequency of the reflected beam is due to the doppler effect (Chapter 24). The velocity of the car is found by measuring the change in frequency, determined by measuring the beats produced by the reflected beam and the original radar source. There are many interesting related phenomena, such as the moiré pattern shown in Figure 23-2, which can be thought of as the beats produced by two sets of parallel lines when the spacing of one set differs slightly from that of the other.

Figure 23-2
Moiré pattern showing beats produced by two sets of parallel lines when the spacing of one set differs slightly from that of the other.

Questions

1. Two violinists are practicing the same piece of music together. Can a listener hear the beats as they play? If beats are heard, what can be done to prevent them?

2. When musical notes are sounded together to make chords, beats are produced. Why are they not noticed as such?

3. Discuss how the phenomenon of beats is used to tune musical instruments.

4. Pianos generally have more than one wire for each note. The wires are struck simultaneously by the same hammer when the note is sounded. What is the effect if these wires are slightly out of tune?

24-2   The Doppler Effect

If a wave source and a receiver are moving relative to each other, the frequency observed by the receiver is not the same as the source frequency. When they are moving toward each other, the observed frequency is greater than the source frequency, and when they are moving away from each other, the observed frequency is less than the source frequency. This is called the *doppler effect.* A familiar example is

Doppler effect

the change in pitch of a train whistle or car horn when the train or car is approaching or receding.

Before we calculate the doppler shift in frequency, we consider the reception of waves by a receiver at rest relative to the source. Figure 24-7 shows a source sending out waves of frequency f_0. This figure can represent either two-dimensional circular waves, e.g., surface water waves, or a two-dimensional drawing of three-dimensional spherical waves, e.g., waves from a point source. Let N be the number of waves emitted in a time Δt. Then $N = f_0 \Delta t$. If v is the speed of the wave relative to the medium, which we assume to be at rest relative to both the source and receiver, these waves will be contained in a distance $v \Delta t$. The wavelength of the waves is the ratio of this distance and the number of waves,

$$\lambda = \frac{v \Delta t}{N} = \frac{v \Delta t}{f_0 \Delta t} = \frac{v}{f_0} \qquad 24\text{-}4$$

The frequency observed by the receiver is the number of waves that pass him per unit time. The number that pass the receiver in time Δt is the number in the distance $v \Delta t$, which is $v \Delta t/\lambda$. The frequency observed by the receiver f_R is then

$$f_R = \frac{v \Delta t/\lambda}{\Delta t} = \frac{v}{\lambda} = f_0 \qquad 24\text{-}5$$

This is, of course, just the frequency of the wave source.

If the medium is not at rest relative to the source and receiver, e.g., there is a wind blowing in the case of sound waves, the wavelength changes but the frequency received is still equal to the source frequency. Let u_w be the speed of the wind, which we assume to be blowing from source to receiver. The speed of the waves relative to the source or receiver is then $v' = v + u_w$. The wavelength λ' between source and receiver is now greater than that with no wind because the same number of waves $N = f_0 \Delta t$ is now contained in the distance $v' \Delta t = (v + u_w) \Delta t$. The wavelength is

$$\lambda' = \frac{v' \Delta t}{N} = \frac{(v + u_w) \Delta t}{f_0 \Delta t} = \frac{v + u_w}{f_0} = \frac{v + u_w}{v} \lambda_0 \qquad 24\text{-}6$$

where $\lambda_0 = v/f_0$ is the original wavelength with no wind. The number of waves received in time Δt is now the number in the distance $v' \Delta t$, which is just $f_0 \Delta t$. Thus the frequency received is again f_0, in agreement with our common experience that the wind does not affect the observed frequency of horns, whistles, or musical instruments. Note that the wavelength and observed frequency with a wind blowing are given by Equations 24-4 and 24-5 with v replaced by v'.

Figure 24-8 shows a point source moving with speed u_S relative to a medium in which the wave speed is v. In front of the source the wavefronts are closer together, and behind the source they are farther apart than for a stationary source. The calculation of the wavelengths is similar to Equations 24-4 and 24-6. In time Δt, the source emits $N = f_0 \Delta t$ waves. The first wavefront travels a distance $v \Delta t$ while the source travels a distance $u_S \Delta t$. In front of the source the N wavefronts occupy the distance $v \Delta t - u_S \Delta t$; behind the source they occupy the distance $v \Delta t + u_S \Delta t$. The wavelength in front of the source is therefore

$$\lambda'_f = \frac{v \Delta t - u_S \Delta t}{f_0 \Delta t} = \frac{v - u_S}{f_0} = \frac{v}{f_0} \left(1 - \frac{u_S}{v}\right) \qquad 24\text{-}7$$

Figure 24-7
Representation of wavefronts from a point source at rest relative to the medium. The diagram can represent either spherical surfaces in three dimensions or circular wavefronts in two dimensions. The wavelength λ_0 is related to the frequency f_0 and the velocity of the wave v by $\lambda_0 = v/f_0$.

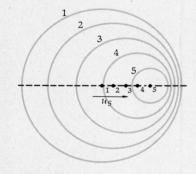

Figure 24-8
Successive wavefronts emitted by a point source moving with speed u_S to the right. Each numbered wavefront was emitted when the source was at the correspondingly numbered position. The wavelength is shorter than λ_0 in front of the source and greater than λ_0 behind the source.

Waves in a ripple tank produced by a source moving to the right with speed less than the wave speed. (*Courtesy of Film Studio, Education Development Center, Newton, Mass.*)

Behind the source the wavelength is

$$\lambda_b' = \frac{v\,\Delta t + u_S\,\Delta t}{f_0\,\Delta t} = \frac{v + u_S}{f_0} = \frac{v}{f_0}\left(1 + \frac{u_S}{v}\right) \qquad 24\text{-}8$$

When we use $\lambda_0 = v/f_0$ for the wavelength of the source at rest, Equations 24-7 and 24-8 can be written

$$\lambda' = \lambda_0\left(1 \pm \frac{u_S}{v}\right) \qquad 24\text{-}9$$

Wavelength in front of or behind moving source

The speed v of the waves depends only on the properties of the medium and not on the motion of the source. The frequency at which the waves pass a point at rest relative to the medium is thus

$$f' = \frac{v}{\lambda_f'} = \frac{f_0}{1 - u_S/v} \qquad 24\text{-}10$$

Frequency in front of moving source

for the source approaching the receiver and

$$f' = \frac{v}{\lambda_b'} = \frac{f_0}{1 + u_S/v} \qquad 24\text{-}11$$

Frequency behind moving source

for the source receding from the receiver.

If the source is at rest and the receiver is moving relative to the medium, there is no change in the wavelength but the frequency of the waves passing the receiver is increased when the receiver moves toward the source and decreased when he moves away from the source. The number of waves that pass a stationary receiver in time Δt is the number in the distance $v\,\Delta t$, which is $v\,\Delta t/\lambda_0$. When the receiver moves toward the source with speed u_R, he passes an additional number $u_R\,\Delta t/\lambda_0$ (Figure 24-9). The total number of waves passing the receiver in time Δt is then

$$N = \frac{v\,\Delta t + u_R\,\Delta t}{\lambda_0} = \frac{v + u_R}{\lambda_0}\,\Delta t$$

The frequency observed is this number divided by the time interval,

$$f' = \frac{N}{\Delta t} = \frac{v + u_R}{\lambda_0} = \frac{v + u_R}{v}\frac{v}{\lambda_0}$$

or

$$f' = f_0\left(1 + \frac{u_R}{v}\right) \qquad 24\text{-}12$$

Figure 24-9
The number of waves which pass a stationary receiver in time Δt is the number in the distance $v\,\Delta t$, where v is the wave speed. If the receiver moves toward the source with speed u_R, he passes the additional number which are in the distance $u_R\,\Delta t$. If λ is the wavelength, the total number of waves passed by the receiver in time Δt is $(v\,\Delta t + u_R\,\Delta t)/\lambda$ and the observed frequency is $f' = (v + u_R)/\lambda$.

If the receiver moves away from the source with speed u_R, similar reasoning leads to the observed frequency,

$$f' = f_0 \left(1 - \frac{u_R}{v}\right) \qquad\qquad 24\text{-}13$$

Frequency observed by receding receiver

The results expressed in Equations 24-10 to 24-13 can be combined when both source and receiver are moving relative to the medium. If the medium is moving, the wave speed v is replaced by $v' = v \pm v_w$, where v_w is the speed of the medium.

Example 24-1 The frequency of a car horn is 400 Hz. What frequency is observed if the car moves toward a stationary receiver with speed $u_S = 100$ ft/sec (about 68 mi/h)?

The velocity of sound relative to air is about 1100 ft/sec. According to Equation 24-7, λ is

$$\lambda'_f = \frac{v - u_S}{f_0} = \frac{1100 - 100 \text{ ft/sec}}{400 \text{ sec}^{-1}} = \frac{1000}{400} \text{ ft} = 2.5 \text{ ft}$$

The frequency observed is

$$f' = \frac{v}{\lambda'_f} = \frac{1100 \text{ ft/sec}}{2.5 \text{ ft}} = 440 \text{ sec}^{-1} = 440 \text{ Hz}$$

Of course we could use Equation 24-10 directly:

$$f' = \frac{f_0}{1 - u_S/v} = \frac{400 \text{ Hz}}{1 - 100/1100} = \frac{1100}{1000} 400 \text{ Hz} = 440 \text{ Hz}$$

We performed the intermediate step of calculating the wavelength first because this effect is easy to remember.

Example 24-2 The horn of a stationary car has a frequency of 400 Hz. What frequency is observed by a receiver moving toward the car at 100 ft/sec?

For a moving receiver, the wavelength does not change; the receiver merely passes more waves in a given time. The observed frequency, according to Equation 24-12, is

$$f' = f_0 \left(1 + \frac{u_R}{v}\right) = (400 \text{ Hz}) \left(1 + \frac{100}{1100}\right) = \frac{1200}{1100} (400 \text{ Hz}) = 436 \text{ Hz}$$

Example 24-3 Work Example 24-2 in the reference frame of the receiver.

In the reference frame of the receiver the car is moving toward the receiver with speed of 100 ft/sec. This situation is not identical to that in Example 24-1 because here the receiver observes an apparent wind of 100 ft/sec in the direction from the car to receiver. The speed of sound waves relative to the receiver is $v' = v + u_w = 1100$ ft/sec + 100 ft/sec = 1200 ft/sec. The wavelength of the waves in front of the car (which is moving relative to the receiver) is given by Equation 24-7 with v' replacing v. Thus

$$\lambda'_f = \frac{v' - u_S}{f_0} = \frac{v + u_w - u_S}{f_0}$$

But the wind speed u_w and the source speed u_S are the same. Both are 100 ft/sec in the frame of the receiver. The wavelength is thus

$$\lambda'_f = \frac{v}{f_0} = \lambda_0 = \frac{1100}{400} \text{ ft} = 2.75 \text{ ft}$$

The observed frequency is

$$f' = \frac{v'}{\lambda'_f} = \frac{1200}{2.75} \text{ Hz} = 436 \text{ Hz}$$

The fact that the wavelength and frequency are the same as in Example 24-2 should not be surprising. In these two examples, identical problems were worked in two different reference frames moving with constant velocity relative to each other.

From the above examples we note that the doppler shift in frequency depends on whether the source or receiver moves relative to the medium. In Example 24-1 the source moved with speed 100 ft/sec relative to the still air, and the frequency shifted from 400 to 440 Hz. In Examples 24-2 and 24-3 the receiver moved with speed 100 ft/sec relative to the still air, and the frequency shifted from 400 to 436 Hz. These shifts are approximately but not exactly equal.

It is interesting to compare these doppler shifts when the speed of the source or receiver u is much less than the wave speed v. According to Equation 24-10, the frequency observed for a source moving toward a receiver with speed u is

$$f' = \frac{f_0}{1 - u/v} = f_0 \left(1 - \frac{u}{v}\right)^{-1}$$

We can compare this with Equation 24-12 for a moving receiver using the binomial expansion

$$(1 + x)^n = 1 + nx + \frac{n(n-1)}{2} x^2 + \cdots$$

For x much less than 1 we may approximate, using only the first few terms. With $x = -u/v$ and $n = -1$, we have

$$\left(1 - \frac{u}{v}\right)^{-1} = 1 + (-1)\left(-\frac{u}{v}\right) + \frac{(-1)(-2)}{2}\left(-\frac{u}{v}\right)^2 + \cdots$$

$$\approx 1 + \frac{u}{v} + \frac{u^2}{v^2}$$

Then Equation 24-14 is approximately

$$f' \approx f_0 \left(1 + \frac{u}{v} + \frac{u^2}{v^2}\right) \qquad\qquad 24\text{-}15$$

On the other hand, if a receiver moves toward a stationary source with speed u, the observed frequency is (Equation 24-12)

$$f' = f_0 \left(1 + \frac{u}{v}\right)$$

These results differ only in terms of order u^2/v^2 or higher.

In many practical situations this difference can be neglected, but the difference is real and of theoretical importance because it shows that these two situations are really different. Not only is the *relative* motion of the source and receiver important, but also the "absolute" motion of both relative to the medium. Thus if we can measure the doppler shift in frequency to order u^2/v^2, we can tell whether it is the source that is moving relative to the medium or the receiver. For sound waves in air, for example, we can also tell which is moving by noting whether it is the source or receiver that feels the wind in his own reference frame. However, a problem arises for light or other electromagnetic waves which propagate through a vacuum. Our equations for the doppler effect seem to imply that we could detect absolute motion relative to the vacuum if we could measure the doppler shift accurately enough, but this contradicts the principle of relativity. Thus either these equations are not correct, or the principle of relativity does not hold. We shall see in our study of special relativity in Chapter 28 that a small but important correction must be made for these equations describing the doppler effect. The correct expression for the doppler shift of light and other electromagnetic waves is

$$f' = \frac{\sqrt{1 - u^2/c^2}}{1 \pm u/c} f_0 \qquad 24\text{-}16$$

Relativistic doppler effect for light

where u is the relative velocity of source and observer and c is the velocity of light. There is no way of distinguishing which is moving; only the relative velocity is important. Comparing this expression with Equations 24-10 and 24-11, we see that the expressions differ by the factor $\sqrt{1 - u^2/c^2}$. This factor arises in the relativistic derivation because the time interval between the emission of the first wave and the Nth wave is not the same when measured by the source and by the receiver, though we have, of course, assumed this in our classical derivation.

In our derivation of the doppler-shift expressions we have assumed that the velocity u of the source or receiver is less than the wave velocity v. If the source moves with velocity greater than the wave velocity, there will be no waves in front of the source. The waves behind the source will be increased in length according to Equation 24-8, but they will be confined to a cone which narrows as u increases. We can easily calculate the angle of this cone. Consider the source at position P_1 at time t_1, as shown in Figure 24-10. After a time Δt, the wave emitted from this point will have traveled a distance $v\,\Delta t$. The source will have traveled a greater distance $u\,\Delta t$ and will be at point P_2. The line from this new position of the source to the wavefront emitted when the source was at P_1 makes an angle θ with the path of the source given by

$$\sin\theta = \frac{v\,\Delta t}{u\,\Delta t} = \frac{v}{u} \qquad 24\text{-}17$$

Figure 24-10
A source moving from P_1 to P_2 with speed u greater than the wave speed v in the medium. There are no wavefronts ahead of the source, and so the envelope of the wavefronts forms a cone with the source at the apex. The angle this cone makes with the direction of motion of the source is given by $\sin\theta = v/u$.

Waves in a ripple tank produced by a source moving to the right with speed greater than the wave speed. (*Courtesy of Film Studio, Education Development Center, Newton, Mass.*)

Equation 24-17 applies to electromagnetic radiation given off when a charged particle moves in a medium with speed u which is greater than the speed of light v in that medium.[1] Called *Čerenkov radiation*, it is confined to the cone with angle given by Equation 24-17.

If the receiver moves toward the source faster than the wave speed, there is no problem. Equation 24-12 holds for the observed frequency. If the receiver moves away from the source faster than the wave speed, the waves never reach the receiver. For light waves, the relativistic expression for the doppler effect given by Equation 24-16 becomes imaginary for u greater than c because of the square-root term in the numerator. According to the special theory of relativity, the relative speed between the source and receiver cannot exceed the speed of light c in vacuum.

Questions

1. Suppose the velocity vector of a receiver makes an angle with the line between him and the source. How will the doppler shift differ from the case discussed in this section? What if the velocity vector makes a right angle with the line joining source and receiver?

2. If the source and receiver are at rest relative to each other but the wave medium is moving relative to them, will the receiver detect any wavelength or frequency shift?

24-3 Interference of Two Point Sources

Figure 24-11 shows the wave pattern produced by two point sources S_1 and S_2 a distance d apart oscillating in phase, each producing circular waves of frequency f, wavelength λ, and speed $v = f\lambda$.

---

[1] It is impossible for a particle to move faster than c, the speed of light in a vacuum. In a medium such as glass, however, electrons and other particles can move faster than the speed of light in that medium.

Figure 24-11
Interference of two point sources in a ripple tank. (*From PCCS Physics, 2d ed., p. 285, D. C. Heath and Company, Lexington, Mass., 1965*)

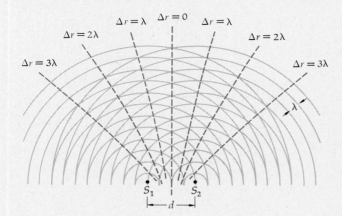

Figure 24-12
Geometric construction of the
interference pattern similar to
Figure 24-11. The wavefronts
add constructively at the
points of intersection. Such
points occur whenever the
path lengths from the two
sources differ by an integral
number of wavelengths.

We can construct a similar pattern (Figure 24-12) with a compass by drawing circular arcs representing wave crests from each source at some particular time. At the points where the crests from each source overlap, the waves add constructively. At these points the paths for the waves from the two sources are either equal in length or differ by an integral number of wavelengths. These path differences are indicated in Figure 24-12. The line through a set of interference maxima for which the path difference is some integral number of wavelengths is a hyperbola. (A hyperbola is in fact defined as the locus of points whose distances from two fixed points differ by a constant amount.) Between each set of interference maxima are interference minima, where the path difference is an odd number of half wavelengths. These lines along which the waves completely cancel are called *nodes* or *nodal lines*. They are also hyperbolas.

We can understand this pattern by applying the results of Section 21-4 for the combination of two harmonic waves having equal frequency, wavelength, and amplitude but a phase difference δ. We found that the resultant of two such harmonic waves is itself a harmonic wave with amplitude

$$A = 2A_0 \cos \tfrac{1}{2}\delta \qquad\qquad 24\text{-}18$$

where A_0 is the amplitude of each wave separately. The phase difference is related to the path difference Δr by

$$\delta = 2\pi \frac{\Delta r}{\lambda} \qquad\qquad 24\text{-}19$$

The interference of two sound sources can be demonstrated by driving two separated speakers with the same amplifier which is fed by an audio signal generator. Moving about the room enables one to detect by ear the positions of constructive or destructive interference. The sound intensity will not actually be zero at the points of destructive interference of the direct sound waves because of sound reflections from the walls and other objects in the room.

In optics, we often observe the intensity pattern on a screen placed parallel to the line of the sources and far away from the sources compared with their separation d. This is called *Young's experiment*, after Thomas Young, who in 1801 used the interference pattern produced by two light sources to demonstrate the wave nature of light. We can calculate the intensity pattern observed when the screen is far from the sources.

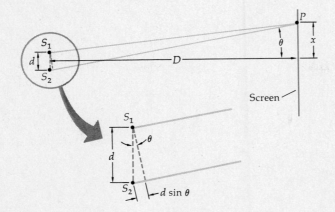

Figure 24-13
Geometry for calculation of
interference pattern observed
on a screen a distance D from
two sources in phase separated by a much smaller distance d. When the screen is
far away, the rays from the
sources to some point P are
approximately parallel and
the path difference is approximately $d \sin \theta$. Constructive
interference occurs when
$d \sin \theta$ is an integral number
of wavelengths. For small θ the
approximation $\sin \theta \approx \tan \theta$
$= x/D$ can be used.

At very large distances from the sources, the lines from the two sources to some point P on the screen are approximately parallel, and the path difference is approximately $d \sin \theta$, as shown in Figure 24-13. We thus have interference maxima at angles given by

$$d \sin \theta = m\lambda \qquad \text{24-20}$$

and minima at

$$d \sin \theta = (m + \tfrac{1}{2})\lambda \qquad \text{24-21}$$

*Two-source interference
maxima and minima*

where m is any integer $(0, 1, 2, \dots)$. The phase difference at a point P is $2\pi/\lambda$ times the path difference $d \sin \theta$:

$$\delta = \frac{2\pi}{\lambda} d \sin \theta \qquad \text{24-22}$$

Phase difference at angle θ

The distance x measured along the screen from the central point to point P is related to θ by $x = D \tan \theta$. We are usually interested in points for which θ is very small, so that $\sin \theta \approx \tan \theta \approx \theta$. Then $\sin \theta \approx x/D$. Substituting this into Equation 24-22, we have for the phase difference at distance x,

$$\delta = \frac{2\pi x d}{\lambda D} \qquad \text{24-23}$$

The amplitude at this distance is

$$2A_0 \cos \tfrac{1}{2}\delta = 2A_0 \cos \frac{\pi x d}{\lambda D}$$

The intensity is proportional to the square of the amplitude and thus is proportional to

$$4A_0^2 \cos^2 \frac{\pi x d}{\lambda D}$$

Figure 24-14 is a plot of the intensity versus $\sin \theta$, which is equivalent to a plot of intensity versus x for small θ since $\sin \theta \approx x/D$.

Since the average value of a cosine-squared function over a cycle is $\tfrac{1}{2}$, the average intensity is proportional to $2A_0^2$, indicated by the dashed line.[1] This is just the intensity which would arise from the two sources

---

[1] For any angle α the identity $\sin^2 \alpha + \cos^2 \alpha = 1$ holds. It is easily seen from a plot of $\sin^2 \alpha$ and $\cos^2 \alpha$ that the average values of these functions over a complete cycle are equal. Thus the average value of either $\sin^2 \alpha$ or $\cos^2 \alpha$ over a cycle is $\tfrac{1}{2}$.

Figure 24-14
Plot of relative intensity versus sin θ observed on a screen far away from two sources in phase as in Figure 24-13. The maximum intensity is proportional to $4A_0^2$ at sin $\theta = m\lambda/d$, where m is an integer and A_0 is the amplitude from each source separately. This is 4 times the intensity of either source acting separately. The average relative intensity $2A_0^2$, indicated by the dashed line, equals twice that of each source acting separately. Since sin $\theta \approx x/D$ for small θ, this is also a plot of relative intensity versus x.

acting separately without interference. We see thus that as a result of the interference of waves from the two sources, the energy is redistributed in space. At a maximum point, the energy is 4 times that from a single source, whereas at a minimum point there is no energy at all; but if we average over many interference maxima and minima, we get the same energy as if the sources acted separately without interference. This is what we should expect from the conservation of energy.

Questions

3. If two nearby sources have the same amplitude but different frequencies, is it possible for them to produce an interference pattern with fixed points of complete destructive interference?

4. The two sources whose resultant amplitude is given by Equation 24-18 were assumed to be vibrating in phase. Discuss what differences might be expected if they differed in phase.

APPENDIX A SI Units

Basic units

Length	The *meter* (m) is the length equal to 1,650,763.73 wavelengths in vacuum of the radiation corresponding to the transition between the $2p_{10}$ and $5d_5$ levels of the ^{86}Kr atom
Time	The *second* (sec) is the duration of 9,192,631,770 periods of the radiation corresponding to the transition between the two hyperfine levels of the ground state of the ^{133}Cs atom
Mass	The *kilogram* (kg) is the mass of the international standard body preserved at Sèvres, France
Current	The *ampere* (A) is that current in two very long parallel wires 1 m apart which gives rise to a magnetic force per unit length of 2×10^{-7} N/m
Temperature	The *kelvin* (K) is 1/273.16 of the thermodynamic temperature of the triple point of water
Luminous Intensity	The *candela* (cd) is the luminous intensity, in the perpendicular direction, of a surface of area 1/600,000 m² of a blackbody at the temperature of freezing platinum at pressure of 1 atm

Derived units

Force	Newton (N)	$1 \text{ N} = 1 \text{ kg-m/sec}^2$
Work, energy	Joule (J)	$1 \text{ J} = 1 \text{ N-m}$
Power	Watt (W)	$1 \text{ W} = 1 \text{ J/sec}$
Frequency	Hertz (Hz)	$1 \text{ Hz} = 1/\text{sec}$
Charge	Coulomb (C)	$1 \text{ C} = 1 \text{ A-sec}$
Potential	Volt (V)	$1 \text{ V} = 1 \text{ J/C}$
Resistance	Ohm (Ω)	$1 \text{ } \Omega = 1 \text{ V/A}$
Capacitance	Farad (F)	$1 \text{ F} = 1 \text{ C/V}$
Magnetic induction	Tesla (T)	$1 \text{ T} = 1 \text{ N/A-m}$
Magnetic flux	Weber (Wb)	$1 \text{ Wb} = 1 \text{ T-m}^2$
Inductance	Henry (H)	$1 \text{ H} = 1 \text{ J/A}^2$

APPENDIX B   Numerical Data

For additional data see the front and back endpapers and the following tables in the text:

Physical constants

Gravitational constant	G	6.672×10^{-11} N-m²/kg²
Speed of light	c	2.997925×10^8 m/sec
Electron charge	e	1.60219×10^{-19} C
Avogadro's number	N_A	6.0220×10^{23} particles/mole
Gas constant	R	8.314 J/mole-K
		1.9872 cal/mole-K
		8.206×10^{-2} ℓ-atm/mole-K
Boltzmann's constant	$k = R/N_A$	1.3807×10^{-23} J/K
		8.617×10^{-5} eV/K
Unified mass unit	u $= 1/N_A$ gm	1.6606×10^{-24} gm
Coulomb constant	$k = 1/4\pi\epsilon_0$	8.98755×10^9 N-m²/C²
Permittivity of free space	ϵ_0	8.85419×10^{-12} C²/N-m²
Magnetic constant	$k_m = \mu_0/4\pi$	10^{-7} N/A² (exact)

Physical constants
(continued)

Permeability of free space	μ_0	$4\pi \times 10^{-7}$ N/A^2
		1.256637×10^{-6} N/A^2
Planck's constant	h	6.6262×10^{-34} J-sec
		4.1357×10^{-15} eV-sec
	$\hbar = h/2\pi$	1.05459×10^{-34} J-sec
		6.5822×10^{-16} eV-sec
Mass of electron	m_e	9.1095×10^{-31} kg
		511.0 keV/c^2
Mass of proton	m_p	1.67265×10^{-27} kg
		938.28 MeV/c^2
Mass of neutron	m_n	1.67495×10^{-27} kg
		939.57 MeV/c^2
Bohr magneton	$m_B = e\hbar/2m_e$	9.2741×10^{-24} A-m^2
		5.7884×10^{-5} eV/T

Terrestrial data

Acceleration of gravity g	9.80665 m/sec^2 standard value
	32.1740 ft/sec^2
At sea level, at equator*	9.7804 m/sec^2
At sea level, at poles*	9.8322 m/sec^2
Mass of earth M_E	5.98×10^{24} kg
Radius of earth R_E, mean	6.37×10^6 m
	3960 mi
Escape velocity $\sqrt{2R_E g}$	1.12×10^4 m/sec
	6.95 mi/sec
Solar constant†	1.35 kW/m^2
Standard temperature and pressure (STP):	
T	273.15 K
P	1.00 atm
	1.01325×10^5 N/m^2
Molecular weight of air	28.97 gm/mole
Density of air (STP), ρ_{air}	1.293 kg/m^3
Speed of sound (STP)	331 m/sec
Heat of fusion of H_2O (0°C, 1 atm)	79.7 cal/gm
Heat of vaporization of H_2O (100°C, 1 atm)	539.6 cal/gm

* Measured relative to the earth's surface.
† Average power incident normally on 1 m^2 outside the earth's atmosphere at the mean distance from the earth to the sun.

Astronomical data

Earth, distance to moon*	3.844×10^8 m
	2.389×10^5 mi
Distance (mean) to sun*	1.496×10^{11} m
	9.30×10^7 mi
	1.00 AU
Orbital speed (mean)	2.98×10^4 m/sec
Moon, mass	7.35×10^{22} kg
Radius	1.738×10^6 m
Period	27.32 d
Acceleration of gravity at surface	1.62 m/sec^2
Sun, mass	1.99×10^{30} kg
Radius	6.96×10^8 m

* Center to center.

Densities of selected substances (STP)

Substance	Density, gm/cm^3*
Hydrogen	8.994×10^{-5}
Helium	1.786×10^{-4}
Air	1.293×10^{-3}
Alcohol (ethanol)	0.806
Water	1.00
Mercury	13.60
Aluminum	2.70
Iron	7.86
Copper	8.96
Lead	11.3
Gold	19.3

* 1 gm/cm^3 = 1000 kg/m^3.

APPENDIX C Conversion Factors

Conversion factors are written as equations for simplicity; relations marked with an asterisk are exact.

Length
*1 in = 2.54 cm

*1 ft = 12 in = 30.48 cm

*1 yd = 3 ft = 91.44 cm

1 m = 1.0936 yd = 3.281 ft = 39.37 in

*1 mi = 5280 ft = 1760 yd

1 mi = 1.609 km

1 light-year = 9.461×10^{15} m

*1 Å = 10^{-10} m

Area
*1 in^2 = 6.4516 cm^2

1 ft^2 = 9.29×10^{-2} m^2

*1 cm^2 = 10^{-4} m^2

*1 acre = 43,560 ft^2

1 mi^2 = 640 acres = 2.590 km^2

Volume
1 in^3 = 16.39 cm^3

1 ft^3 = 1728 in^3 = 28.32 ℓ = 2.832×10^4 cm^3

1 ℓ = 1000 cm^3 = 10^{-3} m^3 = 3.531×10^{-2} ft^3

1 gal = 4 qt = 8 pt = 128 oz = 231 in^3

1 gal = 3.786 ℓ

Time
*1 h = 60 min = 3600 sec

*1 d = 24 h = 1440 min = 8.64×10^4 sec

1 y = 365.24 d = 3.156×10^7 sec

Speed
*1 ft/sec = 0.3048 m/sec

1 mi/h = 0.4470 m/sec

1 mi/h = 1.467 ft/sec

Angle and angular velocity
*π rad = 180°

1 rad = 57.30°

1° = 1.745×10^{-2} rad

1 rev/min = 0.1047 rad/sec

1 rad/sec = 9.549 rev/min

Mass
*1 kg = 10^3 gm

1 slug = 14.59 kg

1 kg = 6.852×10^{-2} slug

1 kg = 6.022×10^{26} u

1 u = 1.6606×10^{-27} kg

Density
1 gm/cm^3 = 10^3 kg/m^3

(1 gm/cm^3)g = 62.4 lb/ft^3

Force
1 lb = 4.4482 N

1 N = 0.2248 lb = 10^5 dyne

(1 kg)g = 2.2046 lb

*1 ton = 2000 lb

Pressure
1 lb/in^2 = 6.895×10^3 N/m^2

*1 atm = 1.01325 bar = 1.01325×10^5 N/m^2

1 mm Hg = 133.32 N/m^2

1 in H_2O = 1.868 mm Hg = 249.1 N/m^2

Energy
1 ft-lb = 1.356 J = 3.766×10^{-7} kW-h = 1.286×10^{-3} Btu

*1 cal = 4.1840 J

1 Btu = 778 ft-lb = 252 cal = 1054 J

1 eV = 1.602×10^{-19} J

1 ℓ-atm = 101.325 J = 24.217 cal

*1 kW-h = 3.6×10^6 J

Power
1 horsepower = 550 ft-lb/sec = 745.7 W

1 Btu/min = 0.02357 horsepower = 17.58 W = 4.200 cal/sec

1 W = 1.341×10^{-3} horsepower = 0.7376 ft-lb/sec

Magnetic induction
*1 G = 10^{-4} T

*1 T = 10^4 G

APPENDIX D   Mathematical Symbols and Formulas

Mathematical Symbols and Abbreviations

$=$	is equal to
$\neq$	is not equal to
$\approx$	is approximately equal to
$\propto$	is proportional to
$>$	is greater than
$\gg$	is much greater than
$<$	is less than
$\ll$	is much less than
Δx	change in x
$n!$	$n(n-1)(n-2) \cdots 1$
Σ	sum
lim	limit
$\Delta t \to 0$	Δt approaches zero
$\int$	integral
$\dfrac{dx}{dt}$	derivative of x with respect to t
$\dfrac{\partial y}{\partial x}$	partial derivative of y with respect to x

Roots of the Quadratic Equation

If
$$ax^2 + bx + c = 0$$
then
$$x = \frac{-b}{2a} \pm \frac{1}{2a}\sqrt{b^2 - 4ac}$$

Binomial Expansion

$$(1 + x)^n = 1 + nx + \frac{n(n-1)}{2!}x^2 + \frac{n(n-1)(n-2)}{3!}x^3 + \cdots$$

To compute $(a + b)^n$ write
$$(a + b)^n = a^n(1 + x)^n \qquad \text{with } x = \frac{b}{a}$$
or
$$(a + b)^n = b^n(1 + y)^n \qquad \text{with } y = \frac{a}{b}$$

Trigonometric Formulas

See also Sec. 1-7.

$$\sin^2\theta + \cos^2\theta = 1 \qquad \sec^2\theta - \tan^2\theta = 1 \qquad \csc^2\theta - \operatorname{ctn}^2\theta = 1$$
$$\sin 2\theta = 2\sin\theta\cos\theta$$
$$\cos 2\theta = \cos^2\theta - \sin^2\theta = 2\cos^2\theta - 1 = 1 - 2\sin^2\theta$$

$$\tan 2\theta = \frac{2 \tan \theta}{1 - \tan^2 \theta}$$

$$\sin \tfrac{1}{2}\theta = \sqrt{\frac{1 - \cos \theta}{2}} \qquad \cos \tfrac{1}{2}\theta = \sqrt{\frac{1 + \cos \theta}{2}} \qquad \tan \tfrac{1}{2}\theta = \sqrt{\frac{1 - \cos \theta}{1 + \cos \theta}}$$

$$\sin (A \pm B) = \sin A \cos B \pm \cos A \sin B$$

$$\cos (A \pm B) = \cos A \cos B \mp \sin A \sin B$$

$$\tan (A \pm B) = \frac{\tan A \pm \tan B}{1 \mp \tan A \tan B}$$

$$\sin A \pm \sin B = 2 \sin [\tfrac{1}{2}(A \pm B)] \cos [\tfrac{1}{2}(A \mp B)]$$

$$\cos A + \cos B = 2 \cos [\tfrac{1}{2}(A + B)] \cos [\tfrac{1}{2}(A - B)]$$

$$\cos A - \cos B = 2 \sin [\tfrac{1}{2}(A + B)] \sin [\tfrac{1}{2}(B - A)]$$

$$\tan A \pm \tan B = \frac{\sin (A \pm B)}{\cos A \cos B}$$

Exponential and Logarithmic Functions

$$e = 2.71828 \qquad e^0 = 1$$

If $y = e^x$, then $x = \ln y$.

$$e^{\ln x} = x$$

$$e^x e^y = e^{(x+y)}$$

$$(e^x)^y = e^{xy} = (e^y)^x$$

$$\ln e = 1 \qquad \ln 1 = 0$$

$$\ln xy = \ln x + \ln y$$

$$\ln \frac{x}{y} = \ln x - \ln y$$

$$\ln e^x = x \qquad \ln a^x = x \ln a$$

$$\ln x = (\ln 10) \log x = 2.3026 \log x$$

$$\log x = \log e \ln x = 0.43429 \ln x$$

$$e^x = 1 + x + \frac{x^2}{2!} + \frac{x^3}{3!} + \cdots$$

$$\ln (1 + x) = x - \frac{x^2}{2} + \frac{x^3}{3} - \frac{x^4}{4} + \cdots$$

APPENDIX E   Derivatives and Integrals

Table E-1 lists some important properties of derivatives and the derivatives of some particular functions which often occur in physics. It is followed by comments aimed at making these properties and rules plausible. More detailed and rigorous discussions can be found in most calculus books. Table E-2 lists some important integration formulas. More extensive lists of differentiation and integration formulas can be found in handbooks, e.g., Herbert Dwight, *Tables of Integrals and Other Mathematical Data*, 4th ed., Macmillan Publishing Co. Inc., New York, 1961.

Table E-1
Properties of derivatives and derivatives of particular functions

---

Linearity

---

1. The derivative of a constant times a function equals the constant times the derivative of the function:

$$\frac{d}{dt}\left[Cf(t)\right] = C\,\frac{df(t)}{dt}$$

2. The derivative of a sum of functions equals the sum of the derivatives of the functions:

$$\frac{d}{dt}\left[f(t) + g(t)\right] = \frac{df(t)}{dt} + \frac{dg(t)}{dt}$$

Chain rule

---

3. If f is a function of x and x is in turn a function of t, the derivative of f with respect to t equals the product of the derivative of f with respect to x and the derivative of x with respect to t:

$$\frac{d}{dt}f(x) = \frac{df}{dx}\frac{dx}{dt}$$

Derivative of a product

4. The derivative of a product of functions $f(t)g(t)$ equals the first function times the derivative of the second plus the second function times the derivative of the first:

$$\frac{d}{dt}\left[f(t)g(t)\right] = f(t)\,\frac{dg(t)}{dt} + \frac{df(t)}{dt}\,g(t)$$

Reciprocal derivative

5. The derivative of t with respect to x is the reciprocal of the derivative of x with respect to t assuming that neither derivative is zero:

$$\frac{dx}{dt} = \left(\frac{dt}{dx}\right)^{-1} \quad \text{if} \quad \frac{dt}{dx} \neq 0$$

Derivatives of particular functions

6. $\dfrac{dC}{dt} = 0 \qquad$ where C is a constant

7. $\dfrac{d(t^n)}{dt} = nt^{n-1}$

8. $\dfrac{d}{dt}\sin\omega t = \omega\cos\omega t$

9. $\dfrac{d}{dt}\cos\omega t = -\omega\sin\omega t$

10. $\dfrac{d}{dt}e^{bt} = be^{bt}$

11. $\dfrac{d}{dt}\ln bt = \dfrac{1}{t}$

Comment on Rules 1 to 5

Rules 1 and 2 follow from the fact that the limiting process is linear. We can understand rule 3, the chain rule, by multiplying $\Delta f/\Delta t$ by $\Delta x/\Delta x$ and noting that since x is a function of t, both Δx and Δf approach zero as Δt approaches zero. Since the limit of a product of two functions equals the product of their limits, we have

$$\lim_{\Delta t\to 0}\frac{\Delta f}{\Delta t} = \lim_{\Delta t\to 0}\frac{\Delta f}{\Delta x}\frac{\Delta x}{\Delta t} = \left(\lim_{\Delta x\to 0}\frac{\Delta f}{\Delta x}\right)\left(\lim_{\Delta t\to 0}\frac{\Delta x}{\Delta t}\right) = \frac{df}{dx}\frac{dx}{dt}$$

Rule 4 is not immediately apparent. The derivative of a product of functions is the limit of the ratio

$$\frac{f(t+\Delta t)g(t+\Delta t) - f(t)g(t)}{\Delta t}$$

If we add and subtract the quantity $f(t+\Delta t)g(t)$ in the numerator, we can write this ratio as

$$\frac{f(t+\Delta t)g(t+\Delta t) - f(t+\Delta t)g(t) + f(t+\Delta t)g(t) - f(t)g(t)}{\Delta t}$$

$$= f(t+\Delta t)\left[\frac{g(t+\Delta t) - g(t)}{\Delta t}\right] + g(t)\left[\frac{f(t+\Delta t) - f(t)}{\Delta t}\right]$$

As Δt approaches zero, the terms in brackets become $dg(t)/dt$ and $df(t)/dt$, respectively, and the limit of the expression is

$$f(t)\,\frac{dg(t)}{dt} + g(t)\,\frac{df(t)}{dt}$$

Rule 5 follows directly from the definition:

$$\frac{dx}{dt} = \lim_{\Delta t \to 0} \frac{\Delta x}{\Delta t} = \lim_{\Delta t \to 0} \left(\frac{\Delta t}{\Delta x}\right)^{-1} = \lim_{\Delta x \to 0} \left(\frac{\Delta t}{\Delta x}\right)^{-1} = \left(\lim_{\Delta x \to 0} \frac{\Delta t}{\Delta x}\right)^{-1}$$

Comment on Rule 7

We can obtain this important result using the binomial expansion (Appendix D). We have

$$f(t) = t^n$$

$$f(t + \Delta t) = (t + \Delta t)^n = t^n \left(1 + \frac{\Delta t}{t}\right)^n$$

$$= t^n \left[1 + n\,\frac{\Delta t}{t} + \frac{n(n-1)}{2!}\left(\frac{\Delta t}{t}\right)^2 + \frac{n(n-1)(n-2)}{3!}\left(\frac{\Delta t}{t}\right)^3 + \cdots\right]$$

Then

$$f(t - \Delta t) - f(t) = t^n \left[n\,\frac{\Delta t}{t} + \frac{n(n-1)}{2!}\left(\frac{\Delta t}{t}\right)^2 + \cdots\right]$$

and

$$\frac{f(t - \Delta t) - f(t)}{\Delta t} = nt^{n-1} + \frac{n(n-1)}{2!}\,t^{n-2}\,\Delta t + \cdots$$

The next term omitted from the last sum is proportional to $(\Delta t)^2$, the following to $(\Delta t)^3$, and so on. Each term except the first approaches zero as Δt approaches zero. Thus

$$\frac{df}{dt} = \lim_{\Delta x \to 0} \frac{f(t + \Delta t) + f(t)}{\Delta t} = nt^{n-1}$$

Comment on Rules 8 and 9

We first write $\sin \omega t = \sin \theta$ with $\theta = \omega t$ and use the chain rule,

$$\frac{d \sin \theta}{dt} = \frac{d \sin \theta}{d\theta}\,\frac{d\theta}{dt} = \omega\,\frac{d \sin \theta}{d\theta}$$

We then use the trigonometric formula for the sine of the sum of two angles θ and $\Delta\theta$:

$$\sin(\theta + \Delta\theta) = \sin \Delta\theta \cos \theta + \cos \Delta\theta \sin \theta$$

Since $\Delta\theta$ is to approach zero, we can use the small-angle approximations

$$\sin \Delta\theta \approx \Delta\theta \qquad \text{and} \qquad \cos \Delta\theta \approx 1$$

Then

$$\sin(\theta + \Delta\theta) \approx \Delta\theta \cos \theta + \sin \theta$$

and

$$\frac{\sin(\theta + \Delta\theta) - \sin \theta}{\Delta\theta} \approx \cos \theta$$

Similar reasoning can be applied to the cosine function to obtain rule 9.

Comment on Rule 10

Again we use the chain rule,

$$\frac{de^\theta}{dt} = b\,\frac{de^\theta}{d\theta} \qquad \text{with } \theta = bt$$

and use the series expansion for the exponential function (Appendix D):

$$e^{\theta+\Delta\theta} = e^{\theta}e^{\Delta\theta} = e^{\theta}\left[1 + \Delta\theta + \frac{(\Delta\theta)^2}{2!} + \frac{(\Delta\theta)^3}{3!} + \cdots\right]$$

Then

$$\frac{e^{\theta+\Delta\theta} - e^{\theta}}{\Delta\theta} = e^{\theta} + e^{\theta}\frac{\Delta\theta}{2!} + e^{\theta}\frac{(\Delta\theta)^2}{3!} + \cdots$$

As $\Delta\theta$ approaches zero, the right side of the equation above approaches e^{θ}.

Comment on Rule 11

Let

$$y = \ln bt$$

Then

$$e^{y} = bt \quad \text{and} \quad \frac{dt}{dy} = \frac{1}{b}e^{y} = t$$

Then using rule 5, we obtain

$$\frac{dy}{dt} = \left(\frac{dt}{dy}\right)^{-1} = \frac{1}{t}$$

Table E-2
Integration formulas*

1. $\displaystyle\int A\,dt = At$	5. $\displaystyle\int e^{bt}\,dt = \frac{1}{b}e^{bt}$
2. $\displaystyle\int At\,dt = \frac{1}{2}At^2$	6. $\displaystyle\int \cos \omega t\,dt = \frac{1}{\omega}\sin \omega t$
3. $\displaystyle\int At^n\,dt = A\,\frac{t^{n+1}}{n+1} \quad n \neq -1$	7. $\displaystyle\int \sin \omega t\,dt = -\frac{1}{\omega}\cos \omega t$
4. $\displaystyle\int At^{-1}\,dt = A\ln t$	

* In these formulas A, b, and ω are constants. An arbitrary constant C can be added to the the right side of each equation.

APPENDIX F   Trigonometric Tables

Angle θ					Angle θ				
Degree	Radian	sin θ	cos θ	tan θ	Degree	Radian	sin θ	cos θ	tan θ
0	0.0000	0.0000	1.0000	0.0000					
1	0.0175	0.0175	0.9998	0.0175	46	0.8029	0.7193	0.6947	1.0355
2	0.0349	0.0349	0.9994	0.0349	47	0.8203	0.7314	0.6820	1.0724
3	0.0524	0.0523	0.9986	0.0524	48	0.8378	0.7431	0.6691	1.1106
4	0.0698	0.0698	0.9976	0.0699	49	0.8552	0.7547	0.6561	1.1504
5	0.0873	0.0872	0.9962	0.0875	50	0.8727	0.7660	0.6428	1.1918
6	0.1047	0.1045	0.9945	0.1051	51	0.8901	0.7771	0.6293	1.2349
7	0.1222	0.1219	0.9925	0.1228	52	0.9076	0.7880	0.6157	1.2799
8	0.1396	0.1392	0.9903	0.1405	53	0.9250	0.7986	0.6018	1.3270
9	0.1571	0.1564	0.9877	0.1584	54	0.9425	0.8090	0.5878	1.3764
10	0.1745	0.1736	0.9848	0.1763	55	0.9599	0.8192	0.5736	1.4281
11	0.1920	0.1908	0.9816	0.1944	56	0.9774	0.8290	0.5592	1.4826
12	0.2094	0.2079	0.9781	0.2126	57	0.9948	0.8387	0.5446	1.5399
13	0.2269	0.2250	0.9744	0.2309	58	1.0123	0.8480	0.5299	1.6003
14	0.2443	0.2419	0.9703	0.2493	59	1.0297	0.8572	0.5150	1.6643
15	0.2618	0.2588	0.9659	0.2679	60	1.0472	0.8660	0.5000	1.7321
16	0.2793	0.2756	0.9613	0.2867	61	1.0647	0.8746	0.4848	1.8040
17	0.2967	0.2924	0.9563	0.3057	62	1.0821	0.8829	0.4695	1.8807
18	0.3142	0.3090	0.9511	0.3249	63	1.0996	0.8910	0.4540	1.9626
19	0.3316	0.3256	0.9455	0.3443	64	1.1170	0.8988	0.4384	2.0503
20	0.3491	0.3420	0.9397	0.3640	65	1.1345	0.9063	0.4226	2.1445
21	0.3665	0.3584	0.9336	0.3839	66	1.1519	0.9135	0.4067	2.2460
22	0.3840	0.3746	0.9272	0.4040	67	1.1694	0.9205	0.3907	2.3559
23	0.4014	0.3907	0.9205	0.4245	68	1.1868	0.9272	0.3746	2.4751
24	0.4189	0.4067	0.9135	0.4452	69	1.2043	0.9336	0.3584	2.6051
25	0.4363	0.4226	0.9063	0.4663	70	1.2217	0.9397	0.3420	2.7475
26	0.4538	0.4384	0.8988	0.4877	71	1.2392	0.9455	0.3256	2.9042
27	0.4712	0.4540	0.8910	0.5095	72	1.2566	0.9511	0.3090	3.0777
28	0.4887	0.4695	0.8829	0.5317	73	1.2741	0.9563	0.2924	3.2709
29	0.5061	0.4848	0.8746	0.5543	74	1.2915	0.9613	0.2756	3.4874
30	0.5236	0.5000	0.8660	0.5774	75	1.3090	0.9659	0.2588	3.7321
31	0.5411	0.5150	0.8572	0.6009	76	1.3265	0.9703	0.2419	4.0108
32	0.5585	0.5299	0.8480	0.6249	77	1.3439	0.9744	0.2250	4.3315
33	0.5760	0.5446	0.8387	0.6494	78	1.3614	0.9781	0.2079	4.7046
34	0.5934	0.5592	0.8290	0.6745	79	1.3788	0.9816	0.1908	5.1446
35	0.6109	0.5736	0.8192	0.7002	80	1.3963	0.9848	0.1736	5.6713
36	0.6283	0.5878	0.8090	0.7265	81	1.4137	0.9877	0.1564	6.314
37	0.6458	0.6018	0.7986	0.7536	82	1.4312	0.9903	0.1392	7.115
38	0.6632	0.6157	0.7880	0.7813	83	1.4486	0.9925	0.1219	8.144
39	0.6807	0.6293	0.7771	0.8098	84	1.4661	0.9945	0.1045	9.514
40	0.6981	0.6428	0.7660	0.8391	85	1.4835	0.9962	0.0872	11.430
41	0.7156	0.6561	0.7547	0.8693	86	1.5010	0.9976	0.0698	14.301
42	0.7330	0.6691	0.7431	0.9004	87	1.5184	0.9986	0.0523	19.081
43	0.7505	0.6820	0.7314	0.9325	88	1.5359	0.9994	0.0349	28.636
44	0.7679	0.6947	0.7193	0.9657	89	1.5533	0.9998	0.0175	57.290
45	0.7854	0.7071	0.7071	1.0000	90	1.5708	1.0000	0.0000	∞

APPENDIX G

Periodic Table of the Elements

The values listed are based on $^{12}_{6}C = 12$ u exactly. For artificially produced elements, the approximate atomic weight of the most stable isotope is given in brackets.

GROUP

PERIOD	SERIES	I	II	III	IV	V	VI	VII	VIII			0
1	1	1 **H** 1.00797										2 **He** 4.003
2	2	3 **Li** 6.942	4 **Be** 9.012	5 **B** 10.81	6 **C** 12.011	7 **N** 14.007	8 **O** 15.9994	9 **F** 19.00				10 **Ne** 20.183
3	3	11 **Na** 22.990	12 **Mg** 24.31	13 **Al** 26.98	14 **Si** 28.09	15 **P** 30.974	16 **S** 32.064	17 **Cl** 35.453				18 **Ar** 39.948
4	4	19 **K** 39.102	20 **Ca** 40.08	21 **Sc** 44.96	22 **Ti** 47.90	23 **V** 50.94	24 **Cr** 52.00	25 **Mn** 54.94	26 **Fe** 55.85	27 **Co** 58.93	28 **Ni** 58.71	
	5	29 **Cu** 63.54	30 **Zn** 65.37	31 **Ga** 69.72	32 **Ge** 72.59	33 **As** 74.92	34 **Se** 78.96	35 **Br** 70.909				36 **Kr** 83.80
5	6	37 **Rb** 85.47	38 **Sr** 87.62	39 **Y** 88.905	40 **Zr** 91.22	41 **Nb** 92.91	42 **Mo** 95.94	43 **Tc** [98]	44 **Ru** 101.1	45 **Rh** 102.905	46 **Pd** 106.4	
	7	47 **Ag** 107.870	48 **Cd** 112.40	49 **In** 114.82	50 **Sn** 118.69	51 **Sb** 121.75	52 **Te** 127.60	53 **I** 126.90				54 **Xe** 131.30
6	8	55 **Cs** 132.905	56 **Ba** 137.34	57-71 Lanthanide series*	72 **Hf** 178.49	73 **Ta** 180.95	74 **W** 183.85	75 **Re** 186.2	76 **Os** 190.2	77 **Ir** 192.2	78 **Pt** 195.09	
	9	79 **Au** 196.97	80 **Hg** 200.59	81 **Tl** 204.37	82 **Pb** 207.19	83 **Bi** 208.98	84 **Po** [210]	85 **At** [210]				86 **Rn** [222]
7	10	87 **Fr** [223]	88 **Ra** [226]	89-103 Actinide series†								

*Lanthanide Series	57 **La** 138.91	58 **Ce** 140.12	59 **Pr** 140.91	60 **Nd** 144.24	61 **Pm** [147]	62 **Sm** 150.35	63 **Eu** 152.0	64 **Gd** 157.25	65 **Tb** 158.92	66 **Dy** 162.50	67 **Ho** 164.93	68 **Er** 167.26	69 **Tm** 168.93	70 **Yb** 173.04	71 **Lu** 174.97
†Actinide Series	89 **Ac** [227]	90 **Th** 232.04	91 **Pa** [231]	92 **U** 238.03	93 **Np** [237]	94 **Pu** [242]	95 **Am** [243]	96 **Cm** [247]	97 **Bk** [247]	98 **Cf** [251]	99 **Es** [254]	100 **Fm** [253]	101 **Md** [256]	102 **No** [254]	103 **Lw** [257]

m/sec (d) at $t = 2$ sec potential energy 296 J, kinetic energy 96 J, total energy 392 J (e) 392 J

31. (a) $\frac{5}{3}$ m/sec (b) 15 J

33. (a) normal force $= 17.6$ N; $\mu = 0.197$ (b) 1.73 W (c) -5.20 J

35. (a) 140 lb (b) 22.3 horsepower (c) work done against air resistance and internal friction

37. 83°

39. (a) 142° (b) 101° (c) 90°

41. $B_z = 0$, $B_y = 2B_x/3$

Problems

3. (a) Assume weight of 700 N (157 lb) is raised 3 cm for each step; then $mgh = 21$ J per step. Using 2000 steps per mile gives 4.2×10^4 J (b) 4.2×10^4 J/1200 sec $= 35$ W. Alternative estimation assumes work is done to accelerate leg to speed v and back to rest in each step. Taking $m = 10$ kg for mass of leg and $v = 1.61$ km/1200 sec gives $2(\frac{1}{2}mv^2) = 18$ J per step, same order of magnitude.

5. (a) $-mg \sin \theta$ (b) $-mgL(1 - \cos \theta_0) = -mgH$

7. (a) $-\frac{3}{8}mv_0^2$ (b) $\mu = \dfrac{3}{16\pi}\dfrac{v_0^2}{rg}$ (c) $\frac{1}{3}$ rev

Chapter 8

True or False

1. False 2. False; only with conservative forces. 3. False 4. True 5. True 6. False

Exercises

1. (a) $W_{AB} = 0$; $W_{BC} = 78.4$ J; $W_{total} = 78.4$ J (b) $W_{AD} = 117.6$ J; $W_{DE} = 0$; $W_{EC} = -39.2$ J; $W_{total} = 78.4$ J (c) $W_{AC} = 78.4$ J

3. (a) from (0,0) to (2,0) $W = 0$; from (2,0) to (2,2) $W = 10$ J; $W_{total} = 10$ J (b) from (0,0) to (0,2) $W = 10$ J; from (0,2) to (2,2) $W = 16$ J; $W_{total} = 26$ J

5. (a) -10 J (b) 0

7. (a) $E_k = 25$ J $= E_{total}$ (b) $E_k = 0$, $U = 25$ J, $E_{total} = 25$ J (c) 5.10 m (d) no

9. (a) -25 J (b) -25 J (c) 100 m/sec

11. (a) -200 J (b) $+200$ J

13. 121 ft

15. (a) $U = -4x + U_0$ (b) $U = -4(x - 6) = 24 - 4x$ (c) $U = -4(x - 6) + 12 = 36 - 4x$

17. (a) 14.1 cm (b) 10 cm

19. conservative: (b), (c), and (e); nonconservative: (a), (d), (f), and (g)

21. (a) $U = -F_0 z$ (b) $U = -F_0(z + 15)$ (c) $U = -F_0(z - 15)$

23. (a) $W = U = 3.12 \times 10^7$ J (b) $mgh = 6.24 \times 10^7$ J (c) force varies from 9.8 N at $r = R_E$ to 2.45 N at $r = 2R_E$

25. (a) 1.88 eV (b) 625 eV (c) 9.38×10^5 MeV (d) 510 keV $= 0.510$ MeV

27. (a) 3.20×10^{-11} J (b) 8.20×10^{10} J

29. (a) 0 at B and E; $+$ at C and D; $-$ at A and F (b) D (c) stable at E; unstable at B

31. (a) $F_x = -U_0/x$ (b) no

33. (a) C/r^2 (b) away; F_r is positive (c) U decreases as r increases (d) if C is negative, force is toward origin and U increases as r increases

35. 203 MeV

37. (a) conservative (b) conservative (c) nonconservative (d) nonconservative

Problems

1. (a) −11 J, −10 J, −7 J, −3 J, 0, +1 J, 0, −2 J, −3 J (b) F_x is given as a function of x only (c) graph should be the negative of that in (a)

3. $U = ax^3/3$

5. (a) minimum of $U(r)$ curve is point of stable equilibrium

7. (a) Along direct path from (4,1) to (4,4) on line $x = 4$ m the work is 36 J. Along path from (4,1) to (0,1) to (0,4) to (4,4) the work is zero. Other similar paths give different results because work along paths parallel to x axis adds to zero while work along vertical path depends on value of x. (b) second path given in (a)

9. (a) $F_r = -dU/dr = 12(U_0/r_0)[(r_0/r)^{13} - (r_0/r)^7]$ (b) $U = 0$ at $r = 2^{-1/6}r_0$; $F_r = 0$ at $r = r_0$ (c) U has minimum value $U = -U_0$ at $r = r_0$

Chapter 9

True or False

1. False 2. True 3. False 4. False 5. True

Exercises

1. (a) 75 J (b) −29.4 J (c) 45.6 J (d) 4.27 m/sec

3. (a) 4.43 m/sec (b) −19.6 J (c) 0.167

5. 2.55 m

7. (a) 294 J (b) 147 J (c) decrease by 147 J (d) −147 J

9. (a) 50 ft-lb (b) $\frac{1}{2}mv_x^2 + \frac{1}{2}mv_y^2 = 18.1$ ft-lb + 31.9 ft-lb; minimum E_k is $\frac{1}{2}mv_x^2 = 18.1$ ft-lb at top of flight (c) 31.9 ft-lb (d) 63.8 ft

11. 3.61 m/sec

15. (a) -6.27×10^9 J (b) -3.14×10^9 J (c) 7.92 km/sec

17. 2.38 km/sec

19. 51.2 km/sec

21. If r increases, U increases, E_k decreases, and E_{total} increases because $\Delta U = -2\Delta E_k$.

23. (a) 128 ft/sec (b) 8.51 atm

25. (a) 12 m/sec (b) 1.33 N/m² = 1.31 atm (c) same

Problems

1. (a) $mg(h - 2R)$ (b) $2g(h - 2R)/R$ (c) $h = 2.5R$

3. (a) $v = \sqrt{2g(2x - L)}$ (b) $a \geq g$

5. (a) 0.989 m   *Note:* The mass falls a distance $h = (4 + x) \sin 30°$, where x is the compression of the spring. If you neglect x in calculating the potential-energy loss, you get 0.885 for x. (b) 0.783 m (c) 1.54 m above spring (d) It will slide up and down a distance which decreases each time and eventually come to rest with the spring compressed about 8.6 cm.

7. (a) $\sqrt{2m_2gy/(m_1 + m_2)}$ (b) $a = m_2g/(m_1 + m_2)$ *Note:* $dy/dt = v$.

9. (b) When r decreases, E_k increases but U and E_{total} both decrease.

11. (b) about 1.6×10^{-10} m and 5×10^{-10} m

13. 6.6

15. (a) 463 m/sec (b) 10.74 km/sec (c) about 8%

Chapter 10

True or False

1. True 2. True 3. True 4. True 5. True 6. True

Exercises

1. $x_{CM} = 5$ m

3. (2 m, 1 m)

5. (a) $3\mathbf{i} - 1.5\mathbf{j}$ m/sec (b) $18\mathbf{i} - 9\mathbf{j}$ kg-m/sec

7. (b) 10.7 ft/sec²

9. (a) 32.7 ft from shore (b) CM 32.7 ft from shore; near end of log 2.7 ft from shore (c) CM 32.7 ft from shore; man and end of log 5.45 ft from shore

11. (a) $x = 0$ (b) $x = -8$ cm, $v = -2$ cm/sec

13. (a) 50 kg-m/sec (b) 50 kg-m/sec (c) 3.57 m/sec

15. 4.55 ft/sec

17. 3.33 m/sec

19. (a) 0.8 m/sec (b) before: heavier car 0.2 m/sec right, lighter car 0.3 m/sec left; after: both cars at rest (c) before: heavier car 1200 J, lighter car 1800 J; after: 0 for both cars

21. (a) 39 J (b) 3 m/sec (c) 2 m/sec to the right and 2 m/sec to the left (d) 12 J (6 J each) (e) $\frac{1}{2}Mv_{CM}^2 = 27$ J $= 39$ J $- 12$ J

23. (a) Both have same velocity, and so there is no rotation. (b) Masses have equal but opposite velocities, and so CM is at rest.

25. (a) Both have same velocity, so that spring remains unstretched and there is no rotation. (b) Masses have equal but opposite velocities, so that CM is at rest. Motion can be oscillation along line of spring, rotation about CM, or some combination.

27. 0.0176 J

31. (a) $3L\lambda_0/2$ (b) $5L/9$

Problems

1. (a) about 2950 mi from center of earth or 1050 mi beneath earth's surface (b) gravitational attraction of sun and other planets; neglecting other planets, $\mathbf{a}_{CM}$ is toward sun (c) about 5900 mi

3. (a) 2 m/sec (b) 8 m/sec (c) $2\frac{2}{3}$ m/sec (d) frictional force exerted by ground on man (e) 1080 J is total increase in kinetic energy

5. $r/6$ from center of large disk along common diameter and away from hole

7. (a) 8 kg-m/sec (b) 1 m/sec for 8-kg mass, 4 m/sec for 2-kg mass (c) 4.12 m/sec and 5.66 m/sec (d) 80 J; 20 J (e) 5 m/sec for 8-kg mass, 2-kg mass is at rest; 80 J; 20 J

9. $x_{CM} = 6.67$ in, $y_{CM} = 3.33$ in

Chapter 11

True or False

1. False 2. False; true only in center-of-mass frame. 3. False; true only in center-of-mass frame. 4. True

Exercises

1. (a) 4 N-sec (b) 2 m/sec

3. (a) 8 N-sec (b) 0.16 sec

5. (a) 15.6 lb-sec (b) 0.31 sec

7. about 2 N

9. (a) 1.4 lb-sec (b) 1400 lb

11. $\sqrt{8mE_k}$

13. 8.33×10^{-4} N; $P = 2.60 \times 10^{-4}$ N/m²

15. 5.65×10^{-21} J = 0.0353 eV

17. (a) about 5×10^{-4} cm (b) about 0.025% of distance traveled due to club

19. (a) 2.4 lb-sec (b) 2400 lb, which is 7500 times weight of ball; yes

25. (b) and (c)

27. 15-gm mass; 3 m/sec to the left; 6-gm mass; 7.5 m/sec to the right

29. (a) 2 m/sec (b) 10-kg mass: 3 m/sec, 6-kg mass: −5 m/sec (c) 10-kg mass: −3 m/sec, 6-kg mass: 5 m/sec (d) 10-kg mass: −1 m/sec, 6-kg mass: 7 m/sec

31. before: $\mathbf{v}_{1i} = 2u\mathbf{i}$, $\mathbf{v}_{2i} = 0$; after: $\mathbf{v}_{1f} = u\mathbf{i} + u\mathbf{j}$, $\mathbf{v}_{2f} = u\mathbf{i} - u\mathbf{j}$, where $u =$ speed of center of mass and ball on right has been assumed initially at rest

33. 1.76 ft/sec

35. 15 gm

37. 447 m/sec

39. (a) 94.9 m/sec (b) 98%

41. 6.16 eV

43. (a) 20% (b) heat (internal energy of ball and surroundings) (c) 0.89

Problems

3. (c) 2.08 N (d) 1.5 N, 2.67 N

5. $a = (100 \text{ ft}/x)g$, where x is distance moved in hand; for $x = 4$ ft, $a = 25g = 800$ ft/sec²; $I = 0.8$ lb-sec; $F_{av} = 8$ lb neglecting weight (8.32 lb including weight), $t = 0.1$ sec; neglecting weight results in about 4% error

7. (a) 4.8 N-sec (b) 1600 N (c) 2.4 N-sec (d) 19.2 N

9. 48 ft/sec

11. (a) 7 m/sec (b) $p_1 = +12$ N-sec, $p_2 = -12$ N-sec (c) $p_1 = -6$ N-sec, $p_2 = +6$ N-sec (d) $v_1 = 5.5$ m/sec, $v_2 = 8$ m/sec (e) 22.5 J

13. $v = [2(m_1 + m_2)/m_1]\sqrt{gL}$

15. (a) 0.72 (b) 42 collisions

Chapter 12

True or False

1. False 2. True 3. True 4. False; e.g., angular displacement. 5. True 6. False 7. True 8. False; zero resultant torque is also necessary. 9. True 10. False

Exercises

1. 1 rad/sec = 9.55 rev/min

3. (a) 0.2 rad/sec (b) 0.955 rev

5. (a) 2.91×10^{-2} rad/sec² (b) 1.75 rad/sec (c) 33.3 rev

7. 0.625 sec

9. (a) 40 cm/sec for 3-kg masses; 80 cm/sec for 1-kg masses; 1.12 J (b) $I = 0.56$ kg-m²

11. (a) 52 kg-m² (b) 25.4 rev/min

13. 28 kg-m²

15. (a) 26 kg-m² (b) $I_{x'} = 18$ kg-m², $I_y = 8$ kg-m²

17. $MR^2/4$

19. $3MR^2/2$

21. (a) 2.4 N-m (b) 66.7 rad/sec² (c) 200 rad/sec (d) 720 J (e) 300 rad (f) (300 rad) (2.4 N-m) = 720 J

23. (a) 0.126 rad/sec^2 (b) 400 N-m (c) 3.18 × 10^3 kg-m^2

25. (a) $\tau = 1.5$ N-m, $I = 1.5 \times 10^{-2}$ kg-m^2, $\alpha = 100$ rad/sec^2 (b) $\omega = 400$ rad/sec, $P = 600$ W

27. 267 horsepower

29. 1.93 m/sec (1.98 m/sec if I is neglected)

31. 26 lb at left and 74 lb at right

33. 354 lb

Problems

1. (a) π rad/sec^2 (b) $3\pi/2$ rad/sec^2

3. (a) 1.97×10^5 J (b) 26.2 N-m (c) 1200 rev

5. (a) $(2m_2 g \sin\theta)/(2m_2 + m_1)$ (b) $(m_1 m_2 g \sin\theta)/(2m_2 + m_1)$ (c) $m_2 gh$ (d) $m_2 gh$ (e) $\sqrt{2gh/(1 + m_1/2m_2)}$ (f) for $\theta = 0$: $a = 0$, $T = 0$, $E = 0$; for $\theta = 90°$ $a = 2m_2 gh/(2m_2 + m_1)$, $T = m_1 m_2 g/(2m_2 + m_1)$, $E = m_2 gh$; for $m_1 = 0$: $a = g \sin\theta$, $T = 0$, $E = m_2 gh$

7. (b) $\omega = \sqrt{2gh(\cos\theta_0 - \cos\theta)/k^2}$ (c) $F_r = mg(7\cos\theta - 6\cos\theta_0)$; $F_t = 2mg \sin\theta$

9. $I = ML^2/6$

13. $\tan\theta = 0.5$, $\theta = 27°$

15. $F = mg\sqrt{2hR - h^2}/(R - h)$

Chapter 13

True or False

1. False; $\mathbf{A} \times \mathbf{B} = -\mathbf{B} \times \mathbf{A}$. 2. True 3. False 4. False; $\mathbf{L}$ must be constant. 5. True 6. True 7. False; f is less than $\mu_s N$ except at limiting angle.

Exercises

1. $\mathbf{F} = -F\mathbf{i}$, $\mathbf{r} = R\mathbf{j}$, $\tau = RF\mathbf{k}$

3. $\tau = -mgx\mathbf{k}$

5. (a) $25\mathbf{k}$ (b) $-25\mathbf{j}$ (c) $8\mathbf{k}$

9. (a) 60 kg-m^2/sec (b) 75 kg-m^2 (c) 0.8 rad/sec

11. (a) doubled (b) doubled

13. (a) 4 N-m (b) $\frac{2}{9}t$ rad/sec

15. $L_{earth} = 7.15 \times 10^{33}$ kg-m^2/sec; $L_{sun} = 2.69 \times 10^{40}$ kg-m^2/sec

17. (a) 132 gm-cm^2/sec (b) 132 gm-cm^2/sec

19. (a) 0.784 N-m (b) $0.26v$ (c) 3.02 m/sec^2

21. (a) $\frac{1}{3}Ml^2\omega$ (b) $\frac{1}{2}l\omega$ (c) $\frac{1}{12}Ml^2\omega$

23. (a) 600 rev/min (b) since $E = L^2/2I$ and $I_f = 3I_i$, $E_f = E_i/3$

25. (a) 6.47 rad/sec (b) $E_{ki} = 41.9$ ft-lb; $E_{kf} = 86.4$ ft-lb (c) 44.5 ft-lb

27. Without smaller rotor, any variation in the angular speed of the main rotor would produce an opposite rotation in the helicopter body because of conservation of angular momentum.

29. (b) no

31. 527 ft-lb

33. (a) 2.88 rad/sec (b) 0.144 m/sec (c) 0.417 m/sec^2 toward pivot (d) $F_{vert} = 19.6$ N; $F_{horiz} = 0.834$ N

35. *Hint:* First find speed v from $v^2 = rg \tan 30°$, where $r = 0.5$ m, as in Example 5-7, page 122. (a) $\mathbf{L} = -2.91\hat{\mathbf{r}} - 1.68\mathbf{k}$ kg-m^2/sec (b) 9.8 N-m

Problems

3. $E_k = \frac{3}{4}MV^2$

5. $2.7R$; $2.5R$

7. 1.36 mi

Chapter 14

True or False

1. False 2. True 3. False; period is independent of amplitude. 4. True 5. True 6. False; it is periodic but not simple harmonic for large amplitudes. 7. True 8. True 9. True 10. True

Exercises

1. (a) 2.5 Hz; 0.4 sec (b) 3 m (c) $x(0) = -3$ m; $x(\frac{1}{2}) = 0$

3. $x = 6 \cos \pi t$ in; $v = -6\pi \sin \pi t$ in/sec; $a = -6\pi^2 \cos \pi t$ in/sec^2

5. (a) 4 ft at $t = \pi/4$ sec (b) $v = 8 \cos 2t$ ft/sec; at $t = 0$, $v = 8$ ft/sec (c) $a = -16 \sin 2t$ ft/sec^2; $a = 0$ at $t = 0$; $a_{max} = 16$ ft/sec^2

7. (a) 2 rad/sec (b) 0.318 Hz; 3.14 sec (c) $x = 40 \cos (2t + \delta)$ cm/sec; $y = 40 \sin (2t + \delta)$ cm/sec, where δ depends on initial position

9. (a) 474 N/m (b) 2.37 J (c) $x(t) = 10 \cos (4\pi t + \delta)$ cm; no

11. (a) 1580 N/m (b) 79.0 m/sec^2 (c) 0.0197 J

13. $E_k = 0.75E$; $E_k = U$ at $x = A/\sqrt{2}$

15. 24.8 cm

17. 9.79 m/sec^2

21. 2.0 sec

23. (a) 2 in; $\frac{1}{3}$ft-lb (b) $\Delta U_{spring} = +\frac{7}{4}$ft-lb; $\Delta U_{gravity} = -1$ ft-lb; $\Delta U_{total} = \frac{3}{4}$ft-lb = $\frac{1}{2}(24 \text{ lb/ft})(\frac{1}{4}\text{ft})^2$ (c) 0.45 sec; 2.2 Hz; 3 in

25. (a) π; 8 cm (b) 0.628 sec

Problems

1. (a) equal (b) equal (c) 2.4 times as far during first second

3. 6.2 cm

5. (b) They meet at the bottom. The period of motion is independent of the amplitude, and so the time to reach the bottom $T/4$ is the same for each mass.

7. (a) $kA/(m_1 + m_2)g$ (b) A and E remain unchanged; ω decreases, $\omega_f = \sqrt{m_1/(m_1 + m_2)}\ \omega_i$; T increases, $T_f = \sqrt{(m_1 + m_2)/m_1}\ T_i$

9. (a) 13 cm (b) 6.5 cm (c) 0.51 sec (d) 0.32 J (e) 0.8 m/sec; 0.13 sec (f) 0.12 sec, 1.13 m/sec

11. (a) $I = ML^2 + \frac{2}{5}Mr^2$ (c) 0.008% error ($= 1.6 \times 10^{-4}$ sec for $T_0 = 2.01$ sec); about 22 cm

13. (a) $d^2x/dt^2 = -(k/m)x$ (b) $E = \frac{1}{2}mv^2 + \frac{1}{2}kx^2 = \frac{1}{2}kA^2$; $v = \sqrt{2E/m - kx^2/m} = \sqrt{k/m}\ \sqrt{A^2 - x^2}$

15. (a) $v_{SHM} = \theta_0 g L$ (b) $v = 2gL(1 - \cos \theta_0)$ (c) $v_{SHM} = 0.5464$ m/sec; $v = 0.5457$ m/sec; difference is 0.07 cm/sec, about 0.13%

19. (a) $dU/dx = -F_x = 0$ at $x = x_0$ (b) $-\frac{1}{2}U_0$ (c) $\omega = \frac{6}{x_0}\sqrt{\frac{U_0}{m}}$

21. 1.28 sec. *Hint:* Use $T = 2\pi \sqrt{L/g'}$, where g' is free-fall acceleration observed in accelerating frame.

Chapter 15

True or False

1. True 2. False 3. True 4. True 5. True 6. False 7. True 8. False 9. True 10. True

Exercises

3. (a) 0.44 sec; 0.18 J (b) 0.045 kg/sec

5. (a) $\frac{3}{4}$

7. 1.0 sec; 2.17 cm

9. (a) $a(t) = (F_0/m) \cos \omega t$; $v(t) = (F_0/m\omega) \sin \omega t$ (b) $x(t) = -(F_0/m\omega^2)(\cos \omega t - 1)$ (c) frequency of oscillation is same but amplitude is different; in steady state, $x(t)$ is given by Equation 15-25

11. for $b = 0$, $A_1/A_2 = \frac{7}{5}$

15. (a) 4.98 cm (5.00 cm neglecting the damping term) (b) $\omega = 14.1$ rad/sec; $f = 2.25$ Hz (c) 35.4 cm

Problems

1. After 14 cycles energy is about 49% of original energy, and amplitude is $0.70A_0$. *Hint:* Easiest to use $E_n = (0.95)^n E_0 = 0.5E_0$ and solve for n.

5. (a) at $t = 3.54$ sec (b) 6 J

7. (a) 219 sec (b) $\omega' \approx \omega_0 = 24.5$ rad/sec; $f' = 3.90$ Hz

9. $A(t + T) = e^{-3.05}A(t) = 4.74 \times 10^{-2}A(t)$; $E(t + T) = e^{-6.1}E(t) = 2.24 \times 10^{-3}E(t)$

Chapter 16

True or False

1. False 2. True 3. True 4. True 5. True 6. False 7. True 8. True 9. True 10. False

Exercises

1. 4.37×10^{11} m

3. 1.50×10^{15} m

5. 84.6 y

7. 6.02×10^{24} kg

9. (a) 0 (b) $\mathbf{g} = -Gm \left[\dfrac{1}{(x - a)^2} + \dfrac{1}{(x + a)^2} \right] \mathbf{i}$

11. (a) 10.8 N (b) at 56° above the x axis (c) $\mathbf{F} = 10\mathbf{i} + 15\mathbf{j}$ N

13. 2.5×10^{-3} N/kg toward the center of the circle

15. (a) $V(x) = -2Gm/(x^2 + a^2)^{1/2}$ (c) $g_x = -Gmx/(x^2 + a^2)^{3/2}$; $x = 0$

17. (a) $V(x) = -GM/(x^2 + r^2)^{1/2}$ (c) at $x = 0$, V is maximum and g is zero

21. (a) Lines cannot cross because direction of $\mathbf{g}$ is ambiguous at intersection. (b) Lines cannot have discontinuous change in direction (kinks) because direction of $\mathbf{g}$ is ambiguous at such a point. (c) Lines diverging from a point imply negative mass at the point, which does not exist.

23. (a) $\mathbf{g} = -2.0 \times 10^{-10} \, \hat{\mathbf{r}}$ N/kg (b) $\mathbf{g} = 0$

25. (c) 6.24×10^7 J/kg (d) 4.99×10^9 J $= 1.39 \times 10^3$ kW-h; about $41.60 (in practice the cost is somewhat greater)

Problems

3. (a) 3.31 y (the semimajor axis is 1.4×10^8 km) (b) 1.49×10^{29} kg (c) m_2 has greater speed and greater total energy (d) $v_P = 1.8v_A$

5. (b) $m_{s_2} = (r_2/r_1)m_{s_1}$; m_{s_1}; toward center of s_1 (c) toward center of s_1 (d) 0 (e) for spherical shell, $m_{s_2} = (r_2^2/r_1^2)m_{s_1}$; the elements would produce equal and opposite fields at point P

7. 198 m/sec $= 444$ mi/h

9. $g_x = -GM/(x_0^2 - L^2/4)$

11. $\omega = \sqrt{4\pi G\rho_0/3}$

Chapter 17   **True or False**   1. True 2. True 3. False 4. False 5. False 6. True

Exercises   1. The system is not in equilibrium when the temperature and pressure readings are taken.

3. (a) adiabatic (b) diathermic (c) adiabatic. *Note:* Both the increase in P_A and the decrease in V_A tend to increase the temperature of A.

5. $t_A \neq t_B$ and $t_B \neq t_C$; no; t_A and t_C may or may not be equal

7. (a) 8.4 cm (b) 107°C

9. (a) 54.9 mm (b) 371 K

11. (a) 33.9 ft (b) 0.89 atm = 673 mm Hg

13. 29.9 in Hg

15. (a) 23.37 lb/in² = 1.59 atm (b) 8.67 lb/in² = 0.59 atm

17. 3.81×10^4 lb

19. (a) 6173 K (b) 10,650°F

21. 37.0°C

23. (a) 10^7 °C (b) about 1.8×10^7 °R (c) about 1.8×10^7 °F

25. (a) 12.3 ℓ (b) 24.6 ℓ (c) 375 K

27. 1.15

29. 5.40×10^3 N due to air inside box; if box is in air at pressure of 1 atm, there will be an opposing force of 4.05×10^3 N due to air outside, giving a net force of 1.35×10^3 N outward.

31. 1.79 moles; 1.08×10^{24} molecules

33. 275 m/sec for argon and 870 m/sec for helium

35. 8.84 K

37. 33×10^{-6} per Celsius degree

39. $1/T = 0.003661$, which differs from 0.003673 by about 0.3%

Problems   1. (a) 6.37 atm (b) 21.4% escapes (c) 3.93 atm

3. (a) 32.0 lb/in² (b) 27.8 lb/in². *Hint:* You must convert gauge pressure to absolute pressure by adding 14.7 lb/in² before using $PV = nRT$.

5. (a) 6.07×10^{-21} J (b) 1.9×10^3 m/sec (c) 7.31×10^3 J (d) 1.9×10^3 J

7. (a) 1.6×10^5 K (b) 1.0×10^4 K (c) yes (see essay in Chapter 9 for complete discussion) (d) about 7.3×10^3 K for O_2 and 4.6×10^2 K for H_2; yes

9. 145°C

11. 5.09 m/sec

Chapter 18   **True or False**   1. False 2. False 3. False 4. False 5. True 6. True 7. True 8. False 9. True 10. False

Exercises   1. 200 kcal

3. (a) 1 Btu = 252 cal (b) 1 Btu = 1054 J (c) 1440 Btu

5. 0.41 cal/gm-°C

7. (a) 0°C (b) 125.6 gm, or 62.8%

9. 49.5 gm

11. (a) 4.18×10^3 J/kg-K (b) 3.33×10^5 J/kg

13. $t_f = 21.54°C$

15. (a) $0.12°C$ (b) $1.73°C$

17. 1 ℓ-atm $= 101.3$ J $= 24.22$ cal

19. (a) 405 J (b) 861 J

21. (a) 507 J (b) 963 J

23. T increases slightly; since U decreases when the atoms are farther apart and E_{total} is constant, E_k and therefore T must increase.

25. (a) 3.00 moles (b) $C_v = 8.96$ cal/K; $C_p = 14.9$ cal/K (c) $C_v = 14.9$ cal/K; $C_p = 20.9$ cal/K

27. (a) $C_v = \frac{3}{2}R$, $C_p = \frac{5}{2}R$, $\gamma = \frac{5}{3}$
    (b) $C_v = \frac{5}{2}R$; $C_p = \frac{7}{2}R$; $\gamma = \frac{7}{5}$
    (c) $C_v = \frac{7}{2}R$, $C_p = \frac{9}{2}R$, $\gamma = \frac{9}{7}$

29. (a) $\Delta U = 894$ cal; $W = 0$; $Q = 894$ cal (b) $\Delta U = 894$ cal; $W = 596$ cal; $Q = 1490$ cal (c) $W = 596$ cal

31. 3.98 gm/mole

35. (a) $V_i = 2.24$ ℓ; $V_f = 5.88$ ℓ (b) $T_f = 143$ K

Problems

1. 34 km; variation in g can be neglected since H/R_E is only about 0.5%; if most of the energy dissipated because of air resistance were absorbed by the ice, air resistance could be neglected. Since much of the energy is probably absorbed by the surrounding air, H would be larger if air resistance were taken into account.

3. Dulong-Petit law gives 6 cal/mole-K, whereas measured value is about 0.5 cal/gm-K $= 9$ cal/mole-K. This could be explained by three degrees of freedom associated with internal energy in addition to the six degrees associated with center-of-mass vibration.

5. $t_f = 28.5°C$; t_i should be about 16°C

9. $C_p' - C_v' = 1.7 \times 10^{-7}$ cal/mole-K

11. (b) calculation gives -65.1 ℓ-atm $= -1.58 \times 10^3$ cal done by gas, that is, 65.1 ℓ-atm done on gas (c) 1.58×10^3 cal removed from gas during cycle (d) Work done by gas for each step is $+22.2$ ℓ-atm during adiabatic expansion, $+8.9$ ℓ-atm during expansion at 1 atm, 0.0 during heating at constant volume, and -96.2 ℓ-atm during compression at 5 atm.

Chapter 19

True or False

1. False 2. False; e.g., isothermal expansion of ideal gas. 3. False 4. False 5. False 6. True 7. False 8. True 9. False 10. True

Exercises

1. (a) 500 J (b) 400 J

3. (a) 40% (b) 335 W

5. 66.7 J absorbed and 46.7 J rejected per cycle

7. *Hint:* Use a perfect refrigerator to transfer 140 cal from the cold to hot reservoir.

9. The reverse process violates the Kelvin-Planck statement in (a) and (b) and the Clausius statement in (c).

13. (a) $33\frac{1}{3}$% (b) $W = 33.3$ cal; $Q_c = 66.7$ cal (c) 2

15. a 5-K decrease in temperature of cold reservoir

17. 224 K

19. (a) 2.75 cal/K = 11.5 J/K (b) 0

21. (a) $\Delta U = +50$ cal (b) $\Delta S = 0.167$ cal/K (c) $\Delta S_u = 0$ (d) parts (a) and (b) have same answers but for part (c) $\Delta S_u > 0$

23. (a) 2.75 cal/K (b) 2.75 cal/K

25. 0.417 cal/K

27. +1.45 cal/K

29. (a) $W = 400$ cal (b) +0.5 cal/K (c) $Q_{out} = 400$ cal; $W_c = 200$ cal, which is 200 cal less than in (a) (d) 200 cal = (0.5 cal/K)(400 K) (e) since Carnot efficiency is 50% here, 100 cal additional work could be done extracting 200 cal from hot reservoir; 100 cal = (0.5 cal/K)(200 K)

31. (a) 1.38 cal/K (b) 413 cal

33. Still air at 25°C has about 102 J more energy, but only air with center-of-mass motion can drive a windmill.

Problems

1. (a) (1) $W = 0$; $Q = 894$ cal; $\Delta U = 894$ cal
(2) $W = 49.2$ ℓ-atm = 1190 cal; $Q = 2980$ cal; $\Delta U = 1790$ cal
(3) $W = 0$; $Q = -1790$ cal; $\Delta U = -1790$ cal
(4) $W = 24.6$ ℓ-atm = 596 cal; $Q = -1490$ cal; $\Delta U = -894$ cal
(b) 15.3%

3. (c) 65% (d) The expansion and compression are not adiabatic, and none of the processes are quasi-static.

5. (a) greatest possible efficiency = 41% (b) 1.68×10^9 J

9. 100 W = 0.135 horsepower

13. (a) 10.2°C (10.0°C if 80 cal/gm is taken for heat of fusion of water) (b) +5.3 cal/K

Chapter 20

True or False

1. True 2. True 3. False 4. False; speed of sound increases by factor $\sqrt{2}$. 5. False

Exercises

3. Segments from $x = 2$ cm to $x = 3$ cm are moving up. Segments from $x = 1$ cm to $x = 2$ cm are moving down. Segment at $x = 2$ cm is at rest.

11. (b) T in pounds; μ in slugs per foot

13. 0.24 sec

15. 924 ft/sec (using $g = 32$ ft/sec²)

17. 776 mi/h

19. 5.06×10^3 m/sec

21. 2.86×10^{10} N/m²

23. $T = 2L/v$; no

25. $T = 4L/v$; no

Problems

1. at 300 K, $v = 0.216$ mi/sec $\approx \frac{1}{5}$ mi/sec (1/v = 4.64 sec/mi); error is about 8%; correction for travel time of light is insignificant

3. (a) 78.4 m (b) 69.8 m (using 347 m/sec for v, which gives 0.226 sec for sound travel time) (c) 70.6 m

5. Approximation gives 347.4 m/sec; exact calculation gives 347.0, assuming that $v = 331$ m/sec at 0°C. Approximation is good to about 0.1%.

7. 2.21 sec

Chapter 21

True or False

1. True 2. True 3. True 4. False; only transverse waves can be polarized. 5. False; 90° out of phase. 6. True 7. True 8. True 9. True 10. False; it has 1000 times the intensity.

Exercises

1. (a) $y(x,t) = y_0 \sin k(x - vt)$ (b) $y(x,t) = y_0 \sin 2\pi\left(\dfrac{x}{\lambda} - ft\right)$

(c) $y(x,t) = y_0 \sin 2\pi\left(\dfrac{x}{\lambda} - \dfrac{t}{T}\right)$ (d) $y(x,t) = y_0 \sin \dfrac{2\pi}{\lambda}(x - vt)$

(e) $y(x,t) = y_0 \sin 2\pi f\left(\dfrac{x}{v} - t\right)$

3. (a) 1.30 m (b) 0.65 m

5. 3000 m for AM; 3 m for FM

7. (a) $y = 0.02 \sin (37.7x - 377t)$ (b) no; any phase constant can be added to the phase

9. (a) linearly polarized (b) circularly polarized if $y_0 = z_0$; elliptically polarized if $y_0 \neq z_0$

11. (a) 0 (b) 3.7×10^{-6} m

13. 8.27×10^{-2} N/m^2

15. (a) 2.1×10^{-11} m (b) 1.1×10^{-11} m

17. 0.035 m

19. (a) 90° (b) $\sqrt{2}\,A$

21. sum is zero

23. (a) 4.74 J (b) 30.6 W

25. (a) 138 N/m^2 (b) 21.6 W/m^2 (c) 0.216 W

27. (a) 10^{-11} W/m^2 (b) 2×10^{-12} W/m^2 (c) 9.2×10^{-5} N/m^2; 4.1×10^{-5} N/m^2

29. 99% (power would have to be reduced by factor of 100)

Problems

3. (a) 0.0023 sec; 440 Hz (b) 316 m/sec (c) 0.719 m; 8.74 m^{-1} (d) $y(x,t) = 5 \times 10^{-4} \sin 2\pi(1.39x - 440t)$ (e) 1.38 m/sec; 3.82×10^3 m/sec^2 (f) 3.02 W

5. (a) one-ninth reflected; eight-ninths transmitted (b) $\frac{1}{3}A$ and $\frac{2}{3}A$

7. (a) 5.46 cm (b) 120° (c) $9I_0$; $2\pi n$, where $n = 1, 2, \ldots$ (e) 240°

11. 26%. This would imply that the noise energy doubles every 3 years, which is probably too great an increase to be reasonable over a long period of time.

Chapter 22

True or False

1. True 2. True 3. True 4. False 5. True

Exercises

1. (a) 440 m/sec (b) 2 m; 220 Hz (c) 440 Hz; 660 Hz

3. 141 Hz

5. (a) 296 m/sec (b) 87.8 N

7. (a) 2 m; 25 Hz (b) $y(x,t) = 0.004 \cos 50\pi t \sin \pi x$

9. (a) 200 m/sec; 0.25 cm (b) 1.26 m (c) 1.26 m

11. (a) 16 m; 5.33 m; 3.2 m (b) 6.25 Hz; 18.75 Hz; 31.25 Hz

13. (a) 4 m; 1.57 m^{-1} (b) 800π rad/sec (c) $y(x,t) = 0.03 \sin \frac{1}{2}\pi x \cos 800\pi t$

15. 17.4 Hz for open; 8.71 Hz for closed

17. (a) 2230 Hz (b) eighth or ninth ($f_9 = 20{,}070$ Hz)

Problems

1. 3.27 cm for A; 6.19 cm for B; 7.56 cm for C; 10 cm for D

3. (a) The powder moves about due to the motion of the gas and collects at the displacement nodes, where the gas is at rest. (b) $v = 2fx$, where x is distance between piles

5. (a) eighth and ninth harmonics (b) 2.16 m (c) 4.32 m

7. 338 m/sec (not accurate because of end correction)

9. (a) 345 m/sec (b) 1.25 cm

11. (a) $v_y = -7.54 \sin 2.36x \sin 377t$ (b) free end at $x = 0.666$ m; maximum speed of this point is 7.54 m/sec (c) $a_y = -2.84 \times 10^3 \sin 2.36x \cos 377t$. The free end at $x = 0.666$ m has the greatest acceleration, which has a maximum value of 2.84×10^3 m/sec^2.

13. this result applies to all harmonics; 1.54%

Chapter 23

True or False

1. True 2. True 3. False 4. True 5. False

Exercises

1. (a) 0.4 cm (b) $y(x,t) = 0.4$ cm $\cos (0.1x - 10t) \cos (5.9x - 590t)$; $v_p = 100$ m/sec (c) $v_g = 100$ m/sec (d) 62.8 m (e) dispersionless

3. (a) $s_1 = s_0 \cos (9.24x - 1000\pi t)$; $s_2 = s_0 \cos (9.33x - 1010\pi t)$; $s = 2s_0 \cos (.046x - 5\pi t) \cos (9.29x - 1005\pi t)$

5. 437 Hz

7. (a) 10 μsec (b) $\Delta f \approx 10^5$ Hz

11. $v_p = v_g = \sqrt{\gamma RT/M}$; no, nondispersive

Problems

3. When the zero of your vernier scale is aligned with the 0-cm mark on the meterstick, the first line on the vernier is 0.1 cm before the 1-cm mark, the second vernier mark is 0.2 cm before the 2-cm mark, etc. When the vernier moves 0.1 cm past the 0-cm mark, the first vernier mark is aligned with the 1-cm mark. The frequency of centimeter marks on the meterstick is 1 per centimeter and the frequency of vernier marks is 1.1 per centimeter. The beat frequency is 0.1 per 1 cm or 1 per 10 cm. The marks are therefore in phase once every 10 cm.

Chapter 24

True or False

1. True 2. False; it also depends on the "absolute" velocity of source or receiver relative to the still air. 3. True 4. False 5. False 6. True

Exercises

1. (a) 8.84×10^{-5} W/m^2 (b) about 80 dB

3. (a) I varies as $1/r$ (b) A varies as $1/\sqrt{r}$

5. (a) $\lambda = v/f_0$; $f = v/\lambda = f_0$ (b) $\lambda' = (v - u_S)/f_0$; $f' = v/\lambda' = vf_0/(v - u_S)$ (c) $\lambda = v/f_0$; $f' = (v + u_R)/\lambda = (v + u_R)f_0/v$

7. (a) 260 m/sec (b) 1.3 m (c) 261.5 Hz

9. (a) 1.7 m (b) 247 Hz

11. 153 Hz

15. (a) 8.3° (b) 16.5° (c) three maxima beyond the $\theta = 0$ maximum

19. (a) $\sin \theta = m/3$, $m = 0, 1, 2, 3$ (b) $\sin \theta = m/9$, $m = 1, 2, 4, 5, 7, 8$

21. 72°

23. (a) 0 (b) $2I_0$ (c) $4I_0$

25. (a) $r_1 - r_2 = (n + \frac{1}{4})\lambda$ (b) $r_1 - r_2 = (n - \frac{1}{4})\lambda$, where $n = 0, 1, 2, \ldots$

Problems

1. (a) 5.3 ft; 207.6 Hz (b) 215 Hz (c) 15 Hz

3. (a) 8.84×10^{-6} W/m² (b) about 69 dB (c) 892 m

5. 23.8 mi/h

7. 3.33 mm

11. (a) $I_1 = 1.99 \times 10^{-5}$ W/m²; $I_2 = 8.84 \times 10^{-6}$ W/m² (b) $I = 5.53 \times 10^{-5}$ W/m² (c) $I = 2.2 \times 10^{-6}$ W/m² (d) $I = 2.87 \times 10^{-5}$ W/m²

13. Speakers are connected properly if they move in phase when driven by a monophonic source. A stereo source is not used because the speakers would not be coherent (they would be driven by different sources). Bass is used so that listener's position is not critical for detection of constructive interference from in-phase speakers and destructive interference from 180°-out-of-phase speakers. For example, if $f = 100$ Hz, $\lambda \approx 11$ ft, and listener need be equidistant from speakers only to within a few feet. If $f = 1000$ Hz, $\lambda \approx 1.1$ ft, and listener's position is critical.

Chapter 25

True or False

1. True 2. False 3. False; it is caused by limiting the wavefront. 4. True 5. True 6. False; the ray approximation is valid for any type of wave if the wavelength is very small. 7. False 8. False; it occurs where the waves from the top and bottom of the slit are in phase. 9. True 10. True

Exercises

5. (a) $\theta_1 = 19.5°$ (b) $\theta_2 = 41.8°$

7. (b) 12 mm

13. $\lambda = 6.7 \times 10^{-29}$ m; no

15. away from the normal because the speed of sound is greater in water than in air

17. (a) 1.46 (b) $\lambda = 2.05$ cm

19. 13.3°

21. 0, 22.0, and 48.6°

Problems

3. (a) 62.7° (b) No; the critical angle for glass-air refraction is 41.8°. For angles greater than 41.8° but less than 62.7° the light rays will enter the water, but they cannot get into the air.

Chapter 26

Exercises

3. 12.4 keV

5. 3×10^{18} Hz

7. 1240 nm; infrared

9. (a) $\theta = 30°$ or $\theta = 150°$ (b) 7.07 m

11. 2.1×10^6 years

13. 10.7 min

15. 92%

17. The angle of refraction is about 27.5° for $\lambda = 400$ nm and about 28.1° for $\lambda = 700$ nm, a difference of about 0.6°.

19. 526 nm (using $n = 1.33$); the swimmer observes the same color

21. 1.68 cm

23. (a) 8.54×10^{-3} rad (b) 6.83 cm

25. (a) 56.4 km = 35.0 mi (b) 56.4 m = 185 ft

27. (a) 0.15 mm (b) 33.3 bands per centimeter

29. 39

31. (a) dark, the ray reflecting from air-glass surface suffers a phase change of 180° (b) 1.75×10^{-4} rad = 0.01°

33. minimum thickness 1.15×10^{-4} mm

35. $\lambda_1 = 486$ nm; $\lambda_2 = 660$ nm

37. (a) $\theta_{579} = 0.1158$ rad, $\theta_{576} = 0.1154$ rad, $\Delta\theta = 4 \times 10^{-4}$ rad (b) 1.44 mm

39. (a) $I_0/8$ (b) $3I_0/32$

41. (a) 30° (b) 1.73

43. 56.3°

Problems

5. (b) 491 (c) 0.99 mm

7. about 6.5×10^6 km using red light ($\lambda = 700$ nm)

9. (c) A transmission interference pattern is produced by the interference of the light directly transmitted with that twice reflected in the air gap. The pattern is the reverse of the reflected pattern. Since only a small fraction of the light is twice reflected, the transmitted light is nearly uniformly bright with weak interference bands. (d) 68 (e) 1.14 cm (f) Since λ is smaller in water than in air, the fringes would be closer together with 0.75 times the original spacing.

11. (a) minimum thickness 6×10^{-7} m (b) 400, 514, and 720 nm (c) 400, 514, and 720 nm

13. (c) $n_{air} = 1.0003$ (d) not necessary

17. (a) 7.94×10^{-4} mm (b) 1.59×10^{-3} mm (c) no; not unless the indexes of refraction varied in just such a way that $\lambda/(n_O - n_E)$ was constant

Chapter 27

True or False

1. True 2. True 3. False 4. True 5. False 6. True 7. False 8. True 9. False; it is smaller than the object. 10. True

Exercises

7. (a) $s' = 33.3$ cm; real, inverted, reduced by $y' = -y/3$
   (b) $s' = 50$ cm; real, inverted, same size
   (c) $s' = \infty$, no image
   (d) $s' = -16.7$ cm, virtual, erect, enlarged $y' = 5y/3$

9. (a) $s' = -20$ cm, virtual, erect, reduced $y' = y/5$
   (b) $s' = -16.7$ cm, virtual, erect, reduced $y' = y/3$
   (c) $s' = -12.5$ cm, virtual, erect, reduced $y' = y/2$
   (d) $s' = -7.14$ cm, virtual, erect, reduced $y' = 0.714\,y$

13. 1.33 cm

15. $s = 10$ cm

17. (a) $s' = -46.15$ cm, virtual (b) $s' = -6.47$ cm, virtual (c) $s' = 44.1$ cm, real

19. (a) 13.6 cm (b) 20 cm (c) −10 cm (d) −40 cm

21. (a) −40 cm (b) +40 cm (c) −40 cm

23. A negative object distance occurs when a surface interrupts light which was converging to a point beyond the surface. The image point is then a virtual object, and the object distance is negative. (a) $s' = +10$ cm, real, erect (b) $s' = +15$ cm, real, erect

25. $s' = +10$ cm; $y' = -1$ cm

27. There are two solutions: (1) $s = 15$ cm produces a real, inverted image at $s' = 30$ cm; (2) $s = 5$ cm produces a virtual, erect image at $s' = -10$ cm.

31. Image is 30 cm to right of second lens. It is erect and twice as large as object.

33. The computed distances from the vertex of the mirror are (to four significant figures) for 0.5 cm, $s' = 3.000$ cm; for 1.0 cm, $s' = 2.998$ cm; for 2.0 cm, $s' = 2.975$ cm; and for 4.0 cm, $s' = 2.674$ cm.

35. Lens should move 2.78 mm forward.

37. $\theta = 8 \times 10^{-5}$ rad; $\Delta x = 1.6$ mm

41. $M_{25} = 2.5$; $M_{50} = 5.0$; for images at infinity, the retinal images are the same size

43. (a) 30 cm (b) −6 (c) −30 (d) 5.83 cm

45. 17.6 cm

Problems

3. (a) $s' = -128$ cm (b) $s' = 14.7$ cm (c) real

7. (b) 2.55 m

9. $f_{\text{blue}} = 17.4$ cm

Chapter 28

True or False

1. True 2. True 3. False 4. True 5. True 6. False 7. False 8. False 9. True 10. True

Exercises

1. (a) 236 μsec (b) 2.36×10^{-12} sec (c) no

3. *Hint:* Use the binomial expansion.

5. (a) 5.96×10^{-8} sec (b) 16.1 m (c) 7.02 m

7. (a) 0.8 m (b) 4.44 nsec

9. 80 c-min

13. 60 min, which is the result of Exercise 12

15. about $0.21c = 39{,}000$ mi/sec

17. $0.6c$

19. (a) $x_2' - x_1' = \gamma(x_2 - x_1)$ (b) Times t_1 and t_2 in Equations 28-19 are equal to t_0, but times t_1' and t_2' in Equations 28-18 are not equal and not known.

21. (a) $u_x = v$; $u_y = c/\gamma$

27. (a) 4.974 MeV/c (b) 0.9948

29. (a) $938\sqrt{3}$ MeV/c = 1625 MeV/c (b) $v/c = \frac{1}{2}\sqrt{3} = 0.866$; $v = 2.60 \times 10^8$ m/sec

31. 6.26 MeV

33. (a) 4.5×10^{-9} u (b) about $8 \times 10^{-9}\%$, a very small error

Problems

3. (c) 0.866 c and 0.9988 c

5. (a) 60 m (b) 0.9756 c (c) 21.95 m (d) 0.25 μsec

11. (a) 120 min (b) 240 min (c) 60 min; 120 min; 240 min; observer in S' makes same table

15. (c) $P' = Mu/\sqrt{1 - u^2/c^2}$ (f) in S: $E_i = E_k + 2mc^2 = 2mc^2\gamma$; $E_f = Mc^2 = 2m\gamma c^2$ since $M = 2m\gamma$; in S': $E_i = mc^2/\sqrt{1 - u'^2/c^2} + mc^2 = 2mc^2\lambda^2$; $E_f = Mc^2\gamma = 2mc^2\lambda^2$

Chapter 29

True or False

1. False; only if the charge is positive. 2. True 3. False; they diverge from a positive point charge. 4. True 5. False; the *net* flux through the surface is zero.

Exercises

1. (a) 6.24×10^{12} (b) 6.24×10^6

3. 230 N

5. $1.5 \times 10^{-2}\mathbf{i}$ N

7. $0.914\ kq^2/L^2$ away from negative charge

9. (a) $8 \times 10^3\mathbf{i}$ N/C at $x = 2$ m; $9.36 \times 10^3\mathbf{i}$ N/C at $x = 10$ m (b) $x = 4$ m (c) **E** points in the positive x direction just to the right of the origin and in the negative x direction just to the left of the origin.

11. (a) $-2.59 \times 10^4\mathbf{j}$ N/C (b) $-5.18 \times 10^{-5}\mathbf{j}$ N

13. (a) $|q_{\text{left}}| = 4|q_{\text{right}}|$ (b) left positive, right negative (c) Field is strong close to charges and between them where lines are most dense. Field is weak away from charges, particularly to the right of the negative charge, where the lines are less dense.

17. 0

19. (a) yes (b) 0 (c) 0

21. (a) 0.053 μC (b) no, only that the net charge inside is zero

23. (a) 1.76×10^{11} C/kg (b) 1.76×10^{13} m/sec² opposite the direction of **E** (c) 0.17 μsec (d) 25.6 cm

25. (a) $-7.04 \times 10^{13}\mathbf{j}$ m/sec² (b) 50 nsec (c) 8.8 cm

27. electric force about 1.46×10^9 times mg

29. $8 \times 10^{-18}\mathbf{i}$ C-m

Problems

1. (a) $0.914\ kq^2/L^2$ toward other positive charge

3. (a) 4 and 2 μC (b) $3 + \sqrt{17}\ \mu$C $= +7.12\ \mu$C and $3 - \sqrt{17}\ \mu$C $= -1.12\ \mu$C

5. (c) For $x \gg a$, the separation of charges is not important, and so you expect the field to be like that of a point charge $+2q$.

7. (a) stable for displacements of q_0 along y axis; unstable for displacements along x axis assuming other charges held fixed (b) stable for displacements of q_0 along x axis and unstable for displacements along y axis assuming other charges held fixed (c) $q_0 = -\frac{1}{4}q$. If none of the charges is held fixed, the equilibrium is unstable for displacement of any of the charges. A stable equilibrium distribution of electric charges is not possible under electric forces only.

Chapter 30

True or False

1. False 2. True 3. True 4. False

Exercises

1. (a) in the negative x direction (b) $E_y = 0$, $E_x = -2kqa/(y^2 + a^2)^{3/2}$

3. (a) $1.42 \times 10^6\mathbf{i}$ N/C (b) $1.92 \times 10^6\mathbf{i}$ N/C (c) $1.77 \times 10^6\mathbf{i}$ N/C (d) $125\mathbf{i}$ N/C

5. (a) $\dfrac{k\lambda}{y}\left(\dfrac{b}{\sqrt{y^2+b^2}}+\dfrac{a}{\sqrt{y^2+a^2}}\right)$

7. (a) $k\pi a^2\sigma/x^2$

11. (a) 9×10^5 N/C (b) 1.798×10^6 N/C (c) 1.796×10^6 N/C (d) 4.50×10^5 N/C (e) 1.12×10^5 N/C. These results for parts (c), (d), and (e) are the same as in Exercise 10, but for parts (a) and (b), $E=0$ in Exercise 10. [Answers to parts (b) and (c) are given to four significant figures, using $k=9\times10^9$ N-m²/C² to bring out the slight variation in E from 9.99 to 10.01 cm.]

13. (a) $\mathbf{E}=\dfrac{kQr}{R^3}\,\hat{\mathbf{r}}$ (b) $\mathbf{E}=\dfrac{kQ}{r^2}\,\hat{\mathbf{r}}$, where $Q=\tfrac43\pi R^3\rho$

Problems

1. *Hint:* Set dE_x/dx equal to zero and solve for x.

3. $E_x=kQx(x^2+\tfrac14L^2)^{-1}(x^2+\tfrac12L^2)^{-1/2}$, where $Q=4L\lambda$. For a ring of radius $r=\tfrac12L$ but carrying the same charge, $E_x=kQx(x^2+\tfrac14L^2)^{-3/2}$. *Hint:* Use Equation 30-9 for the magnitude of the field of each segment, replacing y with $r=(x^2+\tfrac14L^2)^{1/2}$. Then take 4 times the x component of this field.

5. (a) left: $-\sigma/\epsilon_0$; right: $+\sigma/\epsilon_0$; between: zero, where the $+$ direction is to the right (b) left: 0; right: 0; between: $+\sigma/\epsilon_0$

7. (a) $Q=\pi AR^4$ (b) inside: $E_r=Ar^2/4\epsilon_0$; outside: $E_r=AR^4/4\epsilon_0 r^2=kQ/r^2$

Chapter 31 **True or False**

1. False; it is zero in electrostatic equilibrium but not in general. 2. False 3. False 4. False; e.g., a neutral conducting sphere in an external electric field has positive charge on one side and negative charge on the other. 5. True

Exercises

1. (a) 2.85×10^{22} electrons (b) 4.56×10^3 C

3. 1.13×10^4 N/C

5. (a) $7.07\ \mu$C/m² (b) 8.0×10^5 N/C (c) 0 (d) 4.0×10^5 N/C outward both just inside and just outside the hole (if the portion with its charge were replaced, its field would cancel the field inside and add to the field outside)

Problems

3. (c) 14.3 N/m²

Chapter 32 **True or False**

1. False; V must be constant in the region but need not be zero 2. True; but if $V=0$ at a *point*, $\mathbf{E}$ need *not* be zero at that point; if V is zero or constant in a region of space, it cannot be changing from point to point, and so $\mathbf{E}$ must also be zero. 3. False 4. True 5. True 6. True

Exercises

1. (a) 2.4×10^{-2} J (b) -2.4×10^{-2} J (c) -8000 V

3. (a) positive (b) 2.5×10^4 V/m

5. (a) $V(x)=-200x$ (b) $V(x)=4000-200x$ (c) $V(x)=200-200x$, where x is in meters and V in volts

7. (a) C_1 is the potential at $x=0$ (b) $\mathbf{E}=-2C_2x\mathbf{i}$; in negative x direction

9. (a) 4.5 kV (b) 1.35×10^{-2} J (c) 1.35×10^{-2} J (d) 1.35×10^{-2} J

11. (a) 9000 and 8970 V (b) decrease, $-\Delta V/\Delta x=2990$ V/m (c) $E_x=3000$ V/m, same to 0.3% (d) $V(3.00,0.01)=9000$ V, the same as at $x=3.00$ m, $y=0$ m to this accuracy. The change in V for displacements in the y direction is related to E_y, which is zero at the point $x=3.00$ m, $y=0$.

13. (a) 3×10^{-2} J (b) -6×10^{-3} J (c) -1.8×10^{-2} J

15. (a) 0 (b) $\mathbf{E} = 6000\mathbf{i}$ V/m (c) $V(3.01) = -60$ V; $-\Delta V/\Delta x = 6000$ V/m, the same as E_x to this accuracy

17. (a) $V(x) = \dfrac{kq}{|x - a|} + \dfrac{kq}{|x + a|}$ (c) A positive test charge placed at this point will be in stable equilibrium.

19. (a) 9×10^3 V/m just outside; 0 just inside (b) 900 V both just outside and just inside (c) $V = 900$ V, $E = 0$ at center

21. 1.77 mm

25. (a) $Q_2/Q_1 = 2$; $Q_1 + Q_2 = 6 \times 10^{-8}$ C, where Q_1 is charge on 4-cm sphere and Q_2 is charge on 8-cm sphere (b) $Q_1 = 2 \times 10^{-8}$ C; $Q_2 = 4 \times 10^{-8}$ C (c) both at 4.5 kV

27. (a) 0.222 μC (b) $Q_1 = 0.0889$ μC (20-cm sphere); $Q_2 = 0.133$ μC (30-cm sphere) (c) 4 kV (d) $\sigma_1 = 0.177$ μC/m²; $\sigma_2 = 0.118$ μC/m²

Problems

1. (a) $E_k = +ke^2/2r$ (b) $\tfrac{1}{2}mv^2 = 2.18 \times 10^{-18}$ J $= 13.6$ eV; $E = \tfrac{1}{2}mv^2 + U = -13.6$ eV (c) 13.6 eV

3. 4.46×10^{-14} m

5. $V = kqa/z(z - a)$

7. (a) $V = \begin{cases} \sigma x/\epsilon_0 & \text{for } x < 0 \\ 0 & \text{for } 0 \leqslant x \leqslant 0 \\ -\sigma(x - a)/\epsilon_0 & \text{for } x > a \end{cases}$ (b) $V = \begin{cases} 0 & \text{for } x < 0 \\ -\sigma x/\epsilon_0 & \text{for } 0 \leqslant x \leqslant a \\ -\sigma a/\epsilon_0 & \text{for } x > a \end{cases}$

9. $V_a - V_b = \dfrac{2kq}{L} \ln \dfrac{b}{a}$

Chapter 33

True or False

1. False 2. False 3. False 4. True 5. True 6. False 7. True

Exercises

1. (a) 2 pF (b) 200 pF (c) 0.2 μF

3. (a) 9×10^9 m (b) 1410

5. 1.13×10^7 m²; 3.36 km $= 2.09$ mi

7. 466 μF

9. (a) 6.67 μF (b) 40 μC (c) 4 V across 10-μF capacitor and 2 V across 20-μF capacitor

11. (a) 14 μF (b) $\tfrac{8}{7}$ μF

13. (a) 100 (b) 10 V (c) $q = 10$ μC; $V = 1$ kV

15. 10 μF

17. 5×10^{-5} J

19. (a) 0.625 J (b) 1.875 J

21. (a) $\epsilon_0 A/2d$ (b) $2V$ (c) $\epsilon_0 AV^2/d$ (d) $\epsilon_0 AV^2/2d$

23. (a) 10^5 V/m (b) 4.42×10^{-2} J/m³ (c) 8.85×10^{-5} J (d) same, 8.85×10^{-5} J

25. (a) $E = 2.5 \times 10^4$ V/m; $\sigma = 2.21 \times 10^{-7}$ C/m²; $U = 6.64 \times 10^{-7}$ J (b) 6.25 kV/m; 25 V (c) 1.66×10^{-7} J (d) 1.66×10^{-7} C/m²

Problems

3. each capacitor is 5 μF; $C_{\text{eff}} = \tfrac{5}{3}$ μF in series; $C_{\text{eff}} = 7.5$ μF one in parallel with two in series; $C_{\text{eff}} = \tfrac{10}{3}$ μF, two in parallel with one in series

5. (a) $E_r = 2Q/Lr$ for $R_1 < r < R_2$; $E = 0$ elsewhere (b) $dU = (kQ^2/L)$ dr/r (c) $U = (kQ^2/L) \ln (R_2/R_1)$, same as $\tfrac{1}{2}QV$ since $V = (2kQ/L) \ln (R_2/R_1)$

9. (a) 5.0 μF (b) 66.7 V

13. Use 16 capacitors with 4 parallel sets of 4 in series

15. (a) 2.28×10^{-9} F. *Note:* The approximation that this is a parallel-plate capacitor with area $2\pi r L$ and separation $d = 2$ mm gives 2.22×10^{-9} F. (b) about 67 μC

Chapter 34   **True or False**   1. False 2. True 3. False; this is *definition* of resistance. 4. False; true only for conductors obeying Ohm's law 5. True 6. True 7. True

Exercises   1. (a) 600 C (b) 3.75×10^{21} electrons

3. (a) 0.40 A (since ions and electrons flow in opposite directions, their currents add) (b) 566 A/m^2

5. (a) $f = v/2\pi r$ (b) $I = qv/2\pi r$

7. (a) 3.2×10^{13} protons per cubic meter (the proton speed is 6.2×10^7 m/sec obtained from $E_k = \frac{1}{2}mv^2$) (b) 3.75×10^{17} protons (c) $Q = 1.0 \times 10^{-3}t$ C since current is 1.0 mA

9. (a) 1.0 V (b) 0.10 V/m

11. (a) $V_{Cu}/V_{Fe} = 0.17$ (b) E greater in iron

13. (a) 2.75×10^{-2} Ω (b) 3.0×10^{-2} Ω

15. 1.2 Ω

17. 46°C

19. 0.031 Ω

21. (a) 5000 A/m^2 (b) 3.7×10^{-7} m/sec (c) 5.0×10^{-14} sec (d) about 50 Å

23. (a) 5.7 nsec (b) about 15 min

25. (a) 2.42 kW (b) 1.21 kW

27. (a) $R = 48.4$ Ω; $I = 4.55$ A (b) 207 W

29. (a) 0.24 cent (b) 64 cents

Problems   1. (a) 3.12 V (b) $J = 4.59 \times 10^6$ A/m; $E = 7.8 \times 10^{-2}$ V/m (c) 18.7 W

3. (a) 10^{12} electrons (b) 1.6×10^{-4} A (c) 64 kW (d) 640 MW (e) 1/10,000

5. (a) 2.55×10^6 A/m^2 (b) $E_{Cu} = 0.0433$ V/m; $E_{Fe} = 0.255$ V/m (c) $V_{Cu} = 3.46$ V; $V_{Fe} = 12.48$ V (d) 7.97 $\Omega = R_{Cu} + R_{Fe}$, where $R_{Cu} = 1.73$ Ω and $R_{Fe} = 6.24$ Ω

7. $l_{Cu}/l_C = 264$

Chapter 35   **True or False**   1. True 2. True 3. True 4. True 5. False 6. False 7. True

Exercises   1. (a) 0.03 Ω (b) 12.3 V

3. (a) $I = 1.13$ A; $P = 6.79$ W (6.41 W delivered to R)

5. $\mathcal{E} = 3$ V; $r = 1$ Ω

7. (a) 1 A (b) 12 W delivered by 12-V battery; 6 W absorbed by 6-V battery (c) 2 W in the 2-Ω resistor, 4 W in the 4-Ω resistor

9. (a) $\frac{4}{3}$ A (b) 132 J (c) 124 J (d) the 2-V battery absorbs 8 J in this time

11. (a) $I_{2\Omega} = 3$ A; $I_{3\Omega} = 2$ A; $I_{1\Omega} = 1$ A (b) $V_a - V_b = 1$ V (c) $P_{7V} = 21$ W; $P_{5V} = 10$ W

13. (a) $\frac{10}{3}$ Ω (b) 3.6 A in first 2-Ω resistor; 1.2 A in 4-Ω resistor and 2.4 A in second 2-Ω resistor

15. (a) $\frac{48}{7}$ Ω (b) 0.75 A in upper branch; 1.0 A in lower branch with 0.5 A in each of the parallel 8-Ω resistors

17. (a) 5 Ω (b) upper branch: $I_{4\Omega}$ = 1.2 A with 0.72 A in the upper subbranch and 0.48 A in the lower subbranch (5- and 10-Ω resistors); lower branch: $I_{5\Omega}$ = 1.2 A with 0.6 A in each 10-Ω resistor

19. (a) 2 A through 1.5-Ω resistor; 0.75 A through each 4-Ω resistor, 0.5 A through 6-Ω resistor (b) 12 W

21. (a) 600 μC (b) 0.2 A (c) 3 msec (d) 81.2 μC

23. 57.7 MΩ

25. (a) 3.79 μC (b) 2.21 μA (c) 2.21 μA (d) 13.2 μW (e) 4.87 μW (f) 8.37 μW

27. (a) 0.050 Ω (b) 4.9 kΩ

29. (a) 0.100 Ω (b) 0.100 Ω (c) 3.00 MΩ

31. (a) 1.49 kΩ (b) 1.50 kΩ (c) 13.5 kΩ

33. (a) 9.90 kΩ (b) 90.0 kΩ (c) 900 kΩ

35. (a) 43.9 Ω (b) 300 Ω (c) 3800 Ω

Problems

3. (a) 2 A to the right through the 1-Ω and first 2-Ω resistor; 1 A down through the second 2-Ω resistor; 1 A down through the 6-Ω resistor (b) 16 W by the 8-V battery; 8 W by the upper 4-V battery and 4 W *to* the lower 4-V battery

5. $V_a - V_b = 2.4$ V

7. (a) 1.974 A (b) 1.3% (c) 1.48 V (d) 0.001%

9. 600 Ω

11. (b) method a gives R_c = 0.498 Ω; 2.91 Ω; 44.4 Ω; method b gives 0.6 Ω; 3.1 Ω; 80.1 Ω

15. (a) $I = \frac{R_1 + R_2}{R_1 R_2}\varepsilon$ (b) $I = \varepsilon/R_2$ (c) $I(t) = \varepsilon\left(\frac{1}{R_2} + \frac{1}{R_1}e^{-t/R_1C}\right)$ (d) 2.3×10^{-2} sec

Chapter 36

True or False

1. True 2. True 3. True 4. False; the period is independent of the radius. 5. True

Exercises

1. -1.28×10^{-12}j N

3. (a) -7.2×10^{-13}j N (b) 4.8×10^{-13}i N (c) 0 (d) 9.6×10^{-13}i $- 7.2 \times 10^{-13}$j N

5. 1.0 N

7. 20k N/m

9. (a) 2 A-m² (b) 50 A-m

11. (a) 1 dyne-cm/G = 10^{-3} A-m² (b) 1 eV/G = 1.6×10^{-15} A-m²

13. (a) 0.30 A-m² (b) 0.13 N-m

15. (a) 37°; n̂ = 0.8i − 0.6j (b) 0.48n A-m² = 0.38i − 0.29j A-m² (c) 0.58k N-m

17. 3.93×10^{-6} N-m

19. (a) 0.131 μsec (b) 3.83×10^7 m/sec (c) 7.66 MeV

21. (a) 2.7 mm (b) 3.5×10^{10} rad/sec (c) 0.18 nsec

23. (a) 0.13 μsec (b) 2.41×10^7 m/sec (c) 12.0 MeV

25. (a) -10^4k V/m (b) no

27. (a) 6.9 mm (b) 0.75 G

29. (a) 1.44×10^8 rad/sec (b) 27.1 MeV (c) assuming $m_d = 2m_p$, both answers are halved

31. (a) 1.07×10^{-2} cm/sec (b) 5.84×10^{22} electrons/cm^3

33. (a) 3.68×10^{-3} cm/sec (b) 1.47 μV

Problems

1. 0.98 A

3. (a) $B = (Mg/IL) \tan \theta$ (b) $g \sin \theta$ up the rails

Chapter 37

True or False

1. True 2. False 3. False 4. True 5. True

Exercises

1. (a) $4.44 \times 10^{-11}\mathbf{j}$ T (b) $-1.11 \times 10^{-11}\mathbf{j}$ T (c) 0 (d) $-4.44 \times 10^{-11}\mathbf{i}$ T

3. (a) 2×10^{-11} T in direction of the unit vector $\mathbf{n} = -(2/\sqrt{5})\mathbf{i} + (1/\sqrt{5})\mathbf{j}$ (b) $2/\sqrt{5} \times 10^{-11}\mathbf{j}$ T

5. (a) $-8.89 \times 10^{-5}\mathbf{k}$ T (b) 0 (c) $8.89 \times 10^{-5}\mathbf{k}$ T (d) $-1.6 \times 10^{-4}\mathbf{k}$ T

7. (a) $-1.78 \times 10^{-4}\mathbf{k}$ T (b) $-1.33 \times 10^{-4}\mathbf{k}$ T (c) $-1.78 \times 10^{-4}\mathbf{k}$ T (d) $+1.07 \times 10^{-4}\mathbf{k}$ T

9. (a) $6.4 \times 10^{-5}\mathbf{j}$ T (b) $-4.8 \times 10^{-5}\mathbf{k}$ T

11. 0 due to segments along line through P; 5.66×10^{-5} T inward due to each vertical segment, 1.13×10^{-4} T inward due to horizontal segment above P; resultant $\mathbf{B}$ 2.26×10^{-4} T inward

13. 2.36×10^{-5} T

15. (a) $32\sqrt{2}\, k_m I/L = 45.3 k_m I/L$ (b) $4\pi^2 k_m I/L = 39.5 k_m I/L$ (c) the square

17. (a) antiparallel (b) 44.7 mA

19. 28 A

21. (a) 4.5×10^{-4} N/m to right (b) 3×10^{-5} T down

23. (a) $+10\mu_0$ for C_1; 0 for C_2; $-10\mu_0$ for C_3 (b) none of these paths can be used because of lack of symmetry

25. (a) 8 G $= 8 \times 10^{-4}$ T (b) 40 G (c) 28.6 G

27. (a) 6.03×10^{-3} T (b) 0.377 A-m^2 (c) 1.51 A-m (d) 7.9×10^{-9} T using the point pole approximation

29. (a) 0.40 A-m (b) 7.76×10^{-9} N

31. 4800 A/m

33. (a) 1.54×10^6 A/m (b) 1.93 T

35. (a) 0 (b) 1.37×10^{-5} T-m$^2 = 1.37 \times 10^{-5}$ Wb (c) 0 (d) 1.19×10^{-5} Wb

37. 6.74×10^{-3} Wb

39. (a) 1.80×10^{15} N/C-sec (b) $I_d = \epsilon_0 A\, dE/dt = 5$ A (c) 1.60×10^4 A/m^2

Problems

1. The magnetic field due to the cable is 0.05 G at the earth's surface, which is about 7% of magnitude of the earth's field.

3. $v_{||} = (2\pi m/\mu_0 qI)v_t^2$

9. (a) 5.40×10^{-2} T at $x = 5$ cm; 5.39×10^{-2} T at $x = 7$ cm; 5.26×10^{-2} T at $x = 9$ cm; 4.86×10^{-2} T at $x = 11$ cm

11. (a) 5.01×10^{-7} Wb (b) 7.14×10^{-5} N away from wire

13. 1.97×10^{-6} N-m

15. $k_m I$

Chapter 38   **True or False**   1. False; it is proportional to the rate of change of the flux. 2. True 3. False 4. False; it is an independent law. 5. True

Exercises   1. (a) 6.4×10^{-20} N (b) 0.40 V/m (c) 0.12 V

3. (a) 1.6 V (b) 0.8 A counterclockwise (c) 0.128 N (d) 1.28 W; 1.28 W

5. (a) clockwise; repel (b) counterclockwise; attract

7. (a) counterclockwise (b) clockwise

9. 199 T/sec

11. (a) $\mathcal{E} = 0.4 - 0.2t$ V (b) at $t = 0$, $\phi_m = 0$, $\mathcal{E} = 0.4$ V; at $t = 2$ sec, $\phi_m = -0.4$ T-m^2, $\mathcal{E} = 0$; at $t = 4$ sec, $\phi_m = 0$, $\mathcal{E} = -0.4$ V; at $t = 6$ sec, $\phi_m = 1.2$ T-m^2, $\mathcal{E} = -0.8$ V

13. (a) 1.26×10^{-3} C (b) 12.6 mA (c) 0.628 V

15. 0.80 G

17. (a) 24 Wb (b) (−)1.60 kV

19. (a) 60.3 G (b) 7.58×10^{-4} Wb (c) 253 μH (d) 37.9 mV

21. (b) $M = \mu_0 N_1 N_2 A_1 / l_2$ (c) The flux through the solenoid depends on B due to the coil which is not uniform, especially outside the coil.

23. (a) $I = 0$; $dI/dt = 25$ A/sec (b) $I = 2.26$ A; $dI/dt = 20.5$ A/sec (c) $I = 7.90$ A; $dI/dt = 9.20$ A/sec (d) $I = 10.8$ A; $dI/dt = 3.38$ A/sec

25. (a) 13.5 mA (b) 90.8 μA (c) 7.44×10^{-44} A

27. 4.4 msec

29. (a) 44.06 W (b) 40.44 W (c) 3.62 W

31. (a) 2.0 A (b) 4.0 J

33. (a) $W_m = 3.98 \times 10^5$ J (b) $W_e = 4.43 \times 10^{-4}$ J (c) 3.98×10^5 J

35. 1.26 msec

37. (b) third circuit since $I_{max} = \omega Q_0 = \omega CV$ and ω and V are the same for all three circuits

Problems   3. (a) for $0 \le t \le 5$ sec, $\phi_m = 10^{-3}t$ Wb; for 5 sec $\le t \le 10$ sec, $\phi_m = 5 \times 10^{-3}$ Wb; for 10 sec $\le t \le 15$ sec, $\phi_m = (15 - t) \times 10^{-3}$ Wb; for 15 sec $\le t$, $\phi_m = 0$ (b) for $0 \le t < 5$ sec, $\mathcal{E} = -1$ mV; for 5 sec $< t < 10$ sec, $\mathcal{E} = 0$; for 10 sec $< t < 15$ sec, $\mathcal{E} = +1$ mV; for 15 sec $< t$, $\mathcal{E} = 0$

5. $\mu_0 n_1 n_2 \pi r_1^2 l$

7. $R = 10$ Ω; $L = 4$ H

9. (a) 3.53 J (b) 1.61 J (c) 1.92 J

11. (a) $B_o = 3.4$ G; $B_{av} = 6.8$ G (b) 159 T/sec (c) about 80,000 rev (d) 700 G

13. (a) $F = B^2 l^2 v / R$ (c) $I^2 R = (B^2 l^2 v_0^2 / R) e^{-2t/T}$

15. (a) $I^2 R = 2400 e^{-6000t}$ (b) 0.40 J (c) 0.40 J

Chapter 39   **True or False**   1. True; but it is often masked by paramagnetism. 2. True 3. False 4. True 5. True 6. False

Exercises   1. (a) $\mathbf{H} = 8.00 \times 10^3 \mathbf{k}$ A/m; $\mathbf{B} = 101\mathbf{k}$ G (b) $\mathbf{H} = 8.00 \times 10^3 \mathbf{k}$ A/m; $\mathbf{B} = 1.52\mathbf{k}$ T

3. (a) 75 A-m (b) $\mathbf{H}_p = -1.19 \times 10^3 \mathbf{k}$ A/m (c) $\mathbf{H} = +6.81 \times 10^3 \mathbf{k}$ A/m (d) $\mathbf{B} = 714\mathbf{k}$ G

5. H_2, CO_2, and N_2 diamagnetic; O_2 paramagnetic

7. $\mathbf{H} = 8.00 \times 10^3 \mathbf{k}$ A/m; $\mathbf{M} = 0.544\mathbf{k}$ A/m; $\mathbf{B} = 101\mathbf{k}$ G

9. $1.69 m_B$

11. (a) $M_s = 5.6 \times 10^5$ A/m; $\mu_0 M_s = 0.70$ T (b) 5.2×10^{-4} (c) The measured magnetization includes that due to induced moments (diamagnetism), which reduces the net magnetization.

13. $\mu = 1.48 \times 10^{-5}$ H/m; $K_m = 11.7$

15. 11 A

17. (a) 1000 A/m (b) 1.26×10^6 A/m (c) 1.26×10^3

Problems

1. (b) $H = NI/2\pi R$, the same as without core since there are no end effects: $B = \mu_0 NI/2\pi R + \mu_0 M$

Chapter 40

True or False

1. True 2. True 3. True 4. False 5. True 6. True

Exercises

1. (a) 250 rad/sec (b) 4.8π V = 15.1 V

3. (b) 156 V

5. (a) 120π rad/sec = 377 rad/sec (b) $I_{max} = 4.0$ A; $I_{rms} = I_{max}/\sqrt{2} = 2.83$ A (c) 48 W (d) 0 (e) $P_{av} = I_{rms}^2 R = P_{max}/2 = 24$ W

7. (a) 265 Ω (b) 26.5 Ω (c) 2.65 Ω

9. 25.1 mA

11. (a) 15.9 kHz; angular frequency 10^5 rad/sec (b) 159 Hz; angular frequency 10^3 rad/sec (c) 1.59 MHz; angular frequency 10^7 rad/sec

13. (a) 0.377 Ω (b) 3.77 Ω (c) 37.7 Ω

15. 1.59 kHz

17. (a) 7.07×10^3 rad/sec (b) 20 A (c) $X_C = 62.5$ Ω; $X_L = 80$ Ω (d) $Z = 18.2$ Ω; $I_{max} = 5.49$ A (e) $\phi = -74°$

19. (a) 1.13 kHz (b) $X_C = 19.9$ Ω; $X_L = 251 \Omega$ (c) $Z = 231$ Ω; $I_{max} = 0.432$ A (d) $\phi = -89°$

21. 10^4

23. (a) $Q = 10\sqrt{2} = 14.1$ (b) 500 rad/sec (c) 0.275

25. (a) 0.539 (b) 95.3 mA (c) 0.726 W

27. (a) 0.553 (b) 608 mA (c) 37.0 W

29. (a) step down (b) 2.2 V (c) (−)5 A

Problems

3. (a) $L = 0.8$ mH; $C = 12.5$ μF (b) 1.6 (c) for the given values of X_L and X_C, $I_{max} = 2$ A; at resonance $I_{max} = 5.2$ A

11. (a) 856 W (b) 7.07 Ω (c) 102 μF (d) add a 38.4-μF capacitor in parallel or a 19-mH inductor in series

13. (a) 12 Ω (b) $R = 7.2$ Ω, $X = 9.6$ Ω (c) capacitive

Chapter 41

Exercises

1. (a) wave is traveling in $+x$ direction

3. $E_{rms} = 194$ V/m; $B_{rms} = 6.47$ mG

5. (a) 13.3 mG (b) 7.08×10^{-7} J/m^3 (c) 212 W/m^2

Problems   1. $I = 1.91$ kW/m²; $E_{rms} = 849$ V/m; $B_{rms} = 28$ mG

3. (b) 3.9×10^{26} W (c) $E_{rms} = 726$ V/m; $B_{rms} = 24.2$ mG

Chapter 42   **True or False**   1. True 2. True 3. False; it is a property of the metal. 4. True 5. True 6. False 7. True 8. True 9. True 10. True 11. True 12. False 13. True 14. False

Exercises   1. 1.77 to 3.10 eV

3. 4.14×10^{-7} eV

5. (a) 4.13 eV (b) 2.10 eV (c) 1.00 V

7. (a) $f_t = 4.59 \times 10^{14}$ Hz; $\lambda_t = 653$ nm (b) 2.23 V (c) 1.20 V

9. (a) 17.44 keV (b) 0.0760 nm (c) 16.32 keV (d) 1.12 keV

11. (a) 103 nm (b) 97.2 nm (c) 91.2 nm

13. $\lambda_{4 \to 3} = 1876$ nm; $\lambda_{5 \to 3} = 1282$ nm; $\lambda_{6 \to 3} = 1094$ nm; $\lambda_{\infty \to 3} = 820.5$ nm

15. (a) 12.26 Å (b) 1.23 Å (c) 0.388 Å (d) 0.123 Å

17. 2.02 Å

19. about 5×10^{-20} m $= 5 \times 10^{-5}$ fm, where 1 fm $= 10^{-15}$ m is of the order of the diameter of the nucleus

21. 1.95 Å

Problems   1. Plot c/λ versus V_0. (a) 2.05 eV (b) about 5×10^{14} Hz (c) 4.14×10^{-15} V-sec

3. (a) 10^{-22} W (b) about 53 min

7. $\mu/m = 0.99946 = R_H/R_\infty$

9. (b) $E_1 = h^2/m_p r^2 = 6.25 \times 10^{-3}$ eV (c) $T_c \approx 73$ K (d) about 13 eV using $r = 0.53$ Å; $T_c \approx 1.5 \times 10^5$ K

Index